National Center for Construction Education and Research

Electronic Systems Technician Level One

Upper Saddle River, New Jersey
Columbus, Ohio

contren®
Learning Series

National Center for Construction Education and Research

President: Don Whyte
Director of Curriculum Revision and Development: Daniele Dixon
Electronic Systems Technician Project Manager: Rebecca Hassell, Daniele Dixon
Production Manager: Debie Ness
Quality Assurance Coordinator: Jessica Martin
Editor: Brendan Coote
Desktop Publisher: Laura Parker

NCCER would like to acknowledge the contract service provider for this curriculum:
Topaz Publications, Liverpool, New York.

This information is general in nature and intended for training purposes only. Actual performance of activities described in this manual requires compliance with all applicable operating, service, maintenance, and safety procedures under the direction of qualified personnel. References in this manual to patented or proprietary devices do not constitute a recommendation of their use.

10 9 8 7
ISBN 0-13-109195-6

Preface

This volume was developed by the National Center for Construction Education and Research (NCCER) in response to the training needs of the construction, maintenance, and pipeline industries. It is one of many in NCCER's *Contren® Learning Series*. The program, covering training for close to 40 construction and maintenance areas, and including skills assessments, safety training, and management education, was developed over a period of years by industry and education specialists.

NCCER also maintains a National Registry that provides transcripts, certificates, and wallet cards to individuals who have successfully completed modules of NCCER's *Contren® Learning Series*, when the training program is delivered by an NCCER Accredited training Sponsor.

The NCCER is a not-for-profit 501(c)(3) education foundation established in 1995 by the world's largest and most progressive construction companies and national construction associations. It was founded to address the severe workforce shortage facing the industry and to develop a standardized training process and curricula. Today, NCCER is supported by hundreds of leading construction and maintenance companies, manufacturers, and national associations, including the following partnering organizations:

PARTNERING ASSOCIATIONS

- American Fire Sprinkler Association
- American Petroleum Institute
- American Society for Training & Development
- American Welding Society
- Associated Builders & Contractors, Inc.
- Association for Career and Technical Education
- Associated General Contractors of America
- Carolinas AGC, Inc.
- Carolinas Electrical Contractors Association
- Citizens Democracy Corps
- Construction Industry Institute
- Construction Users Roundtable
- Design-Build Institute of America

- Electronic Systems Industry Consortium
- Merit Contractors Association of Canada
- Metal Building Manufacturers Association
- National Association of Minority Contractors
- National Association of State Supervisors for Trade and Industrial Education
- National Association of Women in Construction
- National Insulation Association
- National Ready Mixed Concrete Association
- National Systems Contractors Association
- National Utility Contractors Association
- National Technical Honor Society
- North American Crane Bureau
- North American Technician Excellence
- Painting & Decorating Contractors of America
- Plumbing-Heating-Cooling Contractors National Association
- Portland Cement Association
- SkillsUSA
- Steel Erectors Association of America
- Texas Gulf Coast Chapter ABC
- U.S. Army Corps of Engineers
- University of Florida
- Women Construction Owners & Executives, USA
- Youth Training and Development Consortium

Some features of NCCER's *Contren® Learning Series* are:

- An industry-proven record of success
- Curricula developed by the industry for the industry
- National standardization providing portability of learned job skills and educational credits
- Credentials for individuals through NCCER's National Registry
- Compliance with Apprenticeship, Training, Employer, and Labor Services (ATELS) requirements for related classroom training (CFR 29:29)
- Well-illustrated, up-to-date, and practical information

Acknowledgments

Special thanks to the National Systems Contractors Association (NSCA) for their continued support.

This curriculum was revised as a result of the farsightedness and leadership of the following sponsors:

BICI
Copp Systems Integrator
Electronic Systems Industry
  Consortium

Lincoln Technical Institute
Pratt Landry Associates
Simplex Grinnell
Sound Com Corporation

This curriculum would not exist were it not for the dedication and unselfish energy of those volunteers who served on the Authoring Team. A sincere thanks is extended to:

Stephen Clare
Mark Curry
Brendan Dillon
Mike Friedman
Dick Fyten

Larry Garter
Bruce Nardone
Joe Jones
Ken Nieto
Paul Salyers

Contents

33101-04 Introduction to the Trade 1.i

33102-04 Construction Materials and Methods 2.i

33103-04 Pathways and Spaces 3.i

33104-04 Fasteners and Anchors 4.i

33105-04 Job-Site Safety 5.i

33106-04 Craft-Related Mathematics 6.i

33107-04 Hand Bending of Conduit 7.i

33108-04 Low-Voltage Cabling 8.i

Electronic Systems Technican Level One . . . . .Index

Introduction to the Trade

COURSE MAP

This course map shows all of the modules in the first level of the *Electronic Systems Technician* curriculum. The suggested training order begins at the bottom and proceeds up. Skill levels increase as you advance on the course map. The local Training Program Sponsor may adjust the training order.

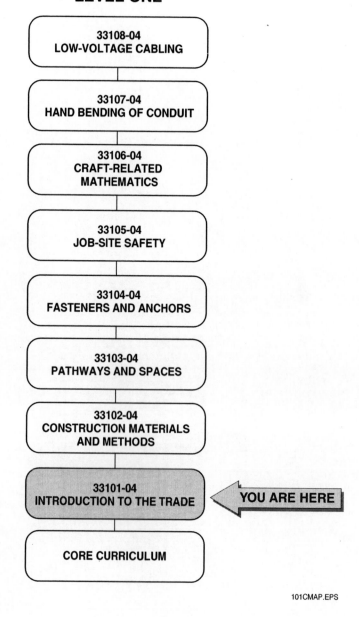

ELECTRONIC SYSTEMS TECHNICIAN
LEVEL ONE

33108-04
LOW-VOLTAGE CABLING

33107-04
HAND BENDING OF CONDUIT

33106-04
CRAFT-RELATED
MATHEMATICS

33105-04
JOB-SITE SAFETY

33104-04
FASTENERS AND ANCHORS

33103-04
PATHWAYS AND SPACES

33102-04
CONSTRUCTION MATERIALS
AND METHODS

33101-04
INTRODUCTION TO THE TRADE

YOU ARE HERE

CORE CURRICULUM

101CMAP.EPS

1.0.0 **INTRODUCTION** 1.1
    1.1.0 Electronic Systems 1.2
    1.2.0 Opportunities in the Industry 1.2
    1.3.0 Integrated Building Management Systems 1.3
    1.4.0 Rules, Regulations, and Standards 1.4

2.0.0 **CERTIFICATION AND LICENSING** .1.4

3.0.0 **YOUR RESPONSIBILITIES AS AN EMPLOYEE** 1.4
    3.1.0 Professional Obligations 1.5
    3.2.0 Company Standards 1.5
    3.3.0 Obligations to Customers 1.5
    3.4.0 Courtesy and Respect 1.6
    3.5.0 Communicating as a Professional 1.6
    3.5.1 Interpreting Instructions 1.7
    3.5.2 Restate Written Instructions Orally 1.8
    3.5.3 Clearly Relate a Customer Requirement 1.8
    3.6.0 Teamwork 1.8
    3.7.0 Conflict Resolution 1.9
    3.7.1 Use Principled Negotiation in Solving a Conflict 1.9

4.0.0 **INDUSTRY STANDARDS AND BUILDING CODES** 1.10
    4.1.0 National Electrical Code® 1.10
    4.2.0 Canadian Electrical Code, Part 1 . . . . .1.11
    4.3.0 National Fire Protection Association (NFPA) 1.11
    4.4.0 National Building Codes 1.11
    4.5.0 International Standards 1.11
    4.6.0 Why Standards? 1.11
    4.6.1 Standards Coordinate Team Activity 1.12
    4.6.2 Standards Reduce Liability 1.12

5.0.0 **DOCUMENTATION AND PAPERWORK** 1.12

6.0.0 **TYPES OF TRAINING PROGRAMS** 1.17
    6.1.0 The History of Apprentice Training 1.17
    6.2.0 Modern Apprenticeship Training 1.17
    6.2.1 ATELS 1.18
    6.2.2 What Apprenticeship Training Means for You 1.18
    6.2.3 OJT + Classroom Training = Highly Skilled Workers 1.19
    6.2.4 NCCER and Your Apprenticeship 1.19

7.0.0 **TOOLS OF THE TRADE** 1.19

SUMMARY 1.22

REVIEW QUESTIONS 1.23

PROFILE IN SUCCESS 1.25

GLOSSARY 1.27

APPENDIX A, National Trade Associations Representing
            the Electronic Systems Industries .1.28

APPENDIX B, Portions of the NEC® Affecting Telecommunications
            and Life Safety Systems 1.32

APPENDIX C, Portions of the CEC Affecting Telecommunications
            and Life Safety Systems 1.34

APPENDIX D, ANSI/NFPA Standards Applicable to
            Low-Voltage Systems 1.35

APPENDIX E, Standards Governing Telecommunications Cabling 1.36

REFERENCES & ACKNOWLEDGMENTS 1.37

Figures

Figure 1   Building automation system 1.3

Figure 2   How communication is interpreted 1.7

Figure 3   Elements of teamwork 1.9

Figure 4   Four basic negotiation steps 1.10

Figure 5   Typical riser diagram 1.13

Figure 6   Typical point-to-point diagram 1.13

Figure 7   Example of a job sheet 1.14

Figure 8   Example of a certificate of completion 1.15–1.16

Figure 9   Cable-stripping and termination tools 1.20

Figure 10   Cable-pulling tools 1.21

Figure 11   Test instruments used in low-voltage work 1.22

Introduction to the Trade

Objectives

When you have completed this module, you will be able to do the following:

1. State the purpose of the electronic systems industry and describe the role of an electronic systems technician in the industry.
2. State the role played by industry associations and be able to identify key associations.
3. State the rules for professional and ethical conduct.
4. Describe the importance of codes and standards and explain how they affect the work of the electronic systems technician.
5. Recognize some of the tools used in the industry.
6. Fill out a time sheet.
7. Fill out a job sheet.

Recommended Prerequisites

Core Curriculum

1.0.0 ◆ INTRODUCTION

There has been an explosion in the development of communications, life safety (fire), security, entertainment, and building control technologies. Consumer demand for electronic systems (also known as **low-voltage** systems) that provide security and life safety, improve communications networking and control, and automate lighting and energy appliances has increased dramatically. Tens of thousands of specialty companies are fueling the need for competent electronic systems technicians (ESTs). There are an estimated 165,000 to 230,000 ESTs employed by businesses in the United States and Canada. The electronic systems industry is among the fastest growing industries in the world.

The demand for qualified technicians is growing and is expected to outpace the supply of skilled workers. Employment opportunities in this field are affected by trends in construction, renovation, and new product development. As the economy grows, more ESTs will be needed to install and maintain systems in homes and businesses. New buildings will be wired during construction to accommodate networks of computers, telecommunications equipment, and control devices. Existing buildings will be modified to incorporate these systems as well. Overall, employment prospects for qualified ESTs should be excellent for decades to come.

The term low-voltage system is often used to describe the electronic systems used in the control of building functions such as lighting, security, and telecommunications. For some time, electronic systems were regarded as part of the electrical contracting industry and its technicians were viewed as electricians. While some licensed electricians install low-voltage systems, the trend has been for low-voltage specialists to handle the newer and

Note: The designations "*National Electrical Code®*" and "NEC®," where used in this document, refer to the *National Electrical Code®*, which is a registered trademark of the National Fire Protection Association, Quincy, MA. *All National Electrical Code® (NEC®) references in this module refer to the 2002 edition of the NEC®.*

more complicated systems, while electricians handle **high-voltage** work. Companies may specialize in security and life safety, entertainment, communications, temperature control, and other functions. They may specialize further in handling residential, commercial, or industrial facilities.

Electronic systems are now more common than ever in both residential and commercial establishments. New construction usually specifies the installation of such systems and there are many opportunities to **retrofit** existing structures to accommodate these systems. One of the most important changes to come along is the integration of control devices with computer systems and telecommunications equipment for remote control and maintenance of building systems.

1.1.0 Electronic Systems

Electronic systems are the components that distribute, carry, capture, and display voice, video, audio, and data signals. These products use electronic signals from **microprocessors** to control mechanical and electrical devices in and around residential and commercial premises. While electronic systems often use 120V power sources, the control devices in these systems typically operate at lower voltages.

1.2.0 Opportunities in the Industry

Typical career paths for ESTs include technician, installer, system engineer, and system designer. ESTs work with low-voltage products or systems designed to be installed and made permanent, rather than those that are portable. The work of an EST involves specialized systems and products used to provide the following functions:

- Entertainment for home and business (video and audio media systems)
- Communications (telephone, fax, **modem**, computer networks, paging, and public address systems)
- Life safety (access control, burglar and fire alarms, and video surveillance)
- Environmental controls (heating, ventilating, and air conditioning [HVAC] and energy management)
- Automation controls for residential and commercial buildings

ESTs may be self-employed, or they can work for either large or small companies. Electronic systems companies differ from electrical contractors who install systems and service products that distribute and use electrical power. Installations occur both during and after building construction, indoors and outdoors. Technicians are often on call for troubleshooting and repair work.

The work of an EST is sometimes strenuous. It may involve standing for a long time, working in awkward or cramped positions, or working on ladders or scaffolds. There is a risk of injury from electrical shock, falls, and other construction hazards. To avoid injury, ESTs must learn and follow strict safety procedures.

ESTs install, connect, calibrate, and service products that carry voice, video, audio, and data within a premises (building, home, apartment, etc.). Some ESTs install and service fire and security alarm systems; others work with telecommunications equipment such as business telephone systems and computer networks.

An EST needs to have a basic understanding of electricity and electronics, microprocessors and computers, and signal/data communications.

EST Definition

The U.S. Department of Transportation (DOT) assigns codes to occupations. The following is the official DOT description for an Electronic Systems Technician:

Occupational Title: Electronic Systems Technician
DOT Code: 823.261-901
ONET Code: 49-2022.03

An EST is an individual whose primary occupation is the design and/or integration, installation, and field maintenance/service of the following:

- Cabling infrastructure and products that transport low voltage (less than 100 volts) voice, video, audio, and data signals in a commercial or residential premises
- Products that capture and display or otherwise annunciate signals
- Products that control signals
- Products that use signals to control mechanical and electrical apparatus

---

A knowledge of the very specialized terminology used in the industry is also essential. Strong familiarity with safety procedures and codes, as well as industry standards and building codes, is critical to success.

In your work, you will review and follow drawings, blueprints, and construction specifications. At the job site, you will perform a variety of tasks, each requiring knowledge of specialized tools, standards, and procedures. These tasks include the following:

- Identifying wire **pathways**
- Installing cable support structures in pathways
- Pulling, securing, and terminating wire and cables
- Installing outlets and connection panels
- Installing, testing, and troubleshooting system electronic and mechanical components
- Programming digital components to perform in the manner specified by the client or by applicable codes

The business focus for each type of company may be different, but all ESTs must have an understanding of electricity and certain mechanical and structural knowledge. Core technical knowledge relates to electronic system interconnection, integration, networking, software programming, calibration of visual displays and sound systems, and user interface design.

1.3.0 Integrated Building Management Systems

One of the most exciting trends in the electronics industry is the integration of all the electronic systems for a single building into a common network controlled from a central computer. This approach allows one individual to monitor and control all building functions from a computer within the building or even in another location many miles away. A technician at a remote site can diagnose problems and help the customer restore the system after an alarm. Specialized computer software is used to accomplish the integration. Special cabling links the components of each subsystem and its controller, which is in turn linked to a central controller that manages the entire network. Selecting, installing, and terminating the network cabling and the components that make the network function are important parts of the job.

While these newer systems provide many benefits, they may also make installation and servicing more complicated. Each type of system has its own set of standards. Some of the standards may overlap, while others may seem to be in conflict. When faced with conflicting standards, it is best to check with your supervisor about how to proceed.

Figure 1 is a simplified schematic diagram of a building control system in which the HVAC, lighting, security, and fire alarm systems are integrated. Although each system has its own controller, central control of all systems is provided by a network controller and monitored/managed at a central facility containing computers, video monitors, and alarm monitors. This building automation system (BAS) allows building managers and life safety service organizations to monitor and manage building systems from distant locations using computers linked by telecommunication lines or satellite communication systems.

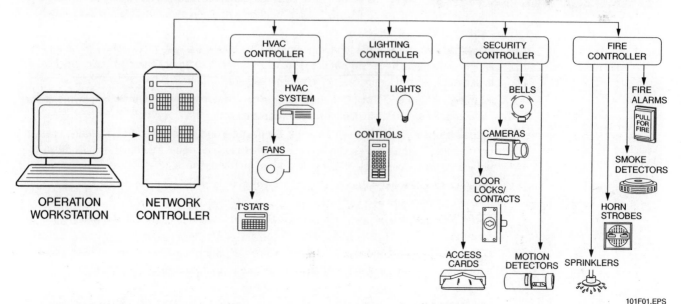

Figure 1 ◆ Building automation system.

101F01.EPS

1.4.0 Rules, Regulations, and Standards

There are many standards, codes, regulations, and rules that govern the electronic systems industry. Each area of specialty will have its own set. For every installation and follow-up, there is probably a code, industry standard, manufacturer's instruction, laboratory requirement, or another written document which serves as the basis for the job. Many regions and localities have adopted their own set of regulations for specific systems. Compliance with codes and standards is required. Non-compliance can put you and your company at risk if something goes wrong.

In civil trials, the courts will frequently focus on the issue of compliance with recognized standards. In the case of a conflict between recognized standards and common industry practice, recognized standards will prevail.

2.0.0 ◆ CERTIFICATION AND LICENSING

Several trade and professional organizations issue certificates to ESTs. Some of the organizations provide training; others provide only testing. The certificate that is issued will certify that the EST has completed a course of instruction, has demonstrated the ability to perform specific job skills, or has passed a test that is recognized and accepted by the industry. A list of industry associations and organizations, including those that provide certification for ESTs, is included in *Appendix A*.

In addition to certification, some local or state authorities may require that you be licensed in order to install and service security and/or telecommunications equipment.

3.0.0 ◆ YOUR RESPONSIBILITIES AS AN EMPLOYEE

Companies that employ ESTs include manufacturers, distributors, contractors, dealers, and service organizations. Each employer is in business to make a profit. In basic terms, profit is the money left over after all expenses such as payroll, rent, insurance, taxes, and other costs of doing business have been covered.

The profit a company makes is used to help the company grow by providing the funds required to buy new equipment, tools, vehicles, and to hire and train new employees. It also helps the company create a reserve that can keep it going in a slow economy. In the case of large companies, the ability of a company to make a profit determines whether investors will buy its stock, supplying the capital necessary to expand and strengthen the company. The stronger a company is financially, the more secure its future.

An important part of your responsibility as an employee, therefore, is to do your part to help your employer be profitable. This means working efficiently and professionally.

Ethical Principles to Live By

Honesty: Be honest and truthful in all dealings. Conduct business according to the highest professional standards. Faithfully fulfill all contracts and commitments. Do not deliberately mislead or deceive others.

Integrity: Demonstrate personal integrity and the courage of your convictions by doing what is right even when there is great pressure to do otherwise. Do not sacrifice your principles for expediency, be hypocritical, or act in an unscrupulous manner.

Loyalty: Be worthy of trust. Demonstrate fidelity and loyalty to companies, employers, fellow craftspeople, and trade institutions and organizations.

Fairness: Be fair and just in all dealings. Do not take undue advantage of another's mistakes or difficulties. Fair people display a commitment to justice, equal treatment of individuals, tolerance for and acceptance of diversity, and open-mindedness.

Respect for others: Be courteous and treat all people with equal respect and dignity regardless of sex, race, or national origin.

Law abiding: Abide by laws, rules, and regulations relating to all personal and business activities.

Commitment to excellence: Pursue excellence in performing your duties, be well-informed and prepared, and constantly endeavor to increase your proficiency by gaining new skills and knowledge.

Leadership: By your own conduct, seek to be a positive role model for others.

The way you conduct yourself on the job has a major impact on your employer and on the electronic systems industry as a whole. Professional and ethical conduct is required of all ESTs, no matter how long you have been on the job. From the very first day, your ability to communicate, your technical competence, and your attention to detail will predict your success in this industry. The five basic rules for professional and ethical conduct follow:

- Be professional at all times.
- Show respect and offend no one.
- Master the technology.
- Work safely.
- Respect and respond to customer requests.

3.1.0 Professional Obligations

The company you work for has the right to expect you to work in the most efficient and practical way possible to keep labor costs down. You should be able to anticipate and solve problems in a way that maintains customer satisfaction and employer confidence. The best employees build the company image by working as though they own the company. Customers have a right to expect professionalism and respect from the company's employees.

As an employee, your first professional obligation is to your employer. Remember, you represent your company. While on the job, all of your actions reflect back on the company.

3.2.0 Company Standards

Many larger companies will provide you with a document that describes company standards for employees. Smaller companies may also have a set of guidelines or expectations. If you are not provided with a document related to company standards, it is a good idea to ask if one exists. Sometimes you will be expected to learn the standards during a period of on-the-job training. If this is the case, make a written note of the things your trainer points out to you as expectations or "the way we do things here."

Company standards differ from industry standards and codes that govern the industry. Company standards exist to provide a measure of consistency in how employees are treated and expected to act on the job. The standards serve to protect both the company and the employee. Company standards provide a set of guidelines or procedures for each employee to use when starting and following through on a job.

Company standards may be gathered from a number of different sources, including the employee handbook, statements of company policy, and instruction or procedure manuals.

3.3.0 Obligations to Customers

No matter what their position, each employee who interacts with customers and others represents their company. Customers form an impression of the company based upon their initial interaction. If the employee does not seem to be attentive to their needs, that all-important first impression will be negative. Poor customer relations may encourage the customer to seek out a competitor's service. One of the keys to good customer relations lies in your ability to be a courteous and effective communicator.

In every business, good customer relations is the key to a company's success. The ability of a company to be profitable is directly related to the number of loyal customers it has. Customer service is the most important aspect of any business. Dissatisfied customers will seek out a competitor and are likely to speak poorly of your company.

Late for Work

Showing up on time is a basic requirement for just about every job. Your employer is counting on you to be there at a set time, ready to work. While legitimate emergencies may arise that may cause you to be late for or even miss work, starting a bad habit of consistent tardiness is not something you want to do.

Drugs and Alcohol

When people use drugs and alcohol, they are putting both themselves and the people around them at serious risk. A construction site can be a dangerous environment, and it is important to be alert at all times. Using drugs and alcohol on the job is an accident waiting to happen. You have an obligation to yourself, your employer, and your fellow employees to work safely. Think about what you would do if you discover someone abusing drugs and/or alcohol at work.

It does not take long for the negative effects of poor customer service to impact your company's profitability.

A company has an obligation to fill the customer's order in a timely manner by providing the service requested. The company must employ competent, licensed (where required) employees to do the work. The company must ensure that all employees are well trained and follow company and industry standards.

The employee has the same obligations to the customer that the company does. The customer has the right to expect that all interactions with company employees will be respectful and courteous. They depend upon you to work safely, and to understand and work to the standards and codes related to the task. Sometimes customers will not understand the procedures or technology behind the system you are installing. Customers usually appreciate it when you take the time to explain what you are about to do. Customers need an opportunity to ask questions and become familiar with the new system.

3.4.0 Courtesy and Respect

Showing respect and using common courtesy is the mark of a professional. Respectful, courteous interactions always make a favorable impression. When you are courteous, you demonstrate that you can put yourself into the other person's shoes. There are some common expectations for good customer relations. It does not matter what your position is in relationship to a work project. All forms of communication should be as follows:

- Honest
- Timely
- Clear and specific
- Free from coarse language or profanity

An EST is expected to communicate certain things at certain times. You must do this to the best of your ability. For example, customers may expect you to communicate the following:

- Project schedules, progress reports, and potential problems or delays
- Safety and security issues
- Requirements or decisions that involve the customer

Supervisors, co-workers, and vendors expect you to clearly communicate the following:

- Schedules and progress reports
- Work responsibilities and specific techniques used to complete a task

- Location information and arrangements for deliveries
- Safety issues

Providing the right information to the right person when needed is a work practice that should not be ignored. You can never go wrong when being courteous.

Respect also extends to personal appearance and work habits. A professional appearance will go a long way towards establishing a positive impression. Pay attention to personal hygiene. Wear clothing that is appropriate for the job. Take the time to appear neat, organized, and safety conscious to create the best possible image. You should always be ready to start a job on time, with the right tools and wearing clothing that is safe and free from offensive slogans.

Learn to plan ahead. Make sure the tools, equipment, and materials needed for the next day's work will be available on time.

Put on the appropriate safety gear for the job. Demonstrate your concern for safety and efficient work practices. At the end of the day or the job, leave the customer's site neat, knowing that all hidden work is safe and correctly installed. It always helps to use a respectful attitude toward co-workers, workers from other trades, vendors, and customers.

3.5.0 Communicating as a Professional

It is rare to have a job where people skills do not count. The way you interact at the job site can make or break your success in this field. Most skilled ESTs recognize that good people skills are valuable tools of the trade. After all, first impressions count. It is not enough just to be technically competent. You must show the customer that you will handle the job and solve any problems efficiently and pleasantly. Every interaction is an opportunity to convey a professional image for you and your company.

Professionals pay attention to all the products of their work, including communication. They always act in a professional and ethical manner. This means demonstrating the traits of honesty, productivity, safety, cooperation, and civility. Just as it is dangerous to ignore safety concerns, it is also risky to ignore how your words and actions may be interpreted by others.

As an EST, you will be working with many different people. In one day, you could interact with a supervisor, co-workers, other tradespeople, customers, and an inspector. Every work site is different. You may be the lone technician or part of a larger team. When communications are positive and effective, the stage is set for a productive working environment. How you treat other people is your personal responsibility. The way you get treated is often a result of how well you interact with others.

Experienced ESTs realize that success in the workplace is determined by a combination of skill, knowledge, and behavior appropriate to the situation. It is important for every EST to convey a professional image. The level of professionalism demonstrated by each technician reflects back on the industry as a whole. Clear, effective communication makes work more productive and pleasant for everyone. If your natural people skills are not what they should be for this kind of work, take the time to learn how to improve them.

3.5.1 Interpreting Instructions

The interpretation and recall of instructions is a very common task in every workplace. Yet the misinterpretation of oral, written, or graphic instructions can lead to costly mistakes. Mistakes can negatively affect safety, quality of work, and the confidence others have in you to do the job correctly.

Communication experts have determined that the words or content of a face-to-face interaction influence less than 10 percent of how the total communication is perceived. Body language and tone of voice provide over 90 percent of the speaker's message. These are the clues we look for when interpreting a message (*Figure 2*). Usually, we pick up on many things besides the actual words spoken. There are even more opportunities for misinterpretation when people communicate by phone or in writing. Just think how much facial expressions or hand gestures contribute to your understanding of what is being said.

Good communication skills include active listening and the precise presentation of information. They are both essential for efficient work practices and avoiding costly mistakes. These people skills are not easy to achieve without a good deal of effort and practice.

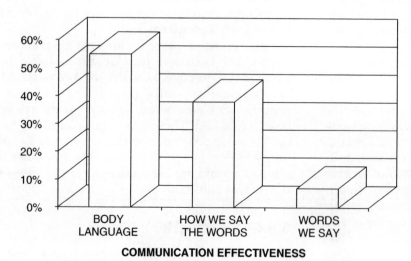

COMMUNICATION EFFECTIVENESS

CUSTOMER SERVICE =
CUSTOMER RESPONSE

101F02.EPS

Figure 2 ◆ How communication is interpreted.

The Customer

When you are on a job site, you should consider yourself to be working for both your employer and your employer's customer. If you are honest and maintain a professional attitude when interacting with customers, everyone will benefit. Your employer will be pleased with your performance, and the customer will be happy with the work that is being done. Try seeing things from a customer's point of view. A good, professional attitude goes a long way toward ensuring repeat business.

Customer Technical Knowledge

When talking with customers, never assume that they do not have technical knowledge or skills. Many customers have a broader technical background and knowledge than some service people.

Everyone has stories about how they were treated as a customer by a representative of a particular company. The situations that were most frustrating are usually the ones where you, as the customer, were not treated with respect. The situations that left you with a positive feeling were very different. If you recall those interactions, you may remember that the employee acted confident, helpful, and professional. Most likely, the service person appeared to really concentrate and listen carefully to what you were asking. When he or she gave you information, it was probably presented clearly and concisely. Even if the situation itself was frustrating, the way you were treated as a customer made a difference. If a problem was handled well, you are more likely to continue to do business there.

The first rule of good communication is to concentrate on the speaker and actively listen to what is being said. This means not interrupting and avoiding the tendency to think about what you are going to say next. There is plenty of time to think of what to say after you are sure you have understood the message. Since what is being said could be open to interpretation, it helps to restate what you think you have been told. Restating the important parts of the message will help you remember it better. When you hear the information and repeat it in your own words, it gets placed into your memory twice. Writing the information down is a third way to keep it in focus.

The key to preventing a misunderstanding is to check out the most important information. Restate what you think are the most important points and watch how the speaker responds. Do not worry about sounding stupid. It is better to get the correct message before you start a job. If there is any doubt about what the speaker meant to say, asking questions is the best way to clear things up. The answer could mean the difference between doing it right the first time and having to waste time on rework.

3.5.2 Restate Written Instructions Orally

Written instructions can often be very short. You may have to read between the lines to understand the full message. The notes you read may be incomplete or difficult to understand. It is always better to get the correct information up front. This is especially true when instructions are critical to a successful installation or follow-up. Again, the trick is to restate the written instructions orally in your own words to check for accuracy.

3.5.3 Clearly Relate a Customer Requirement

Customers may ask you questions or request that you tell a co-worker or supervisor a requirement they have for the job. To convey the information accurately, be sure you understand what the requirement is first. Briefly restate the basics of the requirement back to the customer. He or she will be able to clear up any misunderstandings before you relay the message. If you cannot answer a customer's question or solve a problem, direct the customer to someone who can.

When relaying a message, be sure you have the co-worker or supervisor's full attention. Telling a person something important when they are distracted guarantees that only part of the message will be heard. Even less will be remembered. Gain their full attention by stating why the requirement is important and how it involves them. State the requirement clearly, using a logical sequence. Describe the desired outcome first, then detail the steps required.

State the most important information up front, then repeat it. If the message is complicated, be sure the listener understands each part before going on to the next. You can check for understanding by asking the listener to tell you what they understand about the requirement. Use this as an opportunity to correct any misinformation before mistakes are made.

Finally, follow up to make sure the customer's needs are fulfilled or questions have been answered. Later, ask your co-worker what action was taken. Find out if the customer knows the requirement was acted upon or if delays have been explained. The extra effort you make to get back to the customer will increase their confidence in you as a professional. The customer usually does not care who solves the problem, just that it was solved.

3.6.0 Teamwork

Teamwork is the ability of a group of workers to accomplish a common goal. The workers at any job site will be individuals with different levels of skill and different personalities. The team's ability to get the job done often depends on how well everyone communicates and works together. Each person at a job site will have a particular task to accomplish within a set period of time. With all the different tasks needed to complete a job, it is likely that you will run into a situation where teamwork is important.

The ideal situation is one in which a team of workers agree on the best way to achieve a common goal. They work together, helping to manage the work so that everyone is able to do their own job with the least amount of interference. Sometimes the team is directed by a strong leader who can plan and schedule the work so things run smoothly. However, it is always up to the team members to develop good working relationships

Teamwork

Many of us like to follow sports teams: racing teams, baseball teams, football teams, and soccer teams. Just as in sports, a job site is made up of a team. As a part of that team, you have a responsibility to your teammates.

so that communication flows easily among the team members. To develop good teamwork, work toward the goals shown in *Figure 3*.

Work situations are not always ideal. It is likely that the individuals will have competing priorities. You are required to figure out the best way to work with people you do not know very well. You may also have to deal with a frustrating situation without hurting the feelings of others. This is where your people skills and teamwork skills come into play.

People who work together usually have the same needs, but their methods of achieving results depends upon their personality. Treat supervisors, customers, and co-workers with respect as a first step toward gaining their cooperation. Some common needs follow:

- The need to contribute, to know what your role is in relation to others
- The need to feel competent, to be confident you are doing what is right
- The desire to achieve results, to know how your work measures up to standards
- The desire to have work efforts recognized and rewarded in a timely fashion

GOOD TEAMWORK GOALS:

- Be respectful and maintain the self-esteem of others.
- Develop trustful working relationships.
- Focus on the situation or issue, not on the person.
- Take the initiative to be cooperative.
- Be professional at all times.

101F03.EPS

Figure 3 ◆ Elements of teamwork.

3.7.0 Conflict Resolution

It has been said that conflict is a growth industry. Every day, people from different backgrounds and with differing needs must work together to solve common problems. Whenever people work together, there is a potential for conflict. Conflict starts when two people want different things. They may each have a strong opinion about how a task should be completed.

Like it or not, part of your job will involve negotiating. If you are out in the world interacting with others, you are negotiating. You may not think of yourself as a negotiator, and many people are not good at it. Again, like the other people skills, becoming good at negotiating takes time and practice.

Everyone wants to have a say in the decisions that affect them. Few people are willing to accept decisions dictated by someone else. Negotiation is the basic way you get what you want from others. It does not necessarily result in a win or lose situation. Those skilled at conflict resolution recommend the proven techniques of principled negotiation as a way to manage the back and forth communication required on the job. The best possible outcome of a conflict is when everyone comes out satisfied.

Even though negotiation takes place every day, it is not easy to do it well. If a conflict is handled poorly, each side leaves unhappy and worn out. Unresolved conflicts worsen over time and can lead to negative work relationships. People in conflict start to resent each other. The whole situation can lead to more problems. That is why it is important to resolve conflicts before they grow bigger. Physical violence and intimidation are never acceptable methods of communication.

3.7.1 Use Principled Negotiation in Solving a Conflict

Principled negotiation recognizes that each person brings their own point of view to the table. Trying to understand exactly what these are is the first step in resolving a conflict. Sometimes a conflict is resolved easily when misunderstandings are corrected.

The first step in dealing with the other person is to listen carefully to his or her concerns. Then, try to restate their concerns in your own words.

When you do this, the other person will have more confidence that they are being heard. Sometimes this is all it takes. Take the time to find out where the other person is coming from. Most conflicts can be resolved by mentally stepping into the other person's shoes. Take a few moments to examine the other person's needs from their point of view. If both your needs are reasonable, you can try to find ways to accommodate each other. Suggest things that work for both sides.

Sometimes, each person takes a stand and will not budge. The alternative to a standoff is to change the nature of the game. Good negotiators realize that it is important not to be overwhelmed by an apparent impasse. Instead, you should discuss the conflict calmly and rationally. Let the other person know that their point of view is important to you.

There are four basic steps (*Figure 4*) to negotiate in a way that is more likely to help people agree with one another.

- *Separate the people from the problem* – We all have strong emotions about certain things that affect us. Some feelings come from past experiences, so two people often have very different ways of seeing something. In a conflict, the position we take may be tied up with our own ego. We may not communicate everything that is important, because specific issues may not be important from our standpoint. When you separate the person from the problem, you focus on the issues involved. You are more likely to see yourself as working side by side on a problem, rather than working against the other person.

NEGOTIATING STEPS:

1. Separate the people from the problem.
2. Focus on interests, not positions.
3. Identify several options before deciding what to do.
4. Base expected results on objective standards.

101F04.EPS

Figure 4 ◆ Four basic negotiation steps.

- *Focus on interests, not positions* – It is not easy to reach agreement when people are concerned about their position, rather than working to understand the real problem. A negotiating position may not be what you or the other person really wants. For example, someone may take a certain position because they don't want to look bad in front of others. Try to uncover and focus on the actual need or interest before taking a stand.

- *Identify several options before deciding what to do* – When we have a stake in the outcome of a decision, it is difficult to make a good decision under pressure. Before trying to reach an agreement, take some time to think of other options that may be agreeable to both parties.

- *Base expected results on objective standards* – When discussing possible outcomes, neither person needs to give in. You can decide that a fair solution will be based on a selected standard. The standard could be an expert opinion, completion by a certain time, or quality based on industry standards. This is more likely to lead to a favorable result.

4.0.0 ◆ INDUSTRY STANDARDS AND BUILDING CODES

All telecommunications, life safety, and security systems, as well as the work done by ESTs, are governed by industry standards and building codes. It is important that you become familiar with these standards and codes. The following is a list of standards and codes that govern the work you will do as an EST. During your training, you will become very familiar with these documents. It will become second nature to you to refer to some of these documents in the course of your work. A good rule of thumb is when in doubt, look it up.

In the event of a conflict between two or more standards, the more stringent requirement should be applied. In one sense, the only true conflict would be a situation in which there is no way to comply with all the provisions at the same time.

As an example, if a building code called for manual stations to be mounted at 36" to 56" above the floor, and another standard specified 42" to 60" above the floor, this would generally be considered as an apparent conflict. Because it is possible to comply with both requirements by installing the manual stations at 42" to 56" above the floor, it is not a true conflict.

4.1.0 *National Electrical Code*®

The National Fire Protection Association (NFPA) sponsors, controls, and publishes the *National Electrical Code* (NEC®) within the United States' jurisdiction. The NEC® specifies the minimum provisions necessary to safeguard persons and property from electrical hazards.

Most federal, state, and local municipalities have adopted the NEC®, in whole or in part, as their legal electrical code. Some states or localities adopt the NEC® and add more stringent requirements. The NEC® is used by the following groups:

- Lawyers and insurance companies to determine liability
- Fire marshals and electrical inspectors in loss prevention and safety enforcement
- Designers to ensure a compliant installation

The code sets the minimum standards that must be met to protect people and property from electrical hazards. It is revised every three years. The NEC® is arranged by chapter, article, and section; for example, *NEC Chapter 8, Article 800, Section 800.52*. Portions of the code having significant importance to the electronic system technician are listed in *Appendix B*.

It is important to remember that the NEC® covers only the requirements necessary to ensure a safe environment, not an environment in which the telecommunications systems are guaranteed to operate free of any interference or errors.

4.2.0 *Canadian Electrical Code, Part 1*

The Canadian Standards Association sponsors, controls, and publishes the *Canadian Electrical Code, Part 1 (CEC, Part 1)*. The intent of this code is to establish safety standards for the installation and maintenance of electrical equipment. As with the NEC®, the CEC may be adopted and enforced by the provincial and territorial regulatory authorities.

Telecommunications installers must be familiar with the CEC. *Appendix C* lists sections of the CEC that are of particular interest to the EST.

4.3.0 National Fire Protection Association (NFPA)

In addition to the NEC®, the NFPA and the American National Standards Institute (ANSI) develop and produce other codes that apply to telecommunications, life safety, and security systems. These are listed in *Appendix D*.

4.4.0 National Building Codes

The organizations listed below publish and maintain nationally accepted building codes. State and local governments generally adopt one of these codes. However, the state and local governments may also have additional requirements that must

be met. It is essential that everyone involved in the installation of electronic systems be familiar with the following local and national codes.

- International Code Council (ICC)
- Building Officials and Code Administrators International (BOCA), which publishes the *National Building Code*
- International Conference of Building Officials (ICBO), which publishes the *Uniform Building Code*
- Southern Building Code Congress International (SBCCI), which publishes the *Standard Building Code*

NOTE

Canadian codes must also be followed where applicable.

4.5.0 International Standards

ANSI/TIA/EIA (see *Appendix A*) publishes standards for the manufacturing, installation, and performance of electronic and telecommunications equipment and systems. Five of these ANSI/TIA/EIA standards govern telecommunications cabling in buildings. Each standard covers a specific part of building cabling. They address the required cable, hardware, equipment, design, and installation practices. In addition, each ANSI/TIA/EIA standard lists related standards and other reference materials that deal with the same topics.

Most of the standards include sections that define important terms, abbreviations, and symbols. The ANSI/TIA/EIA standards which govern telecommunications cabling in buildings are listed in *Appendix E*.

The Institute of Electrical and Electronic Engineers also publishes a variety of standards that apply to low-voltage systems. One such standard is *IEEE Standard 1394, High Performance Serial Bus*.

NOTE

The B revisions of *ANSI/TIA/EIA-569* and *570* are scheduled for publication in 2004.)

4.6.0 Why Standards?

Since the earliest recorded time, people have relied upon standards. Without a uniformly recognized system of weights and measures, for example, commerce would not exist.

It would be fairly simple and straightforward if every customer, every style of door, each type of building, or every type of signal could be handled in exactly the same way. Unfortunately, that is impossible. Customers each have a specific need that caused them to contract for our services. In many cases, these needs will be similar, but in others, they will differ. The trick is to develop standards and procedures that allow us to respond to different needs in the same way.

4.6.1 Standards Coordinate Team Activity

Everyone has experienced the frustration of not having the correct tool for a particular job or trying to fix a job completed by someone else. Standardization helps to solve these problems. Following the same procedures on each and every job makes it easier for others to follow up after you. Most companies agree on the specific procedures or devices that will be used. This enables us to have the tools that we need to do the job. Without a standard choice of equipment and a consistent way of doing things, we reinvent each and every job, wasting much time and effort.

4.6.2 Standards Reduce Liability

As mentioned earlier, in civil trials, the courts will frequently focus on the issue of compliance with recognized standards. In the case of a conflict between recognized standards and common industry practice, recognized standards will prevail. For example, an alarm system found to be in violation of the recognized standards after a fatal fire may create a liability for the installer.

Where no particular standards have been legally adopted or are in force in that jurisdiction, national standards may apply. In addition to the moral and social responsibility associated with conducting your work correctly, there are the added civil liability implications. To comply with or exceed the recognized codes and standards is your best protection from liability. When faced with justifying an action in a court proceeding, a company is better off if they can cite recognized standards instead of a common company or industry practice.

5.0.0 ◆ DOCUMENTATION AND PAPERWORK

Every job requires paperwork. At the beginning of the project, you will have drawings and other information describing the project and how it is to be accomplished. This documentation is normally in the form of drawings, including:

- *Work statement* – A detailed description of the work to be performed and the end result expected. It is part of the contract.
- *Floor plan* – A drawing showing the layout of each floor of the building. Separate plans based on the floor plan will show wiring and cable runs. You learned about construction drawings in *Core Curriculum*.
- *Bill of materials* – A detailed list, including quantities, of all system components, cabling, wire, terminations, boxes, raceways, conduits, and other materials needed for an installation. This list is developed by the designer or estimator as part of the **material takeoff**.
- *Riser diagrams* – Diagrams that identify zones within the building, the sequence of device connection, end-of-line devices, and the conductor counts for each cabling run (*Figure 5*).
- *Point-to-point drawings* – Drawings that indicate actual terminal connections and include the connections from the control module through all devices to the terminal device (*Figure 6*). Some point-to-point drawings will show all devices; others will show only typical devices.
- *As-built diagrams* – Diagrams that reflect the finished job. It is not unusual for changes to be made during the course of a project. These changes are marked on a set of drawings as the changes occur. These changes are incorporated into the official drawings, which then become known as the as-builts.

Other paperwork that is an important part of any job includes:

- *Time sheet* – Each person who works on a project must keep an accurate record of the hours they work. This record provides the means for the employer to bill for the work and to verify the accuracy of their price quote. Some employers require employees to punch a time clock at the job site.
- *Job sheet* – The job sheet is used to keep track of all aspects of the job. Job sheets will vary from one company to another. An example is shown in *Figure 7*. In this example, the project leader will summarize the hours spent by each employee, along with the equipment, parts, and material used on the job.
- *Certificate of completion* – This document, which is completed at the end of the project, helps the installer prepare for inspection of the finished work by the client or by an inspection official. A sample from a fire alarm system project is shown in *Figure 8*.

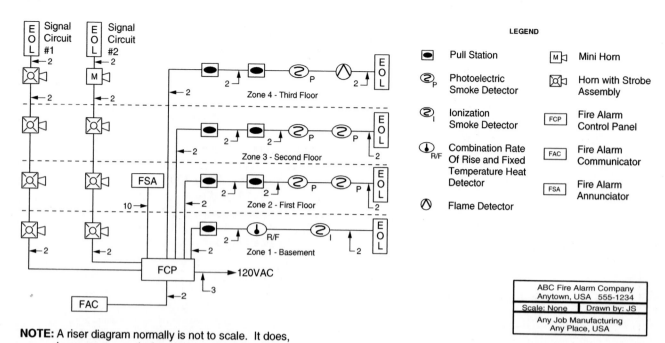

NOTE: A riser diagram normally is not to scale. It does, however, group devices into geographic areas.

Figure 5 ♦ Typical riser diagram.

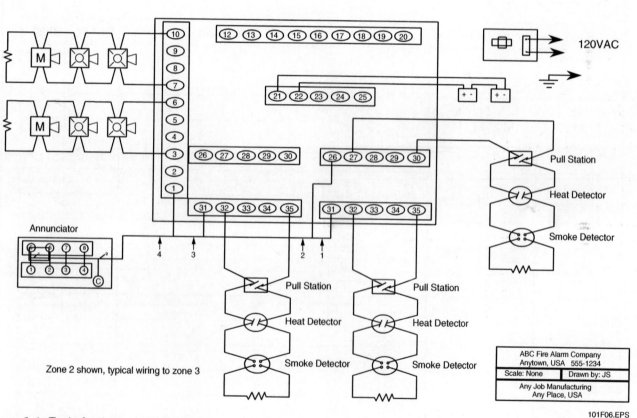

Figure 6 ♦ Typical point-to-point diagram.

- *Change order* – During the course of a project, the client may request changes, or it may turn out that the installation could not be done exactly as planned. (Air conditioning ductwork may have been placed where you planned to run your cable trays, for example.) Each such change must be documented. Before the job is signed off, the changes must also be marked on the as-builts.

JOB SHEET

Work Order No. <u>1005001</u>

Start Date <u>06 July 2004</u>

Customer:

<u>Any Company</u>
<u>123 Fourth St.</u>
<u>Anytown, USA 12345</u>
<u>Phone: (123) 456-7899</u>
<u>Fax: (123) 456-7890</u>

Shipped By:

<u>Another Company</u>
<u>456 Seventh St.</u>
<u>Anothertown, USA 56789</u>
<u>Phone: (111) 555-5555</u>
<u>Fax: (111) 555-4444</u>

Description of Work:

Employee	Hours	Overtime	Date	Quantity	Description	Part No.	Cost

101F07.EPS

Figure 7 ◆ Example of a job sheet.

Name of Protected Property: _____

Address: _____

Rep. of Protected Prop. (name/phone): _____

Authority Having Jurisdiction: _____

Address/Phone Number: _____

1. Type(s) of System or Service

_____ NFPA 72, Chapter 3 — Local

If alarm is transmitted to location(s) off premises, list where received:

_____

_____ NFPA 72, Chapter 3 — Emergency Voice/Alarm Service

Quantity of voice/alarm channels: _____ Single: _____ Multiple: _____

Quantity of speakers installed: _____ Quantity of speaker zones: _____

Quantity of telephones or telephone jacks included in system: _____

_____ NFPA 72, Chapter 4 — Auxiliary

Indicate type of connection:

Local energy: _____ Shunt: _____ Parallel telephone: _____

Location and telephone number for receipt of signals:

_____

_____ NFPA 72, Chapter 4 — Remote Station

Alarm: _____

Supervisory: _____

_____ NFPA 72, Chapter 4 — Proprietary

If alarms are retransmitted to public fire service communications center or others, indicate location and telephone number of the organization receiving alarm:

_____

Indicate how alarm is retransmitted:

_____

_____ NFPA 72, Chapter 4 — Central Station

The Prime Contractor:

_____

Central Station Location:

_____

Means of transmission of signals from the protected premises to the central station:

_____ McCulloh   _____ Multiplex   _____ One-Way Radio
_____ Digital Alarm Communicator _____ Two-Way Radio   _____ Others

Means of transmission of alarms to the public fire service communications center:

(a) _____

(b) _____

System Location: _____

	Organization Name/Phone	Representative Name/Phone
Installer	_____	_____
Supplier	_____	_____
Service Organization	_____	_____

Location of Record (As-Built) Drawings:

_____

Location of Owners Manuals:

_____

Location of Test Reports:

_____

A contract, dated _____ , for test and inspection in accordance with NFPA standard(s) No(s). _____ , dated _____ , is in effect.

101F08A.EPS

Figure 8 ◆ Example of a certificate of completion. (1 of 2)

2. Record of System Installation

(Fill out after installation is complete and wiring checked for opens, shorts, ground faults, and improper branching, but prior to conducting operational acceptance tests.)

This system has been installed in accordance with the NFPA standards as shown below, was inspected by _____ on _____ , includes the devices shown below, and has been in service since _____

_____ NFPA 72, Chapters 1 3 4 5 6 7 (circle all that apply)

_____ NFPA 70, *National Electrical Code*, Article 760

_____ Manufacturer's Instructions

_____ Other (specify): _____

Signed: _____   Date: _____

Organization: _____

3. Record of System Operation

All operational features and functions of this system were tested by _____ on _____ , and found to be operating properly in accordance with the requirements of:

_____ NFPA 72, Chapters 1 3 4 5 6 7 (circle all that apply)

_____ NFPA 70, *National Electrical Code*, Article 760

_____ Manufacturer's Instructions

_____ Other (specify): _____

Signed: _____   Date: _____

Organization: _____

4. Alarm-Initiating Devices and Circuits (use blanks to indicate quantity of devices)

MANUAL

(a) _____ Manual Stations   _____ Noncoded, Activating   _____ Transmitters   _____ Coded

(b) _____ Combination Manual Fire Alarm and Guard's Tour Coded Stations

AUTOMATIC

Coverage: Complete: _____   Partial: _____

(a) _____ Smoke Detectors   _____ Ion   _____ Photo

(b) _____ Duct Detectors   _____ Ion   _____ Photo

(c) _____ Heat Detectors   _____ FT   _____ RR   _____ FT/RR   _____ RC

(d) _____ Sprinkler Waterflow Switches: _____ Transmitters   _____ Noncoded, Activating   _____ Coded

(e) _____ Other (list): _____

5. Supervisory Signal-Initiating Devices and Circuits (use blanks to indicate quantity of devices)

GUARD'S TOUR

(a) _____ Coded Stations

(b) _____ Noncoded Stations, Activating   _____ Transmitters

(c) _____ Compulsory Guard Tour System Comprised of _____ Transmitter Stations and _____ Intermediate Stations

NOTE: Combination devices recorded under 4(b) and 5(a).

SPRINKLER SYSTEM

(a) _____ Coded Valve Supervisory Signaling Attachments
         Valve Supervisory Switches, Activating _____ Transmitters

(b) _____ Building Temperature Points

(c) _____ Site Water Temperature Points

(d) _____ Site Water Supply Level Points

Electric Fire Pump:

(e) _____ Fire Pump Power

(f) _____ Fire Pump Running

(g) _____ Phase Reversal

Engine-Driven Fire Pump:

(h) _____ Selector in Auto Position

(i) _____ Engine or Control Panel Trouble

(j) _____ Fire Pump Running

Engine-Driven Generator:

(k) _____ Selector in Auto Position

(l) _____ Control Panel Trouble

(m) _____ Transfer Switches

(n) _____ Engine Running

101F08B.EPS

Figure 8 ◆ Example of a certificate of completion. (2 of 2)

6.0.0 ◆ TYPES OF TRAINING PROGRAMS

There are two basic forms of training programs that most employers consider. The primary one is on-the-job training (OJT) to improve the competence of their employees in order to provide better customer service and for the continuity and growth of the company. The second is formal apprenticeship training, which provides the same type of training, but also conforms to federal and state requirements under the *Code of Federal Regulations (CFR), Titles 29:29 and 29:30*.

6.1.0 The History of Apprentice Training

Apprenticeship as a means of transferring practical knowledge from one generation to another has a long history. The first mention we have of apprenticeship is found in the Babylonian Code of Hammurabi, which was developed between 1792 and 1750 B.C.E. The code was a series of laws that governed everyday life—marriage, property, crimes, property disputes, and apprenticeship. It stated that if an artisan adopted a son and taught him his craft, he could benefit financially from his adopted son's work. But if the artisan failed to teach him a craft, the adopted son could return to his original family and owe the artisan nothing.

During the Middle Ages (300 to about 1500 C.E.), two large social classes developed: the merchants and the skilled craftsmen. Both classes established occupational guilds, which they formed to keep down competition and regulate training for their own apprentices.

The guilds established the indenture system. Young men were indentured, or contracted, to a master who agreed to train the apprentice in his field as well as to provide food, shelter, and clothing.

The length of apprenticeship varied from two to ten years, depending on the kinds of skills to be learned.

In the 1560s, England adopted the Elizabethan Statute of Artificers, which standardized apprenticeship training and removed it from the control of the guilds. The term of apprenticeship was fixed at seven years. In colonial America, apprenticeship training tended to follow European models, with young men often serving their masters until they were 21.

6.2.0 Modern Apprenticeship Training

Nearly all trade workers learn their skills through an apprenticeship program that combines OJT with related class work. The organization of modern apprenticeship training has its origins in the following events:

- *1800* – Apprenticeships became part of the public education system. Apprentices received wages.
- *1850s* – The first graduated wage scale appeared.
- *1911* – The first law regulating apprenticeship systems was enacted in Wisconsin. This law placed apprenticeship under the authority of an industrial commission.
- *1918–1919* – A building boom and a decrease in the number of skilled foreign workers who could enter the United States led to higher demand for skilled apprentices.
- *1920s* – National employer and labor organizations, educators, government officials, and the construction industry began work on a national apprenticeship system.
- *1937* – The Bureau of Apprenticeship and Training (BAT) was established by the National Apprenticeship Act of 1937 (the Fitzgerald Act). This law ensured the safety and welfare of apprentices.

? **DID YOU KNOW?**

An Ancient Apprenticeship Contract

How did these old apprenticeships work? Here's one example. Historical records include a contract between a young Greek named Heracles and a weaver. In exchange for food, a tunic (a long shirt), and 20 holidays a year, Heracles worked for the weaver for five years. After two and a half years, he was paid 12 drachmas. In his fifth year, his pay was scheduled to double.

In addition to learning to become a journeyman weaver, Heracles most likely worked seven long days each week and had to clean the shop, build fires, pick up supplies, make deliveries, and do whatever other jobs the master weaver needed to have done. And it's also likely that any damage he caused came out of his promised pay.

So how much pay is 12 drachmas? We don't have any way of knowing for certain, but the word drachma means handful—not much pay for almost three years of hard work. Yet Heracles was willing to put in the time to become a skilled master in his chosen trade. As a master weaver, Heracles could look forward to a better income and a better life.

6.2.1 ATELS

The Office of Apprenticeship Training and Employer and Labor Services (ATELS) formerly BAT, administers apprenticeship training at the federal level. ATELS also works closely with State Apprenticeship Councils (SACs), which administer apprenticeship programs at the state level. Programs administered by ATELS/SAC must follow these guidelines:

- Apprentices usually are no younger than 18. However, 16- and 17-year olds may qualify under the Fair Labor Standards Act if certain provisions are met. (Inquire at your local ATELS/SAC office.)
- There must be full and fair opportunity to apply for apprenticeship.
- There must be a schedule of work processes in which an apprentice is to receive training and experience on the job.
- The program must include organized instruction designed to provide apprentices with knowledge in technical subjects related to their trade. A minimum of 144 hours per year is necessary, along with 2,000 hours per year of OJT.
- There must be a progressively increasing schedule of wages.
- There must be proper supervision of on-the-job training with adequate facilities to train apprentices.
- Apprentices' progress, both in job performance and related instruction, must be evaluated periodically, and appropriate records must be maintained.
- There must be no discrimination in any phase of selection, employment, or training.

The apprenticeship system has grown up with the United States and, like the country, it is still growing and changing. Today this system serves a nation that is very different from the way it was in 1937 when BAT was established. Today's apprentices are more likely to use computer-aided designing and cutting tools. They can find jobs anywhere in the world. A global economy, increased competition, and an industry that needs highly skilled and able workers are all part of your future as an electronic systems technician.

6.2.2 What Apprenticeship Training Means for You

For people just starting out in the construction industry, apprenticeship has important advantages. It offers an efficient way to learn skills because the training is planned and organized. The main advantage to you as an apprentice is that you earn as you learn because you are already working in your chosen trade.

An adequate supply of skilled workers is vital to industrial progress. Apprenticeship programs produce competent craftworkers who have the following qualities:

- They are well trained and understand not only how to do a task, but also why a task is done that way.
- They are flexible and can adapt quickly to the changing demands of their jobs.
- They are ready and able to work at all stages in their apprenticeship.

DID YOU KNOW?

Apprenticeships in the United States

In 1999, more than 431,797 apprentices received registered apprenticeship training in 36,903 programs in the United States. Of these workers, 117,380 (27%) were minorities and 31,208 (7%) were women.

6.2.3 OJT + Classroom Training = Highly Skilled Workers

Professionals working in the construction industry identify the skills and knowledge that apprentices will need. They help design courses to give apprentices the necessary hands-on skills and knowledge. Many of these professionals also act as classroom instructors. Classroom instruction is an important part of your apprenticeship program because it helps you understand not only how things are done, but also why they are done.

How does the combination of OJT and classroom training work for you? Here's an example.

In OJT, you will learn and practice basic skills. You'll work under the supervision of a journeyman who will give you specific tasks to accomplish. You'll practice good work habits and hands-on safety. You'll get experience working with others in real-life situations.

Your classroom training is designed to enhance your OJT. In the classroom, you will learn the advantages and limitations of hand and machine operations. You'll learn when and why to select certain tools. You will also learn about safety and what can happen if you don't follow safety guidelines. You'll learn why you must develop good work habits, and you'll find out more about the tools, techniques, and history of your trade. You will also get a chance to practice and learn from your mistakes. You'll be able to take time that might not be available on the job to perfect your skills.

OJT plus classroom training is a winning combination that will help you become a highly skilled electronic systems technician.

6.2.4 NCCER and Your Apprenticeship

This course is part of a curriculum produced by the National Center for Construction Education and Research (NCCER). Like every course in NCCER's curriculum, it was developed by the construction industry for the construction industry. NCCER develops and maintains a training process which is nationally recognized, standardized, and competency-based. A competency-based program requires you to show that you can perform specific job-related tasks safely to receive credit. This approach is unlike other apprenticeship programs that are based on a required number of hours in the classroom and on the job.

The construction industry knows that the future construction workforce will largely be recruited and trained in the nation's secondary and postsecondary schools.

Schools know that to prepare their students for a successful construction career they must use the curriculum that is developed and recognized by the industry. Nationwide, thousands of schools have adopted NCCER's standardized curricula.

The primary goal of NCCER is to standardize construction craft training throughout the country so that both you and your employer will benefit from the training, no matter where you or your job are located. As a trainee in a NCCER-accredited program, you will be listed in the National Registry. You will receive a certificate for each level of training you complete, which can then travel with you from job to job as you progress through your training. In addition, many technical schools and colleges use NCCER's programs.

7.0.0 ◆ TOOLS OF THE TRADE

An EST uses a variety of hand and power tools, as well as common and special test equipment, for installation and troubleshooting of low-voltage equipment. The specific tools and equipment you use will vary to some extent depending on your system specialty (telecommunications, security, entertainment systems, etc.).

In the *Core Curriculum* training modules, you received instruction on basic hand and power tools. In the *Construction Materials and Methods* module in this level, you will learn more about drilling and cutting tools and how they are used in creating cable pathways. You will also learn about conduit bending tools in this level.

The applications of tools and test equipment will be covered as you progress through your training. *Figures 9, 10,* and *11* show some representative examples of special tools and test devices you will use as an EST.

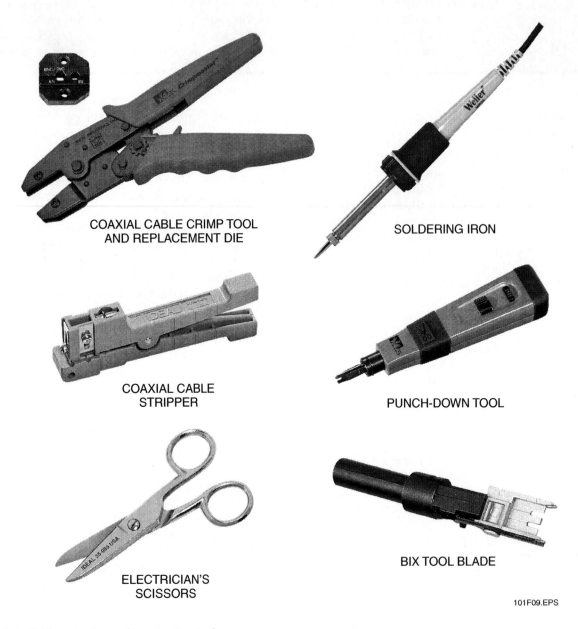

COAXIAL CABLE CRIMP TOOL
AND REPLACEMENT DIE

SOLDERING IRON

COAXIAL CABLE
STRIPPER

PUNCH-DOWN TOOL

ELECTRICIAN'S
SCISSORS

BIX TOOL BLADE

101F09.EPS

Figure 9 ◆ Cable-stripping and termination tools.

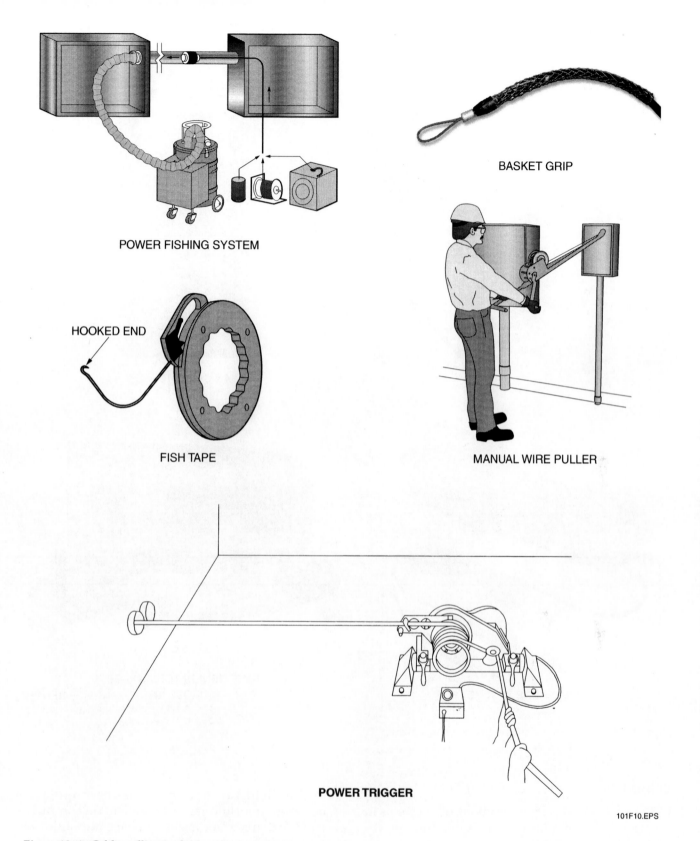

POWER FISHING SYSTEM

BASKET GRIP

HOOKED END

FISH TAPE

MANUAL WIRE PULLER

POWER TRIGGER

101F10.EPS

Figure 10 ◆ Cable-pulling tools.

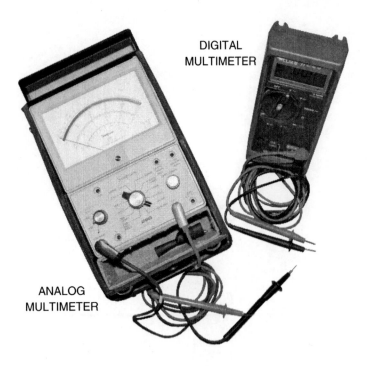

DIGITAL
MULTIMETER

ANALOG
MULTIMETER

LAN CABLE TESTER

TELEPHONE TEST SET

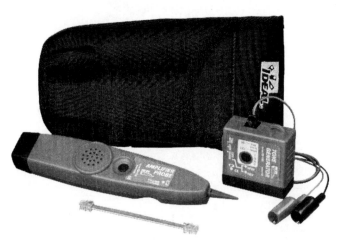

TONE GENERATOR/AMPLIFIER
PROBE KIT

101F11.EPS

Figure 11 ◆ Test instruments used in low-voltage work.

Summary

ESTs install and service equipment and systems in a variety of technology areas, including: alarm and security, communications, entertainment, and integrated building management systems. ESTs work with computer networks, phone systems, audio and video systems, as well as home and business automation systems.

There are approximately 36,000 companies employing at least 165,000 ESTs. The opportunities in this field can only grow as the population becomes more and more dependent on computers and the demand for instant global communication and ready-access entertainment increases.

In addition to learning the technical aspects of their profession, including the safe and efficient use of a variety of tools and test devices, ESTs must become familiar with the numerous installation standards and building codes that govern the industry.

Review Questions

1. All of the following types of systems are installed by ESTs *except* _____.
   a. voice and data
   b. entertainment
   c. communications
   d. power distribution

2. A modem is a device used to _____.
   a. connect computers using communication lines
   b. amplify voice signals
   c. select the operating mode of a security system
   d. turn on emergency lighting during a power failure

3. Which of the following is likely to have a positive effect on your company's profit?
   a. Rework caused by improper installation
   b. Employee tardiness
   c. An increase in insurance costs
   d. Completing a job on time

4. If you are working with others toward a common objective, the best way to resolve a conflict is to _____.
   a. take control of the situation and dictate to the others
   b. try to intimidate anyone who disagrees with you
   c. keep talking until everyone agrees with you
   d. negotiate a solution that everyone can agree with

5. If there is a conflict between two codes or standards that apply to a job, the best approach is to _____.
   a. apply the most demanding standard
   b. apply the least demanding standard
   c. call the organizations that publish the codes
   d. apply the code with the most recent date

6. The *National Electrical Code®* is published by the _____.
   a. National Fire Protection Association
   b. National Electrical Code Association
   c. International Code Council
   d. American National Standards Institute

7. Which of the following is true regarding building codes?
   a. National codes always take precedence over local codes.
   b. Local codes are the same as national codes, so there is no conflict.
   c. Local codes may contain requirements that are not covered in national codes.
   d. Local codes always take precedence over national codes.

8. The ANSI/TIA/EIA standard that governs commercial building pathways and spaces is _____.
   a. *ANSI/TIA/EIA-568-B*
   b. *ANSI/TIA/EIA-569-A*
   c. *ANSI/TIA/EIA-570-A*
   d. *ANSI/TIA/EIA-606*

9. In an ATELS-certified training program, it is necessary to complete a minimum of _____ in each year of the training program.
   a. 150 hours of related instruction
   b. 1,000 hours of OJT
   c. 144 hours of related training and 2,000 hours of OJT
   d. 200 hours of related training and 1,000 hours of OJT

10. A detailed description of the work to be performed and the end result expected is a(n) _____.
    a. bill of materials
    b. work statement
    c. job sheet
    d. certificate of completion

Mark A. Curry, Technical Representative Supervisor
SimplexGrinnell, L.P.

Mark knew from an early age that he wanted a career in electronics, and he didn't wait for it to come to him. He started working toward it in his early teens and got the education and training he needed to succeed.

How did you choose a career in the EST field?
I have had an interest in how things work since my early teens. I tinkered with radios, stereos, and especially telephones and computers. I took some electronics classes in middle school and high school. I knew then that I wanted a career in the electronics field.

What types of training have you been through?
I had three years of high school electronics shop and I received a four-year Bachelor of Science in Electronics Engineering Technology from DeVry Institute of Technology. I also have the NICET® Level II Certification for Fire Alarm Systems. I was trained on a variety of Simplex® fire alarm systems sold in the past 20 years as well as Simplex® brand master clock systems, intercom systems, and electromechanical time clocks. I was also trained on the Iwatsu-based ADIX telephone systems.

What kinds of work have you done in your career?
I started with SimplexGrinnell in 1992 as a time clock technician. I repaired and inspected electromechanical time clocks and master clock systems for schools and businesses. Within a year's time I became an installation technician responsible for installing new fire alarm and communication systems. Over the next six years I installed and serviced a variety of systems in all types of buildings. In late 1998 I moved into the office as a local technical support specialist and systems trainer. I continued to install and service systems in the field, but now my focus was to help out our field technicians when they got in a bind with a technical problem. When not in the field, I would answer support questions for customers, contractors, and technicians. I was also responsible for conducting training programs for new hires and end users. I continued this for the next few years, and in 2002 was promoted to my supervisor position.

Tell us about your present job.
My current position adds all the functions of being a service tech, support specialist, trainer, mentor, and go-to person. It keeps me moving and motivated since each day brings new challenges from all directions. I now supervise nine service technicians and two inventory clerks. I assist them with customer issues ranging from billing, collecting, problem solving, scheduling, and of course technical assistance and training. I am a member of our office safety and security committees, as well as our local information technology representative. I have two other IT technicians who assist me with supporting three servers, 48 laptops, 20 desktop PCs, 114 Nextel phones, 2 fax machines, and 4 multi-function copiers. In addition, I serve on the NCCER committee that developed this EST curriculum.

What factors have contributed most to your success?
Besides training and education, I think my success was due to sheer determination to fix something and my commitment to get the job done correctly on the first try. Nothing is more satisfying than to have a customer call and request your services because of a good experience in the past. Each one of those requests gives you a little more boost to go the extra mile. It shows they trust you and respect you as a person and a professional.

What advice would you give to those new to the EST field?
Stick to the basics! When you are troubleshooting a system, remember that almost any system can be half-split into smaller parts to pinpoint your problem area. Even if you have not had formal training on the system, a few directed questions about what the product should do and what it is not doing now can go a long way toward earning the customer's respect. Continue to learn in the field and get as much training as you can on new products. This will keep you current with technology and keep your mind fresh with new ideas. Don't become stagnant, expand your horizons.

continued

Do you have an interesting career-related fact or accomplishment to share?
With only one year under my belt with SimplexGrinnell I became our only technician to install and support over 30 integrated communications systems for schools. I had no formal training on the product until almost three years later. In 1997, I worked on my first high-rise building. We installed an audio fire alarm system in a 23-story structure for a Fifth Third Bank. In 2001, I worked at the new AM General Hummer plant near South Bend, Indiana, installing their new 12-node networked fire alarm system.

Trade Terms Introduced in This Module

American National Standards Institute (ANSI): An international organization that serves as administrator and coordinator of the U.S. private sector voluntary standardization system. ANSI does not itself develop standards, rather it facilitates development by establishing consensus among qualified groups.

Electronic Industries Alliance (EIA): An international organization whose goal is to enhance the competitiveness of American electronics producers. The organization supports functions for its members in areas of market statistics, technical standards, government relations, and public affairs.

High voltage: As defined by the *National Electrical Code®*, the classification of high voltage covers voltages above 600V.

Low voltage: As defined by the *National Electrical Code®*, the classification of low voltage covers voltages below 600V.

Material takeoff: The process of surveying, measuring, and itemizing all materials and equipment needed for a project.

Microprocessor: A computer chip that can be programmed to perform arithmetic and logic functions and process data.

Modem: Acronym for modulator/demodulator. An electronic device used to connect computers using communication lines. It converts digital signals to analog signals and vice versa.

Pathways: Facilities for the placement of cable.

Retrofit: Convert to new equipment or place new equipment in existing structures.

Telecommunications Industry Association (TIA): An international trade organization that provides communications and information technology products, materials, systems, distribution services, and professional services. It represents suppliers of communications and information technology products on public policy, standards, and market-development issues.

National Trade Associations Representing the Electronic Systems Industries

ALOA
Associated Locksmiths of America
3003 Liveoak Street
Dallas, TX 75204
Phone: (214) 827-1701
Fax: (214) 827-1810
www.aloa.org

The Associated Locksmiths of America, Inc. is a trade association established in 1956 and dedicated to enhancing professionalism, education, and ethics among locksmiths and those in related sectors of the security industry.

Automatic Fire Alarm Association, Inc.
P.O. Box 951807
Lake Mary, FL 32795
Phone: (407) 322-6288
Fax: (407) 322-7488
www.afaa.org

The Automatic Fire Alarm Association was formed in 1953 and is the only national trade association exclusively dedicated to representing the automatic fire detection and fire alarm systems industry. The membership is made up of all segments of industry (manufacturers, distributors, state and regional associations, users, AHJs, engineers, and others).

The Association is committed to influencing codes and standards at all levels to make buildings safer through the proper application of automatic fire detection and fire alarm systems. Significant time and energy has been spent ensuring that the International Building, Fire, and Residential Codes require fire alarm and automatic detection systems for life safety and proper protection. Members also participate in the promulgation of *ANSI/NFPA-101*, *Life Safety Code* and *ANSI/NFPA-72*, *National Fire Alarm Code*.

BICSI
Building Industry Consulting Service International, Inc.
BICSI World Headquarters
8610 Hidden River Parkway
Tampa, FL 33637
Phone: (813) 979-1991 or (800) 242-7405
Fax: (813) 971-4311
www.bicsi.org

BICSI, an international not-for-profit telecommunications association, was founded in 1974 to serve and support telephone company building industry consultants (BICs) responsible for the design and distribution of telecommunications wiring in commercial and multi-family buildings.

BICSI has grown dramatically since those early days and now serves nearly 20,000 members from 80 countries around the world. Their programs and interests cover the broad spectrum of voice, data, and video technologies.

CABA
Continental Automated Buildings Association
1200 Montreal Road, Building M-20
Ottawa, ON, Canada
K1A 0R6
Phone: (613) 990-7407 or (888) 798-CABA (2222)
Fax: (613) 991-9990
www.caba.org

CABA is North America's key source for information, education, and networking relating to home and building automation. Its mission is to encourage the development, promotion, and adoption of business opportunities in the home and building automation industry. Members include manufacturers, dealers, installers, telecommunications companies, energy utilities, builders, consultants, research organizations, publishers, educational institutions, governments, and associations. CABA's numerous publications are recognized by many in the industry for providing more information about the home and building automation market than any other single source in the United States and Canada.

CANASA
Canadian Security Association
610 Alden Road, Suite 100
Markham, ON, Canada
L3R 9Z1
Phone: (905) 513-0622
Fax: (905) 513-0624
www.canasa.org

A non-profit national association established in 1977, CANASA represents the interests of the electronic security alarm industry and helps dealers, distributors, manufacturers, and monitoring companies across Canada succeed in business. Its Professional Development Courses, Information Services, and Membership Advantage Program (MAP) are all part of a comprehensive network of services designed to help members save money and run their businesses faster, safer, and in a professional and ethical manner. CANASA's mission is to promote and protect the interests of member companies.

CANASA is very active on a wide range of issues affecting its members, consumers, and the industry at large. The Association maintains an active dialogue with government officials and regulatory bodies on false alarm policies and prevention methods, industry competition, and licensing. CANASA offers a wide range of benefits and programs for its members, including monthly news updates, consumer publications, benefit plans, opportunities for professional development and education, member meetings, social events, and conferences. CANASA also produces and manages the Security Canada trade shows—the largest security industry shows in Canada. In addition to its national efforts, 13 chapters and subchapters across Canada work to effect positive change on a local level.

CEDIA
Custom Electronic Design and Installation Association
7150 Winton Drive
Suite 300
Indianapolis, IN 46268
Phone: (317) 328-4336
Fax: (317) 280-8527
www.cedia.net

CEDIA is an international, U.S.-based trade association. It is comprised of companies which specialize in planning or installing electronic systems in the home—such as home theaters, single- or multiroom entertainment systems, communications systems, alarm and surveillance systems, lighting control products, integrated systems, and other residential electronics. Founded in 1989, CEDIA's mission is to build recognition and acceptance for the specialized profession and to speak up for its interests by addressing industry, government, and the marketplace.

CEA
Consumer Electronics Association
2500 Wilson Boulevard
Arlington, VA 22201
Phone: (703) 907-7600
Fax: (703) 907-7601
www.ce.org

CEA is a trade association whose primary members are U.S. consumer electronic manufacturers. It is a sector of the Electronic Industries Alliance, which was founded in 1924. CEA has shaped legislation and developed thousands of engineering standards that enable new technologies to be brought to market. CEA sponsors the International Consumer Electronics Show and other trade shows which bring together manufacturers, distributors, retailers, and the press.

EIA
Electronic Industries Alliance
2500 Wilson Boulevard
Arlington, VA 22201
Phone: (703) 907-7500
www.eia.org

EIA is a trade association of the electronics industry that formulates technical standards, disseminates marketing data, and maintains contact with government agencies.

ESIC
Electronic Systems Industry Consortium
4708 Persimmon Way
Tampa, Florida 33624
Phone: (813) 962-7987
Fax: (813) 960-1876
www.hightechjobs.org

In February of 1998, leading trade associations representing electronic systems contracting companies and their suppliers banded together to form the Consortium for Electronic Systems Technician Training. The Consortium's initial goals were to identify and clarify the specific technical competencies sought in technical personnel and to consider options for addressing a chronic shortage of entry-level technical employees. Later that year, the Consortium agreed to join forces with NCCER. The Consortium and NCCER formed a group of subject matter experts (SMEs) who provided the content for the Electronic Systems Technician training. In 2004 the Consortium added a legislative monitoring function since training, apprenticeship and legislation had become intertwined with industry. The name was changed to the Electronic Systems Industry Consortium in response to representing the broader interests of the industry. The Consortium's members represent over 600,000 persons working in the electronic systems industry.

The ESIC is a 501(c)(6) not-for-profit corporation. Regular membership is confined to not-for-profit associations and associate memberships are available for schools, manufacturers, suppliers, schools, and other organizations within the electronic systems industry.

ESTA
Entertainment Services and Technology Association
875 Sixth Avenue
Suite 1005
New York, NY 10001
Phone: (212) 244-1505
Fax: (212) 244-1502
www.esta.org

ESTA is a non-profit trade association representing the North American entertainment technology industry. Our members, who supply a broad spectrum of products and services to the industry, include dealers, manufacturers, representatives, service and production companies, scenic houses, designers, and consultants.

Dedicated to promoting professionalism and growth in the industry, ESTA provides a forum where the industry can come together to exchange ideas and information, create standards and recommend practices, and address issues of training and certification. ESTA provides a wide variety of services to its members in the areas of education and information exchange, member promotion, trade show participation, reduced costs on business services and credit assistance. ESTA's ANSI-accredited Technical Standards Program is the leading standards making program for the entertainment technology industry. ESTA is also bringing the industry together to begin work on the development and implementation of the Entertainment Technician Certification Program.

ICIA
International Communications Industries Association
11242 Waples Mill Road
Suite 200
Fairfax, VA 22030
Phone: (800) 659-7469
Fax: (703) 278-8082
www.infocomm.org

ICIA serves its worldwide membership and the AV communications industry as the pre-eminent provider of education, exhibitions, and information services to enhance their ability to conduct business successfully, profitably and competently.

ICIA's membership is made up of 2,700 companies and individuals located in 56 countries, representing tens of thousands of AV communications professionals. ICIA presents value to its members as an industry-wide non-competitive entity.

NBFAA
National Burglar and Fire Alarm Association
8380 Colesville Road
Suite 750
Silver Spring, MD 20910
Phone: (301) 585-1855
Fax: (301) 585-1866
www.alarm.org

Founded in 1948, NBFAA is organized to pursue the common interests of the industry. The NBFAA is a federation of state associations and is governed by a board of directors selected from each state. Information on the latest technology, techniques, and practices are shared throughout the industry through NBFAA publications, meetings, seminars, and trade shows. Several benefits are available, including reduced rate group health, auto, and liability insurance. The NBFAA is active in false alarm prevention and legislative issues at the federal, state, and local level. The organization has provided its resources and support and played an active role in fashioning alarm industry licensing and fire safety standards in many states. The NBFAA is a leading resource to the nation's news media, the fire service, law enforcement, government, and other organizations on the subject of alarm systems and related fields.

NCCER
National Center for Construction Education and Research
P.O. Box 141104
Gainesville, FL 32614
Phone: (352) 334-0911
Fax: (352) 334-0932
www.nccer.org

NCCER provides a wide variety of construction training programs, maintains a National Registry of the work completed by trainees, and issues certificates to the trainees as they complete each level of an NCCER-accredited training program.

NFPA
National Fire Protection Association
One Batterymarch Park
Quincy, MA 02169
Phone: (617) 770-3000
Fax: (617) 770-0700
www.nfpa.org

NFPA publishes the *National Electrical Code®* and its related materials, along with numerous other codes relating to fire protection and safety.

NICET
National Institute for Certification in Engineering Technologies
1420 King Street
Alexandria, Virginia 22314
Phone: (703) 684-2835 or (800) 787-0034
www.nicet.org

NICET is an organization that administers testing and certification programs in the fire alarm and sound industry. NICET does not provide training.

NSCA
National Systems Contractors Association
625 First Street SE
Suite 420
Cedar Rapids, IA 52401
Phone: (319) 366-6722 or (800) 446-6722
Fax: (319) 366-4164
www.nsca.org

NSCA is a globally recognized trade association working continuously on improving the electronic systems contracting industry. It began as the National Sound and Communications Association but broadened its scope as members broadened their activities. Contractors are predominately commercial. NSCA's mission is to provide members of the NSCA and the electronic systems contracting industry with formal educational opportunities, professional development, information exchange, and member services in response to member-identified needs and priorities and to represent the industry in the external environment.

SIA
Security Industry Association
635 Slaters Lane
Suite 110
Alexandria, VA 22314
Phone: (703) 683-2075
Fax: (703) 683-2469
www.siaonline.org

SIA is an organization of manufacturers and distributors dedicated to the development of professionalism in the security industry. SIA develops equipment standards, has adopted warranty return and repair policies, sponsors market research, participates in false alarm prevention activities, and coordinates trade show exhibits.

TIA
Telecommunications Industry Association
2500 Wilson Boulevard
Suite 300
Arlington, VA 22201
Phone: (703) 907-7700
Fax: (703) 907-7727
www.tiaonline.org

TIA is a national trade organization that represents suppliers of communications and information technology products on public policy, standards, and market-development issues affecting its membership. TIA members provide communications and information technology products, materials, systems, distribution services, and professional services in the United States and around the world. The association's member companies manufacture or supply virtually all of the products used in global communication networks. TIA represents the telecommunications industry with its subsidiary, the Multimedia Telecommunications Association (MMTA), in conjunction with the Electronic Industries Alliance (EIA).

Portions of the NEC®
Affecting Telecommunications
and Life Safety Systems

NEC® Reference	Title	Description
NEC Section 90.2	Scope	The Scope provides information about what is covered in the NEC. This section offers reference to the NESC for industrial or multi-building complexes.
NEC Section 90.3	Code Arrangement	This section explains how the NEC chapters are positioned. Specifically, NEC Chapter 8, Communications Systems, is an independent chapter except where reference is made to other chapters.
NEC Article 100	Definitions	Definitions are those not commonly defined in English dictionaries. Some terms of interest include accessible, bonding, explosion-proof apparatus, ground, premises wiring, and signaling circuit.
NEC Section 110.26	Working Space About Electric Equipment (600V, Nominal, or Less)	This section explains the space for working clearances around electrical equipment. This information is useful when placing a terminal in an electrical closet or electronic components on a communications rack.
NEC Article 250	Grounding	This article is referenced from **NEC Article 800**. It contains specific requirements for the communications grounding and bonding network.
NEC Article 500	Hazardous (Classified) Locations	All of **NEC Article 500** is referenced in **NEC Article 800 (NEC Section 800.8).** This article covers hazardous locations such as gasoline stations and industrial complexes. Additionally, healthcare facilities **(NEC Section 517.80)** are of particular importance. Theaters and marinas are also included in this article.

101A01.EPS

NEC® Reference	Title	Description
NEC Article 725	Class 1, Class 2, and Class 3 Remote-Control, Signaling, and Power-Limited Systems	*NEC Article 725* specifies circuits other than those used specifically for electrical light and power.
NEC Article 760	Fire Alarm	*NEC Article 760* contains requirements for the wiring and equipment used in fire alarm systems.
NEC Article 770	Optical Fiber Cables and Raceways	*NEC Article 770* pertains to optical fiber cables and raceways. Within this section are the requirements for listing of cable, marking, and installation.
NEC Article 800	Communications Systems	*NEC Article 800* contains the requirements for communications systems.
NEC Article 810	Radio and Television Equipment	*NEC Article 810* contains the requirements for radio and television.
NEC Article 820	Community Antenna Television and Radio Distribution Systems	*NEC Article 820* contains requirements for community antenna television and radio distribution systems.

101A02.EPS

Portions of the CEC
Affecting Telecommunications
and Life Safety Systems

CEC Reference	Title	Description
2	General Rules	Provides information on: • Permits • Marking of cables • Flame spread requirements for electrical wiring and cables
10	Grounding and Bonding	Contains detailed grounding and bonding information and requirements for using and identifying grounding and bonding conductors.
12	Wiring Methods	Involves the requirements for installing wiring systems. It outlines: • Raceway systems • Boxes • Other system elements
56	Optical Fiber Cables	Contains the requirements for installing optical fiber cables.
60	Electrical Communication	Contains the requirements for installing communications circuits.

101A03.EPS

ANSI/NFPA
Standards Applicable
to Low-Voltage Systems

Code Number	Title
ANSI/NFPA-13, 13D, 13R	Installation of Sprinkler Systems
ANSI/NFPA-70	National Electrical Code®
ANSI/NFPA-72	National Fire Alarm Code
ANSI/NFPA-75	Protection of Electronic Computer Data Processing Equipment
ANSI/NFPA-101	Life Safety Code
ANSI/NFPA-780	Standard for Installation of Lighting Protection Systems

101A04.EPS

Standards Governing Telecommunications Cabling

ANSI/TIA/EIA-568-A, Commercial Building Telecommunications Cabling Standard:

- *ANSI/TIA/EIA-568-A-1, Propagation Delay and Delay Skew Specifications for 100 Ohm 4-Pair Cable*
- *ANSI/TIA/EIA Telecommunications Systems Bulletin (TSB-67), Transmission Performance Specifications for Field Testing of Unshielded Twisted-Pair Cabling Systems*
- *ANSI/TIA/EIA Telecommunications Systems Bulletin (TSB-72), Centralized Optical Fiber Cabling Guidelines*
- *ANSI/TIA/EIA Telecommunications Systems Bulletin (TSB-75), Additional Horizontal Cabling Practices for Open Offices*

ANSI/TIA/EIA-569-A*, Commercial Building Standard for Telecommunications Pathways and Spaces

ANSI/TIA/EIA-570-A*, Residential and Light Commercial Telecommunications Wiring Standard

ANSI/TIA/EIA-606, Administration Standard for the Telecommunications Infrastructure of Commercial Buildings

ANSI/TIA/EIA-607, Commercial Building Grounding and Bonding Requirements for Telecommunications

*The B revisions of *ANSI/TIA/EIA-569* and *570* are scheduled for publication in 2004.

NOTE

The Institute of Electrical and Electronic Engineers also publishes a variety of standards that apply to low-voltage systems. One such standard is *IEEE Standard 1394, High Performance Serial Bus.*

Additional Resources

This module is intended to be a thorough resource for task training. The following reference works are suggested for further study. These are optional materials for continued education rather than for task training.

National Electrical Code® Handbook. Quincy, MA: National Fire Protection Association.

TIA/EIA Telecommunications Building Wiring Standards. Englewood, CO: Global Engineering.

Figure Credits

Photodisc, Inc.	101F02 (photo), 101F03 (photo), 101F04
Ideal Industries, Inc.	101F10 (coaxial cable crimp tool and replacement die, coaxial cable stripper, punch-down tool, electrician's scissors, and Bix tool blade), 101F11 (LAN cable tester, telephone test set, and tone generator/amplifier probe kit)
Weller® Soldering Products	101F10 (soldering iron)
Topaz Publications, Inc.	101F11 (analog and digital multimeter)

The NCCER makes every effort to keep these textbooks up-to-date and free of technical errors. We appreciate your help in this process. If you have an idea for improving this textbook, or if you find an error, a typographical mistake, or an inaccuracy in NCCER's Contren® textbooks, please write us, using this form or a photocopy. Be sure to include the exact module number, page number, a detailed description, and the correction, if applicable. Your input will be brought to the attention of the Technical Review Committee. Thank you for your assistance.

Instructors – If you found that additional materials were necessary in order to teach this module effectively, please let us know so that we may include them in the Equipment/Materials list in the Instructor's Guide.

Write: Product Development and Revision
National Center for Construction Education and Research
P.O. Box 141104, Gainesville, FL 32614-1104

Fax: 352-334-0932

E-mail: curriculum@nccer.org

Craft _____ Module Name _____

Copyright Date _____ Module Number _____ Page Number(s) _____

Description _____

_____

_____

_____

(Optional) Correction _____

_____

_____

(Optional) Your Name and Address _____

_____

_____

Construction Materials and Methods

COURSE MAP

This course map shows all of the modules in the first level of the *Electronic Systems Technician* curriculum. The suggested training order begins at the bottom and proceeds up. Skill levels increase as you advance on the course map. The local Training Program Sponsor may adjust the training order.

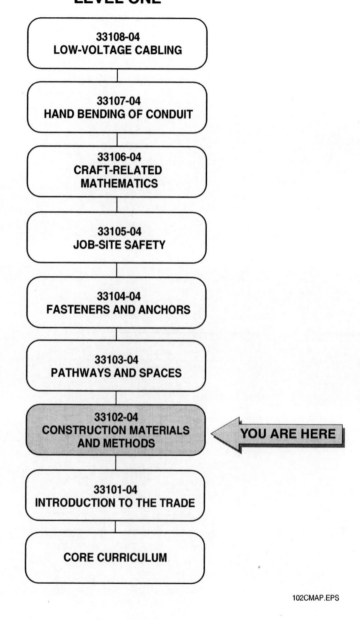

**ELECTRONIC SYSTEMS TECHNICIAN
LEVEL ONE**

33108-04
LOW-VOLTAGE CABLING

33107-04
HAND BENDING OF CONDUIT

33106-04
CRAFT-RELATED
MATHEMATICS

33105-04
JOB-SITE SAFETY

33104-04
FASTENERS AND ANCHORS

33103-04
PATHWAYS AND SPACES

33102-04
CONSTRUCTION MATERIALS
AND METHODS

YOU ARE HERE

33101-04
INTRODUCTION TO THE TRADE

CORE CURRICULUM

102CMAP.EPS

MODULE 33102-04 CONTENTS

1.0.0   **INTRODUCTION** 2.1

2.0.0   **BUILDING MATERIALS** 2.1

    2.1.0   Lumber 2.2

    2.1.1   *Pressure-Treated Lumber* 2.2

    2.2.0   Plywood 2.3

    2.3.0   Building Boards 2.3

    2.3.1   *Hardboard* 2.4

    2.3.2   *Particleboard* 2.4

    2.3.3   *Oriented Strand Board (OSB)* 2.4

    2.3.4   *Mineral Fiberboards* 2.4

    2.3.5   *High-Density Overlay (HDO) and Medium-Density Overlay (MDO) Plywood* 2.5

    2.4.0   Engineered Wood Products 2.5

    2.5.0   Gypsum Board 2.6

    2.5.1   *Types of Gypsum Products* 2.6

    2.6.0   Masonry Materials 2.9

    2.6.1   *Concrete* 2.9

    2.6.2   *Concrete Masonry Units (CMUs)* 2.10

    2.6.3   *Brick* 2.11

    2.6.4   *Stone* 2.11

    2.6.5   *Metal* 2.11

3.0.0   **RESIDENTIAL FRAME CONSTRUCTION** 2.12

    3.1.0   Floor Construction 2.13

    3.1.1   *Girders* 2.14

    3.1.2   *Floor Joists* 2.16

    3.1.3   *Wood I-Beams* 2.17

    3.1.4   *Trusses* 2.17

    3.1.5   *Notching and Drilling of Wooden Joists* 2.17

    3.1.6   *Bridging* 2.18

    3.1.7   *Subflooring* 2.19

    3.2.0   Wall Construction 2.20

    3.2.1   *Corners* 2.21

    3.2.2   *Partition Intersections* 2.21

    3.2.3   *Window and Door Openings* 2.21

    3.2.4   *Firestops* 2.23

    3.2.5   *Bracing* 2.23

    3.2.6   *Sheathing* 2.24

    3.3.0   Ceiling Construction 2.26

3.4.0   Roof Construction 2.27
3.4.1   *Roof Components* 2.29
3.4.2   *Roof Sheathing* 2.30
3.4.3   *Truss Construction* 2.31
3.4.4   *Dormers* 2.32
3.5.0   Plank-and-Beam Framing 2.32
3.6.0   Framing in Masonry 2.33
3.7.0   Walls Separating Occupancies 2.33

4.0.0   **COMMERCIAL CONSTRUCTION METHODS** 2.34
4.1.0   Floors 2.36
4.2.0   Exterior Walls 2.38
4.3.0   Interior Walls and Partitions 2.38
4.3.1   *Metal Framing Materials* 2.38
4.3.2   *Bracing Walls* 2.42
4.3.3   *Metal Joists and Roof Trusses* 2.42
4.4.0   Ceilings 2.43
4.4.1   *Exposed Grid Systems* 2.45
4.4.2   *Metal Pan Systems* .2.47
4.4.3   *Direct-Hung Concealed Grid Systems* 2.48
4.4.4   *Integrated Ceiling Systems* 2.49
4.4.5   *Luminous Ceiling Systems* 2.49
4.4.6   *Suspended Drywall Furring Ceiling Systems* 2.50
4.4.7   *Special Ceiling Systems* 2.51
4.4.8   *General Guidelines for Accessing Suspended Ceilings* 2.52

5.0.0   **FIRE-RATED AND SOUND-RATED CONSTRUCTION** 2.52
5.1.0   Firestopping 2.54
5.2.0   Sound-Isolation Construction 2.57

6.0.0   **TOOLS USED FOR RUNNING CABLE** 2.58
6.1.0   Guidelines for Using All Power Tools 2.58
6.1.1   *Safety Rules Pertaining to All Power Tools* 2.58
6.1.2   *Guidelines Pertaining to the Care of All Power Tools* 2.59
6.2.0   Drilling Tools 2.59
6.2.1   *Portable Drills and Screwguns* 2.59
6.2.2   *Hammer Drills and Rotary Hammers* 2.60
6.2.3   *Special Drilling Equipment* 2.62
6.3.0   Horizontal Directional Drilling 2.65

6.4.0 Cutting Tools 2.66

6.4.1 Reciprocating Saws 2.66

6.4.2 Jig Saws 2.66

6.4.3 Power Cutout Tool 2.67

6.4.4 Drywall Circle Cutter 2.67

6.4.5 Metal Stud Punches 2.67

6.5.0 Pneumatic Nailers and Staplers 2.68

6.6.0 Powder-Actuated Fastening Tools 2.69

6.7.0 Stud Finders 2.70

6.8.0 Fish Tapes 2.70

7.0.0 PROJECT SCHEDULES 2.71

SUMMARY 2.72

REVIEW QUESTIONS 2.72

PROFILE IN SUCCESS 2.74

GLOSSARY 2.75

REFERENCES & ACKNOWLEDGMENTS 2.77

Figures

Figure 1   Types of plywood 2.3

Figure 2   OSB panels 2.4

Figure 3   Examples of engineered wood products 2.6

Figure 4   Glulam beam application 2.6

Figure 5   Typical gypsum wallboard application 2.7

Figure 6   Wall form made from EFCO Hand-E-Form®
           panel system components 2.10

Figure 7   Examples of concrete blocks 2.11

Figure 8   Brick veneer wall 2.12

Figure 9   Stone wall 2.12

Figure 10 Example of rough carpentry
           (western platform framing) 2.13

Figure 11 Foundation form 2.13

Figure 12   Types of slabs 2.14

Figure 13   Concrete block basement wall 2.14

Figure 14   Polystyrene form system 2.14

Figure 15   Typical sill installation 2.15

Figure 16   Typical platform frame floor system 2.15

Figure 17   Typical methods of supporting girders 2.16

Figure 18   Methods of joist framing at a girder 2.17

Figure 19   Typical floor trusses 2.18

Figure 20   Typical floor system constructed with trusses 2.18

Figure 21   Notching and drilling of wooden joists 2.19

Figure 22   Types of bridging 2.19

Figure 23   Subflooring installation 2.20

Figure 24   Wall and partition framing members 2.21

Figure 25   Corner construction 2.22

Figure 26   Constructing nailing surfaces for partitions 2.23

Figure 27   Types of headers 2.24

Figure 28   Cross sections of wood-framed walls 2.25

Figure 29   Firestops 2.25

Figure 30   Metal bracing 2.25

Figure 31   Cutting joist ends to match the roof pitch 2.27

Figure 32   Spliced ceiling joists 2.27

Figure 33   Reinforcing ceiling joists 2.28

Figure 34   Types of roofs 2.28

Figure 35   Roof framing members 2.29

Figure 36   Roof layout factors 2.30

Figure 37   Underlayment installation 2.31

Figure 38   Components of a truss 2.31

Figure 39   Types of trusses 2.32

Figure 40   Shed dormer 2.32

Figure 41   Gable dormer framing 2.33

Figure 42   Example of post-and-beam framing 2.33

Figure 43   Partition backing on a block wall 2.34

Figure 44   Corner construction 2.34

Figure 45   Installing a corner curtain wall panel 2.35

Figure 46   Curtain wall under construction 2.35

Figure 47   Concrete structure 2.35

Figure 48   Tilt-up panel being lifted into place 2.36

Figure 49   Corrugated steel forms 2.37

Figure 50   Flushduct underfloor system 2.37

Figure 51   Trench duct in a cellular floor 2.37

Figure 52   Framing openings in concrete walls 2.38

Figure 53   High fire/noise resistance partition 2.38

Figure 54   Partition wall examples 2.39

Figure 55   Metal trusses 2.39

Figure 56   Standard metal stud stock .2.39

Figure 57   Heavy-duty stud stock 2.40

Figure 58   Metal framing 2.41

Figure 59   Metal studs with concrete floors and ceiling 2.41

Figure 60   Partition held back to allow drywall to slide by 2.41

Figure 61   Plate attached to a beam 2.42

Figure 62   Studs secured to a channel 2.42

Figure 63   Lateral strapping for stud walls 2.43

Figure 64   Diagonal strapping for shear walls 2.44

Figure 65   Heavy-duty bridging 2.44

Figure 66   Fine-gauge lateral bracing .2.44

Figure 67   Examples of metal joist installations 2.45

Figure 68   Installing metal floor joists in a
             slotted foundation wall 2.45

Figure 69   Typical exposed grid system components 2.46

Figure 70   Typical metal pan ceiling components 2.47

Figure 71   Pan removal tool 2.47

Figure 72   Metal pan ceiling 2.47

Figure 73   Typical concealed grid system 2.48

Figure 74   Direct-hung concealed grid system components 2.48

Figure 75   Typical access for concealed grid ceilings 2.49

Figure 76   Typical integrated grid system 2.50

Figure 77   Integrated ceiling layout 2.50

Figure 78   Typical integrated luminous ceiling system 2.50

Figure 79   Carrying channel installed .2.51

Figure 80   Furring channel attached to carrying channel 2.51

Figure 81   Drywall secured to furring channel 2.51

Figure 82   Special metallic system 2.51

Figure 83   Special pan system 2.51

Figure 84   Planar system 2.51

Figure 85   Reflective ceiling 2.52

Figure 86   Translucent panels 2.52

Figure 87   Specifications for typical fire-rated walls 2.54

Figure 88   Example of a fire-rated wall abutting
             a non-rated wall 2.55

Figure 89   Mechanical firestop device 2.55

Figure 90   Fireproof openings 2.56

Figure 91   Extension cord with a GFCI 2.59

Figure 92   Using an electric drill 2.59

Figure 93   Portable drills 2.60

Figure 94   Examples of drill bits 2.60

Figure 95   Power-driven screwdriver 2.61

Figure 96   Hammer drill used to drill holes in masonry 2.61

Figure 97   Hammer drill bits 2.61

Figure 98   Rotary hammer accessories 2.61

Figure 99   Flexible steel drilling system 2.62

Figure 100 90-degree drill 2.62

Figure 101 Core drill 2.65

Figure 102 Horizontal directional drilling rig 2.65

Figure 103 Horizontal directional drilling 2.65

Figure 104 Reciprocating saw 2.66

Figure 105 Reciprocating saw cutting through a floor 2.66

Figure 106 Jig saw 2.66

Figure 107 Power cutout tool 2.67

Figure 108 Circle cutter 2.67

Figure 109 Metal stud punch and grommet 2.67

Figure 110 Pneumatic stapler and nailers 2.68

Figure 111 Gas-driven cordless nail gun 2.69

Figure 112 Powder-actuated fastening tool 2.69

Figure 113 Economical stud locator 2.70

Figure 114 Fish tape installation 2.70

Figure 115 Typical residential construction schedule 2.71

Figure 116 Typical commercial construction schedule 2.72

Tables

Table 1   Nominal and Dressed Sizes of
            Dimension Lumber (in Inches) 2.2

Table 2   Types and Uses of Gypsum Wallboard 2.8

Table 3   Maximum Framing Spacing 2.40

Table 4   Drill Bits and Blades Used for Various Materials ...2.63

Table 5   Drill Bits and Blades Used with Various Tools 2.64

Table 6   Powder Charge Color-Coding System 2.69

Construction Materials and Methods

Objectives

When you have completed this module, you will be able to do the following:

1. Describe the composition and uses of the common types of residential building materials.
2. Identify the major structural components of a residential building.
3. Describe the composition and uses of the common types of commercial building materials.
4. Describe common methods of residential and commercial construction.
5. State the major steps in the construction of a frame residence.
6. Explain common terms used in construction.
7. Identify various types of suspended ceilings.
8. Describe how cable is run from building to building.
9. Select appropriate drills, bits, and cutting tools and make openings in various types of construction materials, including:
   - Lumber
   - Concrete
   - Concrete block
   - Steel
10. Install plywood on a gypsum board wall.

Recommended Prerequisites

Core Curriculum; Electronic Systems Technician Level One, Module 33101-04

Required Trainee Materials

1. Paper and pencil
2. Appropriate personal protective equipment

1.0.0 ◆ INTRODUCTION

Why would someone who installs and services electronic systems need to know how buildings are constructed? The simple answer is that you have to know how the building is put together in order to run cable from place to place within the building, and from one building to another, without doing any damage. Part of that is understanding building materials and how to drill through them.

This module provides an overview of the various types of building materials used in residential and commercial construction and the tools used to penetrate them. We will also cover the construction sequence, so you will know how your work in running and terminating cables and installing distribution boxes fits into the larger scheme of the construction process.

Residential and commercial (including multi-family) construction methods are very different, so they will be covered separately. When we speak of residential, we are referring to single-family and two-family dwellings. Keep in mind, however, that some small commercial buildings, such as apartment buildings and townhouses, may use the same construction techniques and materials as those used in residential buildings.

2.0.0 ◆ BUILDING MATERIALS

Many different materials are used in the construction of a building. Wood frame construction is most common in residential work. Concrete block and brick are also used in residential and light commercial construction.

The construction of large commercial buildings such as office buildings, warehouses, apartment buildings, and parking garages generally involves the use of a steel or concrete support structure and walls made of concrete or steel and glass.

2.1.0 Lumber

The framework of a single-family or two-family dwelling is usually built from lumber, which is divided into five categories:

- Boards – Members up to 1½" thick and 2" wide or wider.
- *Light framing (L.F.)* – Members 2" to 4" thick and 2" to 4" wide.
- *Joists and planks (J&P)* – Members 2" to 4" thick and 6" wide or wider.
- *Beams and **stringers** (B&S)* – Members 5" and thicker by 8" and wider.
- *Posts and timbers (P&T)* – Members 5" × 5" and greater, approximately square.

The vast majority of lumber used in framing a house is softwood such as pine or fir. Hardwoods such as oak and maple are used primarily in furniture and decorative pieces.

Light framing lumber, studs, joists, and planks are all classified as **dimension lumber**.

You are probably familiar with the terms 2 × 4, 1 × 6, and so on. What you may not know is that these numbers represent the nominal (rough) size of the lumber in inches. Once the lumber is dressed (finished) at the lumber mill, it is somewhat smaller, typically ½" to ¾" less than the nominal size in each dimension. *Table 1* shows the final dimensions for some standard sizes of softwood dimension lumber. Note that these dressed dimensions apply only to softwoods; hardwoods have different conversion tables.

2.1.1 Pressure-Treated Lumber

Pressure-treated lumber is softwood lumber protected by chemical preservatives forced deep into the wood through a vacuum-pressure process. Pressure-treated lumber has been used for many years in on-ground and below-ground applications such as landscape timbers, **sill plates**, and foundations. In some parts of the country, it is also

Table 1 Nominal and Dressed Sizes of Dimension Lumber (in Inches)

Nominal	Dressed
2 × 2	1½ × 1½
2 × 4	1½ × 3½
2 × 6	1½ × 5½
2 × 8	1½ × 7¼
2 × 10	1½ × 9¼
2 × 12	1½ × 11¼

102T01.EPS

used extensively in the building of decks, porches, docks, and other outdoor structures. It is popular for these uses in areas where structures are exposed to snow for several months of the year. A major advantage of pressure-treated lumber is its relatively low price in comparison with redwood and cedar. When natural woods such as these are used, only the more expensive heartwood will resist decay and insects.

Because the chemicals used in pressure-treated lumber present some hazards to people and the environment, special precautions apply to its use:

- When cutting pressure-treated lumber, always wear eye protection and a dust mask.
- Wash any skin that is exposed while cutting or handling the lumber.
- Wash clothing that is exposed to sawdust separately from other clothing.
- Do not burn pressure-treated lumber, as the ash poses a health hazard. Bury it or put it in with the trash.
- Be sure to read and follow the manufacturer's safety instructions as defined in the material safety data sheet (MSDS).

One place to look for pressure-treated lumber is any location where wood comes into contact with the ground, or outdoors where the wood is exposed to moisture.

Ghost Wood

Longleaf pine and bald cypress are praised by carpenters for their outstanding beauty and durability. Unfortunately, clear-cutting that occurred in the late 1800s wiped out the two species from the vast forests in the southern United States. Today, lumber companies have resurrected this wood by retracing the rivers that timber companies used to transport the logs to sawmills. Logs of original-growth pine and cypress have been lying along the bottom of these riverbeds for more than one hundred years. What was left behind is now harvested by scuba divers, then sawed, dried, and used for various construction purposes.

2.2.0 Plywood

Plywood is made by gluing together thin layers of wood known as **veneers**. Plywood can have three or more plies (layers). These are bonded together at right angles with glue and heat under tremendous pressure. Putting the plies together at right angles increases the strength; also, the more plies there are, the greater the strength. The ply that is in the center is called the core and each of the exposed plies is called a veneer or face (*Figure 1*). All other plies between the core and veneer are called the crossbands. Constructing the plywood with the grain of adjacent plies running at right angles reduces the possibility of warping.

The average or standard size of plywood is 4'-0" × 8'-0". A few companies produce plywood from 6' to 8' widths and up to 16' in length. **Sheathing**-grade plywood is nominally sized by the manufacturer to allow for expansion; for example, 4'-0" × 8'-0" is really 47¾" × 95¾".

The thickness of plywood will vary from ¾₆" to 1¼". The common sizes are ¼", ½", and ½" for finish paneling and ⅜", ½", ⅝", and ¾" for structural purposes.

Plywood is rated by the American Plywood Association (APA) for interior or exterior use. Exterior-rated plywood is used for sheathing, siding, and other applications where there may be exposure to moisture or wet weather conditions. Exterior plywood panels are made of high-grade veneers bonded together with a waterproof glue that is as strong as the wood itself.

Interior plywood uses lower grades of veneer for the back and inner plies. Although the plies may be bonded with a water-resistant glue, waterproof glue is normally used. The lower-grade veneers reduce the bonding strength, however, which means that interior-rated panels are not suitable for exterior use.

2.3.0 Building Boards

The ingenuity and technology that helped develop the plywood industry also assisted in the development of other materials in sheet form. The main ingredients for these products, known as building boards, are vegetable or mineral fibers. After mixing these ingredients with binder, the mixture becomes very soft.

At this point, the mixture passes through a press, which uses heat and pressure to produce the required thickness and density of the finished board.

Sawdust, wood chips, and wood scraps are the major waste materials at sawmills. These scrap materials are softened with heat and moisture, mixed with a binder and other ingredients, and then run through presses that produce the desired density and thickness.

The finished wood products that come off the presses are classified as hardboard, particleboard, or **oriented strand board (OSB)**.

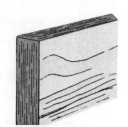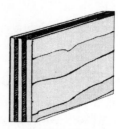

LUMBER CORE   PARTICLEBOARD CORE   VENEER BOARD   FIBERBOARD CORE

102F01.EPS

Figure 1 ◆ Types of plywood.

2.3.1 Hardboard

Hardboard is a manufactured building material, sometimes called tempered board or pegboard. Hardboards are water-resistant and extremely dense. The common thicknesses for hardboards are ³⁄₁₆", ¼", and ⁵⁄₁₆". The standard sheet size for hardboards is 4'-0" × 8'-0". However, they can be made in widths up to 6' and lengths up to 16' for specialized uses.

These boards are susceptible to breaking at the edges if they are not properly supported. Holes must be predrilled for nailing; direct nailing into the material will cause it to fracture.

Three grades of hardboard are manufactured:

- *Standard* – Suitable only for interior use, such as cabinets.
- *Tempered* – The same as standard grade except that it is denser, stronger, and more brittle. Tempered hardboard is suitable for either interior or exterior uses such as siding, wall paneling, and other decorative purposes.
- *Service* – Not as dense, strong, or heavy as standard grade. It can be used for basically everything for which standard or tempered hardboard is used. Service grade hardboard is manufactured for items such as cabinets, parts of furniture, and perforated hardboard.

2.3.2 Particleboard

The main composition of this type of material is small particles or flakes of wood.

Particleboard is pressed under heat into panels. The sheets range in size from ¼" to 1½" in thickness and from 3' to 8' in width. There are also thicknesses of 3" and lengths ranging up to 24' for special purposes. Particleboard has no grain, is smoother than plywood, is more resilient, and is less likely to warp.

Some types of particleboard can be used for **underlayment** if permitted by the local building codes. If particleboard is used as underlayment, it is laid with the long dimension across the joists and the edges staggered. Particleboard can be nailed, although some types will crumble or crack when nailed close to the edges.

2.3.3 Oriented Strand Board (OSB)

Oriented strand board (OSB) is a manufactured structural panel used for wall and roof sheathing and single-layer floor construction. *Figure 2* shows two kinds of OSB panels. OSB consists of compressed wood strands arranged in three perpendicular layers and bonded with phenolic resin. Some of the qualities of OSB are dimensional stability, stiffness, fastener holding capacity, and no

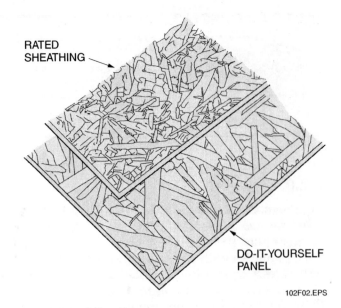

Figure 2 ♦ OSB panels.

voids in the core material. Before cutting into OSB, be sure to check the applicable MSDS for safety hazards. The MSDS is the most reliable source of safety information.

2.3.4 Mineral Fiberboards

The building boards just covered are classified as vegetable fiberboards. Mineral fiberboards fall into the same category as vegetable fiberboards. The main difference is that they will not support combustion. Glass and **gypsum** rock are the most common minerals used in the manufacture of these fiberboards. Fibers of glass or gypsum powder are mixed with a binder and pressed or sandwiched between two layers of asphalt-impregnated paper, producing a rigid insulation board.

Some types of chemical foam mixed with glass fibers will also make a good, rigid insulation. However, this mineral insulation will crush and should not be used when it must support a heavy load.

 WARNING!
Whenever working with older materials that may be made with asbestos, contact your supervisor for the company's policies on safe handling of the material. State and federal regulations require specific procedures to follow prior to removing, cutting, or disturbing any suspect materials. Also, some materials emit a harmful dust when cut. Check the MSDS before cutting. Asbestos can be found in structures built before 1978. It was used in ceiling tiles, siding, floor coverings, shingles, and pipe insulation.

2.3.5 High-Density Overlay (HDO) and Medium-Density Overlay (MDO) Plywood

High-density overlay (HDO) plywood panels have a hard, resin-impregnated fiber overlay heat-bonded to both surfaces. HDO panels are resistant to both abrasion and moisture and can be used for concrete forms, cabinets, countertops, and similar high-wear applications. HDO also resists damage from chemicals and solvents. HDO is available in four common thicknesses: ⅜", ½", ⅝", and ¾".

Medium-density overlay (MDO) panels are coated on one or both surfaces with a smooth, opaque overlay. MDO accepts paint well and is suitable for use as structural siding, exterior decorative panels, and soffits. MDO panels are available in eight common thicknesses ranging from ¹¹⁄₃₂" to ²³⁄₃₂".

Both HDO and MDO panels are manufactured with waterproof adhesive and are suitable for exterior use. If MDO panels are to be used outdoors, however, the panels should be edge-sealed with one or two coats of a good-quality exterior housepaint primer. This is easier to do when the panels are stacked.

2.4.0 Engineered Wood Products

In the past, the primary source of structural beams, timbers, joists, and other weight-bearing lumber was old-growth trees. These trees, which need more than 200 years to mature, are tall and thick and can produce a large amount of high-quality, tight-grained lumber. Extensive logging of these trees to meet demand resulted in higher prices and conflict with forest conservation interests.

The development of wood laminating techniques by lumber producers has permitted the use of younger-growth trees in the production of structural building materials. These materials are given the general classification of engineered lumber products.

Engineered wood products fall into five categories: laminated veneer lumber (LVL), parallel strand lumber (PSL), laminated strand lumber (LSL), wood I-beams, and glue-laminated lumber or glulam (*Figure 3*).

Engineered wood products provide several benefits:

- They can be made from younger, more abundant trees.
- They can increase the yield of a tree by 30% to 50%.
- They are stronger than the same size of structural lumber. Therefore, the same size piece of engineered lumber can bear more weight than that of solid lumber. Or, looked at another way, a smaller piece of engineered lumber can bear equal weight.
- Greater strength allows the engineered lumber to span a greater distance.
- A length of engineered wood is lighter than the same length of solid lumber. It is therefore easier to handle.

LVL is used for floor and roof beams and for **headers** over windows and doors. It is also used in scaffolding and concrete forms. No special cutting tools or fasteners are required.

PSL is used for beams, posts, and columns. It is manufactured in thicknesses up to 7". Columns can be up to 7" wide, and beams range up to 18" in width.

LSL is used for **millwork** such as doors and windows, and any other product that requires high-grade lumber. However, LSL will not support as much of a load as a comparable size of PSL because PSL is made from stronger wood.

Wood I-beams consist of a web with flanges bonded to the top and bottom. This arrangement, which mimics the steel I-beam, provides exceptional strength. The web can be made of OSB or plywood. The flanges are grooved to fit over the web. Wood I-beams are used as floor joists, **rafters**, and headers. Because of their strength, wood I-beams can be used in greater spans than a comparable length of dimension lumber. Lengths of up to 80' are available.

Glulam is made from several lengths of solid lumber that have been glued together. It is popular in architectural applications where exposed beams are used (*Figure 4*). Because of its exceptional strength and flexibility, glulam can be used in areas subject to high winds or earthquakes.

Fire-Retardant Building Materials

Lumber and sheet materials are sometimes treated with fire-retardant chemicals. The lumber can either be coated with the chemical in a non-pressure process or impregnated with the chemical in a pressure-treating process. Fire-retardant chemicals react to extreme heat, releasing vapors that form a protective coating around the outside of the wood. This coating, known as char, delays ignition and inhibits the release of smoke and toxic fumes.

PSL

LVL

LSL

WOOD I-BEAMS

GLULAM BEAM

102F03.EPS

Figure 3 ◆ Examples of engineered wood products.

102F04.EPS

Figure 4 ◆ Glulam beam application.

Glulam beams are available in widths from 2½" to 8¾". Depths range from 5½₀" to 28½". They are available in lengths up to 40'. They are used for many purposes, including: ridge beams; basement beams; headers of all types; stair treads, supports, and stringers; and **cantilever** and **vaulted ceiling** applications.

2.5.0 Gypsum Board

Gypsum wallboard, also known as gypsum drywall, is one of the most popular and economical methods of finishing the interior walls and ceilings of wood-framed and metal-framed buildings. Properly installed and finished, drywall can give a wall or ceiling made from many panels the appearance of being made from one continuous sheet.

Gypsum board is a generic name for products consisting of a noncombustible core. It is rated as limited combustible because of the paper. This product is made primarily of gypsum with a paper surfacing covering the face, back, and long edges. A typical board application is shown in *Figure 5*.

2.5.1 Types of Gypsum Products

Many types of gypsum board are available for a variety of building needs (see *Table 2*). Gypsum board panels are mainly used as the surface layer for interior walls and ceilings; as a base for ceramic, plastic, and metal tile; for exterior soffits; for elevator and other shaft enclosures; and to provide fire protection for architectural elements.

Gypsum board products are available with reflective aluminum foil backing, which provides an effective vapor barrier for exterior walls. When applied with the foil surface against the framing, with a minimum of ¾" enclosed air space adjacent to the foil, additional insulating efficiency is achieved.

This combination effectively reduces radiant heat loss in the cold season and radiant heat gain in the warm season. However, foil-backed gypsum

Use of Engineered Wood Products

Engineered wood products are used in a wide array of applications that were once exclusively served by cut lumber. For example, PSL is used for columns, ridge beams, and headers. LVL is also used for form headers and beams. Wood I-beams are used to frame roofs as well as floors. An especially noteworthy application is the use of LSL studs, top plates, and soleplates in place of lumber to frame walls.

The Way It Was

Until the 1930s, walls were typically finished by installing thin, narrow strips of wood or metal known as lath between studs, and then coating the lath with wet plaster. Skilled plasterers could produce a very smooth wall finish, but the process was time-consuming and messy. In the early 1930s, paper-bound gypsum board was introduced and soon came into widespread use as a replacement for the tedious lath and plaster process.

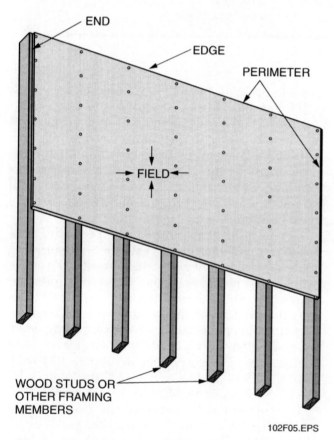

102F05.EPS

Figure 5 ◆ Typical gypsum wallboard application.

- ¼" *gypsum board* – A lightweight, low-cost board used as a base in a multi-layer application for improving sound control, to cover existing walls and ceilings in remodeling, for curved walls, and for barrel ceilings.

- ⁵⁄₁₆" *gypsum board* – A lightweight board developed for use in manufactured construction, primarily mobile homes.

- ⅜" *gypsum board* – A lightweight board principally applied in a double-layer system over wood framing and as a face layer in repair and remodeling.

- ½" *gypsum board* – Generally used for single-layer wall and ceiling construction in residential work and in double-layer systems for greater sound and **fire ratings**.

- ⅝" *gypsum board* – Used in quality single-layer and double-layer wall systems. The greater thickness provides additional fire resistance, higher rigidity, and better impact resistance. It is also used to separate occupied and unoccupied areas, such as a house from a garage or an office from a warehouse.

- 1" *gypsum board (either a single 1" board or two ½" factory-laminated boards)* – Used as a liner or as a core board in shaft walls and in semi-solid or solid gypsum board partitions. It is also known as coreboard.

Standard gypsum boards are 4' wide and 8', 10', or 14' long. The width is compatible with the standard framing of studs or joists spaced 16" or 24" on center.

Regular gypsum board is used as a surface layer on walls and ceilings. Type X gypsum board is available in ½" and ⅝" thicknesses and has an improved fire resistance made possible by the use

board is not used as a backing material for tile, as a second face ply on a two-ply system, in conjunction with heating cables, or when laminating directly to masonry, ceiling, and roof assemblies.

Various thicknesses of gypsum wallboard are available in regular, Type X, water-resistant, and predecorated boards.

Table 2 Types and Uses of Gypsum Wallboard

Type	Thickness	Sizes	Use
Regular, paper faced	¼" ⅜" ½", ⅝"	4' × 8' to 10' 4' × 8' to 14' 4' × 8' to 16'	Recovering old gypsum walls Double-layer installation Standard single-ply installation
Regular with foil back	½", ⅝"	4' × 8' to 14'	Use as a vapor barrier or radiant heat retarder
Type X, fire-retardant	⅜",½", ⅝"	4' × 8' to 16'	Use in garages, workshops, and kitchens, as well as around furnaces, fireplaces, and chimney walls; ⅝" is ¾-hour fire rated
Moisture-resistant	½", ⅝"	4' × 6' to 16'	For tile backing in areas not exposed to constant moisture
Architectural panels	5⁄16"	4' × 8'	Any room in the house
Gypsum lath	⅜", ½", ⅝"	16" × 4' 2' × 8' to 12'	Use as a base for plaster Use ⅜" for 16" OC stud spacing; ½" or ⅝" for 24" OC stud spacing
Gypsum coreboard	1"	2' × 8' to 12'	Shaft liner Laminated partitions

102T02.EPS

of special core additions. It is also available with a predecorated finish. Type X gypsum board is used in most fire-rated assemblies.

Architectural (predecorated) gypsum board has a decorated surface which does not require further treatment. The surfaces may be coated, printed, or have a vinyl film. Textured patterns are also available. It requires additional trim, dividers, and corners.

Water-resistant gypsum board, also known as green board, has a water-resistant gypsum core and water-repellent paper. The facing typically has a light green color. It is available with a regular or Type X core and in ½" or ⅝" thicknesses. Water-resistant gypsum board is not recommended for use in tubs and shower enclosures and other areas exposed to water.

A special type of wallboard is replacing water-resistant gypsum wallboard as a backing for tile in damp areas such as baths and shower stalls. One type is known as cement board. It is made from a slurry of Portland cement mixed with glass fibers. It is colored light blue for easy recognition. These backer boards, in addition to their use as a tile backer, can be used as a floor underlayment, countertop base, heat shield for stoves, and as a base for exterior finishes such as **stucco** and brick veneer. They are available in 4" × 8" and 3" × 5" panels. Common thicknesses are ¼", 7⁄16", and ½".

Gypsum backing board is designed to be used as a base layer or backing material in multi-layer systems. It is available with aluminum foil backing and with regular or Type X cores.

Gypsum core board is available as a 1"-thick solid core board or as a factory-laminated board composed of two ½" boards. It is used in shaft walls and laminated gypsum partitions with additional layers of gypsum board applied to the core board to complete the wall assembly. It is available in a width of 24" and with a variety of edges (square and tongue-and-groove are the most common).

Gypsum sheathing is used as a protective, fire-resistive membrane under exterior wall surfacing materials such as wood siding, masonry veneer, stucco, and shingles. It also provides protection against the passage of water and wind and adds structural rigidity to the framing system. The noncombustible core is surfaced with firmly bonded, water-repellent paper. In addition, a water-repellent material may be incorporated in the core. It is available in 2' and 4' widths, and ½" to ⅝" thicknesses. ⅝"-thick boards are available with Type X cores.

Gypsum board **substrate** for floor or roof assemblies has a ½"-thick Type X core and is available in 24" or 48" widths. It is used under combustible roof coverings to protect the structure from fires originating on the roof. It can also serve as an underlayment when applied to the top surfaces of floor joists and under **subflooring**. It may also be used as a base for built-up roofing applied over steel decks.

Gypsum form board has a fungus-resistant paper and is used as a support and permanent form for poured-in-place reinforced gypsum concrete roof decks.

Gypsum base for veneer plaster is used as a base for thin coats of hard, high-strength gypsum veneer plaster.

Gypsum lath is a board product used as a base to receive hand- or machine-applied plaster. It is available in ⅜" or ½" thicknesses and in widths of 16" or 24". Gypsum lath is normally available in 48" lengths. Other lengths are available by special order.

2.6.0 Masonry Materials

For this module, the term masonry includes construction using stone, brick, concrete block, and poured concrete. These materials are used extensively in residential and commercial construction. Special tools and fasteners are used with these materials.

2.6.1 Concrete

Concrete is a mixture of four basic materials: Portland cement, fine aggregates, coarse aggregates, and water. When first mixed, concrete is in a semi-liquid state and is referred to as **plastic concrete**. When the concrete hardens, but has not yet gained structural strength, it is called **green concrete**. After the concrete has hardened and gained its structural strength, it is called cured concrete. Various types of concrete can be obtained by varying the basic materials and/or by adding other materials to the mix. These added materials are called **admixtures**.

The desirable properties of concrete in the plastic state are as follows:

- *Moldability* – Plastic concrete may be molded by forms into almost any shape. This is often used to obtain a decorative effect.
- *Portability* – Plastic concrete may be moved in mixing trucks, motorized buggies, wheelbarrows, or by belt conveyors or hydraulic pumps.

The desirable properties of cured concrete are:

- *High structural strength* – Unreinforced concrete has great compressive strength. **Reinforced concrete**, **pre-stressed concrete**, or **post-tensioned concrete** has high structural strength under compression, tension, and lateral pressure.
- *Watertightness* – Although water is used to prepare concrete and concrete can harden under water, properly proportioned and mixed concrete is virtually watertight in most cases.
- *Durability* – Properly mixed and placed concrete usually continues to gain strength for several years and becomes almost as durable and abrasion-resistant as the hardest natural stone.

Portland cement is a finely ground powder consisting of varying amounts of lime, silica, alumina, iron, and other trace components. While dry, it may be moved in bulk or can be bagged in moisture-resistant sacks and stored for relatively long periods of time. Portland cement is a hydraulic

Special-Use Wallboard

Regular ½" and ⅝" gypsum wallboard are the most common types. There are, however, several types of gypsum wallboard designed for special applications. These include:

- Type X gypsum wallboard provides improved fire ratings because its core material is mixed with fire-retardant additives. Type X is often used on walls that separate occupancies. Examples are walls and ceilings between apartments or a wall separating a garage from the living area of a house. Use of Type X is normally specified by local building codes for protection of occupants.
- Flexible ¼" drywall panels have a heavy paper face and are designed to bend around curved surfaces.
- Special high-strength drywall panels are made for ceiling applications. The core of these panels is specially treated to resist sagging.
- A weather-resistant drywall panel is available for installation on soffits, porch ceilings, and carport ceilings.

Gypsum sheathing panels are used in cases where the required fire rating of exterior walls exceeds that available with OSB, plywood, or other types of sheathing. Gypsum sheathing panels have a water-resistant core covered on both sides with water-repellent paper. Gypsum sheathing panels are widely used in commercial construction.

cement because it will set and harden by reacting with water with or without the presence of air. This chemical reaction is called hydration and can occur even when the concrete is submerged in water. The reaction creates a calcium silicate hydrate gel and releases heat. This reaction begins the instant water is mixed with the cement and continues as the mixture hardens and cures. The reaction occurs rapidly at first, depending on how finely the cement is ground and what admixtures are present. Then, after its initial cure and strength are achieved, a cement mixture continues to slowly cure over a longer period of time until its ultimate strength is attained.

Because it is in a semi-liquid form when poured, concrete is placed in reinforced forms made of wood, metal, or other materials (*Figure 6*). Concrete floors, walls, and columns can be poured on site. Walls and other structural concrete components are sometimes prefabricated off site and moved to the site on a truck. They are then lifted into place with cranes.

In residential construction, concrete may be used in foundation walls and **footings**, basement floors, or as the foundation slab if the house has no basement.

In commercial construction, the entire structure, including floors, walls, and support columns, may be made of concrete. Walls can be anywhere from a few inches to several feet thick.

The ratio of basic ingredients in concrete is determined by a number of variables, such as the application or weather conditions. A common mix for do-it-yourself applications is 3:2:1—one part Portland cement, two parts sand, three parts aggregate, with enough water to make the mix workable. In the construction trades, the correct ratio for a given situation is determined much more scientifically, and is usually done by an engineer. Admixtures may be added to affect drying time, increase strength, and add color.

CAUTION

Those working with cement should be aware that it is harmful. Dry cement dust can enter open wounds and cause blood poisoning. When the cement dust comes in contact with body fluids, it can cause chemical burns to the membranes of the eyes, nose, mouth, throat, or lungs. Wet cement or concrete can also cause chemical burns to the eyes and skin. Make sure that appropriate personal protective equipment is worn when working with dry cement or wet concrete. If wet concrete enters waterproof boots from the top, remove the boots and rinse your legs, feet, boots, and clothing with clear water as soon as possible. Repeated contact with cement or wet concrete can cause an allergic reaction in certain individuals.

2.6.2 Concrete Masonry Units (CMUs)

Commonly known as concrete block, concrete masonry units (CMUs) are one of the most common building materials in both residential and commercial construction. *Figure 7* shows samples of these blocks. They are made from a mixture of Portland cement, aggregates such as sand and gravel, and water.

Hollow concrete block is used in all kinds of residential and commercial applications. Residential basement walls are usually made of concrete block and it is often used as a base for finish materials such as brick and stucco.

The typical size of a concrete block used in loadbearing construction is 7⅝" wide, 7⅝" high, and 15⅝" long. This is known as an 8" × 8" × 16" unit because it is designed for a ⅜" mortar joint. Mortar is a bonding agent made of cement, fine aggregate such as sand, and water. It is used to provide a watertight bond between blocks.

Sometimes, tiny foam beads are poured into concrete block walls to provide insulation. If you drill a hole though the block, the beads will begin to pour out and will not stop until the beads in that vertical channel have escaped. When installing

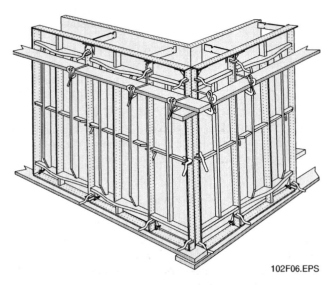

102F06.EPS

Figure 6 ◆ Wall form made from EFCO Hand-E-Form® panel system components.

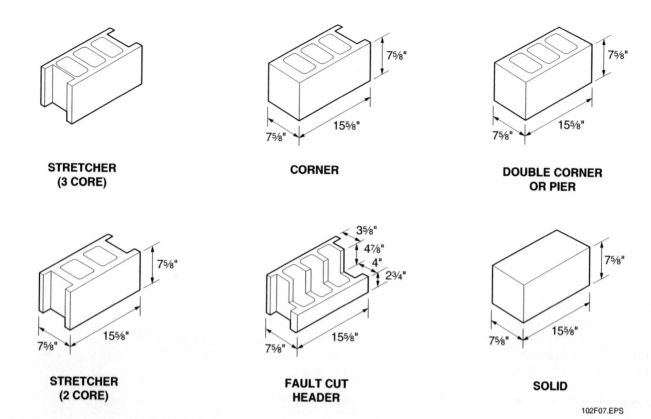

**STRETCHER
(3 CORE)**

CORNER

**DOUBLE CORNER
OR PIER**

**STRETCHER
(2 CORE)**

**FAULT CUT
HEADER**

SOLID

102F07.EPS

Figure 7 ◆ Examples of concrete blocks.

low-voltage conduit, be sure you have the conduit ready to insert into the hole or have plugs available when you drill.

In some cases, CMU construction is reinforced by placing rebar in the openings and then filling the openings with a thinned mortar known as grout. In such cases, drilling through the wall will be much more difficult than it is when the blocks remain hollow.

2.6.3 Brick

Brick is commonly used as a veneer for residential and commercial buildings. Brick is made from pulverized clay that is mixed with water and then molded into various shapes, primarily rectangular. Once the brick hardens and dries, it is fired in a furnace to provide the necessary hardness. Although there are many sizes available, a standard brick is 2¼" × 3¾" × 8".

Like cement block, bricks are bonded together with mortar. Brick is typically laid against a supporting structure such as a concrete block wall or a frame wall sheathed with plywood (*Figure 8*). An air space is maintained between the two walls to allow moisture to escape. A weep hole is provided to drain condensation that develops in the air space. The main difference between conventional

frame construction and brick facing is that the foundation wall is extended to provide support for the brick.

Although concrete block and brick are hard, they can be readily penetrated with the correct drill and bit in order to install cable runs. These tools are covered later in this module.

2.6.4 Stone

Like brick, stone is used primarily as a facade over block or frame walls. Stone used for this purpose can be as much as 6" thick. However, in renovating very old homes, you may find stone foundations and walls a foot or more thick, and they are very difficult to drill through. *Figure 9* shows a diagram of a stone veneer wall with the stone laid in a random pattern.

2.6.5 Metal

Metals have a variety of applications, especially in commercial construction. Lightweight steel and aluminum studs are used in framing walls, floors, and roofs. Metal sheet material is common in walls and roofs of commercial buildings. **Corrugated** steel decking is used as a base for poured concrete floors in multi-story commercial buildings.

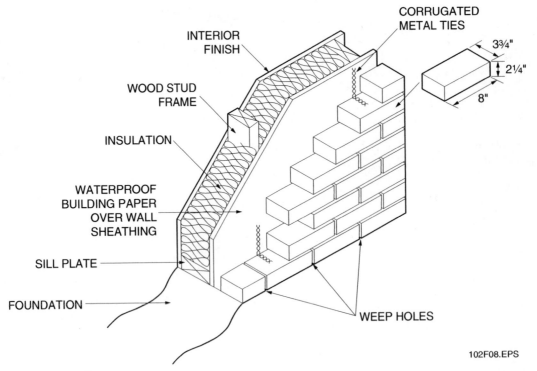

Figure 8 ◆ Brick veneer wall.

Figure 9 ◆ Stone wall.

Heavy-gauge structural steel **girders** and beams are used as the horizontal and vertical support members in many commercial buildings. Steel reinforcing bars and mesh are used to strengthen poured concrete in all applications.

3.0.0 ◆ RESIDENTIAL FRAME CONSTRUCTION

Wood frame construction (*Figure 10*) has been in common use since the 1800s. Frame construction begins by building a foundation, which usually consists of a poured concrete footing. In cold climates, the footing must be built below the frost line to prevent it from cracking. If there is no basement, a short foundation wall of poured concrete is set onto poured concrete footings.

It is common to use wooden forms to shape the poured concrete footing (*Figure 11*), and then to use edge forms to make the slab floor. In some cases, the two pours are combined to make a monolithic pour (*Figure 12*). Reinforcing bars are embedded in the concrete both to reinforce it and to provide a connection to the adjoining concrete.

If the house is to have a basement, the basement walls, usually made of concrete block, are set onto the footings (*Figure 13*), which are below ground level.

Reinforced polystyrene foam wall forms (*Figure 14*) have become popular for basement walls because they are easy to build and can be left in place after the wall is poured. In addition, they provide substantial insulation. The concrete walls made with these forms can range from 3" or 4" to 10" thick.

A sill plate, which acts as the anchor for the wood framing, is installed onto the foundation wall (*Figure 15*). Anchor bolts or straps embedded in the concrete are used to attach the sill plate to the foundation. The sills are often made from pressure-treated lumber. Otherwise, a vapor barrier must be placed between the sill and the foundation.

The sills provide a means of leveling the top of the foundation wall and also prevent the other wood framing lumber from making contact with the concrete or masonry, which can cause the lumber to rot.

Figure 10 ◆ Example of rough carpentry (western platform framing).

Today, sills are normally made using a single layer of 2 × 6 lumber. Local codes normally require that pressure-treated lumber and/or foundation-grade redwood lumber be used for the sill whenever it comes into direct contact with any type of concrete. However, where codes allow, untreated softwood can be used.

3.1.0 Floor Construction

Floor systems provide a base for the remainder of the structure to rest on. They transfer the weight of people, furniture, and materials from the subfloor, to the floor framing, to the foundation wall, to the footing, then finally to the earth. Floor systems are built over basements or crawl spaces. Single-story structures built on slabs do not have floor systems; however, multi-level structures may have both a slab and a floor system. *Figure 16* shows a typical platform floor system and identifies the various parts.

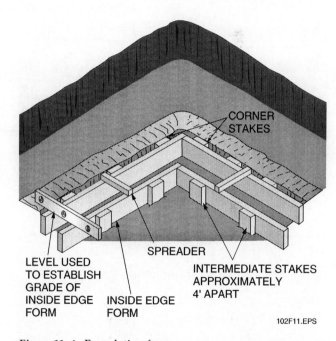

Figure 11 ◆ Foundation form.

Framing Methods

Western platform framing is a method of construction in which a first floor deck is built on top of the foundation walls. Then, the first floor walls are erected on top of the platform. Upper floor platforms are built on top of the first floor walls, and upper floor walls are erected on top of the upper floor platforms. In balloon framing, which is a method seldom used today, the studs extend from the sill plate to the rafter plate. Balloon framing requires the use of much longer studs.

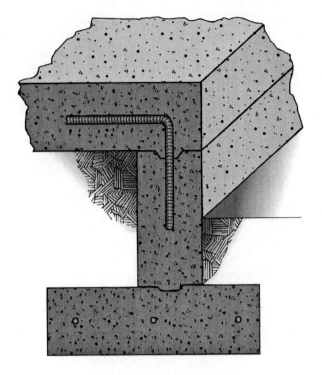

SLAB WITH FOUNDATION

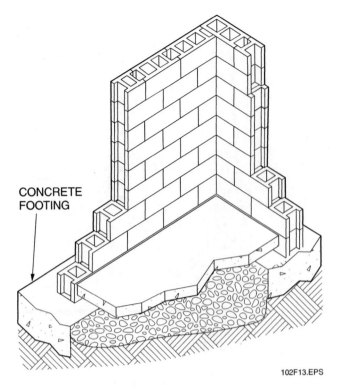

102F13.EPS

Figure 13 ◆ Concrete block basement wall.

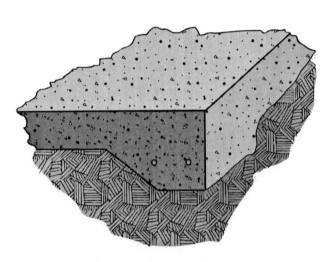

SLAB WITH THICKENED EDGE

102F12.EPS

Figure 12 ◆ Types of slabs.

102F14.EPS

Figure 14 ◆ Polystyrene form system.

3.1.1 Girders

Floor joists rest on the sill and provide the support for the floor, as well as an attaching surface for the ceiling of the floor below, if applicable.

The distance between two outside walls is frequently too great to be spanned by a single joist. When two or more joists are needed to cover the span, support for the inboard joist ends must be provided by one or more beams, commonly called girders. Girders carry a very large portion of the weight of the building. They must be well designed, rigid, and properly supported at the foundation walls and on the supporting posts or columns. They must also be installed so that they will properly support the floor joists. Girders may be made of solid timbers, built-up lumber, engineered lumber, or steel beams. In some instances, precast reinforced concrete girders may be used.

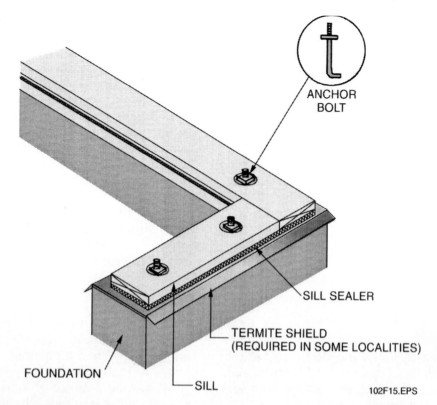

ANCHOR
BOLT

SILL SEALER

TERMITE SHIELD
(REQUIRED IN SOME LOCALITIES)

FOUNDATION

SILL

102F15.EPS

Figure 15 ◆ Typical sill installation.

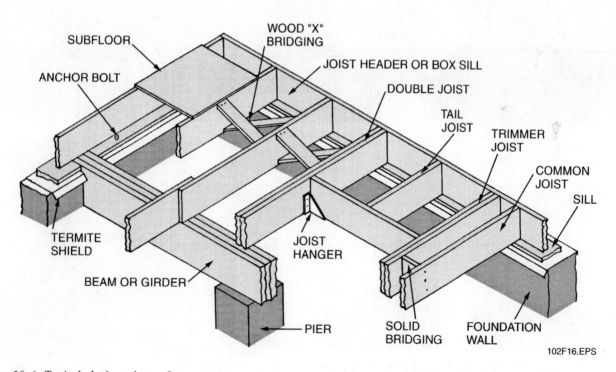

SUBFLOOR

WOOD "X"
BRIDGING

JOIST HEADER OR BOX SILL

ANCHOR BOLT

DOUBLE JOIST

TAIL
JOIST

TRIMMER
JOIST

COMMON
JOIST

SILL

TERMITE
SHIELD

JOIST
HANGER

BEAM OR GIRDER

PIER

SOLID
BRIDGING

FOUNDATION
WALL

102F16.EPS

Figure 16 ◆ Typical platform frame floor system.

Girders and beams must be properly supported at the foundation walls, and at the proper intervals in between, either by supporting posts, columns, or piers (*Figure 17*). Solid or built-up wooden posts installed on pier blocks are commonly used to support floor girders, especially for floors built over a crawl space.

Four-inch round steel columns filled and reinforced with concrete, called lally columns, are commonly used as support columns in floors built over basements. Some types of lally columns must be cut to the required height, while others have a built-in jack screw that allows the column to be adjusted to the proper height. Metal plates are installed at the top and bottom of the column to distribute the load over a wider area. The plates normally have predrilled holes so that they may be fastened to the girder.

3.1.2 Floor Joists

Floor joists are a series of parallel, horizontal framing members that make up the body of the floor frame (*Figure 16*). They rest on and transfer the building load to the sills and girders.

Joists are normally placed 16" on center (OC). However, there are applications when joists can be set as close as 12" OC or as far apart as 24" OC. These distances are used because they accommodate 4' × 8' subfloor panels and provide a nailing surface where two panels meet. Joists can be supported by the top of the girder or may be framed to the side. *Figure 18* shows several methods for joist framing at the girder. If joists are lapped over the girder, the minimum amount of lap is 4" and the maximum amount of lap is 12".

There are many different types of joist hangers that can be used to fasten joists to girders and other support framing members. Joist hangers are used where the bottom of the girder must be flush with the bottoms of the joists. At the sill end of the joist, the joist should rest on at least 1½" of wood. In platform construction, the ends of all the joists are fastened to a header joist, also called a band joist or rim joist, to form the box sill.

Joists are doubled where extra loads need to be supported. When a partition runs parallel to the joists, a double joist is placed underneath. Joists must also be doubled around all openings in the floor frame for stairways, chimneys, etc., to reinforce

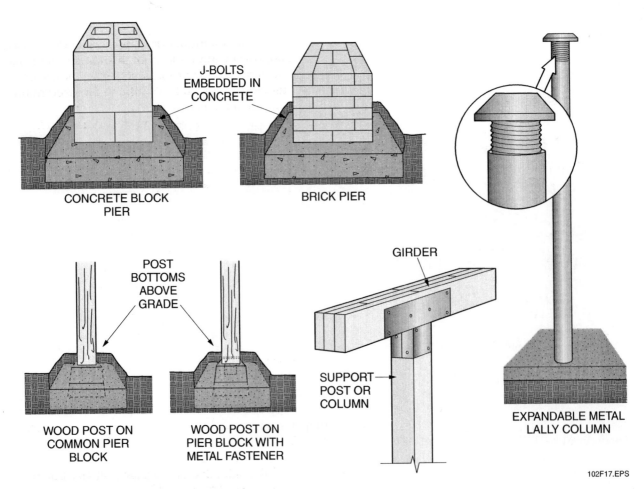

Figure 17 ◆ Typical methods of supporting girders.

102F17.EPS

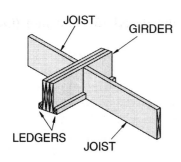
JOIST GIRDER

LEDGERS JOIST

JOIST NOTCHED AROUND LEDGERS

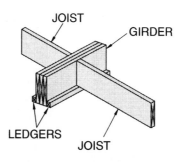
JOIST GIRDER

LEDGERS JOIST

JOIST SITS ON LEDGERS

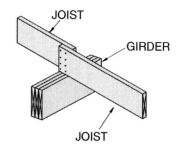
JOIST GIRDER

JOIST

JOIST OVERLAP ON GIRDER

102F18.EPS

Figure 18 ◆ Methods of joist framing at a girder.

the rough opening in the floor. These additional joists used at such openings are called **trimmer joists**.

In residential construction, floors traditionally have been built using wooden joists. However, the use of prefabricated engineered wood products such as wood I-beams and various types of **trusses** is also becoming common.

I-Beams

The first plywood I-beam was created in 1969. In 1977, the first I-beam was created using LVL. This new construction offered superior strength and stability. In 1990, OSB web material, constructed of interlocking fibers, began to be used in I-beams, as shown here. OSB is less expensive than plywood and is not as prone to warping or cracking. Engineered wood products were once only available through a handful of companies that pioneered the industry. Today, engineered lumber and lumber systems are offered by a wide variety of companies.

102SA01.EPS

3.1.3 Wood I-Beams

Wood I-beam joists are typically manufactured with 1½" diameter, pre-stamped knockout holes in the web about 12" OC that can be used to accommodate wiring. Other holes or openings can be cut into the web, but these can only be of a certain size and at the locations specified by the I-beam manufacturer. Under no circumstances should the flanges of I-beam joists be cut or notched.

3.1.4 Trusses

Trusses are manufactured joist assemblies made of wood or a combination of steel and wood (*Figure 19*). Solid light-gauge steel and open-web steel trusses are also made, but these are used mainly in commercial construction. Like the wood I-beams, trusses are stronger than comparable lengths of dimension lumber, allowing them to be used over longer spans. Longer spans allow more freedom in building design because interior load bearing walls and extra footings can often be eliminated. Trusses are generally faster and easier to erect, with no need for trimming or cutting in the field. They also provide the additional advantage of permitting ductwork, plumbing, and wiring to be run easily between the open webs. *Figure 20* shows a typical floor system constructed with trusses.

3.1.5 Notching and Drilling of Wooden Joists

When it is necessary to notch or drill through a floor joist, most building codes will specify how deep a notch can be made. For example, the *International Building Code* (IBC) or *NFPA 5000 Building Code* specifies that notches on the ends of joists shall not exceed one-fourth the depth. Therefore, in a 2 × 10 floor joist, the notch could not exceed 2½" (see *Figure 21*).

This code also states that notches for pipes in the top or bottom shall not exceed one-sixth the

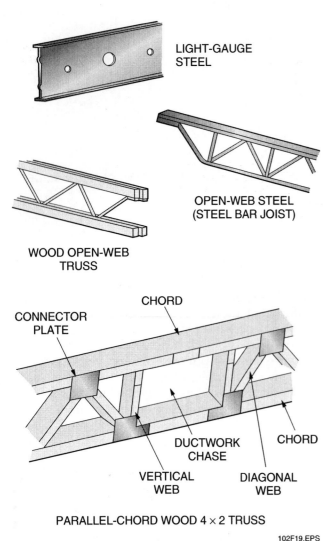

LIGHT-GAUGE
STEEL

OPEN-WEB STEEL
(STEEL BAR JOIST)

WOOD OPEN-WEB
TRUSS

CONNECTOR
PLATE

CHORD

CHORD

DUCTWORK
CHASE

VERTICAL
WEB

DIAGONAL
WEB

PARALLEL-CHORD WOOD 4 × 2 TRUSS

102F19.EPS

Figure 19 ◆ Typical floor trusses.

depth, and shall not be located in the middle third of the span. Therefore, when using a 2 × 10 floor joist, a notch cannot be deeper than 1⅝". This notch can be made either in the top or bottom of the joist, but it cannot be made in the middle third of the span. This means that if the span is 12', the middle span from 4' to 8' may not be notched.

This code further requires that holes bored for pipe or cable shall not be within 2" of the top or bottom of the joist, nor shall the diameter of any such hole exceed one-third the depth of the joist. This means that if a hole needs to be drilled, it may not exceed 3" in diameter if a 2 × 10 floor joist is used. Always check the local codes.

When working with wood I-beams, never notch or drill through the beam flange or cut other openings in the web without checking the manufacturer's specification sheet. Also, do not drill or notch other types of engineered lumber, such as LVL, PSL, and glulam, without first checking the specification sheets.

3.1.6 Bridging

Bridging is used to stiffen the floor frame and to enable an overloaded joist to receive some support from the joists on either side. Most building codes require that bridging be installed in rows between the floor joists, at intervals of not more than 8'. For example, floor joists with spans of 8' to 16' need one row of bridging in the center of the span.

Three types of bridging (*Figure 22*) are commonly used: wood cross-bridging, solid wood bridging, and metal cross-bridging. Wood and

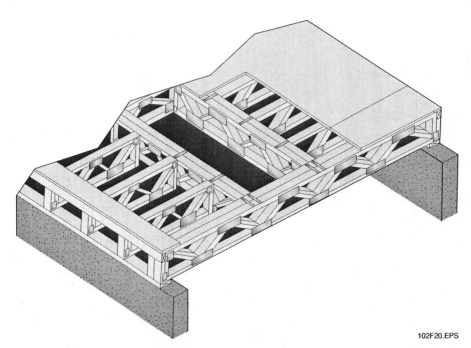

102F20.EPS

Figure 20 ◆ Typical floor system constructed with trusses.

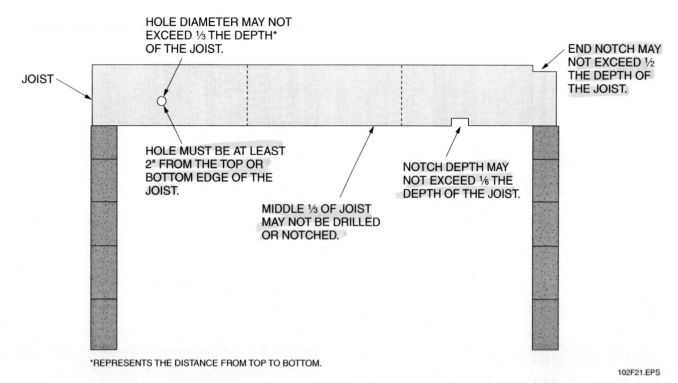

HOLE DIAMETER MAY NOT EXCEED ⅓ THE DEPTH* OF THE JOIST.

JOIST

END NOTCH MAY NOT EXCEED ½ THE DEPTH OF THE JOIST.

HOLE MUST BE AT LEAST 2" FROM THE TOP OR BOTTOM EDGE OF THE JOIST.

NOTCH DEPTH MAY NOT EXCEED ⅙ THE DEPTH OF THE JOIST.

MIDDLE ⅓ OF JOIST MAY NOT BE DRILLED OR NOTCHED.

*REPRESENTS THE DISTANCE FROM TOP TO BOTTOM.

102F21.EPS

Figure 21 ◆ Notching and drilling of wooden joists.

metal cross-bridging are composed of pieces of wood or metal set diagonally between the joists to form an X. Wood cross-bridging is typically 1 × 4 lumber placed in double rows that cross each other in the joist space.

Metal cross-bridging is installed in a similar manner. Metal cross-bridging comes in a variety of styles and different lengths for use with a particular joist size and spacing. It is usually made of 18-gauge steel and is ¾" wide. Solid bridging, also called **blocking**, consists of solid pieces of lumber (usually the same size as the floor joists) installed between the joists. The bridging pieces are offset from one another to enable end nailing.

3.1.7 Subflooring

Subflooring consists of panels or boards laid directly on and fastened to floor joists (*Figure 23*) in order to provide a base for underlayment and/or the finish floor material. Underlayment is a material, such as particleboard or plywood, laid on top of the subfloor to provide a smoother surface for finish flooring. The subfloor adds rigidity to the structure and provides a surface upon which walls and other framing can be laid out and constructed. Subfloors also act as a barrier to cold and dampness, thus keeping the building warmer and drier in winter. Subflooring can be constructed of plywood, OSB or other manufactured board panels, or common wooden boards.

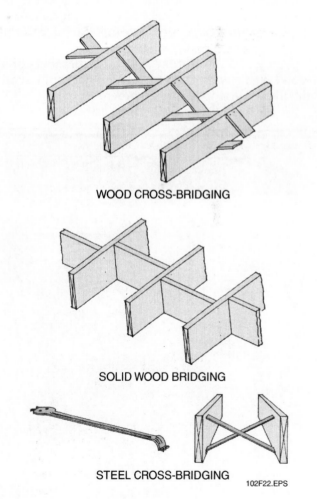

WOOD CROSS-BRIDGING

SOLID WOOD BRIDGING

STEEL CROSS-BRIDGING

102F22.EPS

Figure 22 ◆ Types of bridging.

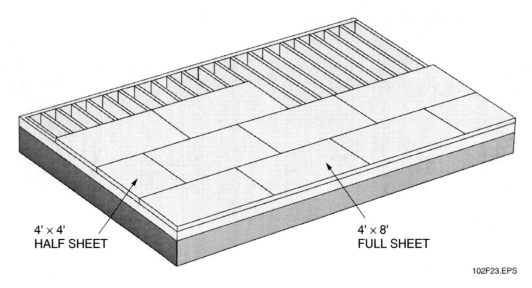

4' × 4'
HALF SHEET

4' × 8'
FULL SHEET

102F23.EPS

Figure 23 ◆ Subflooring installation.

3.2.0 Wall Construction

Wall framing is generally done with 2 × 4 studs spaced 16" OC. In many cases, 24" spacing is used on interior walls. Some codes permit 24" spacing on exterior walls for one-story buildings. If 24" spacing is used in a two-story building, the lower floor must be framed with 2 × 6 lumber.

Figure 24 identifies the structural members of a wood frame wall. Each of the members shown on the illustration is described here.

OSB Subflooring

INSIDE TRACK

Today, many builders prefer to use OSB for subfloors. It offers acceptable structural strength at a reduced price.

102SA02.EPS

NOTE

Codes may require variations in structure for seismic and other hazards.

- *Blocking (spacer)* – A wood block that is used as a filler piece and support between framing members. Blocking also provides a surface for attaching equipment, etc.
- *Cripple stud* – In wall framing, this is a short framing stud that fills the space between a header and a **top plate** or between the sill and the **soleplate**.
- *Double top plate* – This is a plate made of two members to provide better stiffening of a wall. It is also used for connecting splices, corners, and partitions that are at right angles (perpendicular) to the wall.
- *Header (lintel)* – This is a horizontal structural member that supports the load over an opening such as a door or window.
- *King stud* – This is the full-length stud next to the **trimmer stud** in a wall opening.
- *Partition* – This is a wall that subdivides space within a building. A bearing partition or wall is one that supports the floors and roof directly above in addition to its own weight.
- *Rough opening* – This is an opening in the framing formed by framing members, usually for a window or a door.
- *Rough sill* – This is the lower framing member attached to the top of the lower cripple studs to form the base of a rough opening for a window.

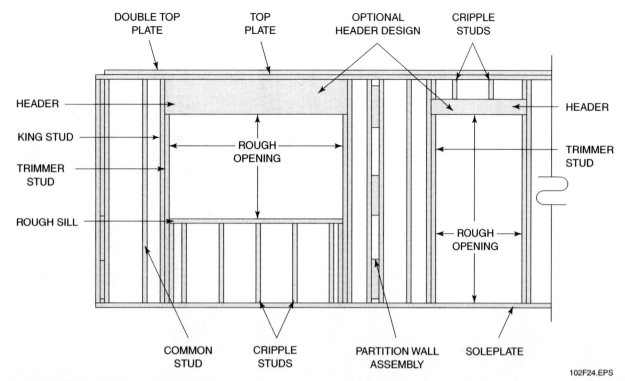

Figure 24 ◆ Wall and partition framing members.

- *Soleplate* – This is the lowest horizontal member of a wall or partition to which the studs are nailed. It rests on the rough floor.
- *Stud* – The main vertical framing member in a wall or partition.
- *Top plate* – The upper horizontal framing member of a wall used to carry the roof trusses or rafters.
- *Trimmer stud* – The vertical framing member that forms the sides of rough openings for doors and windows. It provides stiffening for the frame and supports the weight of the header.

3.2.1 Corners

A wall must have solid corners that can take the weight of the structure. In addition to contributing to the strength of the structure, corners must provide a good nailing surface for sheathing and interior finish materials. Building contractors generally select the straightest, least defective studs for corner framing.

There are many methods for constructing corners. Two are shown in *Figure 25*. Some builders will construct the corner in place, then plumb and brace it before raising the wall frames. This approach makes it easier to plumb and brace the frame, but it prevents installation of the sheathing before the frame is erected. If the corners are included in the frame, then a portion of the corner is included with each of the mating frame sections.

3.2.2 Partition Intersections

Interior partitions must be securely fastened to outside walls. For that to happen, there must be a solid nailing surface where the partition intersects the exterior frame. There are several methods used to construct framing for partition Ts. Some of them are shown in *Figure 26*.

3.2.3 Window and Door Openings

When wall framing is interrupted by an opening such as a window or door, a method is needed to distribute the weight of the structure around the opening. This is done by the use of a header. The header is placed so that it rests on the trimmer studs, which transfer the weight to the soleplate or subfloor and then to the foundation.

Headers are made of solid or built-up lumber. Laminated lumber and beams have become popular as header material, especially where the load is heavy.

Built-up headers are usually made from 2" lumber separated by ½" plywood spacers (*Figure 27*). A full header is used for large openings and fills the area from the rough opening to the bottom of the top plate. A small header with cripple studs is suitable for average-size windows and doors and is usually made from 2 × 4 or 2 × 6 lumber. Built-up headers are sometimes made by gluing and nailing ½" plywood the entire length of the header, instead of inserting

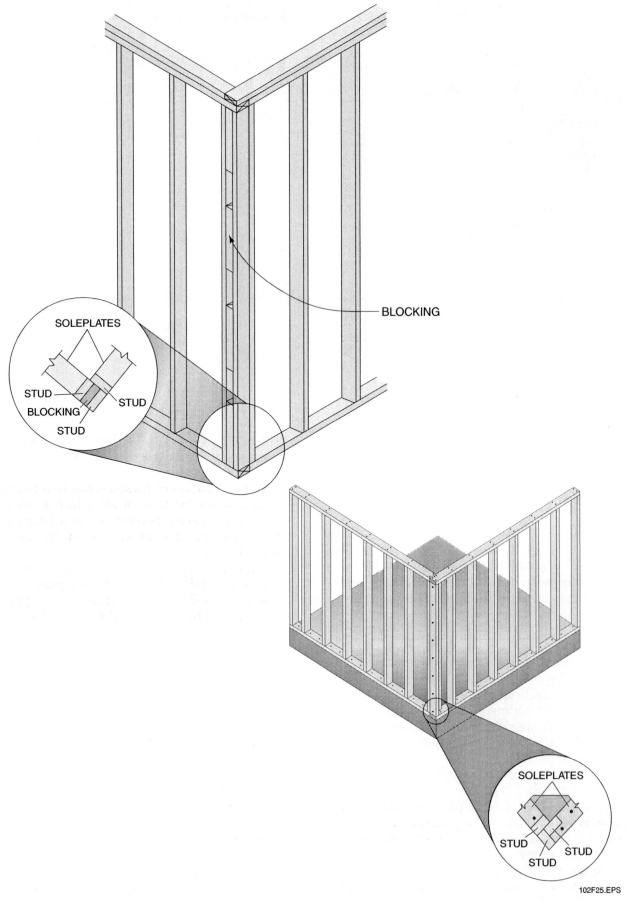

SOLEPLATES

STUD

STUD

BLOCKING

STUD

BLOCKING

SOLEPLATES

STUD

STUD

STUD

102F25.EPS

Figure 25 ◆ Corner construction.

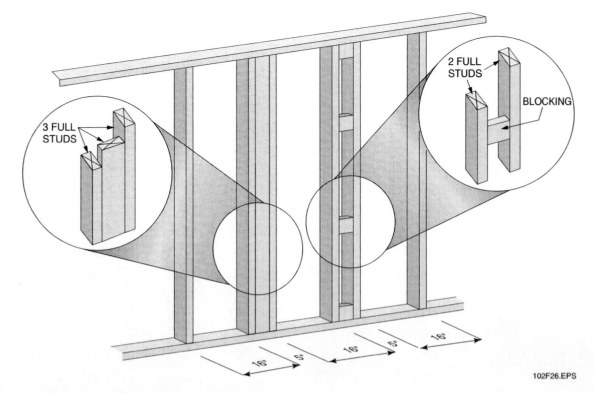

Figure 26 ◆ Constructing nailing surfaces for partitions.

plywood blocks. This method allows the framing crew to make a long section (16') of built-up header, then cut what they need for each opening from that section. The crew may use the same header for all openings. This saves time because it eliminates the need for cutting and installing cripple studs.

Truss headers are used when the load is especially heavy or the span is extra wide. The design of the trusses is generally included in the architect's plans.

Other types of headers used for heavy loads are wood or steel I-beams and box beams. The latter are made of plywood webs connected by lumber flanges in a box configuration.

The width of a header is equal to the rough opening plus the thickness of the trimmer studs. For example, if the rough opening for a 3'-wide window is 38" and the thickness of the trimmer studs measures 3", the width of the header would be 41".

Figure 28 shows cross sections of typical wood-framed walls.

3.2.4 Firestops

In some areas, local building codes may require **firestops**. Firestops are short pieces of 2 × 4 blocking (or 2 × 6 pieces if the wall is framed with 2 × 6 lumber) that are nailed between studs. See *Figure 29*.

Without firestops, the space between the studs will act like a flue in a chimney. Any holes drilled through the soleplate and top plate create a draft,

and air will rush through the space. In a fire, air, smoke, gases, and flames can race through the chimney-like space.

The installation of firestops has two purposes. First, it slows the flow of air, which feeds a fire through the cavity. Second, it can actually block flames (temporarily at least) from traveling up through the cavity.

If the local code requires firestops, it may also require that holes through the soleplate and top plate (for plumbing or electrical runs) be plugged with a **firestopping** material to prevent airflow.

3.2.5 Bracing

Bracing is important in the construction of exterior walls. Many local building codes require bracing if certain types of sheathing are used. In areas where high winds or earthquakes are a hazard, lateral bracing may be required even when ½" plywood is used as the sheathing.

Several methods of bracing have been used since the early days of construction. One method is to cut a notch (let-in) for a 1 × 4 or 1 × 6 at a 45-degree angle on each corner of the exterior walls. Another method is to cut 2 × 4 braces at a 45-degree angle for each corner. Still another type of bracing (used where permitted by the local code), is metal strap bracing (*Figure 30*). This product is made of galvanized steel.

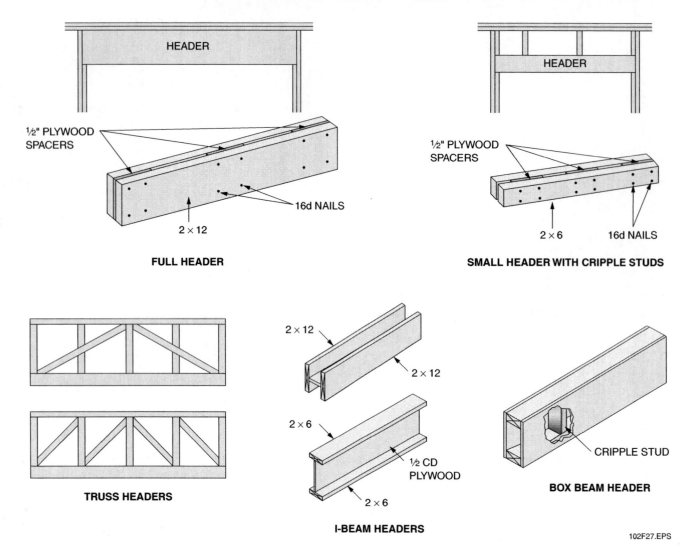

Figure 27 ◆ Types of headers.

Metal strap bracing is easier to use than let-in wood bracing. Instead of notching out the studs for a 1 × 4 or 2 × 4, a circular saw is used to make a diagonal groove in the studs, top plate, and soleplate for the rib of the bracing strap. The strap is then nailed to the framing.

With the introduction of plywood, some areas of the country have done away with corner bracing. However, along with plywood came different types of sheathing that are byproducts of the wood industry and do not have the strength to withstand wind pressures. When these are used, permanent bracing is needed. Building codes in some areas will allow a sheet of ½" plywood to be used on each corner of the structure in lieu of diagonal bracing when the balance of the sheathing is fiberboard. In other areas, the use of bracing is required regardless of the type of sheathing used. Always check local codes.

3.2.6 Sheathing

Sheathing is the material used to close in the walls. **APA-rated** material, such as plywood and non-veneer panels, are generally used for sheathing.

When plywood is used, the panels will range from ⁵⁄₁₆" to ¾" thick. A minimum thickness of ⅜" is recommended when siding is to be applied. The higher end of the range is recommended when the sheathing acts as the exterior finish surface. The panels may be placed with the grain running horizontally or vertically. If they are placed with the grain running horizontally, local building codes may require that blocking be used along the top edges.

Typical nailing requirements call for 6d (6 penny) nails for panels ½" thick or less and 8d nails for thicker panels. Nails are spaced 6" apart at the panel edges and 12" apart at intermediate studs.

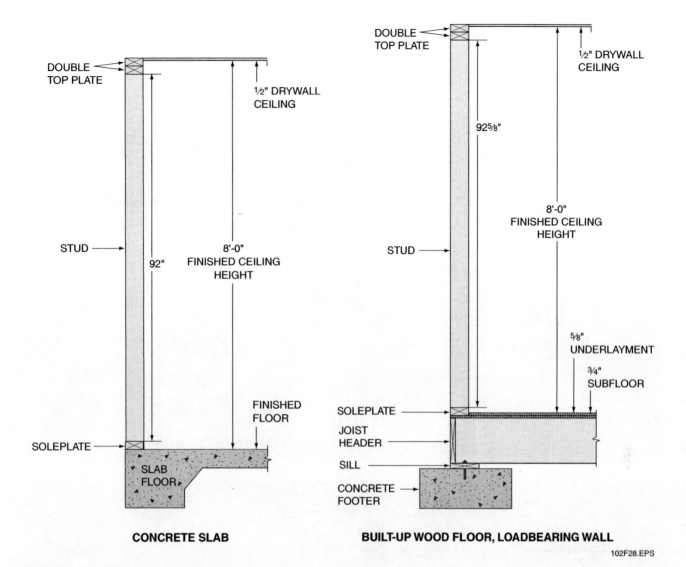

CONCRETE SLAB

BUILT-UP WOOD FLOOR, LOADBEARING WALL

102F28.EPS

Figure 28 ◆ Cross sections of wood-framed walls.

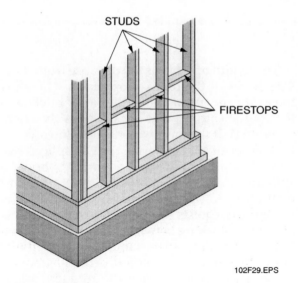

102F29.EPS

Figure 29 ◆ Firestops.

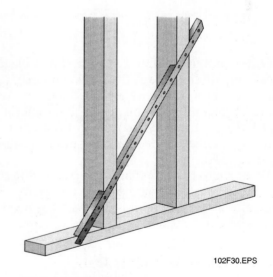

102F30.EPS

Figure 30 ◆ Metal bracing.

Headers

Headers can be constructed in many ways, some of which are shown here.

HEADER WITH CRIPPLE STUDS

SOLID HEADER

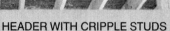

GARAGE DOOR HEADER USING
ENGINEERED LUMBER

102SA03.EPS

Other materials that are sometimes used as sheathing are fiberboard (insulation board), rigid foam sheathing, and exterior-rated gypsum wallboard. A major disadvantage of these materials is that siding cannot be nailed to them. It must either be nailed to the studs or special fasteners must be used.

When material other than rated panels is used as sheathing, rated plywood panels may be installed vertically at the corners to eliminate the need for corner bracing.

3.3.0 Ceiling Construction

Ceiling joists are usually laid across the width of a building at the same positions as the wall studs.

The length of a joist is the distance from the outside edges of the double top plates. The ends of the joists are cut to match the rafter pitch so that the roof sheathing will lay flush on the framing (*Figure 31*). If the joist exceeds the allowable span, two pieces of joist material must be spliced over a bearing wall or partition. *Figure 32* shows two splicing methods. There should be a minimum overlap of 6". Another method of splicing is to place the two joists on either side of the rafter with a piece of blocking between the joists at the splice.

If the spacing is the same as that of the wall studs, the joists are nailed directly above the studs. This makes it easier to run ductwork, piping, flues, and wiring above the ceiling. Metal joist hangers can be used in place of nailing.

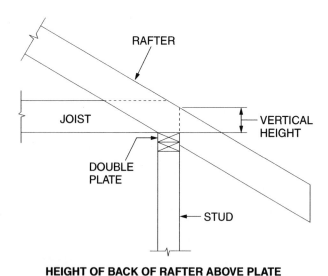

HEIGHT OF BACK OF RAFTER ABOVE PLATE

102F31.EPS

Figure 31 ◆ Cutting joist ends to match the roof pitch.

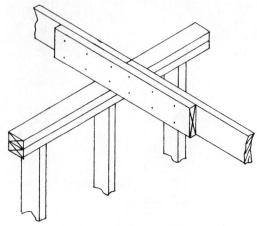

CEILING JOISTS LAPPED OVER
BEARING PARTITION

CEILING JOISTS BUTTED OVER
BEARING PARTITION

102F32.EPS

Figure 32 ◆ Spliced ceiling joists.

After the joists are installed, a **ribband** or **strongback** is nailed across them to prevent twisting or bowing (*Figure 33*). The strongback is used for larger spans. In addition to holding the joists in line, it provides support for the joists at the center of the span.

3.4.0 Roof Construction

The most common types of roofs used in residential construction are shown in *Figure 34* and described here.

- *Gable roof* – A gable roof has two slopes that meet at the center (ridge) to form a gable at each end of the building. It is the most common type of roof because it is simple, economical, and can be used on any type of structure.
- *Hip roof* – A hip roof has four sides or slopes running toward the center of the building. Rafters at the corners extend diagonally to meet at the ridge. Additional rafters are framed into these rafters.
- *Gable and valley roof* – This roof consists of two intersecting gable roofs. The part where the two roofs meet is called a valley.
- *Mansard roof* – The mansard roof has four sloping sides, each of which has a double slope. As compared with a gable roof, this design provides more available space in the upper level of the building.

INSIDE TRACK

Mansard Roof

Mansard roofs are popular in the design of many fast-food restaurants and small office buildings.

102SA04.EPS

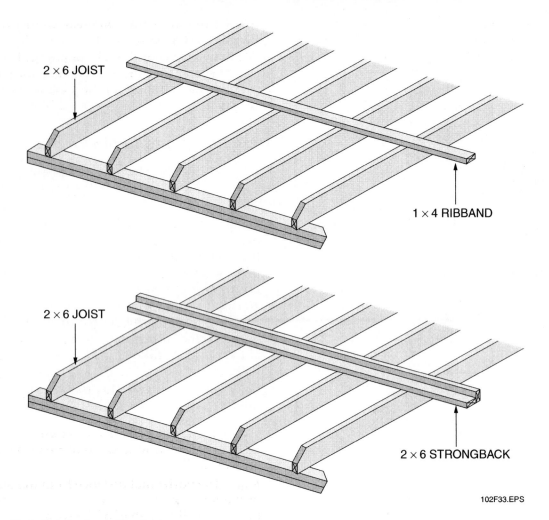

2 × 6 JOIST

1 × 4 RIBBAND

2 × 6 JOIST

2 × 6 STRONGBACK

102F33.EPS

Figure 33 ◆ Reinforcing ceiling joists.

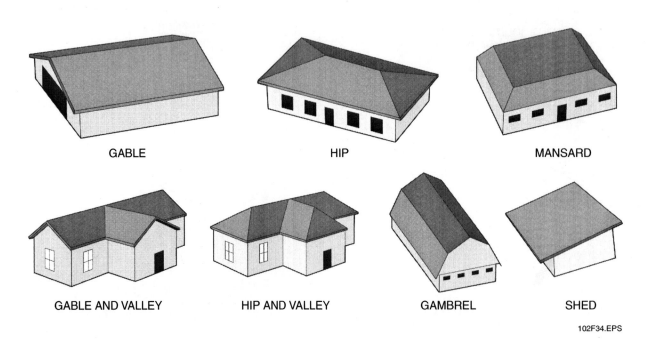

GABLE

HIP

MANSARD

GABLE AND VALLEY

HIP AND VALLEY

GAMBREL

SHED

102F34.EPS

Figure 34 ◆ Types of roofs.

- *Gambrel roof* – The gambrel roof is a variation on the gable roof in which each side has a break, usually near the ridge. The gambrel roof provides additional space in the upper level.
- *Shed roof* – Also known as a lean-to roof, the shed roof has a flat, sloped construction. It is commonly used in high-ceiling contemporary residences and for additions.

There are two basic roof framing systems. In stick-built framing, ceiling joists and rafters are laid out and cut by the builder on the site and the frame is constructed one stick at a time.

In truss-built construction, the roof framework is prefabricated off site. The truss contains both the rafters and the ceiling joist. Trusses and truss construction will be discussed later in this module.

3.4.1 Roof Components

Rafters and ceiling joists provide the framework for all roofs. The main components of a roof are shown in *Figure 35* and described here.

- *Ridge (ridgeboard)* – The highest horizontal roof member. It helps to align the rafters and tie them together at the upper end. The ridgeboard is one size larger than the rafters.
- *Common rafter* – A structural member that extends from the top plate to the ridge in a direction perpendicular to the wall plate and ridge. Rafters often extend beyond the roof plate to form the overhang (eaves) that protect the side of the building.
- *Hip rafter* – A roof member that extends diagonally from the corner of the plate to the ridge.
- *Valley rafter* – A roof member that extends diagonally from the plate to the ridge along the lines where two roofs intersect.
- *Jack rafter* – A roof member that does not extend the entire distance from the ridge to the top plate of a wall. Hip jacks and valley jacks are shown in *Figure 35*. A rafter fitted between a hip rafter and a valley rafter is called a cripple jack. It touches neither the ridge nor the plate.
- *Plate* – The wall framing member that rests on top of the wall studs. It is sometimes called the rafter plate because the rafters rest on it. It is also referred to as the top plate.

On any pitched roof, rafters rise at an angle to the ridgeboard. Therefore, the length of the rafter is greater than the horizontal distance from the plate to the ridge. In order to calculate the correct rafter length, the builder must factor in the slope of the roof. Here are some additional terms that apply to roof layout (see *Figure 36*).

- *Span* – The horizontal distance from the outside of one exterior wall to the outside of the other exterior wall.
- *Run* – The horizontal distance from the outside of the top plate to the center line of the ridgeboard (usually one-half of the span).

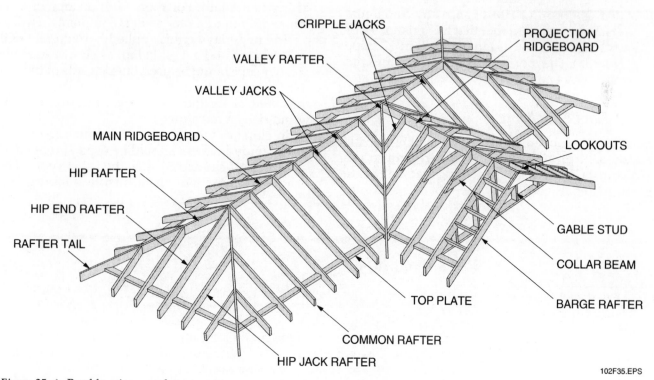

Figure 35 ◆ Roof framing members.

102F35.EPS

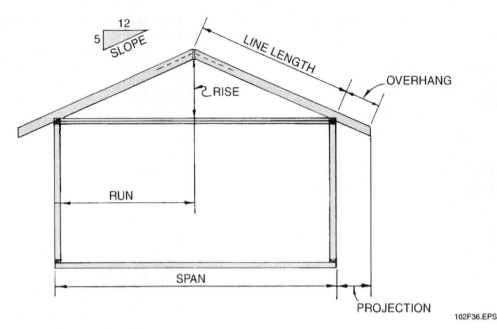

Figure 36 ◆ Roof layout factors.

- *Rise* – The total height of the rafter from the top plate to the ridge. This is stated in inches per foot of run.
- *Pitch* – The angle or degree of slope of the roof in relation to the span. Pitch is expressed as a fraction. For example, if the total rise is 6' and the span is 24', the pitch would be 1/4 (6 over 24).
- *Slope* – The inclination of the roof surface expressed as the relationship of rise to run. It is stated as a unit of rise to so many horizontal units. For example, a roof that has a rise of 5" for each foot of run is said to have a 5 in 12 slope (*Figure 36*). The roof slope is sometimes referred to as the roof cut.

3.4.2 Roof Sheathing

Sheathing is applied as soon as the roof framing is finished. It provides additional strength to the structure and a base for the roofing material. Some of the materials commonly used for sheathing are plywood, OSB, waferboard, **shiplap**, and common boards. When composition shingles are used, the sheathing must be solid. If wood **shakes** are used, the sheathing boards may be spaced. When solid sheathing is used, a ⅛" space is left between panels to allow for expansion.

Once the sheathing has been installed, an underlayment of asphalt-saturated felt or other specified material is installed to keep moisture out until the shingles are laid. For roofs with a slope of 4" or more, 15-pound roofer's felt is commonly used.

The underlayment is applied horizontally with a 2" top lap and a 4" side lap, as shown in *Figure 37*. A 6" lap should be used on each side of the center line of hips and valleys. A metal drip edge is installed along the rakes and eaves to keep out wind-driven moisture.

In climates where snow accumulates, a waterproof underlayment should be used at roof edges and around chimneys, skylights, and vents. This underlayment has an adhesive backing that

Pitch and Slope

The terms pitch and slope may be used interchangeably on the job site, but the two terms actually refer to two different concepts. Slope is the amount of rise per foot of run and is always referred to as a number in 12. For example, a roof that rises 6" for every foot of run has a 6 in 12 slope (the 12 simply refers to the number of inches in a foot). Pitch, on the other hand, is the ratio of rise to the span of the roof and is expressed as a fraction. For example, a roof that rises 8' over a 32' span is said to have a pitch of 1/4 (8/32 = 1/4).

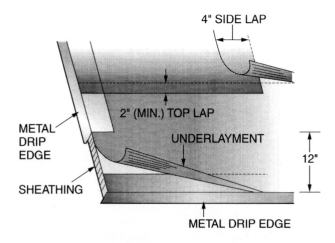

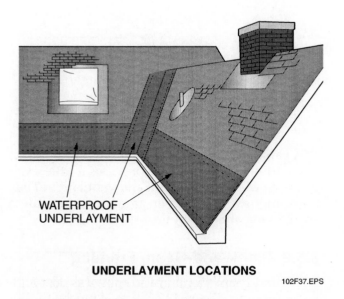

UNDERLAYMENT OVERLAP

UNDERLAYMENT LOCATIONS

102F37.EPS

Figure 37 ◆ Underlayment installation.

adheres to the sheathing. It protects against water damage that can result from melting ice and snow that backs up under the shingles. Sheet metal or other material is used at roof intersections and around chimneys, vents, and skylights to prevent water from entering. In snowy climates, sheet metal eave flashing is often installed at the edge of a roof to prevent ice dams from forming.

3.4.3 Truss Construction

In most cases, it is much faster and more economical to use prefabricated trusses in place of rafters and joists. Even if a truss costs more to buy than the comparable framing lumber (and this is not always the case), it takes significantly less labor than stick framing. Another advantage is that a truss will span a greater distance without a bearing wall than stick framing. Just about any type of roof can be framed with trusses. Some of the special terms used to identify the members of a truss are shown in *Figure 38*.

A truss is a framed or jointed structure. It is designed so that when a load is applied at any intersection, the stress in any member is in the direction of its length. *Figure 39* shows some of the many kinds of trusses.

Even though some trusses look nearly identical, there is some variation in the interior (web) pattern. Each web pattern distributes weight and stress a little differently, so different web patterns are used to deal with different loads and spans. The decision of which truss to use for a particular application will be made by the architect or engineer and will be shown on the blueprints.

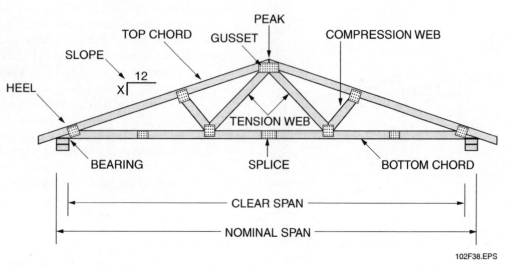

102F38.EPS

Figure 38 ◆ Components of a truss.

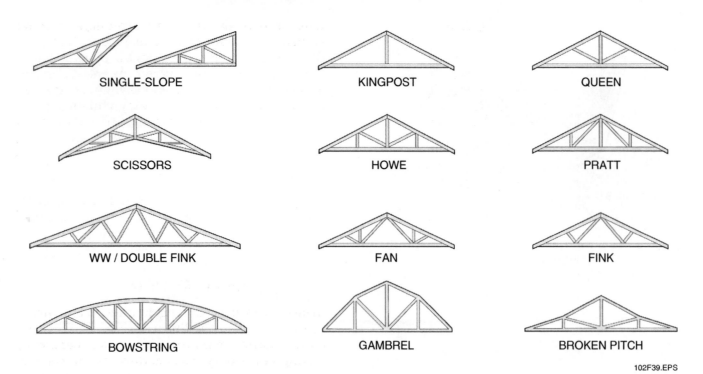

Figure 39 ◆ Types of trusses.

3.4.4 Dormers

A **dormer** is a framed structure that projects out from a sloped roof. A dormer provides additional space and is often used in a Cape Cod style home, which is a single-story dwelling in which the attic is often used for sleeping rooms.

A shed dormer (*Figure 40*) is a good way to obtain a large amount of additional living space. If it is added to the rear of the house, it will not affect the appearance of the house from the front.

102F40.EPS

Figure 40 ◆ Shed dormer.

A gable dormer (*Figure 41*) serves as an attractive addition to a house. It provides a little extra space, as well as some light and ventilation. They are sometimes used over garages to provide a small living area or studio.

3.5.0 Plank-and-Beam Framing

Plank-and-beam framing, also known as post-and-beam framing (*Figure 42*), employs much sturdier framing members than common framing. It is often used in framing roofs for luxury residences, churches, and lodges, as well as other public buildings where a striking architectural effect is desired.

Because the beams used in this type of construction are very sturdy, wider spacing may be used. Vertical supports are typically spaced 48" OC, as compared with 16" OC used in conventional framing. When plank-and-beam framing is used for a roof, the beams and planking can be finished and left exposed. The underside of the planking takes the place of an installed ceiling.

In lighter construction, solid posts or beams such as 4 × 4s are used. In heavier construction, laminated beams made of glulam, LVL, and PSL are used.

In post-and-beam framing, plank subfloors or roofs are usually of 2" nominal thickness, supported on beams spaced up to 8' apart. The ends of the beams are supported on posts or piers. Wall spaces between posts are provided with supplementary framing as required for attachment of

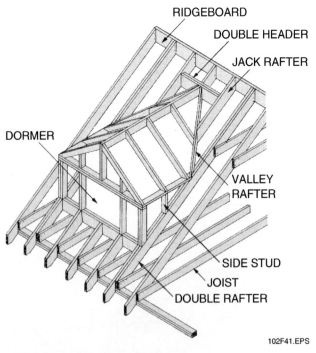

Figure 41 ◆ Gable dormer framing.

Labels in figure: RIDGEBOARD, DOUBLE HEADER, JACK RAFTER, DORMER, VALLEY RAFTER, SIDE STUD, JOIST, DOUBLE RAFTER

102F41.EPS

Figure 42 ◆ Example of post-and-beam framing.

102F42.EPS

exterior and interior finishes. This additional framing also provides lateral bracing for the building.

If local building codes allow end joints in the planks to fall between supports, planks of random lengths may be used and the beam spacing adjusted to fit the house dimensions. Windows and doors are normally located between posts in the exterior walls, eliminating the need for headers over the openings. The wide spacing between posts permits ample room for large glass areas.

A combination of conventional framing with post-and-beam framing is sometimes used where the two adjoin each other.

Where a post-and-beam floor or roof is supported on a stud wall, a post is usually placed under the end of the beam to carry a conventional load. A conventional roof can be used with post-and-beam construction by installing a header between posts to carry the load from the rafters to the posts.

3.6.0 Framing in Masonry

In order to install cabling in buildings constructed of masonry, you must be aware of the methods used in furring masonry walls. As a general rule, furring of masonry walls is done on 16" centers. Some contractors will apply 1 × 2 **furring strips** 24" OC. This may save material, but it does not provide the same quality as a wall done on 16" centers.

In addition to the furring strips, 1 × 4 and 1 × 6 stock is used. All material that comes in contact with concrete or masonry must be pressure-treated.

Backing for partitions against a masonry block wall is done using one of the methods shown in *Figure 43*.

When preparing the corners of the block wall to receive the furring strips, enough space is left for the drywall to slip by the furring strips (*Figure 44*).

A 1 × 4 is used at floor level to receive the baseboard. Either a narrow or wide baseboard can be used. Some builders will install a simple furring strip at floor level and depend on the vertical strips for baseboard nailing. Once the drywall has been installed, it is difficult to find the strips when nailing the baseboard.

3.7.0 Walls Separating Occupancies

Every wall, floor, and ceiling in a building is rated for its fire resistance, as established by building codes. The fire rating is stated in terms of hours; for example, one-hour wall, two-hour wall, and so on. The rating denotes the length of time an assembly can withstand fire and give protection from it as determined under laboratory conditions. The greater the fire rating, the thicker the wall is likely to be. This subject is covered further in the section on commercial construction.

In multi-family residential construction, such as apartments and townhouses, the walls and ceilings dividing the occupancies must meet special fire and

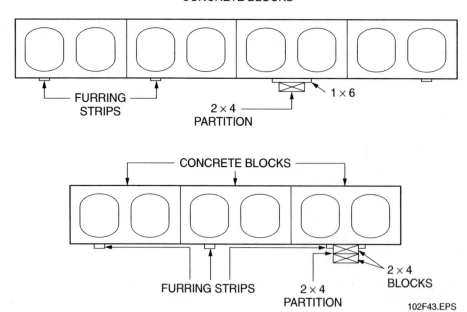

CONCRETE BLOCKS

FURRING STRIPS

2 × 4 PARTITION

1 × 6

CONCRETE BLOCKS

FURRING STRIPS

2 × 4 PARTITION

2 × 4 BLOCKS

102F43.EPS

Figure 43 ◆ Partition backing on a block wall.

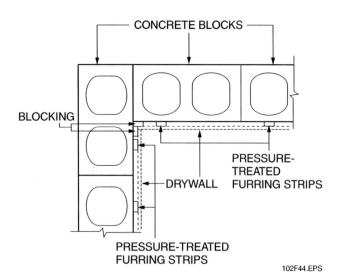

CONCRETE BLOCKS

BLOCKING

PRESSURE-TREATED FURRING STRIPS

DRYWALL

PRESSURE-TREATED FURRING STRIPS

102F44.EPS

Figure 44 ◆ Corner construction.

soundproofing requirements. The code requirements will vary from one location to another and may even vary within areas of a jurisdiction. That is, dwellings in high-risk areas may have stiffer standards than those in other areas of the same city or county. In some cases, the code may require a masonry wall between occupancies. This masonry wall may even be required to penetrate the roof of the building so that if a fire occurs, it is contained within the unit in which it started, because it is unable to travel through the walls or across the attic space.

There are many different construction methods for multi-dwelling (party) walls. Each is designed to meet different fire and soundproofing standards. The wall is likely to be more than 3" thick and contain several layers of gypsum wallboard and insulation.

The important thing to note is that there are many variations, so you must know what you are drilling into before you start drilling. It is also possible that the codes will not permit you to run a cable from one unit to another in a multi-family occupancy. In addition, if drilling is permitted, you will probably have to use firestopping materials to seal off the opening.

4.0.0 ◆ COMMERCIAL CONSTRUCTION METHODS

The structural framework of large buildings, such as office buildings, hospitals, apartment houses, and hotels, is usually made from concrete or structural steel. The exterior finish is often concrete panels that are either prefabricated and raised into place or poured into forms built at the site. Floors are usually made of concrete that is poured at the site using wood, metal, or fiberglass forms. Exterior walls (curtain walls) may also be made of glass in a metal or concrete framework. *Figure 45* shows such a curtain wall section being installed. Before the concrete is poured, provision must be made for cabling pathways.

102SA05.EPS

102F45.EPS

Figure 45 ◆ Installing a corner curtain wall panel.

In some buildings, the framework is made of structural steel. Panels fabricated off site are lifted into place and bolted or welded to the steel (*Figure 46*).

Figure 47 shows the structure of a building in which all the structural framework is made of concrete poured at the site. Each component of the structure requires a different type of form. In this case, the floor and beams were made in a single pour using integrated floor and beam forms, which were removed once the concrete hardened.

In some specialized commercial applications, tilt-up concrete construction is used. In tilt-up construction, the wall panels are usually poured on the concrete floor slab, then tilted into place on the footing using a crane (*Figure 48*). The panels are welded together.

102F46.EPS

Figure 46 ◆ Curtain wall under construction.

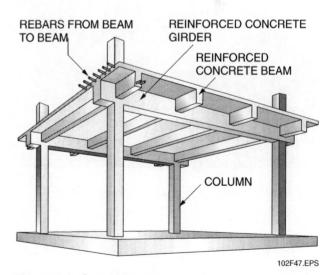

REBARS FROM BEAM TO BEAM

REINFORCED CONCRETE GIRDER

REINFORCED CONCRETE BEAM

COLUMN

102F47.EPS

Figure 47 ◆ Concrete structure.

Masonry Curtain Wall

This masonry curtain wall panel combines 2"-thick architectural precast concrete brick with a heavy-gauge stainless steel frame and insulated stainless steel anchor doors.

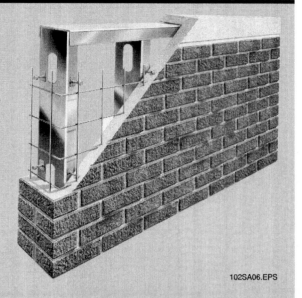

102SA06.EPS

Tilt-Up Records

The Tilt-Up Concrete Association (www.tilt-up.org) keeps records of tilt-up projects. As of 2002, several amazing statistics had been recorded, including:

- Heaviest tilt-up panel – 310,000 pounds
- Largest tilt-up panel by area – 1,815 square feet, including window openings (30' × 60'-6")
- Tallest tilt-up panel – 91'-7¼"
- Largest number of panels in a single building – 1,310
- Largest tilt-up building (floor area) – 1,750,000 square feet

102F48.EPS

Figure 48 ◆ Tilt-up panel being lifted into place.

The main difference between tilt-up and other types of large commercial construction is that there is no steel or concrete framework in tilt-up construction. The walls and floor slab bear the entire load. Tilt-up is most common in one- or two-story buildings with a slab at grade (no below-grade foundation). It is popular for warehouses, low-rise offices, churches, and a variety of other commercial and multi-family residential applications. Tilt-up panels of 50' in height are not uncommon. They typically range from 5" to 8" thick, but thicker walls can be obtained when using lighter-weight concrete.

4.1.0 Floors

Once the framework is in place, the concrete floors are poured using deck forms. Shoring is placed under the form to support it until the concrete hardens. *Figure 49* shows cellular floors poured over corrugated steel forms, which remain in place, providing channels though which cabling can be run.

A section of metal, plastic, or fiber sleeve is often inserted vertically into the form before the concrete is poured to allow for electrical, communications, and other cabling to pass through the floor.

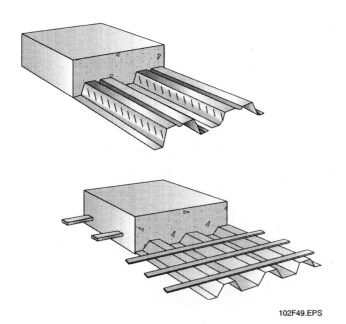

Figure 49 ◆ Corrugated steel forms.

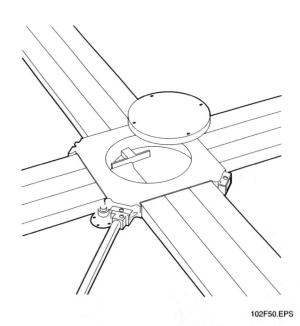

Figure 50 ◆ Flushduct underfloor system.

In some installations, underfloor duct systems are embedded in the concrete floor and are used to provide horizontal distribution of cables. Vertical access ports (handholes) are embedded in the form so that cable can be fished to various locations in the space. *Figure 50* shows a single-level feeder duct system. In two-level systems, one level carries electrical power cables and the other carries low-voltage cables.

Trench ducts are metal troughs that are embedded in the concrete floor and used as feeder ducts for electrical power and telecommunication lines. *Figure 51* shows a trench duct in a cellular floor.

Access floors consist of modular floor panels supported by pedestals. They may or may not have horizontal bracing in addition to the pedestals. This type of structure is used in computer rooms, intensive care facilities, and other areas where a lot of cabling is required. In some applications, such as a factory, a trench may be formed in the concrete floor to accommodate cabling and other services.

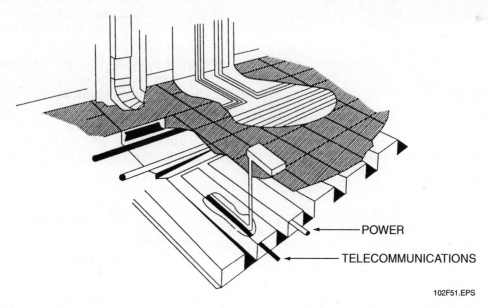

POWER

TELECOMMUNICATIONS

Figure 51 ◆ Trench duct in a cellular floor.

4.2.0 Exterior Walls

When walls are formed of concrete, openings for doors and windows are made by inserting wooden or metal bucks in the form, as shown in *Figure 52*. Openings for services such as piping and cabling are accommodated with fiber, plastic, or metal tubes inserted into the form.

4.3.0 Interior Walls and Partitions

The construction of walls and partitions in commercial applications is driven by the fire and soundproofing requirements specified in local building codes. In some cases, a frame wall with ½" gypsum drywall on either side is satisfactory. In extreme cases, such as the separation between offices and manufacturing space in a factory, it may be necessary to have a concrete block wall combined with fire-resistant gypsum wallboard, along with rigid and/or fiberglass insulation, as shown in *Figure 53*. This is especially true if there is any explosion or fire hazard.

While they are sometimes used in residential construction, steel studs are the standard for framing walls and partitions for commercial construction. Once the studs are installed, one or more layers of gypsum wallboard and insulation are applied. The type and thickness of the wallboard and insulation depend on the fire rating and soundproofing requirements. Soundproofing needs vary from one use to another and are often based on the amount of privacy required for the intended use. For example, executive and physician offices may require more privacy than general offices.

The requirements for sound reduction and fire resistance can significantly affect the thickness of a wall. For example, a wall with a high sound transmission class (STC) and fire resistance might have a total thickness of nearly 6", while a low-rated wall might have a thickness of only 3" using steel studs and 2¼" using wooden studs. (See *Figure 54*.)

As discussed previously, the fire rating specified by the applicable building code determines the types and amount of material used in a wall or partition. As shown in *Figure 54*, a one-hour rated wall might be made of single sheets of ⅝" gypsum wallboard on wooden or 25-gauge metal studs. A two-hour rated wall requires heavy-gauge metal studs and two layers of fire-resistant gypsum wallboard.

4.3.1 Metal Framing Materials

Metal framing components include metal studs and, in some cases, metal joists and metal roof trusses (*Figure 55*). The vertical and horizontal framing members serve as structural load-carrying components for a variety of low- and high-rise structures. Metal stud framing is compatible with all types of surfacing materials.

The advantages of metal framing include noncombustibility, uniformity of dimension, lightness of weight, freedom from rot and moisture, and ease of construction. The components of metal frame systems are manufactured to fit together easily. There are a variety of metal framing systems, both loadbearing and nonbearing types. Some nonbearing partitions are designed to be demountable or moveable and still meet the requirements of sound

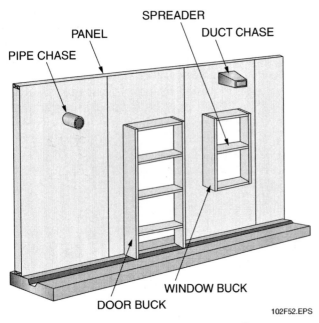

Figure 52 ◆ Framing openings in concrete walls.

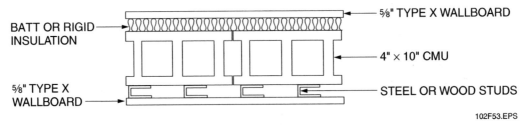

Figure 53 ◆ High fire/noise resistance partition.

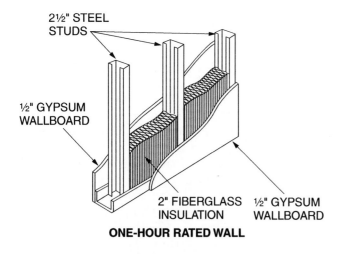

2½" STEEL STUDS

½" GYPSUM WALLBOARD

2" FIBERGLASS INSULATION

½" GYPSUM WALLBOARD

ONE-HOUR RATED WALL

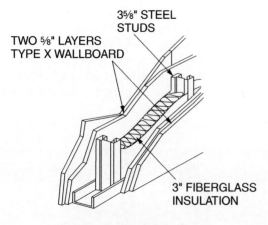

3⅝" STEEL STUDS

TWO ⅝" LAYERS TYPE X WALLBOARD

3" FIBERGLASS INSULATION

TWO-HOUR RATED WALL

102F54.EPS

Figure 54 ◆ Partition wall examples.

102F55.EPS

Figure 55 ◆ Metal trusses.

insulation and fire resistance when covered with the proper gypsum system.

When metal studs are used for drywall framing systems, the channel stock features knurled sides for positive screw settings and comes in two grades. The first grade is the standard drywall stud (*Figure 56*). Standard studs come in widths of 1⅝" to 6". The flanges are 1⅜" × 1¼". Lengths of 6' to 16' are commercially available. The standard drywall stud is 25-gauge steel (the higher the gauge, the lighter the metal). Depending on the product number, lengths range from 8' to 12'; other lengths are available by special order.

The second grade is the extra heavy drywall stud (*Figure 57*). These studs have knurled sides for positive screw settings. They also have cutouts and utility knockout holes 12" from each end and at the mid-point of the stud.

The width of the extra heavy studs will also vary from 1⅝" to 6". The flanges are 1⅜" × 1¼". The extra heavy drywall stud is 20 gauge. This type of stud can be ordered in any length that is needed.

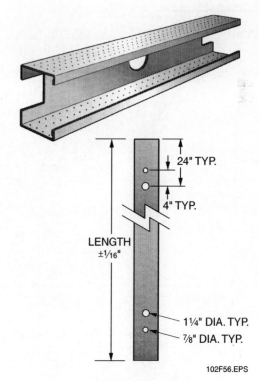

24" TYP.

4" TYP.

LENGTH ±1/16"

1¼" DIA. TYP.

⅞" DIA. TYP.

102F56.EPS

Figure 56 ◆ Standard metal stud stock.

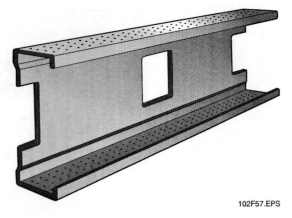

Figure 57 ◆ Heavy-duty stud stock.

102F57.EPS

Metal studs are also available in greater strengths of 18 gauge, 16 gauge, 12 gauge, and 10 gauge. These strengths are classified as structural steel studs. They are available in widths of 2½" to 8". The flanges are 1⅝" × 2" or 2½". They can be ordered in whatever length is needed.

Although different materials are used, the general approach to framing with metal studs is the same as that used for wooden studs. In fact, metal studs can be used with either wood plates or metal runners.

Like wood framing, metal framing is installed 12", 16", or 24" OC, openings are framed with headers and cripples, and special framing is needed for corners and partition Ts.

Depending on the load, reinforcement may be needed when framing openings. Bracing of walls to keep them square and plumb is also required. The illustrations in this section show examples of common framing techniques. *Table 3* shows the framing spacing for various gypsum drywall applications.

The erection of metal studs typically starts by laying metal tracks in position on the floor and ceiling and securing them (*Figure 58*). If the tracks are being applied to concrete (*Figure 59*), a low-velocity powder-actuated fastener is generally used. If the tracks are being applied to wood joists, such as in a residence, screws can be driven with a screw gun.

Table 3 Maximum Framing Spacing

	Single-Ply Gypsum Board Thicknesses	Application to Framing	Maximum OC Spacing of Framing
Ceilings	⅜"	Perpendicular	16"
	½"	Perpendicular or Parallel	16"
	½"	Perpendicular	24"
	⅝"	Perpendicular	24"
Sidewalls	⅜"	Perpendicular or Parallel	16"
	½" or ⅝"	Perpendicular or Parallel	24"

Fasteners Only – No Adhesive Between Plies					
	Multi-Ply Gypsum Board Thicknesses		Application to Framing		Maximum OC Spacing of Framing
	Base	Face	Base	Face	
Ceilings	⅜"	⅜"	Perpendicular	Perpendicular	16"
	½"	⅜"	Parallel	Perpendicular	16"
		½"	Parallel	Perpendicular	16"
	½"	½"	Perpendicular	Perpendicular	24"
	⅝"	½"	Perpendicular	Perpendicular	24"
		⅝"	Perpendicular	Perpendicular	24"

Sidewalls*

* For two-layer applications with no adhesive between plies, ⅜", ½", or ⅝" gypsum board may be applied perpendicularly (horizontally) or parallel (vertically) on framing spaced a maximum of 24" OC. Maximum spacing should be 16" OC when ⅜" board is used as the face layer

102T03.EPS

Once the tracks are in place, the studs and openings are laid out in the same way as a wood frame wall. The studs may be secured to the tracks with screws or they may be welded. In some cases, the entire wall will be laid out on the floor, then raised and secured. When heavy-gauge walls are used, they may be assembled and welded in a shop and brought to the site.

There are some differences between installing metal nonbearing partitions and wooden nonbearing partitions. When building with wood, all partitions must be nailed together. With metal studs, this is not required.

As shown in *Figure 60*, the partitions are held back from the other partitions so that the drywall will slide past. Note the conduit fed through the openings in the stud.

When metal studs are used to frame around steel beams, the metal studs are secured to the metal beam with powder-actuated fasteners (if allowed) and the support members are screwed to the metal studs (*Figure 61*). Note the wire hanger for the suspended ceiling at the right of the picture.

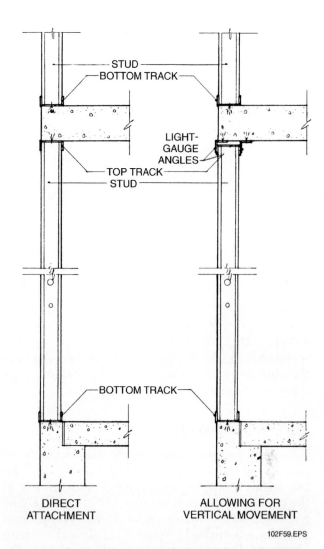

102F59.EPS

Figure 59 ◆ Metal studs with concrete floors and ceiling.

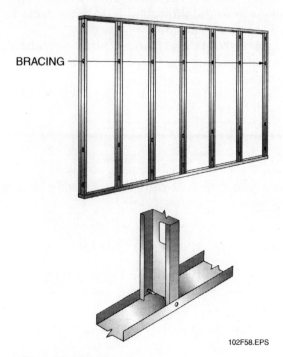

102F58.EPS

Figure 58 ◆ Metal framing.

102F60.EPS

Figure 60 ◆ Partition held back to allow drywall to slide by.

Figure 61 ◆ Plate attached to a beam.

102F61.EPS

Figure 62 ◆ Studs secured to a channel.

102F62.EPS

When the metal studs are installed against metal channels or flanges, the studs are secured to the channel with scrap pieces of metal studs, as shown in *Figure 62*.

4.3.2 Bracing Walls

Different forms of bracing are used to support metal stud walls. Lateral bracing using continuous metal strapping is always recommended as the minimum support for metal stud walls (*Figure 63*). Diagonal bracing using metal strapping is sometimes required (*Figure 64*). This is done with 20-gauge, 2" wide metal straps placed close to the end of the wall. Lateral and diagonal braces can be screwed and/or welded to the studs.

For heavier studs (6" and wider), steel channel threaded through the openings in the studs and welded to angle clips is sometimes required (*Figure 65*). Fine-gauge lateral bracing, fed through the openings in the studs and welded to each stud, is also used in some applications, as shown in *Figure 66*.

4.3.3 Metal Joists and Roof Trusses

In commercial work, metal studs are commonly used to frame interior nonbearing walls and partitions. In residential work, an entire house can be framed with steel studs, joists, and roof trusses.

Steel joists are available in the same sizes as wood joists. Joists can rest directly on concrete or masonry or they can be attached to a wood sill plate or top plate. See *Figure 67*.

One method of installing floor joists in a poured concrete foundation wall is to form slots in the wall to accept the joists (*Figure 68*).

Metal roofs are framed with prefabricated trusses in which the framing members are welded together.

Identifying Structural Studs

Structural studs are marked with a color code for easy identification. The coding is as follows:

Gauge	Color
20	White
18	Yellow
16	Green
14	Blue
12	Red

Note that there are both light and structural gauge studs made of 20-gauge steel. The difference is in the dimensions.

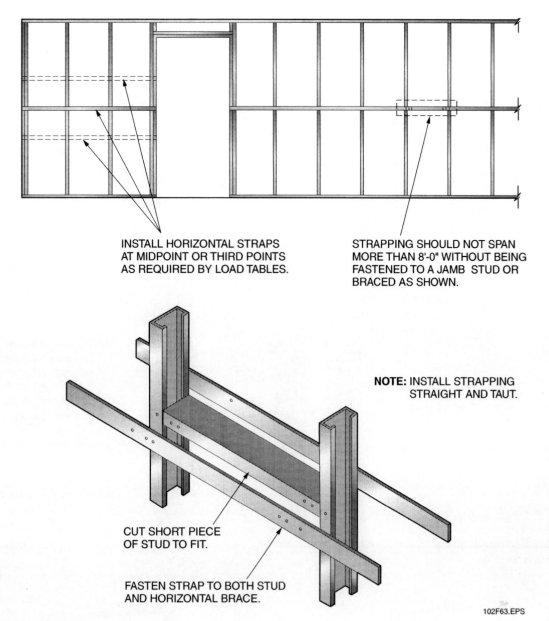

INSTALL HORIZONTAL STRAPS
AT MIDPOINT OR THIRD POINTS
AS REQUIRED BY LOAD TABLES.

STRAPPING SHOULD NOT SPAN
MORE THAN 8'-0" WITHOUT BEING
FASTENED TO A JAMB STUD OR
BRACED AS SHOWN.

NOTE: INSTALL STRAPPING
STRAIGHT AND TAUT.

CUT SHORT PIECE
OF STUD TO FIT.

FASTEN STRAP TO BOTH STUD
AND HORIZONTAL BRACE.

102F63.EPS

Figure 63 ◆ Lateral strapping for stud walls.

4.4.0 Ceilings

Although suspended ceilings are sometimes found in residential applications, they are most commonly used in commercial construction. Suspended ceilings have a number of advantages in commercial work:

- They provide excellent noise suppression.
- They provide an area in which horizontal runs of cabling, piping, heating and cooling ducts, and other services can be readily accessed.
- In many commercial buildings, the area between the suspended ceiling and the floor above acts as the return air **plenum** for air conditioning and heating, eliminating the need for some of the sheet metal ductwork.

- The use of suspended ceilings eliminates the need for ceiling framing, as well as the need to box in horizontal runs of ductwork and piping.

There are a wide variety of suspended acoustical ceiling systems. They use the same basic materials, but their appearances are completely different. The focus in this module is on the following systems:

- Exposed grid systems
- Metal pan systems
- Direct-hung concealed grid systems
- Integrated ceiling systems
- Luminous ceiling systems
- Suspended drywall furring ceiling systems
- Special ceiling systems

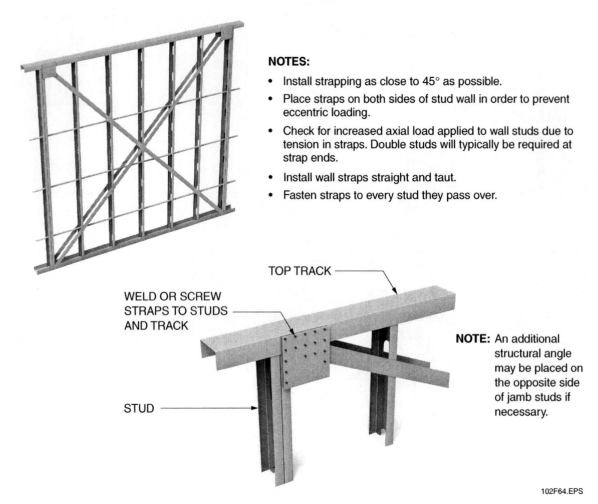

NOTES:

- Install strapping as close to 45° as possible.
- Place straps on both sides of stud wall in order to prevent eccentric loading.
- Check for increased axial load applied to wall studs due to tension in straps. Double studs will typically be required at strap ends.
- Install wall straps straight and taut.
- Fasten straps to every stud they pass over.

WELD OR SCREW STRAPS TO STUDS AND TRACK

TOP TRACK

STUD

NOTE: An additional structural angle may be placed on the opposite side of jamb studs if necessary.

102F64.EPS

Figure 64 ◆ Diagonal strapping for shear walls.

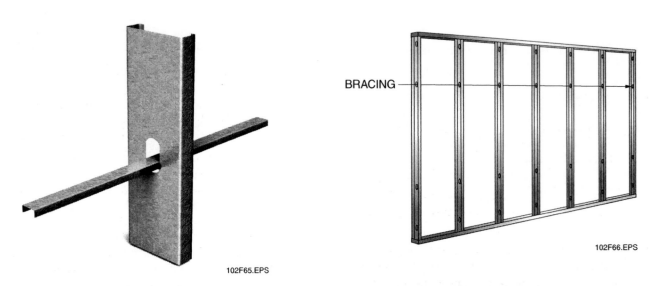

102F65.EPS

Figure 65 ◆ Heavy-duty bridging.

BRACING

102F66.EPS

Figure 66 ◆ Fine-gauge lateral bracing.

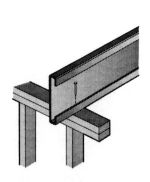 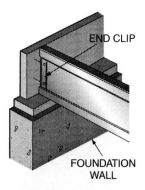 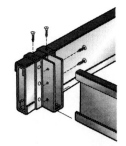 

| JOIST APPLIED DIRECTLY TO DOUBLE TOP PLATE | JOIST ATTACHED TO WOOD SILL PLATE AND HEADER JOIST | METAL JOIST ATTACHED TO METAL HEADER JOIST | METAL JOIST ATTACHED TO CONCRETE FOUNDATION |

102F67.EPS

Figure 67 ◆ Examples of metal joist installations.

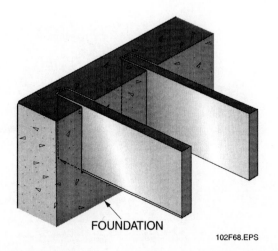

102F68.EPS

Figure 68 ◆ Installing metal floor joists in a slotted foundation wall.

4.4.1 Exposed Grid Systems

For an exposed grid suspended ceiling, also called a direct-hung system, a light metal grid is hung by wire from the original ceiling or the deck above. Ceiling panels, which are usually 2' × 2' or 2' × 4', are then placed in the frames of the metal grid. Exposed grid systems are constructed using the components and materials shown in *Figure 69* and described here:

- *Main runners* – These are the primary support members of the grid system for all types of suspended ceiling systems. They are 12' in length and are usually made in the form of an inverted T. When it is necessary to lengthen the main runners, they are usually spliced together using extension inserts. However, the method of splicing the main runners will vary with the type of system being used.

- *Cross runners (cross ties or cross tees)* – These supports are inserted into the main runners at right angles and spaced an equal distance from each other, forming a complete grid system. They are held in place by either clips or automatic locking devices. Typically, they are either 4' or 2' in length and are usually constructed in the form of an inverted T. Note that 2' cross runners are only required for use with 2' × 2' ceiling panels.

- *Wall angle* – These supports are installed on the walls to support the exposed grid system at the outer edges.

- *Ceiling panels* – These panels are laid in place between the main runners and cross ties to provide an acoustical treatment. Acoustical panels used in suspended ceilings stop sound reflection and reverberation by absorbing sound waves. These panels are typically designed with numerous tiny sound traps consisting of drilled or punched holes or fissures, or a combination of both. A wide variety of ceiling panel designs, patterns, colors, facings, and sizes are available, allowing most environmental and appearance demands to be met. Panels are typically made of glass or mineral fiber. Generally, glass panels have a higher sound absorbency than mineral fiber panels. Panel facings are typically made of embossed vinyl and are available in a variety of patterns, such as fissured, pebbled, and **striated**. The specific ceiling panels used must be compatible with the ceiling suspension system, however, because there are variations among manufacturers' standards and not all panels fit all systems.

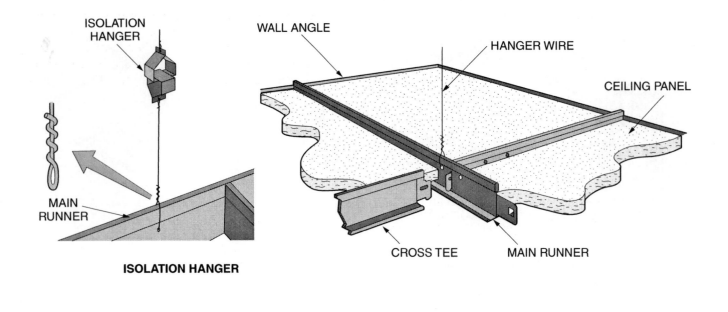

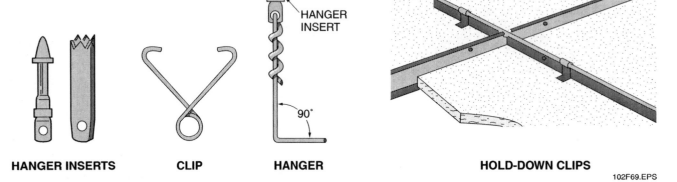

HANGER INSERTS   **CLIP**   **HANGER**

HOLD-DOWN CLIPS

102F69.EPS

Figure 69 ◆ Typical exposed grid system components.

- *Hanger inserts and clips* – There are many types of fastening devices used to attach the grid system hangers or wires to the building's horizontal structure above the suspended ceiling. Screw eyes and star anchors are commonly used, and require an electric hammer for installation. Eye pin fasteners are also commonly used to fasten into reinforced concrete with a powder-actuated fastening tool. Clips are used where beams are available and are typically installed over the beam flanges, then the hanger wires are inserted through the loops in the clips and secured. These devices must be adequate to handle the load.

- *Hangers* – These are attached to the hanger inserts, pins, and clips to support the suspended ceiling's main runners. The hangers can be made of No. 12 wire or heavier rod stock. Ceiling isolation hangers are also available that isolate ceilings from noise traveling through the building structure.

- *Hold-down clips* – These clips are used in some systems to hold the ceiling panels in place.

- *Nails, screws, rawls, toppets, molly bolts* – These fasteners are used to secure the wall angle to the wall. The specific item used depends on the wall construction and material.

4.4.2 Metal Pan Systems

The metal pan system is similar to the conventional suspended acoustical ceiling system, but metal tiles or pans are used in place of the conventional acoustical panel. See *Figure 70*.

The pans are made of steel or aluminum and are generally painted white; however, other colors are available by special order. Pans are also available in a variety of surface patterns. Tests have indicated that metal pan ceiling systems are effective for sound absorption. They are durable and easily cleaned and disinfected. In addition, the finished ceiling has little or no tendency to have sagging joint lines or drooping corners. The metal pans are die-stamped and have crimped edges that snap into the spring-locking main runner and provide a flush ceiling.

Take care in handling the pans if you have to remove them. Use white gloves or rub your hands with cornstarch to keep any perspiration marks from the surface of the pans. If care is not taken, fingerprints will be plainly visible when the units are reinstalled.

When removing or installing pans, grasp the pan at its edge and force its crimp into the tee bar slots. Use the palms of your hands to seat the pan. After installing several of the pans as noted above, slide them along the tee bars into position. Use the side of your closed fist to bump the pan into level position if it does not seat readily. If metal pan hoods are required, slip them into position over the pans as they are installed. The purpose of the hood is to reduce the travel of sound through the ceiling into the room.

If a metal pan must be removed, a pan pulling device is available (*Figure 71*). To pull out a pan, insert the free ends of the device into two of the perforations at one corner of the pan and pull down sharply. Repeat this at each corner of the pan. By following this removal procedure, there is no danger of bending the pan out of shape. A metal pan ceiling is shown in *Figure 72*.

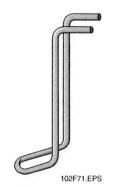

102F71.EPS

Figure 71 ◆ Pan removal tool.

102F72.EPS

Figure 72 ◆ Metal pan ceiling.

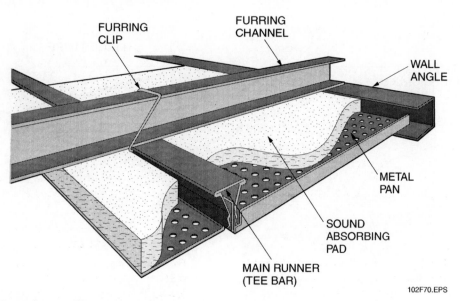

FURRING CLIP

FURRING CHANNEL

WALL ANGLE

METAL PAN

SOUND ABSORBING PAD

MAIN RUNNER (TEE BAR)

102F70.EPS

Figure 70 ◆ Typical metal pan ceiling components.

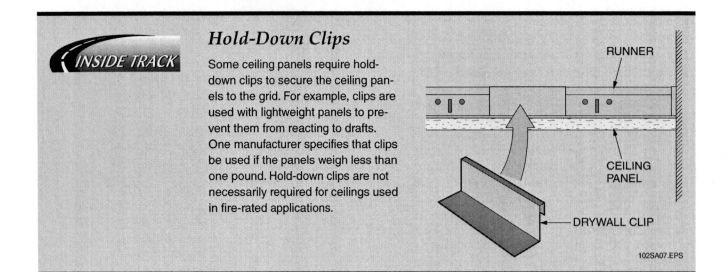
4.4.3 Direct-Hung Concealed Grid Systems

In this type of suspended acoustical ceiling system, the support runners are hidden from view, resulting in a patterned ceiling that is not broken by the pattern of the runners. See *Figure 73*.

The tiles used for this system are similar in composition to conventional acoustical tile, but are manufactured with a **kerf** on all four edges. Kerfed and **rabbeted** 12" × 12" or 12" × 24" tiles are used with this system. Tiles of various colors and finishes are available. Refer to *Figure 74* for a diagram of a concealed grid system installation.

If regular access is needed to the area above the ceiling, special access systems can be incorporated into the ceiling. See *Figure 75*.

102F73.EPS

Figure 73 ◆ Typical concealed grid system.

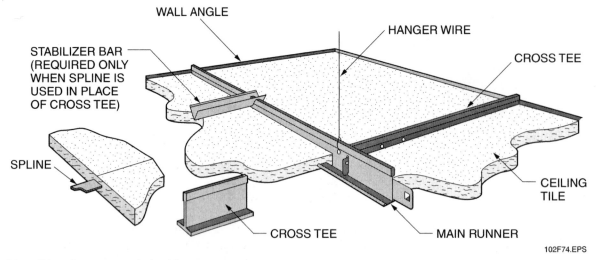

WALL ANGLE

HANGER WIRE

STABILIZER BAR (REQUIRED ONLY WHEN SPLINE IS USED IN PLACE OF CROSS TEE)

CROSS TEE

SPLINE

CEILING TILE

CROSS TEE

MAIN RUNNER

102F74.EPS

Figure 74 ◆ Direct-hung concealed grid system components.

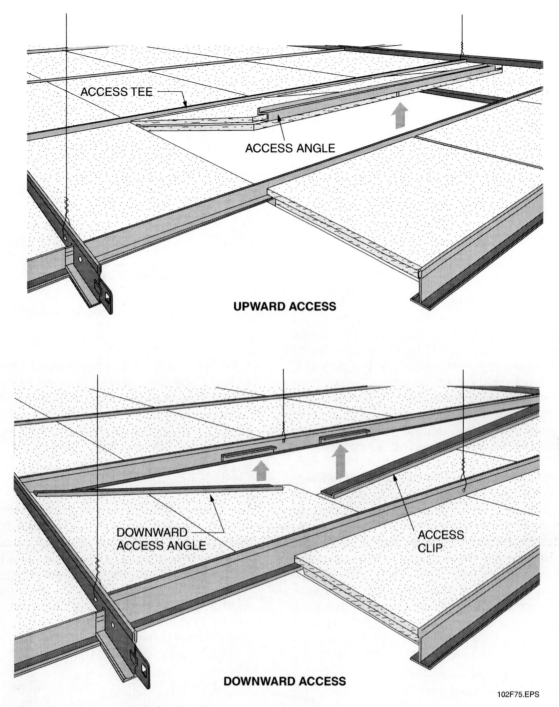

ACCESS TEE

ACCESS ANGLE

UPWARD ACCESS

DOWNWARD ACCESS ANGLE

ACCESS CLIP

DOWNWARD ACCESS

102F75.EPS

Figure 75 ◆ Typical access for concealed grid ceilings.

4.4.4 Integrated Ceiling Systems

As indicated by its name, the integrated ceiling system incorporates the lighting and/or air supply diffusers as part of the overall ceiling system, as shown in *Figures 76* and *77*.

This system is available in units called modules. The common sizes are 30" × 60" and 60" × 60". The dimensions refer to the spacing of the main runners and cross tees.

4.4.5 Luminous Ceiling Systems

Luminous ceiling systems are available in many styles, such as exposed-grid systems with drop-in plastic light diffusers and aluminum or wood framework with translucent acrylic light diffusers. Refer to *Figure 78*.

Fluorescent fixtures are generally installed above the translucent diffusers. Standard modules of 2' × 2' up to sizes of 5' × 5' are available, as are

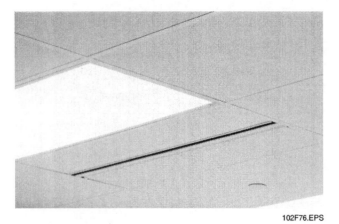

Figure 76 ◆ Typical integrated grid system.

custom sizes for special applications. There are two types of luminous ceilings—standard and non-standard. Standard systems are, as their name indicates, those that are available in a series of standard sizes and patterns. Non-standard systems deviate from the normal spacing of main supports and/or have unusual sizes, shapes, and configurations of diffusing panels.

All surfaces in the luminous space, including pipes, ductwork, ceilings, and walls, are painted with a 75% to 90% reflectance matte white finish. Any surfaces in this area that might tend to flake, such as fireproofing and insulation, should receive an approved hard surface coating prior to painting to prevent flaking onto the ceiling below.

The installation of a standard luminous system is the same as for the exposed grid suspended system, with the exception of the border cuts. Luminous ceilings are placed into the grid members in full modules. Any remaining modules are filled in with acoustical material that has been cut to size.

Figure 78 ◆ Typical integrated luminous ceiling system.

With a 2' × 2' or 2' × 4' standard exposed grid system, luminous panels are used to provide the light diffusing element in the system. These panels are laid in between the runners. A variety of sizes and shapes of panels are available.

4.4.6 Suspended Drywall Furring Ceiling Systems

The suspended drywall furring system is used when it is desirable or specified to use a drywall finish or drywall backing for an acoustical tile ceiling.

When this type of ceiling is installed, the first step is to install a carrying channel, as shown in *Figure 79*. Furring channels are then installed at right angles to the carrying channels. *Figure 80* shows an example in which a hat-type metal furring channel is used.

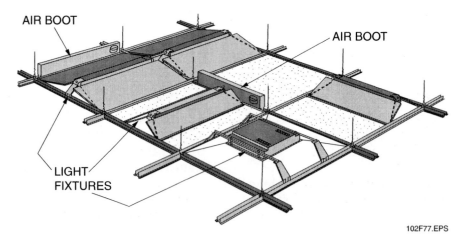

Figure 77 ◆ Integrated ceiling layout.

After the furring channels are in place, the drywall sheets are installed with drywall screws driven into the furring channel (*Figure 81*).

In some cases, the furring channels are attached directly to structural members such as steel beams or wooden joists, instead of to suspended carrying channels. In other cases, ceiling tiles are attached to the drywall.

4.4.7 Special Ceiling Systems

There are numerous special ceiling systems that differ from those covered in this module. Some of these are the special metallic system, special pan system, planar system, mirrored (reflective) system, and translucent panel system (*Figures 82* through *86*).

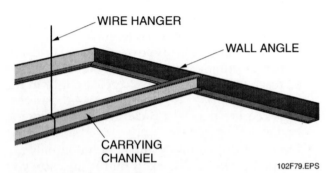

102F79.EPS

Figure 79 ◆ Carrying channel installed.

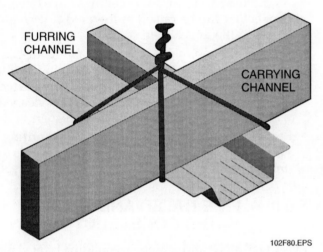

102F80.EPS

Figure 80 ◆ Furring channel attached to carrying channel.

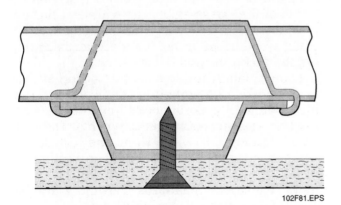

102F81.EPS

Figure 81 ◆ Drywall secured to furring channel.

102F82.EPS

Figure 82 ◆ Special metallic system.

102F83.EPS

Figure 83 ◆ Special pan system.

102F84.EPS

Figure 84 ◆ Planar system.

Figure 85 ◆ Reflective ceiling.

Figure 86 ◆ Translucent panels.

4.4.8 General Guidelines for Accessing Suspended Ceilings

In new construction, the cable installer sometimes has the luxury of running cable before the suspended ceiling grid and panels are installed. More often, however, you will be faced with the retrofit of an existing system, or with a situation in which the ceiling has already been installed in the new building by the time you get there.

Keep in mind that the ceiling panels are delicate and the grid system is not capable of sustaining much weight. In addition, as you have already seen, there are many different types of ceiling systems, each of them with its own special requirements.

The following are some general guidelines for working with suspended ceilings:

- Contact building maintenance personnel to find out how the ceiling is constructed and how to obtain spare panels in case some of the existing panels get damaged. They should also have the special tools you will need to get access to some types of ceilings. One type of concealed grid system, for example, has a special hook that is used to reach under the panel and release it from the cross member. As previously discussed, pan ceilings require special procedures for removing and installing pans.

- Do not force ceiling panels. Some panels are clipped to the gridwork. If that is the case, you will need to find the panel that is not clipped and start there. A special tool may be needed to release the clips.

- As discussed earlier, some ceilings have hinged panels that can be raised or lowered to provide access to the area above.

- Keep your hands clean to avoid staining the ceiling panels. If a panel gets dirty, try cleaning it with a damp sponge or an art gum eraser. Vinyl-faced fiberglass and mylar-faced ceilings can be cleaned with mild detergents or germicidal cleaners.

- Pan ceiling panels require special handling. Wear gloves or rub cornstarch on your hands to prevent the transfer of fingerprints to the panels.

5.0.0 ◆ FIRE-RATED AND SOUND-RATED CONSTRUCTION

Every wall, floor, and ceiling in a building is rated for its fire resistance, as established by building codes. The fire rating is stated in terms of hours, such as one-hour wall or two-hour wall. The rating denotes the length of time an assembly can withstand fire and provide protection from it, as determined under laboratory conditions (*Figure 87*). The greater the fire rating, the thicker the wall is likely to be.

In multi-family residential construction, such as apartments and townhouses, the walls and ceilings dividing the occupancies must meet special fire and soundproofing requirements. The code requirements will vary from one location to another and may even vary within areas of a jurisdiction. For example, dwellings in high-risk areas may have stricter standards than those in other areas of the same city or county.

Plenum Ceilings

The systems that provide heating and cooling for most commercial buildings are forced-air systems. Blower fans are used to circulate the air. The blower draws air from the space to be conditioned and then forces the air over a heat exchanger, which cools or heats the air. In a cooling system, for example, the air is forced over an evaporator coil that has very cold refrigerant flowing through it. The heat in the air is transferred to the refrigerant, so the air that comes out the other side of the evaporator coil is cold. In homes, the air is delivered to the conditioned space and returned to the air conditioning/heating system through ductwork that is usually made of sheet metal. In commercial buildings with suspended ceilings, the space between the ceiling and the overhead decking is often used as the return air plenum. (A plenum is a sealed chamber at the inlet or outlet of an air handler.) This approach saves money by eliminating about half the cost of materials and labor associated with ductwork.

One thing to keep in mind is that anything in the plenum space (electrical or telecommunications cable, for example) must be specifically rated for plenum use in order to meet fire ratings. Plastic sheathing used on standard cables gives off toxic fumes when burned. Plenum-rated cable uses non-toxic sheathing.

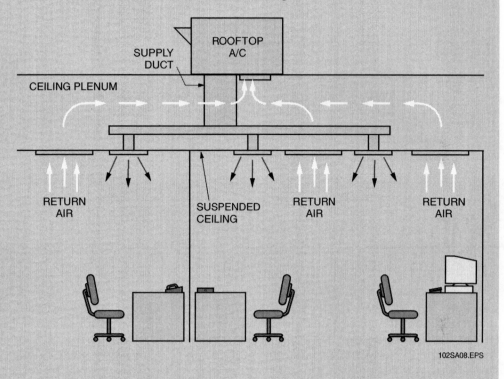

102SA08.EPS

Drilling Fire-Rated Walls

There are many wall variations, so you must first establish the type of construction before undertaking any invasive action, such as drilling. If drilling is permitted, you may have to use firestopping materials to seal off the opening.

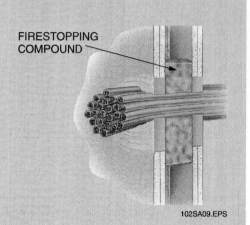

FIRESTOPPING COMPOUND

102SA09.EPS

QUICK SELECTOR FOR FIRE-RATED ASSEMBLIES
PARTITIONS/WOOD FRAMING (LOAD BEARING)

SINGLE LAYER	REF.	DESIGN NO.	DESCRIPTION	STC	TEST NO.
45 MIN.	UL FM	U317 WI-45 MIN	½" FIRE-SHIELD GYPSUM WALLBOARD NAILED ON BOTH SIDES 2 × 4 STUDS, 16" OC.	34	NGC 2161
1 HR.	UL FM	U305 WI6A-1HR WP 3605	⅝" FIRE-SHIELD GYPSUM WALLBOARD OR ⅝" FIRE-SHIELD MR BOARD NAILED ON BOTH SIDES 2 × 4 WOOD STUDS, 16" OC.	35	NGC 2403
1 HR.	UL FM	U309 WI6B-1HR WP 3605	⅝" FIRE-SHIELD GYPSUM WALLBOARD OR ⅝" FIRE-SHIELD MR BOARD NAILED ON BOTH SIDES 2 × 4 WOOD STUDS, 24" OC.	38	NGC 2404
1 HR.	FM GA	WIA-1HR (WP) 45 WP-1200	⅝" FIRE-SHIELD GYPSUM WALLBOARD OR ⅝" FIRE-SHIELD MR BOARD SCREW ATTACHED HORIZONTALLY TO BOTH SIDES 3⅝" SCREW STUDS, 24" OC. ALL WALLBOARD JOINTS STAGGERED.	42	NGC 2385
	OSU	T-1770	⅝" FIRE-SHIELD GYPSUM WALLBOARD SCREW ATTACHED VERTICALLY TO BOTH SIDES 3⅝" SCREW STUDS, 24" OC. ALL WALLBOARD JOINTS STAGGERED.		
DOUBLE LAYER					
2 HR.	UL FM	U301 BASED ON WP 4135	2 LAYERS ⅝" FIRE-SHIELD GYPSUM WALLBOARD NAIL APPLIED TO 2 × 4 WOOD STUDS SPACED 16" OC. BOARDS MAY BE APPLIED HORIZONTALLY OR VERTICALLY WITH ALL JOINTS STAGGERED.	40	NGC 2363
2 HR.	OSU GA	T-1771 BASED ON WP 1711	FIRST LAYER ⅝" FIRE-SHIELD GYPSUM WALLBOARD SCREW ATTACHED VERTICALLY TO BOTH SIDES 3⅝" SCREW STUDS, 24" OC. SECOND LAYER LAMINATED VERTICALLY ON BOTH SIDES. VERTICAL JOINTS STAGGERED.	48	NGC 2282

102F87.EPS

Figure 87 ◆ Specifications for typical fire-rated walls.

In some cases, the code may require a masonry wall between occupancies. This masonry wall may even be required to penetrate the roof of the building so that if a fire occurs, it is contained within the unit in which it started because it is unable to travel through the walls or across the attic space.

There are many different construction methods for so-called party walls. Each is designed to meet different fire and soundproofing standards. The wall is likely to be more than 3" thick and contain several layers of gypsum wallboard and insulation. A fire-rated wall may abut a non-rated partition or wall. In this case, the rated wall must be carried through to maintain the fire rating. *Figure 88* shows an example of how this is done.

5.1.0 Firestopping

Firestopping means cutting off the air supply so that fire and smoke cannot readily move from one location to another. You will hear the term firestop used in two different ways.

In frame construction, a firestop is a piece of wood or fire-resistant material inserted into an opening such as the space between studs. This firestop acts as a barrier to block airflow that would allow the space to act as a chimney, carrying fire rapidly to upper floors. It does not put out the fire, but it slows the fire's progress.

In commercial construction and some residential applications, firestopping material is used to close wall penetrations such as those created to run conduit, piping, and air conditioning ducts. If such openings are not sealed, fire will travel through the openings in its search for oxygen.

In order to meet the fire rating standards established by the building and fire codes, the openings must be sealed. The firestopping methods used for this purpose are classified as mechanical and nonmechanical.

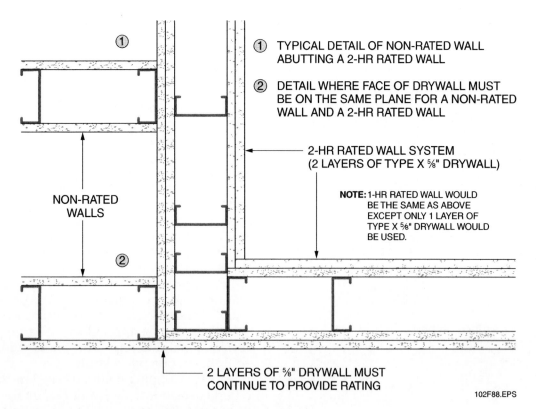

① TYPICAL DETAIL OF NON-RATED WALL
   ABUTTING A 2-HR RATED WALL

② DETAIL WHERE FACE OF DRYWALL MUST
   BE ON THE SAME PLANE FOR A NON-RATED
   WALL AND A 2-HR RATED WALL

2-HR RATED WALL SYSTEM
(2 LAYERS OF TYPE X ⅝" DRYWALL)

NOTE: 1-HR RATED WALL WOULD
BE THE SAME AS ABOVE
EXCEPT ONLY 1 LAYER OF
TYPE X ⅝" DRYWALL WOULD
BE USED.

NON-RATED
WALLS

2 LAYERS OF ⅝" DRYWALL MUST
CONTINUE TO PROVIDE RATING

102F88.EPS

Figure 88 ◆ Example of a fire-rated wall abutting a non-rated wall.

NOTE

As an EST, you may be required to install fire-stopping in openings that you create for cable runs. You should be aware that in some jurisdictions, specially licensed firestop technicians must perform all firestopping work.

Mechanical firestops are devices such as the one shown in *Figure 89* that mechanically seal the opening.

Nonmechanical firestops are fire-resistant materials, such as caulks and putties, that are used to fill the space around the conduit or piping. You may be required to install various nonmechanical firestopping materials when working with fire-rated walls and floors. Holes or gaps affect the fire rating of a floor or wall. Properly filling these penetrations with firestopping materials maintains the rating. Firestopping materials are typically applied around all types of piping, electrical conduit, ductwork, electrical and communication cables (*Figure 90*), and similar devices that run through openings in floor slabs, walls, and other fire-rated building partitions and assemblies.

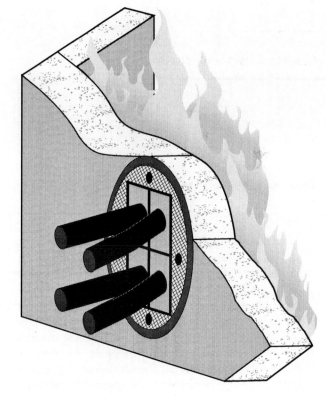

102F89.EPS

Figure 89 ◆ Mechanical firestop device.

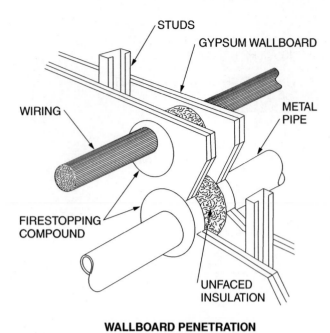

WALLBOARD PENETRATION

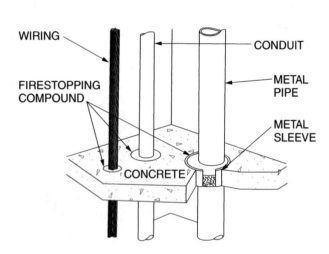

CONCRETE PENETRATION

102F90.EPS

Figure 90 ◆ Fireproof openings.

Nonmechanical firestopping materials are classified as intumescent or endothermic. Both are formulated to help control the spread of fire before, during, and after exposure to open flames. When subjected to the extreme heat of a fire, intumescent materials expand (typically up to three times their original size) to form a strong insulating material that seals the opening for three to four hours. Should the insulation on the cables or pipes passing through the penetration become consumed by the fire, the expansion of the firestopping material also acts to fill the void in the floor or wall in order to help stop the spread of smoke and other toxic products of combustion.

Endothermic materials block heat by releasing chemically bound water, which causes them to absorb heat. Some firestopping materials are ablative, which means that they form a hard char when exposed to flame. The char inhibits the passage of flame and smoke.

Firestopping materials are formulated in such a way that when activated, they are free of corrosive gases, reducing the risks to building occupants and sensitive equipment.

Firestopping materials are made in a variety of forms including composite sheeting, caulks, silicone sealants, foams, moldable putty, wrap strips, and spray coatings. They come in both one-part and two-part formulations. The installation of these materials must always be done in accordance with the applicable building codes and the manufacturer's instructions for the product being used. Depending on the product, firestopping materials can be applied via spray equipment, conventional caulking guns, pneumatic pumping equipment, or a putty knife.

Any firestopping materials used must meet the criteria of standard *ASTM E814, Fire Test*, as tested under positive pressure. They must also have an hourly rating that is equal to or greater than the hourly rating of the floor or wall being penetrated. Based on *ASTM E814/UL 1479* tests, one of four ratings, measured in time, may be applied to firestopping materials and systems. These ratings are as follows:

- *F rating* – A firestopping system meets the requirements of an F rating if it remains in the opening during the fire test for the rating period without permitting the passage of flames through the opening or the occurrence of flaming on any element of the unexposed side of the assembly.

- *FT rating* – A firestopping system meets the requirements of an FT rating if it remains in the opening during the fire test within the limitations as specified for an F rating. In addition, the transmission of heat through the firestopping system during the rated period shall not have been such as to raise the temperature of any thermocouple on the unexposed surface of the firestopping system by more than 347.8°F (181°C) above its initial temperature.

- *FH rating* – A firestopping system meets the requirements of an FH rating if it remains in the opening during the fire test within the limitations for an F rating. In addition, during a hose stream test, the firestopping system shall not develop any opening that would permit a projection of water from the stream to the unexposed side.

Avoid Back-to-Back Fixtures

Medicine cabinets; electrical, telephone, television, and intercom outlets; and plumbing, heating, and air conditioning ducts should not be installed back-to-back. Any opening for such fixtures, piping, and electrical outlets should be carefully cut to the proper size and caulked.

Firestopping Materials

There are a wide variety of firestopping materials on the market. Shown here are just a few examples. Firestopping and fireproofing are not the same thing. Firestopping is intended to prevent the spread of fire and smoke from room to room through openings in walls and floors. Fireproofing is a thermal barrier that causes a fire to burn more slowly and retards the spread of fire.

FIRESTOP SEALANT

CABLE PROTECTION SPRAY

INTUMESCENT PUTTY

INTUMESCENT PIPE SLEEVE

102SA10.EPS

- *FTH rating* – A firestopping system shall be considered as meeting the requirements of an FTH rating if it remains in the opening during the fire test and hose stream test within the limitations as described for FT and FH ratings.

5.2.0 Sound-Isolation Construction

The first step for airborne sound isolation of any assembly is to close off air leaks and flanking paths. Since noise can travel over, under, or around walls, through the windows and doors adjacent to them, through air ducts, and through floors and crawl spaces, these paths must be correctly treated.

Buildings are generally required to meet a STC rating. The STC is a numeric rating representing the effectiveness of the construction in isolating airborne sound transmission. The higher the STC rating, the better the sound absorption. Hairline cracks and other openings can have an adverse affect on the ability of a building to achieve its STC rating, particularly in higher-rated construction.

Where a very high STC performance is needed, air conditioning, heating, and ventilating ducts should not be included in the assembly. Failure to observe special construction and design details can destroy the effectiveness of the best assembly. Improved sound isolation is obtained by the following:

- Separate framing for the two sides of a wall
- Resilient channel mounting for the gypsum board
- Using sound-absorbing materials in wall cavities
- Using adhesive-applied gypsum board of varying thicknesses in multi-layer construction
- Caulking the perimeter of gypsum board partitions, openings in walls and ceilings, partition/mullion intersections, and outlet box openings
- Locating recessed wall fixtures in different stud cavities

The entire perimeter of sound-isolating partitions should be caulked around the gypsum board edges to make it airtight. The caulking should be a non-hardening, non-shrinking, non-bleeding, non-staining, resilient sealant.

Sound-control sealing must be covered in the specifications, understood by all related tradespeople, supervised by the appropriate party, and inspected carefully as the construction progresses.

6.0.0 ◆ TOOLS USED FOR RUNNING CABLE

When you install low-voltage cable, it may be necessary to drill or cut through wood, steel, concrete, masonry, gypsum wallboard, and other building materials. It is important that you be able to select the correct tool and the correct bit or blade for each job.

The intent of this section is to familiarize you with each of the tools and the related safety rules that apply when using them. Before you will be allowed to operate a specific power tool, you must be able to show that you know the safety rules associated with it. As your training progresses, you will learn how to operate each of the tools while under the supervision of your instructor and/or supervisor. Specific operating procedures and safety rules for using a tool are provided in the operator's/user's manual supplied by the manufacturer with each tool. Before operating any power tool for the first time, you should always read this manual to familiarize yourself with the tool. If the manual is missing, you or your supervisor should contact the manufacturer for a replacement. It is often possible to download the manual from the manufacturer's website.

6.1.0 Guidelines for Using All Power Tools

Before proceeding with our descriptions of power tools, it is important to review the general safety rules that apply when using all power tools, regardless of type. It is also important to overview the general guidelines that should be followed in order to properly care for power tools.

> **NOTE**
> Power tools may be operated by electricity (AC or DC current), air, combustion engines, or explosive powder.

6.1.1 Safety Rules Pertaining to All Power Tools

Power tools can be dangerous. It is important to use them safely. The rules for the safe use of all power tools are as follows:

- Do not attempt to operate any power tool before being checked out by the instructor on that particular tool.
- Always wear eye protection, hearing protection, and a hard hat when operating all power tools.
- Wear face protection when necessary.
- Wear proper respirator equipment when necessary.
- Wear the appropriate clothing for the job being done. Never wear loose clothing that could become caught in the moving tool. Roll up long sleeves, tuck in shirttails, and tie back long hair.
- Do not distract others or let anyone distract you while operating a power tool.
- Do not engage in horseplay in the shop.
- Do not run or throw objects in the shop.
- Consider the safety of others, as well as yours.
- Do not leave a power tool running while it is unattended.
- Assume a safe and comfortable position before using a power tool.
- Be sure that the power tool is properly grounded before using it. Use a **ground fault circuit interrupter (GFCI)**, if possible (*Figure 91*).
- Be sure that the power tool is disconnected before performing maintenance or changing accessories.
- Do not use a dull or broken tool or accessory.
- Use a power tool only for its intended purpose.

Figure 91 ◆ Extension cord with a GFCI.

- Keep your feet, fingers, and hair away from the blade and/or other moving parts of a power tool.
- Do not use a power tool with the guards or safety devices removed.
- Do not operate a power tool if your hands or feet are wet.
- Keep the work area clean at all times.
- Become familiar with the correct operation and adjustments of a power tool before attempting to use it.
- Keep a firm grip on the power tool at all times.
- Use electric extension cords of sufficient size to service the particular power tool you are using.
- Check cords for frayed insulation or missing ground prong.
- Report unsafe conditions to your instructor or supervisor.

6.1.2 Guidelines Pertaining to the Care of All Power Tools

Power tools require proper care and maintenance. Guidelines for the proper care of power tools follow:

- Don't hold a power tool by the cord.
- Keep all tools clean and in good working order.
- Keep all machine surfaces clean and waxed.
- Follow the manufacturer's maintenance procedures.
- Protect cutting edges.
- Keep all tool accessories, such as blades and bits, sharp.
- When using a circular cutting tool, always use the appropriate blade for the arbor size.
- Report any unusual noises, sounds, or vibrations to your instructor or supervisor.
- Regularly inspect all tools and accessories.

6.2.0 Drilling Tools

A wide variety of tools and drill bits are used to penetrate wood, metal, and masonry. Selection is based on the type of material, as well its thickness and hardness. *Figure 92* shows examples of how drills are used by cable installers.

6.2.1 Portable Drills and Screwguns

Portable drills (*Figure 93*) are made in a great number of types and sizes. Light-duty drills generally have a pistol grip. Heavy-duty drills may have a spade-shaped or D-shaped handle and a side handle to provide a secure grip for better control on

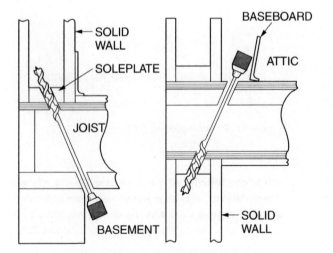

DRILLING CABLE ACCESS HOLES IN A WOOD FRAME BUILDING

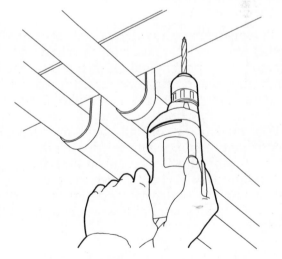

DRILLING A HOLE IN A METAL I-BEAM

Figure 92 ◆ Using an electric drill.

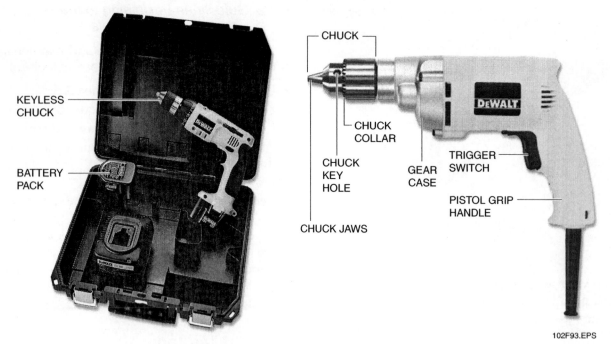

Figure 93 ◆ Portable drills.

large drilling jobs. Drill sizes are based on the diameter of the largest drill shank that will fit into the chuck of the drill; ¼", ⅜", and ½" are common. Most drills have variable speed and reversible controls. Twist drill bits are used in electric drills to make holes in wood and metal. For boring larger holes in wood, hole saws and spade and power bore bits are used. *Figure 94* shows examples of common drill bits. Drills can be used for many operations, including the following:

• Boring and drilling
• Cutting holes with hole saws
• Mixing materials
• Driving screws

Power-driven screwdrivers (*Figure 95*), also called screwguns, are used for the rapid and efficient driving or removal of all types of screws, including wood, machine, and thread-cutting screws. Heavy-duty types can be used for driving and removing lag bolts, flooring screws, etc. Electric screwdrivers normally have an adjustable depth control to prevent over-driving the screws. Many have a clutch mechanism that disengages when the screw has been driven to a preset depth. Some power screwdrivers are designed to perform specific fastening jobs, such as fastening drywall to walls and ceilings.

6.2.2 Hammer Drills and Rotary Hammers

Hammer drills (*Figure 96*) and rotary hammers are special types of power drills. When equipped

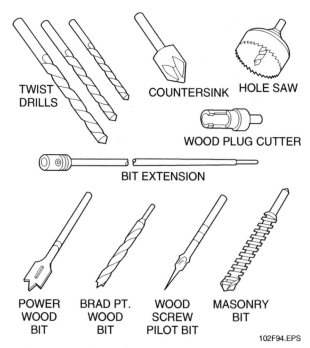

Figure 94 ◆ Examples of drill bits.

with a carbide-tipped percussion bit, they are used mainly to drill holes in concrete and other masonry materials. With different bits or cutters (*Figure 97*), they can also be used for the following:

• Drilling holes in wood and other materials
• Setting anchors
• Performing light chipping work
• Mixing materials

Figure 95 ◆ Power-driven screwdriver.

Figure 96 ◆ Hammer drill used to drill holes in masonry.

The hammer drill is a lighter-duty tool used for drilling smaller holes; the rotary hammer is a heavier-duty tool used to drill larger holes. Both the hammer drill and rotary hammer operate with a dual action. They rotate and hammer at the same time, enabling them to drill holes much faster than can be done with a standard drill equipped with a masonry bit. Most models are reversible and can be easily switched to a standard rotary-action drill. They also have a depth gauge that can be set to control the depth of the hole being drilled. A cold chisel bit can be used with some models of rotary hammers for chipping and edging concrete. Note that chipping hammers, similar to rotary hammers, are also made specifically for use in chipping masonry and concrete.

A heavy-duty rotary hammer can accommodate a 6" core bit, as well as a variety of chisels used to penetrate or break up concrete and stone (*Figure 98*).

Rules for the safe use of portable drills and hammer drills are as follows:

- Hold the tool firmly.
- Always remove the chuck key before starting the drill.
- Be sure the drill or tool is secure in the chuck before starting the drill.
- Use eye protection.
- Never attempt to stop the drill by taking hold of the chuck.
- Do not force the drill into the material.
- Be sure the material is properly secured before drilling.
- Never point the drill at anyone.

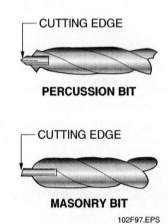

Figure 97 ◆ Hammer drill bits.

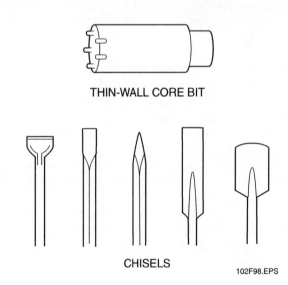

Figure 98 ◆ Heavy-duty rotary hammer and accessories.

Hammer Drill Safety

Make sure that you have a firm grip on the side handle when using a hammer drill. You should never hold on to just the main handle. Use both hands to equalize the rotation of the drill. Most hammer drills have enough torque to break your wrist.

Rules for the safe use of an electric screwdriver (screwgun) are as follows:

- Hold the tool firmly.
- Use the correct type and size bit for the screws being used.
- Set the gun for the proper depth.
- Never place the screw point against any part of your body.
- Never hold your hand behind the material into which you are driving the screw.

Rules for the safe use of rotary hammers and chipping hammers are as follows:

- Do not force or overload the hammer.
- Use the correct tool for the job being done.
- Keep your hands and feet clear of the tool.
- Never point the hammer at anyone while it is running.
- Do not use the point or chisel for prying.
- Be sure the tools are properly secured in the hammer.

6.2.3 Special Drilling Equipment

Some special drilling tools are used by electronic systems technicians to assist in running cable. *Figure 99* shows a system used to run cable after the finish work has been done. This system combines a flexible steel bit with a spring steel shaft. Once the bit is through to the other side, a hole in the bit is used to connect the cable, which can then be fished through the hole by reversing the drill through the hole in the bottom plate, then pulling it through the opening in the wall.

Other drill bits especially designed for wiring work contain a hole that can be used to fish a cable back through the drilled opening.

In some tight spots, there is not enough room for a standard drill. For that reason, tool manufacturers have developed the 90-degree drill (*Figure 100*). Another drill designed for working in close quarters has the head positioned at a 55-degree angle.

Because of the wide variety of applications and tools used to drill or cut through various types of materials, two tables are provided for reference. *Table 4* relates the type of material to the tools that

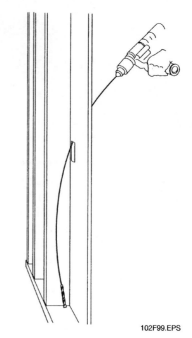

102F99.EPS

Figure 99 ◆ Flexible steel drilling system.

102F100.EPS

Figure 100 ◆ 90-degree drill.

can be used to bore or cut through it. *Table 5* relates various types and sizes of bits and blades to the tools with which they are used.

A core drill (*Figure 101*) is a heavy-duty drill designed for drilling through reinforced concrete, brick, block, and stone. They are usually attached to the wall for horizontal drilling. They are mounted on a fixture for vertical drilling. Core drills equipped with diamond bits are capable of drilling a 12"-diameter hole. The bit, which is like a hole saw, is cooled and lubricated by running water during drilling. This type of tool requires special training.

Table 4 Drill Bits and Blades Used for Various Materials

TYPE & TYPICAL SIZES	MATERIAL										
	Wood	Steel	Metal Studs	Vinyl Siding	Alum. Siding	Drywall	Plaster	Ceiling Tile	Formica & Laminates	Asphalt Roofing	Metal Siding
Twist Bits, Standard Shank from 1/16" – 1/2"	●	●	●	●	●	●		●	●	●	●
Twist Bits, 1/2" – 1"	●		●	●	●	●		●	●	●	●
Brad Point Wood Bit (same as twist bit size)	●			●		●		●	●	●	●
Knockout Punch, Various Sizes & Shapes		●	●								
Metal Stud Punch, 7/8" – 1-3/8"			●								
Stepper Bits, 1/8" – 1-3/8"		●	●		●						●
Spade Bits, 1/4" – 1-1/2"	●					●		●	●		
Easy Bore Bits, 1/2" – 4-5/8"	●					●				●	
Bell Hanger Bits, 1/4" – 3/8"	●			●	●	●		●	●	●	●
Hole Saws, 9/16" – 6"	●			●		●		●	●	●	
Bimetal Hole Saws, 9/16" – 6"	●	●	●	●	●	●		●	●	●	●
Forstner Bits (Precision Boring), 1/4" – 2-1/8"	●			●		●		●	●		
Carbide Easy Bore Bits, 3/4" – 2-1/2"	●			●	●	●	●	●		●	
Auger Type, 9/16" – 1-1/2"	●					●			●		
Around the Corner Bits (Cuts Curved Holes), 3/4" – 1-1/8"	●			●		●		●			
Type "C" Combination Flex Bit, 4' – 6' Long 1/4" – 1" Dia.	●		●	●		●		●		●	
Type "B" Combination Flex Bit, 4' – 6' Long 3/8" – 9/16"	●					●					
Auger Flex Bit, 4' – 6' Long 3/8" – 1" Dia.	●										
Wallboard Saw						●		●			
Jab Saw with Saws-All Blade	●			●		●	●	●			
Utility Knife						●					
Saws-All Blades, 3" – 12"	●	●	●	●	●	●	●	●	●	●	●

MASONRY							
	Concrete	Brick	Stone	Ceramic & Mosaic Floor & Wall Tile	Plaster with or without Wire Mesh	Corian & Granite	Block
Masonry Twist Bit from 3/16" to 1/2"	●	●		●	●	●	●
Percussion Carbide Bit from 3/16" to 1/2"	●	●	●	●	●	●	●
Type "M" Flex Bits from 1/4" to 3/4"	●			●	●		●
Hammer Core Bits from 2" to 6"	●	●	●				●

102T04.EPS

Table 5 Drill Bits and Blades Used with Various Tools

TYPE & TYPICAL SIZES	SUGGESTED TOOL FOR CUT OR HOLE							
	Standard 3/8" & 1/2" Drill	Cordless 3/8" & 1/2" Drill	Hammer Drill	Close Quarter Drill	1/2" Hammer Drill	1/2" Hole Hawg Drill	Hand Auger	1/2" 90° Angle Drill
Twist Bits, Standard Shank from 1/16" – 1/2"	●	●	●	●	●			
Twist Bits, 1/2" – 1"	●	●	●		●			
Brad Point Wood Bit (same as twist bit size)	●	●	●	●	●			
Stepper Bits, 1/8" – 1-3/8"	●	●	●	●	●			
Spade Bits, 1/4" – 1-1/2"	●	●	●	●	●			
Easy Bore Bits, 1/2" – 4-5/8"	1/2" recommended	●	●		●			●
Bell Hanger Bits, 1/4" – 3/8"	●	●	●	●	●		●	
Hole Saws, 9/16" – 6"	1/2" required	●	●		●	●		●
Bimetal Hole Saws, 9/16" – 6"	1/2" required	●	●		●			●
Forstner Bits (Precision Boring), 1/4" – 2-1/8"	●	●	●		●			●
Carbide Easy Bore Bits, 3/4" – 2-1/2"						●		●
Auger Type, 9/16" – 1-1/2"	●				●	●		●
Around the Corner Bits (Cuts Curved Holes), 3/4" – 1-1/8"	●	●			●	●		●
Type "C" Combination Flex Bit, 4' – 6' Long 1/4" – 1" Dia.	1/2" HD					●		●
Type "B" Combination Flex Bit, 4' – 6' Long 3/8" – 9/16"	1/2" HD	●			●	●		●
Auger Flex Bit, 4' – 6' Long 3/8" – 1" Dia.	1/2" HD				●	●		●

MASONRY					
	Standard 3/8" & 1/2" Drill	Cordless Drill	Hammer Drill	Rotary Hammer	Demolition Hammer
Masonry Twist Bit from 3/16" to 1/2"	●	●	●		
Percussion Carbide Bit from 3/16" to 1/2"			●		
Type "M" Flex Bits from 1/4" to 3/4"			●		
Hammer Core Bits from 2" to 6"				●	●

102T05.EPS

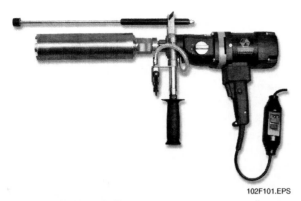

102F101.EPS

Figure 101 ◆ Core drill.

102F102.EPS

Figure 102 ◆ Horizontal directional drilling rig.

6.3.0 Horizontal Directional Drilling

A horizontal directional drilling rig like the one shown in *Figure 102* is used to create cable pathways under roads, waterways, and other obstructions. The drilling mechanism is pushed through the ground to create the opening (*Figure 103*). Once the opening is drilled the conduit is pulled back through the opening. Then the entire assembly is pulled back through the opening.

Like any other rotating machines, these drilling rigs are inherently dangerous. Do not get anywhere near the drilling mechanism while it is operating. Anyone working around one of these rigs must receive special safety training in the hazards related to horizontal directional drilling.

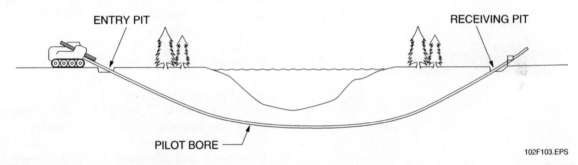

ENTRY PIT

RECEIVING PIT

PILOT BORE

102F103.EPS

Figure 103 ◆ Horizontal directional drilling.

Drill Rod Hazard

A three-man crew was installing an underground telephone cable in a residential area. They had just completed a bore hole under a driveway using a horizontal boring machine. The bore hole rod had been removed from the hole. While the rod was still rotating, the operator straddled it and stooped over to pick it up. His trouser leg became entangled in the rotating rod and he was flipped over, striking tools and materials. He died as a result of his injuries.

The Bottom Line: Never step over a rotating drill rod, no matter how safe it looks.

Source: The Occupational Safety and Health Administration

DRILL PIPE

102SA11.EPS

6.4.0 Cutting Tools

The reciprocating saw and the jig saw are the most commonly used tools for cutting openings in wood, metal, wallboard, and other building materials. Other specialty tools are also used to make openings in gypsum wallboard and metal studs.

6.4.1 Reciprocating Saws

Reciprocating saws (*Figures 104* and *105*) are heavy-duty saws with a horizontal back and forth movement of the blade. They are an all-purpose saw that can be used for cutting or notching wood and metal. When a reciprocating saw is used to cut a section out of material, as shown in *Figure 105*, a starter hole must be drilled first.

Reciprocating saw models with variable speeds ranging from 0 to 2,400 strokes per minute (SPM) are common. Speed selection is made with a variable control at the trigger on/off switch. Greater horsepower and slower speeds are generally needed when cutting through metals or when cutting along a curved or angled line. The typical length of the horizontal sawing stroke is 1⅛". A multi-positioned foot at the front of the saw can be put in three different positions for use in flush cutting, **ripping**, and **crosscutting**.

A wide variety of blades are made for use with reciprocating saws. Each type of blade is designed to make an optimum cut in a different kind of material. The blade length determines the thickness of the material that can be cut. Use the shortest blade that will do the job. Reciprocating saw blade lengths range from 3½" to 12". The number of teeth range from 3½ to 32 per inch. Blades with 3½ to 6 teeth per inch are generally used for sawing wood, while blades with 6 to 10 teeth per inch are used for general-purpose sawing. Blades with 10 to 18 teeth per inch are used for cutting metal. Always use the blade recommended by the blade manufacturer for the type of material being cut.

6.4.2 Jig Saws

Jig saws (*Figure 106*), also commonly called saber saws or bayonet saws, are lighter-duty saws than reciprocating saws.

With the proper blade, jig saws can cut wood, metal, plastic, and other materials. Variable-speed models with speeds ranging from 0 to 3,200 SPM are common. The typical length of the vertical sawing stroke is 1". Jig saws have a baseplate or shoe. The broad surface of the shoe helps keep the blade aligned. It also helps prevent the work from vibrating and allows the teeth to bite into the material. The baseplate can be tilted for making bevel cuts. Many jig saws have a large scrolling knob which can be unlocked from a stationary position, then used to rotate the blade while sawing the material. This makes it easier to cut tight curves, corners, and patterns.

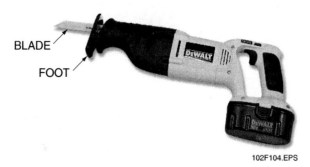

BLADE

FOOT

102F104.EPS

Figure 104 ◆ Reciprocating saw.

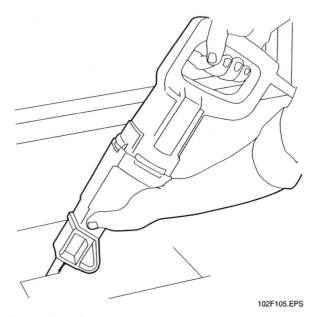

102F105.EPS

Figure 105 ◆ Reciprocating saw cutting through a floor.

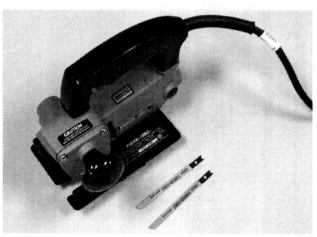

102F106.EPS

Figure 106 ◆ Jig saw.

Wood-cutting, metal-cutting, and special-purpose blades are available. Use the shortest blade that will do the job. Blades for cutting wood have as few as 6 teeth per inch for fast, coarse cutting, and as many as 14 teeth per inch for fine work. Tapered-ground blades are made that produce splinter-free cuts in plywood. Blades made for cutting both metals and plastic laminates typically have between 12 and 32 teeth per inch. Always use the blade recommended by the blade manufacturer for the type of material being cut.

6.4.3 Power Cutout Tool

This power tool (*Figure 107*), also known as a wall router, is used to cut openings in gypsum drywall. It uses a special cutting drill bit to penetrate and cut through the wallboard. Other bits are available to cut wall tile and cement board, which is commonly used as both a tile backer in showers and in subflooring.

6.4.4 Drywall Circle Cutter

The circle cutter (*Figure 108*) has a calibrated steel shaft that allows accurate cuts up to 16" in diameter. The cutter wheel and center pin are heat treated.

6.4.5 Metal Stud Punches

Metal studs usually come from the factory with pre-punched openings for conduit and piping.

A metal stud punch (*Figure 109*) is available for punching additional openings if needed. This tool

works with studs up to 20 gauge. When electrical or telecommunications cabling is routed through the openings, grommets like the one shown in *Figure 109* should be inserted in the openings to protect the cabling from sharp edges. Other types of devices are made to eliminate conduit rattle.

Figure 107 ◆ Power cutout tool.

102F107.EPS

Figure 108 ◆ Circle cutter.

102F108.EPS

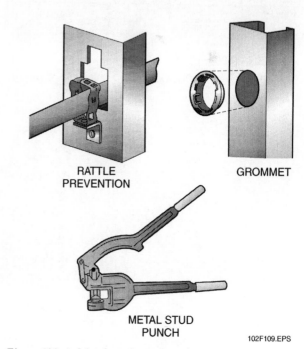

RATTLE PREVENTION

GROMMET

METAL STUD PUNCH

102F109.EPS

Figure 109 ◆ Metal stud punch and grommet.

6.5.0 Pneumatic Nailers and Staplers

Pneumatic nailers and staplers (*Figure 110*) are fastening tools powered by compressed air which is fed to the tool through an air hose connected to an air compressor. These tools, known as guns, are widely used for quick, efficient fastening of framing, subflooring, sheathing, etc. Nailers and staplers are made in a variety of sizes to serve different purposes. Under some conditions, staples have some advantages over nails. For example, staples do not split wood as easily as a nail when driven near the end of the board. Staples are also excellent for fastening sheathing, shingles, building paper, and other materials because their two-legged design covers more surface area. However, both fasteners are sometimes used to accomplish the same fastening jobs.

For some models of fasteners, the nails or staples come in strips and are loaded into a magazine, which typically holds 100 or more fasteners. Some tools have an angled magazine, which makes it easier for the tool to fit into tight places. Coil-fed models typically use a coil of 300 nails loaded into a circular magazine. Lightweight nailing guns can handle tiny finishing nails. Larger framing nailers can shoot smooth-shank nails up to 3¼" in length.

Rules for the safe use of pneumatic fasteners are as follows:

- Be sure all safety devices are in good shape and are functioning properly.
- Use the pressure specified by the manufacturer.
- Always assume that the fasteners are loaded.
- Never point a pneumatic fastener at yourself or anyone else.
- Be sure the fastener is disconnected from the power source before making adjustments or repairs.
- Use caution when attaching the fastener to the air supply because the fastener may discharge.
- Never leave a pneumatic fastener unattended while it is still connected to the power source.
- Use nailers and staplers only for the type of work for which they were intended.
- Use only nails and staples designed for the fastener being used.
- Never use fasteners on soft or thin materials that nails may completely penetrate.

Nailers and staplers are also made in cordless models (*Figure 111*). These tools use a tiny internal combustion engine powered by a disposable fuel

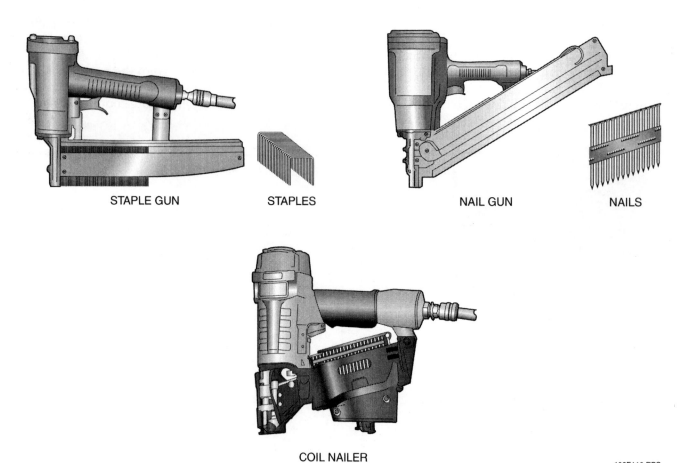

STAPLE GUN   STAPLES   NAIL GUN   NAILS

COIL NAILER

102F110.EPS

Figure 110 ◆ Pneumatic stapler and nailers.

cell and a rechargeable battery. The action of the piston drives the fastener. A cordless stapler can drive about 2,500 staples with one fuel cell. A cordless framing nailer can drive about 1,200 nails on one fuel cell. The battery on a cordless tool must be periodically recharged. It pays to have a spare battery to use while one is being charged. The rules for the safe operation of a cordless nailer or stapler are basically the same as those described above for pneumatic nailers and staplers.

6.6.0 Powder-Actuated Fastening Tools

A powder-actuated fastening tool (*Figure 112*) is a low-velocity fastening system powered by gunpowder cartridges, commonly called boosters. Powder-actuated tools are used to drive specially designed fasteners into masonry and steel.

Manufacturers use color-coding schemes to identify the strength of a powder load charge. It is extremely important to select the right charge for the job, so learn the color-coding system that applies to the tool you are using. *Table 6* shows an example of a color-coding system.

102F111.EPS

Figure 111 ◆ Gas-driven cordless nail gun.

Other rules for safely operating a powder-actuated tool are as follows:

- Do not use a powder-actuated tool unless you are certified.
- Follow all safety precautions in the manufacturer's instruction manual.

 WARNING!
OSHA requires that all operators of powder-actuated tools be qualified and certified by the manufacturer of the tool. Certification cards must be carried whenever using the tool. If the gun does not fire, hold it against the work surface for at least 30 seconds. Follow the manufacturer's instructions for removing the cartridge. Do not try to pry it out, as some cartridges are rim-fired and could explode.

Table 6 Powder Charge Color-Coding System

Power Level*	Color
1	Gray
2	Brown
3	Green
4	Yellow
5	Red
6	Purple

*From least powerful (1) to the most powerful (6).

102T06.EPS

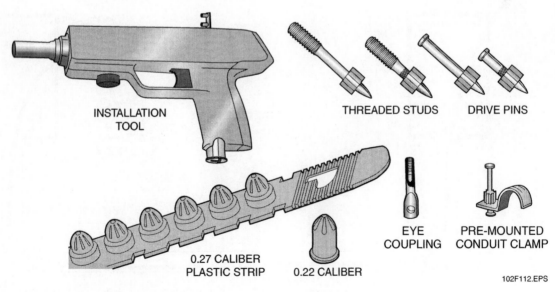

Figure 112 ◆ Powder-actuated fastening tool.

INSTALLATION TOOL

THREADED STUDS   DRIVE PINS

0.27 CALIBER PLASTIC STRIP

0.22 CALIBER

EYE COUPLING

PRE-MOUNTED CONDUIT CLAMP

102F112.EPS

- Always wear safety goggles and a hard hat when operating a powder-actuated tool.
- Use the proper size pin for the job you are performing.
- When loading the driver, put the pin in before the charge.
- Use the correct booster (powder load) according to the manufacturer's instructions.
- Never hold the end of the barrel against any part of your body or cock the tool against your hand.
- Never hold your hand behind the material you are fastening.
- Do not shoot close to the edge of concrete.
- Never attempt to pry the booster out of the magazine with a sharp instrument.
- Always wear ear protection.
- Don't fire on an angle. The gun must be perpendicular to the surface.
- Check local codes for restrictions on use.

6.7.0 Stud Finders

When you are running cable in a finished building, it is essential to find the studs behind the wallboard or other finish panels in order to mount connection boxes. There are two types of stud finders. One is magnetic and reacts to the nails or screws used to secure the panels to the studs. Another type of stud finder senses density. As the device is passed over a panel, it will detect the existence of a mass in an otherwise hollow area. Some very sophisticated types of stud finders are capable of differentiating between steel studs and copper piping and can also locate electrical wires. They can also be used to locate the steel rebars and other material embedded in concrete up to 6" thick.

The cost of stud finders ranges from a few dollars for a basic type (*Figure 113*) to more than a hundred dollars for the multi-function type.

6.8.0 Fish Tapes

Special devices known as fish tapes are used to fish wire and cable through walls, conduit, and other openings. *Figure 114* shows a basic fish tape and its use.

The tape is fed through an opening, then the wire is connected to the hook on the end of the tape and carefully pulled back through the opening.

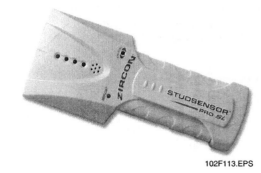

102F113.EPS

Figure 113 ◆ Economical stud locator.

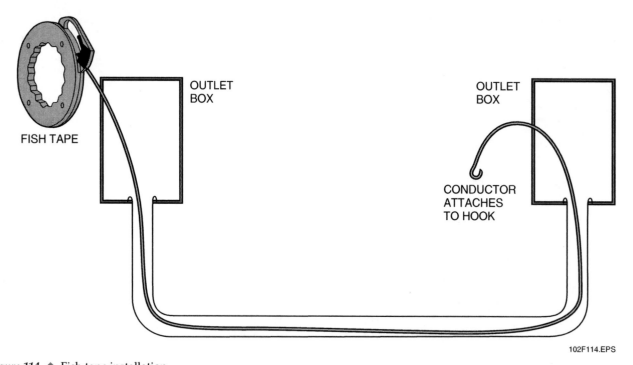

102F114.EPS

Figure 114 ◆ Fish tape installation.

There are several types of fishing tools, and some of them are designed to pull heavy bundles of cables. We will discuss various fishing tools in more detail in the conductor installation module.

7.0.0 ◆ PROJECT SCHEDULES

A construction project requires a lot of planning and scheduling because different trades, equipment, and materials are needed at different times in the process. Electrical and communications cabling is normally installed when the building has been dried-in (i.e., the exterior siding and roofing are applied so the building remains dry, but the framing is exposed in the interior of the building).

Project planning and scheduling will be covered in more detail later in your training. For now, *Figures 115* and *116* provide an overview of where each trade fits into the construction process for residential and commercial projects, respectively.

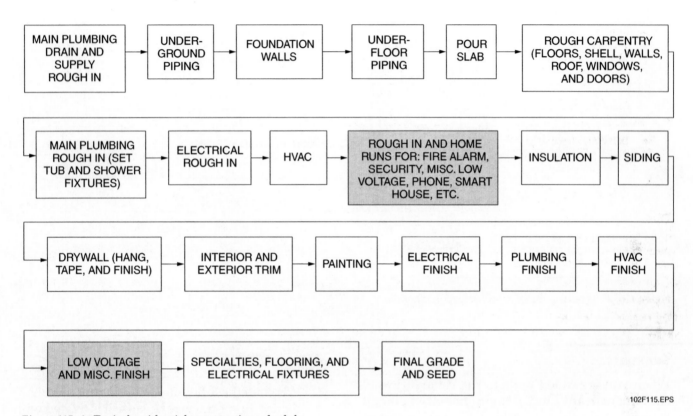

102F115.EPS

Figure 115 ◆ Typical residential construction schedule.

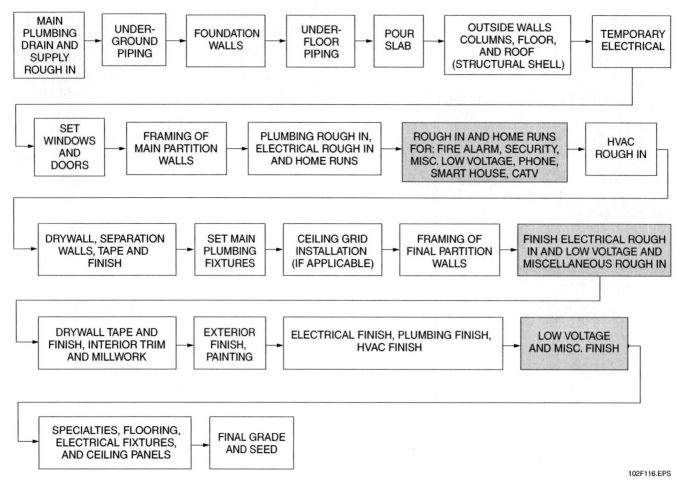

Figure 116 ◆ Typical commercial construction schedule.

102F116.EPS

Summary

When you are called upon to run cable or install equipment in any kind of environment, whether it is residential or commercial, new construction or modification, it will be important for you to know how the building is put together. With that knowledge, you can anticipate potential problems. You will also be able to select the right drilling or cutting tools for the job.

As you now realize, there are many different types of construction. You also know that you will not get very far by guessing what might be behind a wall. It could be anything. Armed with a basic knowledge of construction principles, however, you will be able to face a new project with confidence.

In addition to knowing construction materials and methods, you must also know what tool to use in a given situation. You must also be familiar with the various blades, bits, and other attachments used with these tools so that you can select the one that is appropriate for each situation.

Review Questions

1. Which of the following materials must be handled with special care because it is treated with hazardous chemicals?

   a. Gypsum drywall
   b. Pressure-treated lumber
   c. Brick
   d. Plywood

2. Gypsum wallboard with foil backing is used as a _____.

   a. backer for tile
   b. decorator panel
   c. vapor barrier
   d. liner in elevator shafts

3. The typical concrete block used in loadbearing construction is about _____ deep.

   a. 2"
   b. 4"
   c. 6"
   d. 8"

4. All of the following are true about trusses *except* _____.

   a. ductwork and wiring are easily run through a truss's webbing
   b. trusses are generally faster and easier to erect
   c. trusses place more restrictions on building design than dimension lumber
   d. trusses are stronger than comparable lengths of dimension lumber

5. The main horizontal framing member of a floor is known as a _____.

   a. girder
   b. joist
   c. lally column
   d. rafter

6. If you are required to drill through a 2" × 12" floor joist, the diameter of the hole may *not* exceed _____.

   a. 1"
   b. 2"
   c. 3"
   d. 4"

7. The purpose of a strongback is to _____.

   a. provide a foundation for the ribband
   b. attach the joist to the sill plate
   c. support ceiling joists
   d. brace studs

8. In plank-and-beam construction, framing members are typically installed _____ OC.

   a. 12"
   b. 16"
   c. 24"
   d. 48"

9. Floors in large office buildings are typically made of _____.

   a. concrete
   b. metal joists and wood sheathing
   c. steel beams
   d. galvanized aluminum

10. Concrete tilt-up panels are typically _____ thick.

   a. 1" to 2"
   b. 2" to 3"
   c. 3" to 4"
   d. 5" to 8"

11. The wall shown in *Figure 1* is most likely located between _____.

   a. a doctor's office and the waiting room
   b. the garage and kitchen of a home
   c. a manufacturing area and an office
   d. a bedroom and a bathroom

12. The metal studs used in the construction of a nonbearing partition are usually _____ gauge.

   a. 25
   b. 20
   c. 18
   d. 16

13. When drywall is used in large commercial construction projects, the drywall sheets are typically attached _____.

   a. directly to the underside of the concrete floor above using powder-actuated fasteners
   b. to the wood joists
   c. to suspended furring channels
   d. to steel trusses

14. Which of the following tools would you use to drill a hole through a concrete wall?

   a. Rotary hammer with a core bit
   b. Hammering drill with a hole saw
   c. Reciprocating saw with a concrete blade
   d. Rotary hammer with an auger bit

15. When drilling a 3" diameter hole in gypsum drywall, you would probably use a _____.

   a. twist bit
   b. power cutout tool
   c. percussion bit
   d. core bit

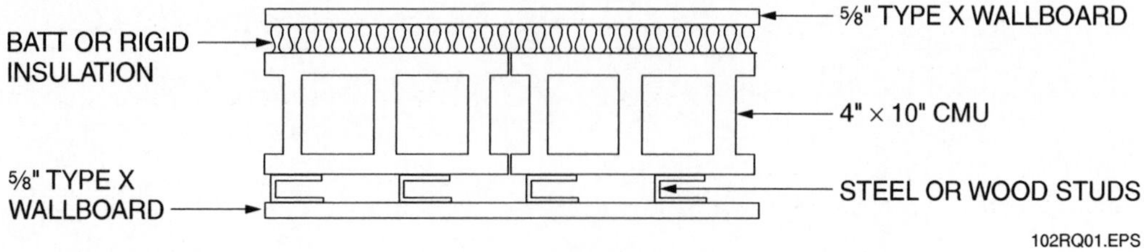

BATT OR RIGID INSULATION
⅝" TYPE X WALLBOARD
4" × 10" CMU
⅝" TYPE X WALLBOARD
STEEL OR WOOD STUDS

102RQ01.EPS

Figure 1

Bruce Nardone, RCDD®, Master Instructor
BICSI

Many young men and women receive technical training and work experience while in the military service. Bruce received training as a military telecommun-ications installer. He knew then that he had found his career niche and went on to achieve success in the telecommunications field in civilian life.

How did you get started in the EST field?
I joined the Marines when I was 19 and then later went into the Army. While in the service, I received training as a telecommunications installer. I enjoyed the challenges and the constant change in the technology. I feel most comfortable working in an exacting technical field.

What types of training have you received in your career?
I have been trained as a telecommunications installer on a variety of systems. I have also had extensive training in network design and installation. I hold BICSI's Registered Communications Distribution Designer (RCDD®) designation. I have also had training in both safety supervision and confined space safety.

What kinds of work have you done in your career?
I have worked as a telecommunications installer and technician as well as a project manager and site manager. During my career, I have conducted training courses for installers, technicians, and company executives. I have also worked as an estimator and network engineer.

What do you do in your present job?
BICSI is an international telecommunications association that provides skill training and industry certification programs, such as the RCDD®, which is the most widely recognized credential in the industry. As a BICSI master instructor, I conduct training programs in design and installation of commercial and residential telecommunications systems and equipment. I also provide tech support for BICSI members.

What factors do you think have contributed to your success?
My desire to excel, to help people, and to be an asset to my employer. I also think my training and experience in the military, as well as the discipline and structure of the military environment, really gave me a good start on my career.

What advice would you give to those who are new to the field?
Decide what you want and don't stop until you get it. Take advantage of any training that is available to you. Join and participate in professional associations in order to keep abreast of the changing technology and also to give something back to the industry.

Trade Terms Introduced in This Module

Admixture: Any material that is added to a concrete mixture to obtain additional properties.

APA-rated: Building material that has been rated by the American Plywood Association for a specific use.

Blocking: A wood block used as a filler piece and support member between framing members.

Bridging: Wood or metal pieces placed diagonally between joists to provide added support.

Cantilever: A beam, truss, or floor that extends beyond the last point of support.

Corrugated: Material formed with parallel ridges or grooves.

Cripple stud: In wall framing, a short framing stud that fills the space between the header and the top plate or between the sill and the soleplate.

Crosscutting: Cutting across the grain of lumber.

Dimension lumber: Any lumber within a range of 2" to 5" thick and up to 12" wide.

Dormer: A framed structure that projects out from a sloped roof.

Double top plate: A length of lumber laid horizontally over the top plate of a wall to add strength to the wall.

Fire rating: A classification indicating in time (hours) the ability of a structure or component to withstand fire conditions.

Firestop: A piece of lumber or fire-resistant material installed in an opening to prevent the passage of fire.

Firestopping: A material or mechanical device used to block openings in walls, ceilings, and floors to prevent the passage of fire and smoke.

Footing: The foundation for a column or the enlargement placed at the bottom of a foundation wall to distribute the weight of the structure.

Furring strips: Strips of wood or metal applied to a wall or other surface to make it level, form an air space, and/or provide a fastening surface for finish covering.

Gable: The triangular wall enclosed by the sloping ends of a ridged roof.

Girder: The main steel or wood supporting beam for a structure.

Green concrete: Concrete that has hardened, but has not yet gained its full structural strength.

Ground fault circuit interrupter (GFCI): A protective device that instantly de-energizes a circuit when a current to ground exceeds some predetermined value.

Gypsum: A chalky type of rock that serves as the basic ingredient of plaster and gypsum wallboard.

Gypsum wallboard: A generic term for gypsum core panels covered with paper on both sides. It is commonly used to finish walls.

Header: A horizontal member that supports the load over an opening such as a door or window. Also known as a lintel.

Joists: Equally spaced framing members that support floors and ceilings.

Kerf: A groove or notch made by a saw.

Millwork: Various types of manufactured wood products such as doors, windows, and moldings.

Oriented strand board (OSB): Panels made from layers of wood strands bonded together.

Plastic concrete: Concrete in a liquid or semi-liquid workable state.

Plenum: A sealed chamber for moving air under slight pressure at the inlet or outlet of an air conditioning system. In some commercial buildings, the space above a suspended ceiling often acts as a return air plenum.

Post-tensioned concrete: Concrete placed around steel reinforcement such as rods or cables that are isolated from the concrete. After the concrete has cured, tension is applied to the rods or cables to provide greater structural strength.

Pre-stressed concrete: Concrete that is placed around pre-stressed reinforcing steel in a casting bed. This type of concrete cannot be cut without first consulting a structural engineer.

Rabbeted: A board or panel with a groove cut into one or more of its edges.

Rafter: A sloping structural member of a roof frame to which sheathing is attached.

Reinforced concrete: Concrete that has been placed around some type of reinforcing material, usually steel.

Ribband: A 1 × 4 nailed to ceiling joists to prevent twisting and bowing of the joists.

Ripping: Cutting with the grain of the lumber.

Shakes: A handsplit wood shingle.

Sheathing: The sheet material or boards used to close in walls and roofs.

Shiplap: Lumber with edges that are shaped to overlap adjoining pieces.

Sill plate: A horizontal timber that supports the framework of a building. It forms the transition between the foundation and the frame.

Soleplate: The lowest horizontal member of a wall or partition. It rests directly on the rough floor.

Striated: A surface design that has the appearance of fine parallel grooves.

Stringer: The support member at the sides of a staircase; also, a timber used to support form-work for a concrete floor.

Strongback: An L-shaped arrangement of lumber used to support ceiling joists and keep them in alignment. In concrete work, it represents the upright support for a form.

Stucco: A type of plaster used to coat exterior walls.

Subfloor: Panels or boards fastened to the tops of floor joists.

Substrate: The underlying material to which a finish is applied.

Top plate: The upper horizontal member of a wall or partition frame.

Trimmer joist: A full-length horizontal member that forms the sides of a rough opening in a floor. It provides stiffening for the frame.

Trimmer stud: The vertical framing member that forms the sides of a rough opening for a door or window. It provides stiffening for the frame and supports the weight of the header.

Truss: An engineered assembly made of wood or metal that is used in place of individual structural members such as the joists and rafters used to support floors and roofs.

Underlayment: A material such as plywood or particleboard that is installed on top of a subfloor to provide a smooth surface for the finish flooring.

Vaulted ceiling: A high, open ceiling that generally follows the roof pitch.

Veneer: The covering layer of material for a wall or the facing materials applied to a substrate.

Additional Resources

This module is intended to be a thorough resource for task training. The following reference works are suggested for further study. These are optional materials for continued education rather than for task training.

Carpentry, 1997. Leonard Koel. Homewood, IL: American Technical Publishers.

Modern Carpentry, 2000. Willis H. Wagner and Howard Bud Smith. Tinley Park, IL: The Goodheart-Willcox Company, Inc.

Figure Credits

Trus Joist	102F03 (PSL, LVL, LSL, wood I-beams), 102SA01
Topaz Publications, Inc.	102F03 (glulam beam construction), 102F04, 102F14, 102F40, 102F55, 102F95, 102F96, 102F98, 102F104, 102F106, 102F113,102SA02–102SA04, 102SA11, 102SA12
Gypsum Association	102F05
EFCO	102F06
Greenstreak, Inc.	102F09
Southern Forest Products Association	102F42
Benson Group Companies	102F45, 102F46

Tilt-Up Concrete Association	102F48
BICSI	102F51
Alcan Building Products	102F85
Armstrong World Industries, Inc.	102F72, 102F73, 102F77
BPB Celotex–Capaul Series	102F76
Ceilings Plus	102F86
Chicago Metallic Corporation	102F64, 102F65, 102F84
Coleman Cable, Inc.	102F91
DeWalt Industrial Tool Company	102F93, 102F100
Easi-Set Industries	102SA06
Erico Inc.	102F109
Florida Chapter of the Associated Builders and Contractors	102F60–102F62
W.R. Grace & Company	102SA10
Integrated Ceilings, Inc.	102F78, 102F82, 102F83
National Gypsum	102SA05, 102SA09
Solaris RotoZip	102F107
The Stanley Works	102F108
CS Unitec, Inc., www.csunitec.com	102F101 (END130/3P core drill)
Vermeer Manufacturing Company	102F102

The NCCER makes every effort to keep these textbooks up-to-date and free of technical errors. We appreciate your help in this process. If you have an idea for improving this textbook, or if you find an error, a typographical mistake, or an inaccuracy in NCCER's Contren® textbooks, please write us, using this form or a photocopy. Be sure to include the exact module number, page number, a detailed description, and the correction, if applicable. Your input will be brought to the attention of the Technical Review Committee. Thank you for your assistance.

Instructors – If you found that additional materials were necessary in order to teach this module effectively, please let us know so that we may include them in the Equipment/Materials list in the Instructor's Guide.

Write: Product Development and Revision
National Center for Construction Education and Research
P.O. Box 141104, Gainesville, FL 32614-1104

Fax: 352-334-0932

E-mail: curriculum@nccer.org

Craft _____ Module Name _____

Copyright Date _____ Module Number _____ Page Number(s) _____

Description _____

_____

_____

_____

(Optional) Correction _____

_____

_____

(Optional) Your Name and Address _____

_____

_____

Pathways and Spaces

COURSE MAP

This course map shows all of the modules in the first level of the *Electronic Systems Technician* curriculum. The suggested training order begins at the bottom and proceeds up. Skill levels increase as you advance on the course map. The local Training Program Sponsor may adjust the training order.

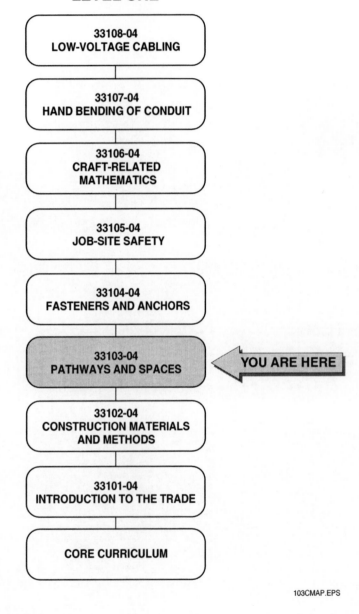

ELECTRONIC SYSTEMS TECHNICIAN
LEVEL ONE

33108-04
LOW-VOLTAGE CABLING

33107-04
HAND BENDING OF CONDUIT

33106-04
CRAFT-RELATED
MATHEMATICS

33105-04
JOB-SITE SAFETY

33104-04
FASTENERS AND ANCHORS

33103-04
PATHWAYS AND SPACES ⟵ YOU ARE HERE

33102-04
CONSTRUCTION MATERIALS
AND METHODS

33101-04
INTRODUCTION TO THE TRADE

CORE CURRICULUM

103CMAP.EPS

1.0.0 INTRODUCTION 3.1

2.0.0 RACEWAYS 3.2

3.0.0 CONDUIT 3.2

    3.1.0   Types of Conduit 3.2

    3.1.1   *Electrical Nonmetallic Tubing* 3.2

    3.1.2   *Inner Duct* 3.3

    3.1.3   *Electrical Metallic Tubing* 3.3

    3.1.4   *Rigid Metal Conduit* 3.5

    3.1.5   *Galvanized Rigid Steel Conduit* 3.6

    3.1.6   *Plastic-Coated GRC* 3.6

    3.1.7   *Aluminum Conduit* 3.6

    3.1.8   *Intermediate Metal Conduit* 3.7

    3.1.9   *Rigid Nonmetallic Conduit* 3.7

    3.1.10 *Liquidtight Flexible Nonmetallic Conduit* 3.8

    3.1.11 *Flexible Metal Conduit* 3.8

4.0.0 METAL CONDUIT FITTINGS 3.10

    4.1.0   Couplings 3.10

    4.2.0   Conduit Bodies 3.10

    4.2.1   *Type C Conduit Bodies* 3.10

    4.2.2   *Type L Conduit Bodies* 3.10

    4.2.3   *Type T Conduit Bodies* 3.11

    4.2.4   *Type X Conduit Bodies* 3.11

    4.2.5   *Threaded Weatherproof Hubs* 3.11

    4.3.0   Insulating Bushings 3.12

    4.3.1   *Nongrounding Insulating Bushings* 3.12

    4.3.2   *Grounding Insulating Bushings* 3.12

    4.4.0   Offset Nipples 3.12

5.0.0 BUSHINGS AND LOCKNUTS 3.13

6.0.0 SEALING FITTINGS 3.14

7.0.0 CABLE AND RACEWAY SUPPORTS 3.14

    7.1.0   Straps 3.14

    7.2.0   Standoff Supports 3.14

    7.3.0   Electrical Framing Channels 3.15

    7.4.0   Beam Clamps 3.16

    7.5.0   Cable Supports 3.16

    7.5.1   *Cable Ties* 3.16

    7.5.2   *Cable Hangers* 3.16

8.0.0 SURFACE METAL AND NONMETALLIC RACEWAYS 3.18

    8.1.0   Pole Systems 3.20

    8.2.0   Underfloor Systems 3.20

8.3.0   Cellular Metal Floor Raceways 3.20

8.4.0   Cellular Concrete Floor Raceways 3.21

9.0.0   **CABLE TRAYS** 3.21

9.1.0   Cable Tray Fittings 3.22

9.2.0   Cable Tray Supports 3.23

9.2.1   *Direct Rod Suspension* 3.23

9.2.2   *Trapeze Mounting and Center-Hung Support* 3.23

9.2.3   *Wall Mounting* 3.23

9.2.4   *Pipe Rack Mounting* 3.24

10.0.0   **STORING RACEWAYS** 3.24

11.0.0   **HANDLING RACEWAYS** 3.24

12.0.0   **UNDERGROUND SYSTEMS** 3.24

12.1.0   Duct Materials 3.26

12.2.0   Plastic Conduit 3.26

12.3.0   Monolithic Concrete Duct 3.26

12.4.0   Controlled Environment Vaults 3.26

12.5.0   Pedestals and Cabinets 3.26

13.0.0   **BOXES** 3.27

13.1.0   Metal Boxes 3.27

13.1.1   *Pryouts* 3.28

13.1.2   *Knockouts* 3.28

13.2.0   Nonmetallic Boxes 3.28

13.3.0   Low-Voltage Boxes 3.29

14.0.0   **MAKING A CONDUIT-TO-BOX CONNECTION** 3.29

15.0.0   **CONSTRUCTION PROCEDURES** 3.29

15.1.0   Masonry and Concrete Flush-Mount Construction 3.29

15.2.0   Metal Stud Environment 3.32

15.3.0   Wood-Frame Environment 3.32

15.4.0   Steel Environment 3.33

15.5.0   Suspended Ceilings 3.34

16.0.0   **OVERVIEW OF CABLE DISTRIBUTION** 3.34

16.1.0   Pathways 3.36

16.2.0   Spaces 3.38

SUMMARY 3.39

REVIEW QUESTIONS 3.39

PROFILE IN SUCCESS 3.41

GLOSSARY 3.43

REFERENCES & ACKNOWLEDGMENTS 3.44

Figures

Figure 1   ENT and fittings 3.2

Figure 2   Examples of inner ducts 3.3

Figure 3   EMT conduit comparison 3.4

Figure 4   Compression fittings 3.4

Figure 5   Setscrew fittings 3.4

Figure 6   Rigid metal conduit 3.6

Figure 7   PVC conduit 3.7

Figure 8   PVC expansion coupling 3.8

Figure 9   Flex connectors 3.8

Figure 10   Flexible metal conduit 3.9

Figure 11   Combination couplings 3.9

Figure 12   Conduit and coupling 3.10

Figure 13   Metal conduit couplings 3.10

Figure 14   Type C conduit body 3.10

Figure 15   Type L conduit bodies and how to identify them 3.11

Figure 16   Type T conduit body 3.11

Figure 17   Type X conduit body 3.11

Figure 18   Threaded weatherproof hubs 3.12

Figure 19   Insulating bushings 3.13

Figure 20   Grounding insulating bushings 3.13

Figure 21   Offset nipples 3.13

Figure 22   Bushings 3.13

Figure 23   Locknuts 3.13

Figure 24   Sealing fittings 3.14

Figure 25   Straps 3.14

Figure 26   Standoff support 3.15

Figure 27   Electrical framing channels 3.15

Figure 28   Beam clamp 3.16

Figure 29   Cable ties 3.16

Figure 30   J-hooks and bridle rings 3.17

Figure 31   Hardware used to manage cables and wiring 3.17

Figure 32   Perimeter raceway 3.18

Figure 33   Examples of surface raceway 3.19

Figure 34   Low-voltage raceway box .3.19

Figure 35   Pancake raceway 3.19

Figure 36   Pole base 3.20

Figure 37   Underfloor raceway duct 3.21

Figure 38   Cross section of a cellular floor 3.21

Figure 39   Cable tray system 3.22

Figure 40 Direct rod suspension 3.23

Figure 41 Trapeze mounting and center-hung support 3.23

Figure 42 Wall mounting 3.23

Figure 43 Typical cable maintenance hole 3.25

Figure 44 Installing underground entrances 3.25

Figure 45 Examples of pedestals 3.27

Figure 46 Boxes used in raceway systems 3.27

Figure 47 Pryout removal 3.28

Figure 48 Knockout removal 3.29

Figure 49 Knockout punch kit 3.29

Figure 50 Low-voltage boxes and accessories 3.30

Figure 51 Conduit-to-box connection .3.30

Figure 52 Correct entrance angle 3.30

Figure 53 Concrete flush-mount installation 3.31

Figure 54 Concrete outlet box 3.31

Figure 55 4-S extension ring used to bring the box
           to the masonry surface 3.31

Figure 56 Three-gang switch box 3.31

Figure 57 Caddy-fastening devices 3.32

Figure 58 Installing wire or conduit in a
           wood-frame building 3.33

Figure 59 Steel strut system 3.34

Figure 60 Raceway installed above a suspended ceiling 3.34

Figure 61 Building distribution system 3.35

Figure 62 Telecommunications room layout (top view) 3.36

Figure 63 Pathways in a typical commercial building 3.37

Figure 64 Typical sleeve and slot sizes 3.38

Figure 65 Typical telecommunications room 3.38

Pathways and Spaces

Objectives

When you have completed this module, you will be able to do the following:

1. Describe various types of cable trays and raceways.
2. Identify and select various types and sizes of raceways and fittings.
3. Identify and select various types and sizes of cable trays.
4. Identify various methods used to install raceways.
5. Demonstrate knowledge of NEC® raceway requirements.
6. Describe procedures for installing raceways and boxes on various surfaces.
7. Make a conduit-to-box connection.
8. Select cable support hardware for various applications.
9. Install a cut-in box in drywall and run inner duct from the box to the ceiling.

Recommended Prerequisites

Core Curriculum; Electronic Systems Technician Level One, Modules 33101-04 through 33102-04

Required Trainee Materials

1. Paper and pencil
2. Appropriate personal protective equipment
3. Copy of the latest edition of the *National Electrical Code®*

1.0.0 ◆ INTRODUCTION

As you have already learned, the proper selection, installation, and termination of wiring and cables associated with low-voltage systems are important elements of an EST's job. In this module, you will learn about the **conduit**, **raceways**, and other types of supports used in managing the hundreds, and often thousands, of cables and wires used to connect telecommunications and security equipment within a building.

Some of the knowledge and skills you gained in the *Construction Materials and Methods* module will be helpful as you learn the proper mounting techniques for raceways and electronic equipment.

Along with *ANSI/TIA/EIA-569*, the following NEC® articles should be referenced:

- *NEC Article 250* – *Grounding*
- *NEC Article 342* – *Intermediate Metal Conduit*
- *NEC Article 344* – *Rigid Metal Conduit*
- *NEC Article 348* – *Flexible Metal Conduit*
- *NEC Article 350* – *Liquidtight Flexible Metal Conduit*
- *NEC Article 352* – *Rigid Nonmetallic Conduit*
- *NEC Article 356* – *Liquidtight Flexible Nonmetallic Conduit*
- *NEC Article 358* – *Electrical Metallic Tubing*
- *NEC Article 362* – *Electrical Nonmetallic Tubing*
- *NEC Article 392* – *Cable Trays*
- *NEC Article 725* – *Class 1, Class 2, and Class 3 Remote-Control, Signaling, and Power-Limited Circuits*
- *NEC Article 760* – *Fire Alarm Systems*

Note: The designations "*National Electrical Code®*" and "NEC®," where used in this document, refer to the *National Electrical Code®*, which is a registered trademark of the National Fire Protection Association, Quincy, MA. *All National Electrical Code® (NEC®) references in this module refer to the 2002 edition of the NEC®.*

- **NEC Article 770** – Optical Fiber Cables and Raceways
- **NEC Articles 800, 810, 820,** and **830** – Communications Systems

NOTE

Mandatory rules in the NEC® are characterized by the use of the word shall. Explanatory material is in the form of Fine Print Notes (FPNs). When referencing specific sections of the NEC®, always check to see if any exceptions apply.

Some of the NEC® articles referenced in this module are intended to establish safe practices for high-voltage applications. Although electrical safety may not be an issue in some low-voltage applications, the NEC® requirements represent good practices that have been established and refined over many years of use. It is therefore in your interest to follow these practices, regardless of the voltage level. Moreover, there will be situations in which high voltage and low voltage share a raceway. In these situations, the high-voltage requirements must be followed.

2.0.0 ◆ RACEWAYS

The term raceway refers to a wide range of circular and rectangular enclosed channels used to house electrical wiring. Raceways can be metallic or nonmetallic and come in different shapes. Depending on the particular purpose for which they are intended, raceways include enclosures such as underfloor raceways, flexible metal conduit, wireways, surface metal raceways, and surface nonmetallic raceways.

3.0.0 ◆ CONDUIT

Conduit is a raceway with a circular cross section, similar to pipe, that contains wires or cables. Conduit is used to provide protection for **conductors** and route them from one place to another. In addition, conduit makes it easier to replace or add wires to existing structures.

3.1.0 Types of Conduit

Many types of conduit are used in the construction industry. The size of conduit to be used is determined by engineering specifications, local codes, and the NEC®. Refer to *NEC Chapter 9* and *Annex C* for information on the allowable conduit fill with various conductors. We will examine several common types of conduit in this section.

3.1.1 Electrical Nonmetallic Tubing

Electrical nonmetallic tubing (ENT) is a corrugated raceway that can be bent by hand (*Figure 1*). It is made of polyvinyl chloride (PVC) plastic and comes in diameters ranging from ½" to 2". It is available in coils of 100' to 200' and in reels ranging from 500' to 1,500'. ENT is available in a color-coded form that conforms to the following code:

- *Yellow* – Communications and signal cable
- *Red* – Fire alarm circuits
- *Blue* – Power circuits

103F01.EPS

Figure 1 ◆ ENT and fittings.

NEC Section 362.10 permits ENT to be exposed when used in a building not exceeding three floors. In buildings greater than three floors, the construction must be **fire-rated** and the conduit must be concealed in walls, floors, or ceilings. (The conduit must be fire-rated if it is installed in a plenum ceiling of any building.)

NOTE

Refer to *NEC Section 362.12* for restrictions that apply to ENT.

If it is necessary to **splice** sections of ENT, standard and quick-connect couplings are available.

ENT is also available as a pre-wired assembly. The conductors are installed at the factory under conditions that will prevent damage to the insulation. A special tool is required when cutting pre-wired ENT in order to prevent the conductor insulation from being cut.

Color Me Blue

ENT is also known in the industry as Smurf tube because the blue color used for power conductors is reminiscent of the Smurf cartoon characters.

3.1.2 Inner Duct

Inner duct is a flexible, nonmetallic tubing for use in walls, floors, slabs, and ceilings. It is intended to be pulled through an existing conduit system, as shown in *Figure 2A*. Inner duct is very similar in construction to ENT. Like ENT, inner duct comes in colors; however, the color scheme is slightly different. The following color code has been established:

- *Orange* – Riser-rated communications and signal cable (note the difference from ENT)
- *White* – Plenum-rated communications and signal cable
- *Red* – Fire alarm circuits
- *Blue* – Power circuits

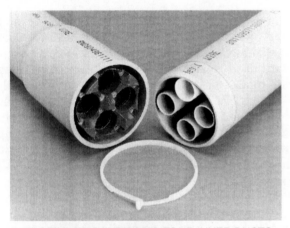

(A) CONDUIT CONTAINING FOUR INNER DUCTS

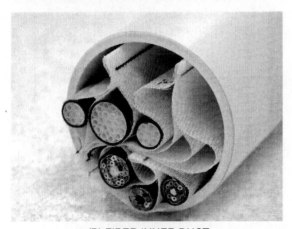

(B) FIBER INNER DUCT

103F02.EPS

Figure 2 ◆ Examples of inner ducts.

Inner duct is available in rolls of 100' and 200', as well as fixed lengths of 10'. Inside diameters range from ½" to 1¼". It normally comes with a pull rope installed, but is available without it.

Some of the advantages of inner duct include its relatively low cost and that its use tends to reduce pulling tension, especially when multiple inner ducts are installed in conduit. A disadvantage is that because it is flexible, it must be carefully secured to the supporting structure to prevent kinking while the cable is being pulled through it.

Various connectors and terminations are available, as are adapters to transition from inner duct to rigid PVC.

Inner duct is often used for running optical fiber cables, as shown in *Figure 2B*. Inner duct must have the appropriate fire rating for the environment in which it is being installed.

3.1.3 Electrical Metallic Tubing

Electrical metallic tubing (EMT) is the lightest duty tubing available for enclosing and protecting wiring. EMT is widely used for residential, commercial, and industrial wiring systems. It is lightweight, easily bent and/or cut to shape, and is the least costly type of metallic conduit. Because the wall thickness of EMT is less than that of rigid conduit, it is often referred to as thinwall conduit. A comparison of the inside diameter (ID) and the outside diameter (OD) of EMT to rigid metal conduit and intermediate metal conduit (IMC) is shown in *Figure 3*.

NEC Section 358.10(A) permits the installation of EMT for either exposed or concealed work where it will not be subject to severe physical damage during installation or after construction. The installation of EMT using waterproof fittings is permitted in wet locations such as outdoors or indoors in dairies, laundries, and canneries.

NOTE

Refer to *NEC Section 358.12* for restrictions that apply to the use of EMT.

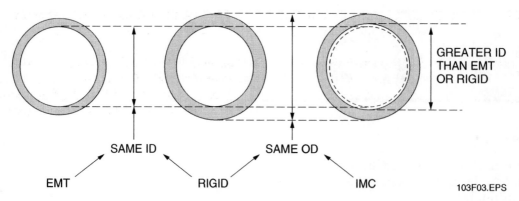

Figure 3 ◆ EMT conduit comparison.

EMT shall not be used (1) where, during installation or afterward, it will be subject to severe physical damage; (2) where protected from corrosion solely by enamel; (3) in cinder concrete or cinder fill where subject to permanent moisture unless protected on all sides by a layer of non-cinder concrete at least 2" thick or unless the tubing is at least 18" under the fill; (4) in any hazardous (classified) locations, except as permitted by *NEC Sections 502.4, 503.3,* and *504.20;* or (5) for the support of fixtures or other equipment.

In a wet area, EMT and other conduit must be installed to prevent water from entering the conduit system. In locations where walls are subject to regular wash-down (*NEC Section 300.6*), the entire conduit system must be installed to provide a ¼" air space between it and the wall or supporting surface. The entire conduit system is considered to include the conduit, boxes, and fittings. To ensure resistance to corrosion caused by wet environments, EMT is galvanized. The term galvanized is used to describe the procedure in which both the interior and exterior surfaces of the conduit are coated with a corrosion-resistant zinc compound.

Because EMT is a good conductor of electricity, it may be used as an equipment **grounding** conductor. In order to qualify as an equipment grounding conductor [see *NEC Section 250.118(4)*], the conduit system must be tightly connected at each joint and provide a continuous grounding path. The connectors used in an EMT system ensure electrical and mechanical **continuity** throughout the system.

NOTE

Support requirements for EMT are covered in *NEC Section 358.30.* Various types of supports will be discussed later in this module.

EMT fittings are manufactured in two basic types. One type is the compression coupling (*Figure 4*).

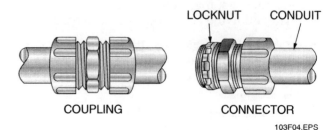

Figure 4 ◆ Compression fittings.

Because EMT is too thin for threads, special fittings must be used. For wet or damp locations, compression fittings such as those shown in *Figure 4* are used. These fittings contain a compression ring made of metal that forms a watertight seal.

When EMT compression couplings are used, they must be securely tightened, and when installed in masonry concrete, they must be of the concrete-tight type. If installed in a wet location, they must be of the raintight type. Refer to *NEC Section 358.42.*

EMT fittings for dry locations can be either the setscrew type or the indenting type. To use the setscrew type, the ends of the EMT are inserted into the sleeve and the setscrews are tightened to make the connection. Various types of setscrew couplings are shown in *Figure 5.*

Figure 5 ◆ Setscrew fittings.

EMT sizes of 2½" and larger have the same outside diameter as corresponding sizes of galvanized rigid steel conduit (GRC). GRC threadless connectors may be used to connect EMT.

NOTE

EMT connectors, although they are the same size as GRC threadless connectors, may not be used to connect GRC.

Both setscrew and compression couplings are available in die-cast or steel construction. Steel couplings are stronger than die-cast couplings and have superior quality.

Support requirements for EMT are presented in *NEC Section 358.30*. As with most other metal conduit, EMT must be supported at least every 10' and within 3' of each outlet box, junction box, cabinet, fitting, or terminating end of the conduit. An exception to *NEC Section 358.30* allows the fastening of unbroken lengths of EMT to be increased to a distance of 5' (1.52 m) where structural members do not readily permit fastening within 3' (914 mm).

3.1.4 Rigid Metal Conduit

Rigid metal conduit (RMC) is conduit that is constructed of metal having sufficient thickness to permit the cutting of pipe threads at each end. Rigid metal conduit provides the best physical protection for conductors of any of the various types of conduit. Rigid metal conduit is supplied in 10' lengths including a threaded coupling on one end.

INSIDE TRACK

EMT Installation

When installing EMT, hook your index finger up through the box to check that the conduit is seated in the connector. If you feel a lip between the conduit and the connector, the conduit is not properly seated.

103SA01.EPS

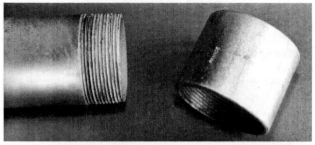

Figure 6 ◆ Rigid metal conduit.

Rigid metal conduit may be fabricated from steel or aluminum. Rigid metal steel conduit may either be galvanized or enamel-coated inside and out. Because of its threaded fittings, rigid metal conduit provides an excellent equipment grounding conductor, as defined in *NEC Section 250.118(2)*. A piece of rigid metal conduit is shown in *Figure 6*. The support requirements for rigid metal conduit are presented in *NEC Section 344.30(B)(2)*.

Rigid metal conduit may be used in underground installations if proper corrosion protection is used.

3.1.5 Galvanized Rigid Steel Conduit

Galvanized rigid steel conduit (GRC) is mostly used in industrial applications. GRC is heavier than EMT and IMC. It is more difficult to cut and bend, requires threading of each end, and has a higher purchase price than EMT and IMC. As a result, the cost of installing GRC is generally higher than the cost of installing EMT and IMC.

3.1.6 Plastic-Coated GRC

Plastic-coated GRC has a thin coating of PVC over the GRC. This combination is useful when an environment calls for the ruggedness of GRC along with the corrosion resistance of PVC. Typical installations where plastic-coated GRC may be required are:

• Chemical plants
• Food plants
• Refineries
• Fertilizer plants
• Paper mills
• Wastewater treatment plants

Plastic-coated GRC requires special threading and bending techniques.

3.1.7 Aluminum Conduit

Aluminum conduit has several characteristics that distinguish it from steel conduit. Because it has better resistance to wet environments and some chemical environments, aluminum conduit generally requires less maintenance in installations such as sewage treatment plants.

Direct burial of aluminum conduit results in a self-stopping chemical reaction on the conduit surface that forms a coating on the conduit. This coating acts to prevent further corrosion, increasing the life of the installation.

Because aluminum conduit is lighter than steel conduit, there are some installation advantages to using aluminum. For example, a 10' section of 3" aluminum conduit weighs about 23 pounds, compared to the 68-pound weight of its steel counterpart.

Rigid Metal Conduit Installations

Use rigid metal conduit in hazardous environments or in areas where there is a chance of physical abuse or extreme moisture. The NEC® does allow EMT to be buried in the ground or in concrete, but galvanized rigid metal conduit is more commonly used.

Because of its cost, aluminum conduit is not widely used. In addition, its use is limited by code. Because it is nonmagnetic, however, aluminum conduit can be used near magnetic resonance imaging (MRI) equipment.

3.1.8 Intermediate Metal Conduit

Intermediate metal conduit (IMC) has a wall thickness that is less than that of rigid metal conduit but greater than that of EMT. The weight of IMC is approximately two-thirds that of rigid metal conduit. Because of its lower purchase price, lighter weight, and thinner walls, IMC installations are generally less expensive than comparable rigid metal conduit installations. However, IMC installations still have high strength ratings.

With the proper corrosion protection, IMC is suitable for use in underground applications.

> **NOTE**
> Additional information on intermediate metal conduit may be found in **NEC Article 342**.

The OD of a given size of IMC is the same as that of the comparable size of rigid metal conduit. Therefore, rigid metal conduit fittings may be used with IMC. Since the threads on IMC and rigid metal conduit are the same size, no special threading tools are needed to thread IMC. Some technicians feel that threading IMC is more difficult than threading rigid metal conduit because IMC is somewhat harder.

The ID of a given size of IMC is somewhat larger than the internal diameter of the same size of rigid metal conduit because of the difference in wall thickness. Bending IMC is considered easier than bending rigid metal conduit because of the reduced wall thickness. However, bending is sometimes complicated by kinking, which may be caused by the increased hardness of IMC.

The NEC® requires that intermediate metal conduit be identified along its length at 5' intervals with the letters IMC. *NEC Sections 110.21* and *342.120* describe this marking requirement.

Intermediate metal conduit, like rigid metal conduit, is permitted to act as an equipment grounding conductor, as defined in *NEC Section 250.118(3)*.

The use of IMC may be restricted in some jurisdictions. It is important to investigate the requirements of each jurisdiction before selecting any materials.

3.1.9 Rigid Nonmetallic Conduit

The most common type of rigid nonmetallic conduit (RNC) is manufactured from polyvinyl chloride (PVC). Because PVC conduit is noncorrosive, chemically inert, and non-aging, it is often used for installation in wet or corrosive environments and for most underground applications. Corrosion problems found with steel and aluminum rigid metal conduit do not occur with PVC. However, PVC conduit may deteriorate under some conditions, such as long periods of direct sunlight. It is also affected by higher-than-usual ambient temperatures.

All PVC conduit is marked according to standards established by the National Electrical Manufacturers' Association (NEMA) or **Underwriters Laboratories (UL)**. A section of PVC conduit is shown in *Figure 7*.

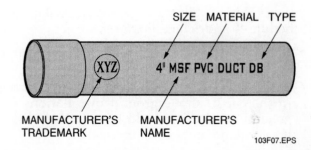

Figure 7 ◆ PVC conduit.

Because PVC conduit is lighter than steel or aluminum rigid conduit, IMC, or EMT, it is considered easier to handle. PVC conduit can usually be installed much faster than other types of conduit because the joints are made up with cement and require no threading.

PVC conduit contains no metal. This characteristic reduces the voltage drop of conductors carrying alternating current in PVC compared to identical conductors in steel conduit.

Because PVC is nonconducting, it cannot be used as an equipment grounding conductor. An equipment grounding conductor sized in accordance with *NEC Table 250.122* must be pulled in each PVC conductor run (except for underground service-entrance conductors).

PVC is available in lengths up to 20', but some local codes require PVC to be cut to 10' lengths prior to installation because it expands and contracts significantly when exposed to changing temperatures. This expansion and contraction characteristic is worse in long runs. To avoid damage to PVC conduit caused by temperature changes, expansion couplings such as the one shown in *Figure 8* are used. The inside of the coupling is sealed with one

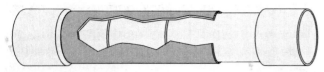

Figure 8 ◆ PVC expansion coupling.

103F08.EPS

or more O-rings. This type of coupling may allow up to 6" of movement. Check the requirements of the local codes prior to installing PVC.

PVC conduit is manufactured in two types:

- *Type EB* – Thin wall for underground use only when encased in concrete. Also referred to as Type I.
- *Type DB* – Thick wall for underground use without encasement in concrete. Also referred to as Type II.

Type DB is available in two wall thicknesses, Schedule 40 and Schedule 80:

- Schedule 40 is heavy wall for direct burial in the earth and above-ground installations.
- Schedule 80 is extra heavy wall for direct burial in the earth, above-ground installations for general applications, and installations where the conduit is subject to physical damage.

Support requirements for rigid nonmetallic conduit (PVC) are found in *NEC Table 352.30(B)*. As with other conduit, it must be supported within 3' of each termination, but the maximum spacing between supports depends upon the size of the conduit. Some of the regulations for the maximum spacing of supports follow:

- *½" to 1" conduit* – every 3'
- *1¼" to 2" conduit* – every 5'
- *2½" to 3" conduit* – every 6'
- *3½" to 5" conduit* – every 7'
- *6" conduit* – every 8'

3.1.10 Liquidtight Flexible Nonmetallic Conduit

Liquidtight flexible nonmetallic conduit (LFNC) was developed as a raceway for industrial equipment where flexibility was required and protection of conductors from liquids was also necessary. This conduit is covered in *NEC Article 356*. The use of LFNC has been expanded from industrial applications to outside and direct burial usage where listed and marked.

Several varieties of LFNC have been introduced. The first product (LFNC-A) was commonly referred to as hose. It consisted of an inner and outer layer of neoprene with a nylon reinforcing web between the layers. A second-generation product (LFNC-B) consisted of a smooth wall, flexible PVC with a rigid PVC integral reinforcement rod. The third product (LFNC-C) was a nylon corrugated shape without any integral reinforcements. These three permitted LFNC raceway designs must be flame-resistant with fittings **approved** for installation of electrical conductors. Nonmetallic connectors are listed for use and some liquidtight metallic flexible conduit connectors are dual-listed for both metallic and nonmetallic liquidtight flexible conduit.

LFNC is sunlight-resistant and suitable for use at conduit temperatures of 80°C dry and 60°C wet. It is available in ⅜" through 4" sizes. *NEC Section 350.12* states that LFNC cannot be used where subject to physical damage or where any combination of ambient and conductor temperature would produce damaging operating temperatures.

Liquidtight flexible metal conduit is a raceway with a circular cross section having an outer liquidtight, nonmetallic, sunlight-resistant jacket over an inner flexible metal core with associated couplings and connectors covered by *NEC Article 350*.

Flex connectors are used to connect flexible conduit to boxes or equipment. They are available in straight, 45-degree, and 90-degree configurations (*Figure 9*).

3.1.11 Flexible Metal Conduit

Flexible metal conduit, sometimes called flex, may be used for many kinds of wiring systems. Flexible metal conduit is made from a single strip of steel or

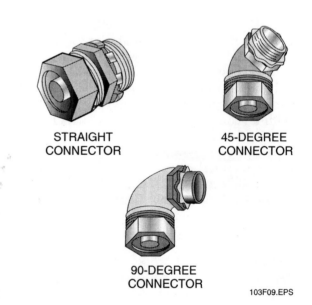

STRAIGHT CONNECTOR

45-DEGREE CONNECTOR

90-DEGREE CONNECTOR

103F09.EPS

Figure 9 ◆ Flex connectors.

Liquidtight Conduit

INSIDE TRACK

Liquidtight conduit protects conductors from vapors, liquids, and solids. Liquidtight conduit that includes an inner metal core is widely used in commercial construction.

103SA02.EPS

aluminum, wound and interlocked. It is typically available in sizes from ⅜" to 4" in diameter. Flexible metal conduit is shown in *Figure 10*.

Flexible metal conduit is often used to connect equipment or machines that vibrate or move slightly during operation. It may also be used in the final connection to equipment having an electrical connection point that is difficult to access.

Flexible metal conduit is easily bent, but the minimum bending radius is the same as for other types of conduit. It should not be bent more than the equivalent of four quarter bends (360 degrees total) between pull points, such as conduit bodies and boxes. It can be connected to boxes with a flexible conduit connector and to rigid conduit or EMT by using a combination coupling.

Two types of combination couplings are shown in *Figure 11*.

103F10.EPS

Figure 10 ◆ Flexible metal conduit.

 NOTE
When using a combination coupling, be sure the flexible conduit is pushed as far as possible into the coupling. This covers the end and protects the conductors from damage.

Flexible metal conduit is generally available in two types: non-liquidtight and liquidtight. *NEC Articles 348* and *350* cover the uses of flexible metal conduit.

Liquidtight flexible metal conduit has an outer covering of liquidtight, sunlight-resistant, flexible material that acts as a moisture seal. It is intended for use in wet locations. It is used primarily for equipment and motor connections when movement of the equipment is likely to occur. The number of bends, size, and support requirements for liquidtight conduit are the same as for all flexible conduit. Fittings used with liquidtight conduit must also be of the liquidtight type.

Support requirements for flexible metal conduit are found in *NEC Sections 348.30* and *350.30*. Straps or other means of securing the flexible metal conduit must be spaced every 4½' and within 12" of each end. (This spacing is closer together than for rigid conduit.) However, at terminals where flexibility is necessary, lengths of up to 36" without support are permitted. Failure to provide proper support for flexible conduit can make pulling conductors difficult.

 NOTE
The NEC® specifies that conduit bends must be made so that the conduit is not damaged and the internal diameter of the conduit is not effectively reduced.

There are raceways specifically designed to maintain the correct bend radii for Category 5, Category 5e, and optical fiber installations.

FLEXIBLE TO EMT   FLEXIBLE TO RIGID

103F11.EPS

Figure 11 ◆ Combination couplings.

4.0.0 ◆ METAL CONDUIT FITTINGS

Manufacturers design and build conduit fittings for a multitude of applications. The type of conduit fitting used in a particular application depends upon the size and type of conduit, the type of fitting needed for the application, the location of the fitting, and the installation method. The requirements and proper applications of boxes and fittings (conduit bodies) are found in *NEC Section 300.15*. Some of the more common types of fittings are examined in the following sections.

4.1.0 Couplings

Couplings are sleeve-like fittings that are typically threaded inside to join two male threaded pieces of rigid conduit or IMC. A piece of conduit with a coupling is shown in *Figure 12*.

Other types of couplings may be used, depending upon the location and type of conduit. Several types are shown in *Figure 13*.

4.2.0 Conduit Bodies

Conduit bodies are a separate portion of a conduit or tubing system that provide access through a removable cover to the interior of the system. They are used at a junction of two or more sections of the system or at a terminal point of the system. They are usually cast and are significantly higher in cost than the stamped steel boxes permitted with EMT. However, there are situations in which conduit bodies are preferable, such as in outdoor locations, for appearance's sake in an **exposed location**, or to change types or sizes of raceways. Also, conduit bodies do not have to be supported, as do stamped steel boxes. They are also used when elbows or bends would not be appropriate or to provide wire pulling locations in longer conduit runs.

4.2.1 Type C Conduit Bodies

Type C conduit bodies may be used to provide a pull point in a long conduit run or a conduit run that has bends totaling more than 360 degrees. A Type C conduit body is shown in *Figure 14*.

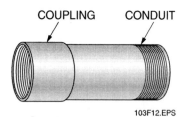

COUPLING   CONDUIT

103F12.EPS

Figure 12 ◆ Conduit and coupling.

103F14.EPS

Figure 14 ◆ Type C conduit body.

4.2.2 Type L Conduit Bodies

When referring to conduit bodies, the letter *L* represents an elbow. A Type L conduit body is used as a pulling point for conduit that requires a 90-degree change in direction. Because of the 90-degree bend, Type L conduit bodies are not acceptable for use with high-performance cable. The cover is removed, then the wire is pulled out, coiled on the ground or floor, reinserted into the other conduit body's opening, and pulled. The cover and its associated gasket are then replaced. Type L conduit bodies are available with the cover on the back (Type LB), on the sides (Type LL or LR), or on both sides (Type LRL). Several Type L conduit bodies are shown in *Figure 15*. Specialized LB bodies are available for high-performance cable.

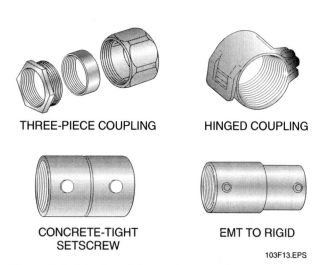

THREE-PIECE COUPLING   HINGED COUPLING

CONCRETE-TIGHT   EMT TO RIGID
SETSCREW
                              103F13.EPS

Figure 13 ◆ Metal conduit couplings.

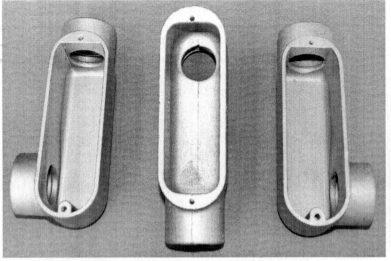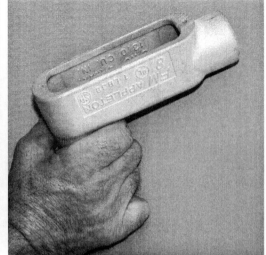

103F15.EPS

Figure 15 ◆ Type L conduit bodies and how to identify them.

To identify Type L conduit bodies, use the following method:

Step 1 Hold the body like a pistol.

Step 2 Locate the opening on the body:
- If the opening is to the left, it is a Type LL.
- If the opening is to the right, it is a Type LR.
- If the opening is on the top (back), it is a Type LB.
- If there are openings on both the left and the right, it is a Type LRL.

4.2.3 Type T Conduit Bodies

Type T conduit bodies are used to provide a junction point for three intersecting conduits and are used extensively in conduit systems. A Type T conduit body is shown in *Figure 16*.

4.2.4 Type X Conduit Bodies

Type X conduit bodies are used to provide a junction point for four intersecting conduits. The removable cover provides access to the interior of the X so that wire pulling and splicing may be performed. A Type X conduit body is shown in *Figure 17*.

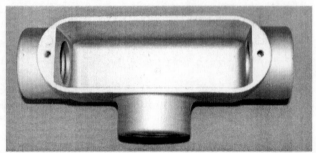

103F16.EPS

Figure 16 ◆ Type T conduit body.

103F17.EPS

Figure 17 ◆ Type X conduit body.

4.2.5 Threaded Weatherproof Hubs

Threaded weatherproof hubs are used for conduit entering a box in a wet location. *Figure 18* shows typical threaded weatherproof hubs.

103F18.EPS

Figure 18 ◆ Threaded weatherproof hubs.

4.3.0 Insulating Bushings

An insulating bushing is either nonmetallic or has an insulated throat. Insulating bushings are installed on the threaded end of conduit that enters a sheet metal enclosure.

4.3.1 Nongrounding Insulating Bushings

The purpose of a nongrounding insulating bushing is to protect the conductors from being damaged by the sharp edges of the threaded conduit end. *NEC Section 312.5(B)* states that where conductors enter a box, fitting, or other enclosure, a bushing must be provided to protect the wire from abrasion. *NEC Section 312.6(C)* references *NEC Section 300.4(F)*, which states where ungrounded conductors (No. 4 or larger) enter a raceway in a cabinet or box enclosure, the conductors shall be protected by a substantial fitting providing a smoothly rounded insulating surface, unless the conductors are separated from the raceway fitting by substantial insulating material securely fastened in place. An exception is where threaded hubs or bosses that are an integral part of a cabinet, box enclosure, or raceway provide a smoothly rounded or flared entry for conductors. Insulating bushings are shown in *Figure 19*.

4.3.2 Grounding Insulating Bushings

Grounded insulating bushings, usually called grounding bushings, are used to protect conductors and also have provisions for connection of an equipment grounding conductor. The ground wire, once connected to the grounding bushing, may be connected to the enclosure to which the conduit is connected. Grounding insulating bushings are shown in *Figure 20*.

4.4.0 Offset Nipples

Offset nipples are used to connect two pieces of electrical equipment in close proximity where a slight offset is required. They come in sizes ranging from ½" to 2" in diameter. See *Figure 21*.

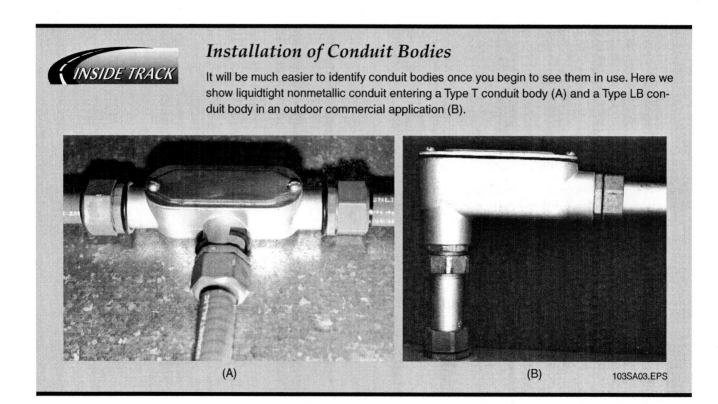

INSIDE TRACK

Installation of Conduit Bodies

It will be much easier to identify conduit bodies once you begin to see them in use. Here we show liquidtight nonmetallic conduit entering a Type T conduit body (A) and a Type LB conduit body in an outdoor commercial application (B).

(A)

(B)

103SA03.EPS

Figure 19 ◆ Insulating bushings.

103F19.EPS

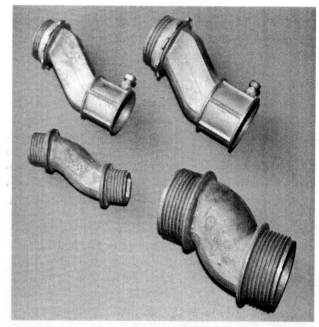

Figure 21 ◆ Offset nipples.

103F21.EPS

Figure 20 ◆ Grounding insulating bushings.

103F20.EPS

Figure 22 ◆ Bushings.

103F22.EPS

5.0.0 ◆ BUSHINGS AND LOCKNUTS

Conduit is joined to boxes by connectors, adapters, threaded hubs, or locknuts.

Bushings protect the wires from the sharp edges of the conduit. Bushings are usually made of plastic or metal. Some metal bushings have a grounding screw to permit a **bonding conductor** to be installed. Some different types of plastic and metal bushings are shown in *Figure 22*.

Locknuts are used on the inside and outside walls of the box to which the conduit is connected. A grounding locknut may be needed if a bonding wire is to be installed. Special sealing locknuts are also used in wet locations. Several types of locknuts are shown in *Figure 23*.

103F23.EPS

Figure 23 ◆ Locknuts.

6.0.0 ◆ SEALING FITTINGS

Hazardous locations in manufacturing plants and other industrial facilities involve a wide variety of flammable gases and vapors and ignitable dusts. Since these hazardous substances have widely different flash points, ignition temperatures, and flammable limits, fittings are required to seal the conduit runs. Sealing fittings are installed in conduit runs to minimize the passage of gases, vapors, or flames through the conduit and reduce the accumulation of moisture. They are required by *NEC Article 500* in hazardous locations where explosions may occur. They are also required where conduit passes from a hazardous location of one classification to another classification or to an unclassified location. Several types of sealing fittings are shown in *Figure 24*.

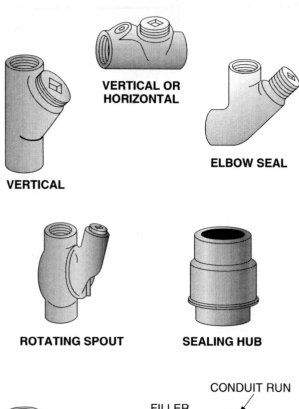

VERTICAL OR HORIZONTAL

ELBOW SEAL

VERTICAL

ROTATING SPOUT

SEALING HUB

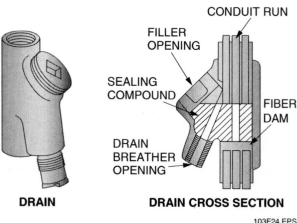

CONDUIT RUN

FILLER OPENING

SEALING COMPOUND

FIBER DAM

DRAIN BREATHER OPENING

DRAIN

DRAIN CROSS SECTION

103F24.EPS

Figure 24 ◆ Sealing fittings.

7.0.0 ◆ CABLE AND RACEWAY SUPPORTS

Cable and raceway supports are available in many types and configurations. This section discusses the most common cable and conduit supports found in low-voltage cable installations. *NEC Section 300.11* discusses the requirements for branch circuit wiring that is supported from above. Equipment and raceways must have their own supporting methods and may not be supported by the supporting hardware of a fire-rated roof/ceiling assembly.

7.1.0 Straps

Straps are used to support conduit to a surface (see *Figure 25*). The spacing of these supports must conform to the minimum support spacing requirements for each type of conduit. One-hole and two-hole straps are used for all types of conduit: EMT, GRC, IMC, PVC, and flex. The straps can be flexible or rigid. Two-part straps are used to secure conduit to electrical framing channels (struts). Parallel and right angle beam clamps are also used to support conduit from structural members.

Clamp back straps can also be used with a backplate to maintain the ¼" spacing from the surface required for installations in wet locations.

7.2.0 Standoff Supports

The standoff support, often referred to as a Minerallac (the name of a manufacturer of this type of support), is used to support conduit away from the supporting structure. In the case of the one-hole and two-hole straps, the conduit must be kicked up wherever a fitting occurs. If standoff supports are

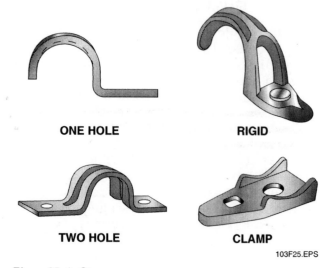

ONE HOLE

RIGID

TWO HOLE

CLAMP

103F25.EPS

Figure 25 ◆ Straps.

Installing Sealing Fittings

These fittings must be sealed after the wires are pulled. A fiber dam is first packed into the base of the fitting between and around the conductors, then the liquid sealing compound is poured into the fitting.

103SA04.EPS

used, the conduit is held away from the supporting surface and no offsets (**kicks**) are required in the conduit at the fittings. Standoff supports may be used to support all types of conduit including GRC, IMC, EMT, PVC, and flex, as well as tubing installations. A standoff support is shown in *Figure 26*.

7.3.0 Electrical Framing Channels

Electrical framing channels or other similar framing materials are used together with Unistrut-type conduit clamps to support conduit (see *Figure 27*). They may be attached to a ceiling, wall, or other surface or be supported from a trapeze hanger.

Figure 26 ◆ Standoff support.

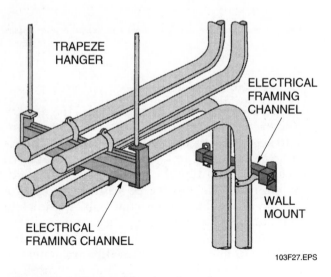

103F27.EPS

Figure 27 ◆ Electrical framing channels.

7.4.0 Beam Clamps

Beam clamps are used with suspended hangers. The raceway is attached to or laid in the hanger. The hanger is suspended by a threaded rod. One end of the threaded rod is attached to the hanger and the other end is attached to a beam clamp. The beam clamp is then attached to a beam. A beam clamp is shown in *Figure 28.*

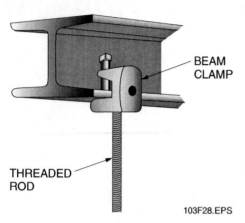

BEAM CLAMP

THREADED ROD

103F28.EPS

Figure 28 ◆ Beam clamp.

7.5.0 Cable Supports

All cable runs must be securely fastened to the building structure. Several types of mechanical devices are used to support cable.

NOTE

Never use ceiling gridwires to support cabling. Only use hangers appropriately attached to the building structure. Hangers must be placed 48" to 60" apart.

7.5.1 Cable Ties

Ties are used for a variety of purposes (*Figure 29*). The basic tie can be wrapped around a cable bundle to keep it neatly dressed. The lashing tie or velcro tie can be used to keep cables temporarily in place while additional cables are being pulled. The mounting tie and the tie with the mounting base can be used to secure small cable bundles to a flat surface. The mounting bases are available with adhesive backing or a screw hole. With the exception of the velcro tie, these ties are generally made of nylon. Ties must be loose enough to avoid distorting the cable.

When installing ties, keep the following precautions in mind:

- Fire-rated (plenum-rated) cable ties must be used in cases where cables run through a ceiling plenum.
- Ties should be loosely connected to prevent pinching the cable; otherwise, the performance of the cable will be affected.

7.5.2 Cable Hangers

J-clamps (J-hooks) and bridle rings are among the most common types of cable hangers (*Figure 30*). These devices can be mounted in a variety of ways.

When high-performance cable such as telecommunications/data cabling is involved, bridle rings and ties are not suitable because they can crimp the cable and thereby reduce its performance. In such cases, J-hooks spaced every four or five feet are generally recommended. J-hooks have a wider base and are therefore less likely to crimp the cable. Wide strap-type hangers are also available to handle bundles from 4" to 6" in diameter.

Cables may not be laid on a suspended ceiling. They must be routed through suitable hangers or raceways.

Other types of cable supports are D-rings, half D-rings, and mushroom posts (*Figure 31*). D-rings come in a variety of sizes and colors, and are available in aluminum or plastic.

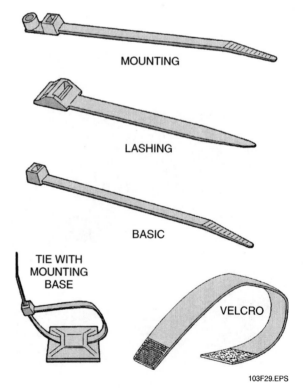

MOUNTING

LASHING

BASIC

TIE WITH MOUNTING BASE

VELCRO

103F29.EPS

Figure 29 ◆ Cable ties.

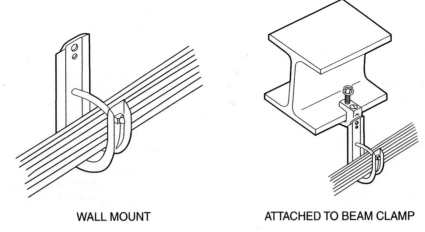

WALL MOUNT **ATTACHED TO BEAM CLAMP**

J-HOOKS

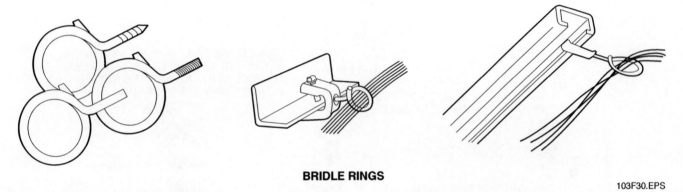

BRIDLE RINGS

103F30.EPS

Figure 30 ◆ J-hooks and bridle rings.

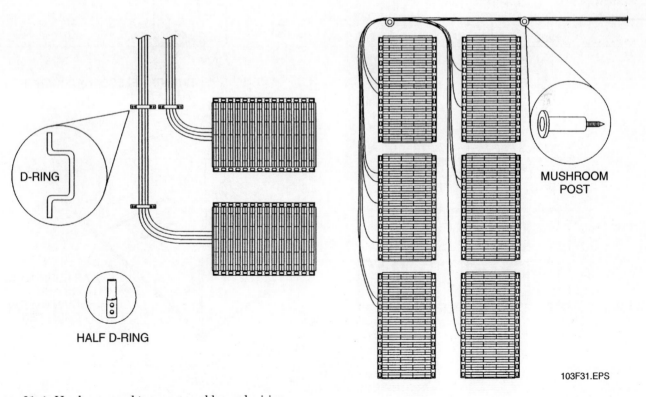

D-RING

HALF D-RING

MUSHROOM POST

103F31.EPS

Figure 31 ◆ Hardware used to manage cables and wiring.

8.0.0 ◆ SURFACE METAL AND NONMETALLIC RACEWAYS

Surface metal raceways, sometimes known as Wiremold, consist of a wide variety of special raceways designed primarily to carry power and communications wiring to locations on the surface of ceilings or walls of building interiors. They can be made of metal or plastic.

Low-voltage perimeter raceway (*Figure 32*) is specifically designed to route, protect, and seal data, voice, video, optical fiber, or power cabling. Data, voice, video, and optical fiber cable have minimum bend radii that must be observed.

There are three types of surface raceway (*Figure 33*). One is a single-channel, one-piece type. Another is a one-piece, self-latching model designed for low-capacity applications, such as one- and two-channel. This type is available with a peel-and-stick adhesive system.

The third type of low-voltage raceway is a two-piece model with a base that can be screwed or nailed to a wall, floor, or ceiling. A compatible raceway cover fits over the base and locks into place. This type of raceway is used for multi-channel applications and has available divider walls to separate power and low-voltage cables.

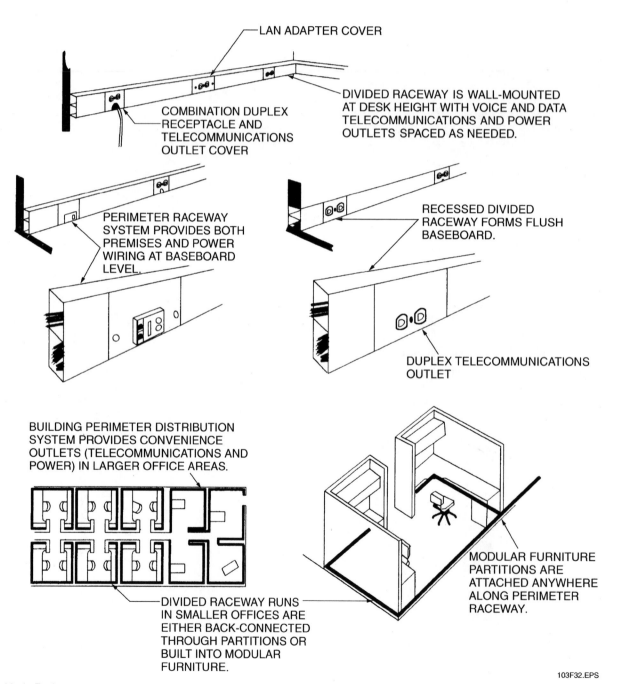

Figure 32 ◆ Perimeter raceway.

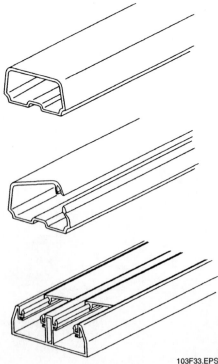

Figure 33 ◆ Examples of surface raceway.

The perimeter raceways shown in *Figure 33* are available in widths ranging from ¾" to over 7".

Accessories are available to connect the 8' or 10' section of raceway, create junctions, and make corners. Corners are compatible with the minimum 1" bend radius required by TIA/EIA 568-A. A selection of termination boxes and faceplates is also available. See *Figure 34* for an example.

Installation specifications of both surface metal raceways and surface nonmetallic raceways are listed in detail in *NEC Articles 386* and *388*, respectively. All these raceways must be installed in dry, interior locations. The number of conductors, their amperage, and the allowable cross-sectional area

of the conductors are specified in *NEC Tables 310.16* and *310.18*.

One use of surface metal raceways is to protect conductors that run to nonaccessible outlets.

Other surface metal raceway designs are referred to as pancake raceways because of their flat cross sections. Their primary use is to extend power, lighting, telephone, or signal wire to locations away from the walls of a room without embedding them under the floor. A pancake raceway is shown in *Figure 35*.

There are also surface metal raceways available that house two or three different conductor raceways. These are referred to as twin duct or triple duct. These raceways permit different circuits, such as power and signal circuits, to be placed within the same raceway.

NEC Section 800.52 specifies minimum separations between power and communications cable.

The reason for separating these cables is to limit the effect that electromagnetic interference (EMI) has on communications systems. EMI is basically electronic noise that is generated by high-voltage systems and by appliances such as microwave ovens. This noise can interfere with, and even interrupt, communications lines.

While communications cable can share **pathways** with other low-voltage cables in most instances, communications and power cables must be separated by a barrier if they are run in the same raceway. If the cables are not run in a raceway, there must be a 2" separation.

The number and types of conductors permitted to be installed and the capacity of a particular surface raceway must be calculated and matched with NEC® requirements, as discussed previously. *NEC Tables 310.16* through *310.19* are used for surface raceways in the same manner in which they are used for wireways. For surface raceway installations with more than three conductors in each raceway, refer to *NEC Table 310.15(B)(2)(a)*.

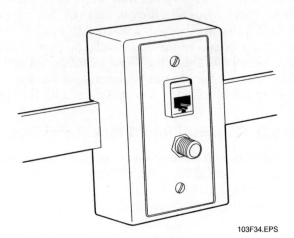

Figure 34 ◆ Low-voltage raceway box.

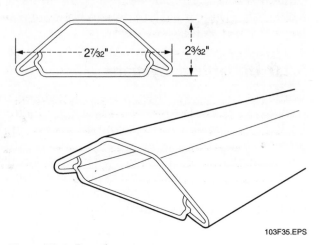

Figure 35 ◆ Pancake raceway.

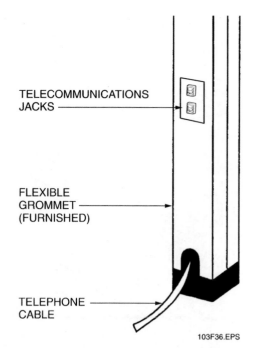

TELECOMMUNICATIONS JACKS

FLEXIBLE GROMMET (FURNISHED)

TELEPHONE CABLE

103F36.EPS

Figure 36 ◆ Pole base.

> **NOTE**
> Inserts must be installed so that they are flush with the finished grade of the floor.

8.1.0 Pole Systems

There are many situations in which cables and wires have to be carried from overhead wiring systems to devices that are not located near existing wall outlets or control circuits. This type of wiring is typically used in open office spaces where cubicles are provided by temporary dividers. Poles are used to accomplish this. Some common manufacturers' names for these poles include Tele-Power poles, Quick-E poles, and Walkerpoles. The poles usually come in lengths suitable for 10', 12', or 15' ceilings. *Figure 36* shows a pole base. There must be a divider between electrical and low-voltage cabling.

8.2.0 Underfloor Systems

Underfloor raceway systems were developed to provide a practical means of bringing conductors for lighting, power, and signaling to cabinets and consoles. Underfloor raceways are available in 10' lengths and widths of 4" and 8". The sections are made with inserts spaced every 24". The inserts can be removed for outlet installation. These are explained in *NEC Article 390*.

Junction boxes are used to join sections of underfloor raceways. Conduit is also used with underfloor raceways by using a raceway-to-conduit connector (conduit adapter). A typical underfloor raceway duct is shown in *Figure 37*.

This wiring method makes it possible to place a desk or table in any location where it will always be over, or very near to, a duct. The wiring method for lighting and power between cabinets and the raceway junction boxes may be conduit, underfloor raceway, wall elbows, and cabinet connectors. Optional dividers are available with some junction boxes to allow power and low-voltage conductors to share the same box. Special collars and flanges are also available to elevate the surface of the junction box so it is even with the floor.

8.3.0 Cellular Metal Floor Raceways

A cellular metal floor raceway is a type of floor construction designed for use in steel-frame buildings. In these buildings, the members supporting the floor between the beams consist of

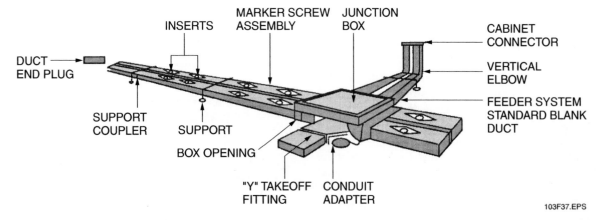

Figure 37 ♦ Underfloor raceway duct.

sheet steel rolled into shapes. These shapes are combined to form cells, or closed passageways, which extend across the building. The cells are of various shapes and sizes, depending upon the structural strength required. The cells of this type of floor construction form the raceways, as shown in *Figure 38*.

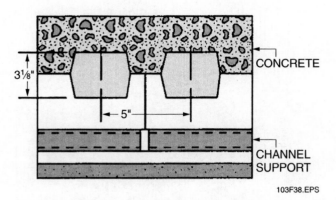

Figure 38 ♦ Cross section of a cellular floor.

Connections to the cells are made using headers which extend across the cells. A header connects only to those cells which are to be used as raceways for conductors. A junction box or access fitting is necessary at each joint where a header connects to a cell. Two or three separate headers, connecting to different sets of cells, may be used for different systems. For example, light and power, signaling systems, and public telephones would each have a separate header. A special elbow fitting is used to extend the headers up to the distribution equipment on a wall or column.

8.4.0 Cellular Concrete Floor Raceways

The term pre-cast cellular concrete floor refers to a type of floor used in steel-frame, concrete-frame, and wall-bearing construction. In this type of system, the floor members are pre-cast with hollow voids which form smooth, round cells. The cells form raceways which can be adapted for use as underfloor raceways by using special fittings. A pre-cast cellular concrete floor is fire-resistant and requires no further fireproofing. The pre-cast reinforced concrete floor members form the structural floor and are supported by beams or bearing walls. Connections to the cells are made with headers which are secured to the pre-cast concrete floor. *NEC Article 372* covers the installation of cellular concrete floor raceways.

9.0.0 ♦ CABLE TRAYS

Cable trays function as a support for conductors and tubing (see *NEC Article 392*). A cable tray has the advantage of easy access to conductors, and thus lends itself to installations where the addition or removal of conductors is a common practice. Cable trays are fabricated from aluminum, steel, and fiberglass.

Cable trays are available in three basic forms: ladder, trough, and basket. Ladder tray, as the name implies, consists of two parallel channels connected by rungs. Trough-type trays consist of two parallel channels (side rails) having a corrugated, ventilated bottom, or a corrugated, solid bottom. Wire basket tray is usually made of 2" × 4" wire mesh. It is lightweight and easy to bend. It is commonly used for telecommunications cabling. There is also a special center rail cable tray available for use in telephone and sound wiring.

Cable trays are commonly available in 12' and 24' lengths. They are usually available in widths of 6", 9", 12", 18", 24", 30", and 36", and load depths of 4", 6", and 8".

Cable trays may be used in most installations. Cable trays may be used in air handling (plenum) ceiling spaces, but only to support the wiring methods permitted in such spaces by *NEC Section 300.22(C)(1)*. Also, cable trays may be used in Class 1, Division 2 locations according to *NEC Section 501.4(B)*. Cable trays may also be used above a suspended ceiling that is not used as an air handling space. Some manufacturers offer an aluminum cable tray that is coated with PVC for installation in caustic environments. A typical cable tray system with fittings is shown in *Figure 39*.

Wire and cable installation in cable trays is defined by the NEC®. Read *NEC Article 392* to become familiar with the requirements and restrictions made by the NEC® for safe installation of wire and cable in a cable tray.

Metallic cable trays that support electrical conductors must be grounded as required by *NEC*

Article 250. Where steel and aluminum cable tray systems are used as equipment grounding conductors, all of the provisions of *NEC Section 392.7* must be complied with.

 WARNING!
Do not stand on, climb in, or walk on a cable tray.

9.1.0 Cable Tray Fittings

Cable tray fittings are part of the cable tray system and provide a means of changing the direction or dimension of the different trays. Some of the uses of horizontal and vertical tees, horizontal and vertical bends, horizontal crosses, reducers, barrier strips, covers, and box connectors are shown in *Figure 39*.

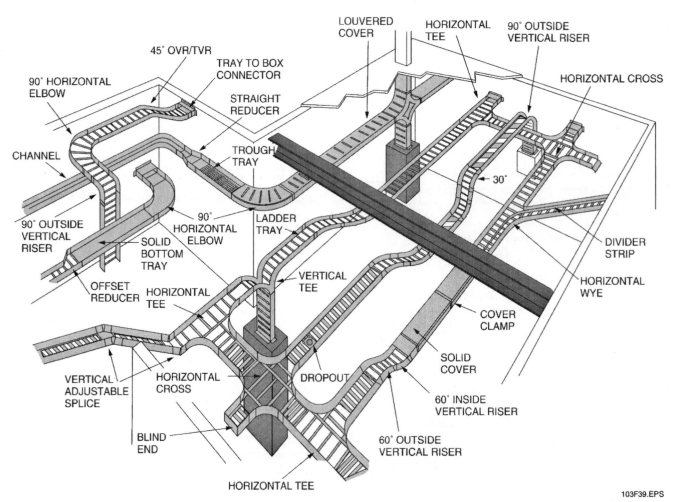

Figure 39 ◆ Cable tray system.

9.2.0 Cable Tray Supports

Cable trays are usually supported in one of five ways: direct rod suspension, trapeze mounting, center hung, wall mounting, and pipe rack mounting.

9.2.1 Direct Rod Suspension

Direct rod suspension uses threaded rods and hanger clamps to support cable trays. One end of the threaded rod is connected to the ceiling or other overhead structure. The other end is connected to hanger clamps that are attached to the cable tray side rails. A direct rod suspension assembly is shown in *Figure 40*.

9.2.2 Trapeze Mounting and Center-Hung Support

Trapeze mounting is similar to direct rod suspension mounting. The difference is in the method of attaching the cable tray to the threaded rods. A structural member, usually a steel channel or strut, is connected to the vertical supports to provide an appearance similar to a swing or trapeze. The cable tray is mounted to the structural member. Often, the underside of the channel or strut is used to support conduit. A trapeze mounting assembly is shown in *Figure 41*.

The center-hung support method is very similar to trapeze mounting. However, only one rod is used, and it is centered between the cable tray side rails.

9.2.3 Wall Mounting

Wall mounting is accomplished by supporting the cable tray with structural members attached to a wall. This method of support is often used in tunnels and other underground or sheltered installations where large numbers of conductors interconnect equipment that is separated by long distances. A wall mounting assembly is shown in *Figure 42*.

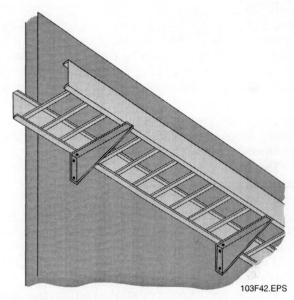

Figure 42 ◆ Wall mounting.

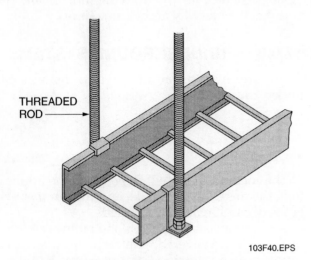

THREADED ROD

103F40.EPS

Figure 40 ◆ Direct rod suspension.

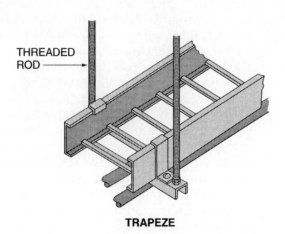

THREADED ROD

TRAPEZE

Figure 41 ◆ Trapeze mounting and center-hung support.

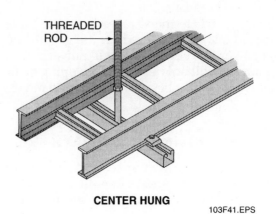

THREADED ROD

CENTER HUNG

103F41.EPS

9.2.4 Pipe Rack Mounting

Pipe racks are structural frames used to support piping that interconnects equipment in outdoor industrial facilities. Usually, some space on the rack is reserved for conduit and cable tray. Pipe rack mounting of cable tray is often used when power distribution and electrical wiring is routed over a large area.

10.0.0 ◆ STORING RACEWAYS

Proper and safe methods of storing conduit, wireways, raceways, and cable trays may sound like a simple task, but improper storage techniques can result in wasted time and damage to the raceways, as well as personal injury. There are correct ways to store raceways that will help avoid costly damage, save time in identifying stored raceways, and reduce the chance of personal injury.

Pipe racks are commonly used for storing conduit. The racks provide support to prevent bending, sagging, distorting, scratching, or marring of conduit surfaces. Most racks have compartments where different types and sizes of conduit can be separated for ease of identification and selection. The storage compartments in racks are usually elevated to help avoid damage that might occur at floor level. Conduit that is stored at floor level is easily damaged by people and other materials or equipment in the area.

The ends of stored conduit should be sealed to help prevent contamination and damage. Conduit ends can be capped, taped, or plugged.

Always inspect raceway before storing it to make sure that it is clean and is not damaged. Also, make sure that the raceway is stored securely so that when someone comes to get it for a job, it will not fall in any way that could cause injury.

To prevent contamination and corrosion of stored raceway, it should be covered with a tarpaulin or other suitable covering. It should also be separated from non-compatible materials, such as hazardous chemicals.

Wireways, surface metal raceways, and cable trays should always be stored off the ground on boards in an area where people will not step on it and equipment will not run over it. Stepping on or running over raceway bends the metal and makes it unusable.

11.0.0 ◆ HANDLING RACEWAYS

Raceway is made to strict specifications. It can easily be damaged by careless handling. From the time raceway is delivered to a job site until the installation is complete, use proper and safe handling techniques. These are a few basic guidelines for handling raceway that will help avoid damaging or contaminating it:

- Never drag raceway off a delivery truck or off other lengths of raceway, and never drag it on the ground or floor. Dragging raceway can cause damage to the ends.
- Keep the thread protection caps on when handling or transporting conduit raceway.
- Keep raceway away from any material that might contaminate it during handling.
- Flag the ends of long lengths of raceway when transporting it to the job site.
- Never drop or throw raceway when handling it.
- Never hit raceway against other objects when transporting it.
- Always use two people when carrying long pieces of raceway. Make sure that you both stay on the same side and that the load is balanced. Each person should be about one-quarter of the length of the raceway from the end. Lift and put down the raceway at the same time.

12.0.0 ◆ UNDERGROUND SYSTEMS

There are three different ways to install cable underground:

- Duct
- Conduit
- Direct burial

The method used will depend on the application, the materials available, and the number and types of conductors to be pulled.

A duct consists of at least one pathway placed in a trench and covered with earth. In some cases, conduit can be classified as a pathway. Pathways are available as either a single duct or multiple ducts (two, three, four, or six pathways per section). The depth at which the duct will be placed is determined using *NEC Table 300.5*. The conduit pathways are encased in concrete or other materials. This provides good mechanical strength.

In underground cable installations, a duct is a buried conduit through which a cable passes. Maintenance holes are set at intervals in an underground duct run. Maintenance holes provide access through throats (sometimes called chimneys). At ground level, or street surface level, a maintenance hole cover closes off the maintenance hole area tightly. An individual cable length running underground normally terminates at a maintenance hole, where it is spliced to another length of cable. A duct may consist of a single conduit or several, each carrying a cable length from one maintenance hole to the next. See *Figure 43*.

Maintenance holes provide room for installing lengths of cable in conduit lines (*Figure 44*). They are also used for maintenance work and for performing tests. Workers enter a maintenance hole from above. In a two-way maintenance hole, cables enter and leave in two directions. There are also three-way and four-way maintenance holes. Maintenance holes are often located at the intersection of two streets so that they can be used for cables leaving in four directions. Maintenance holes are usually constructed of brick or concrete. Their design must provide room for drainage and for workers to move around inside them. A similar opening, known as a handhole, is sometimes provided for splicing on lateral two-way ducts.

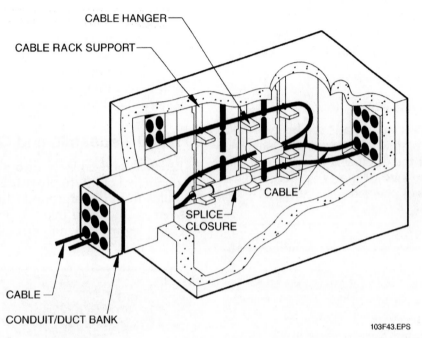

Figure 43 ◆ Typical cable maintenance hole.

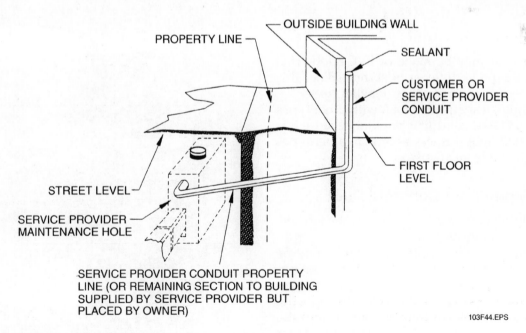

Figure 44 ◆ Installing underground entrances.

For direct-buried cable, filled polyethylene insulated conductor (PIC) cable is the only type of copper cable recommended. It contains a gel which inhibits water penetration and migration, and therefore protects the integrity of the cable. Direct-buried cable may require an armored sheath to resist damage from rodents and other sources.

NOTE

The difference between direct-buried cable and underground cable is that underground cable is run through a conduit and/or maintenance hole.

12.1.0 Duct Materials

Underground ducts can be made of fiber, vitrified tile, iron conduit, plastic, or poured concrete. The inside diameter of the ducting for a specific job is determined by the size of the cable that will be drawn into the duct. Sizes from 2" to 6" (ID) are available.

WARNING!

Be careful when working with unfamiliar duct materials. In older installations, asbestos/cement duct may have been used. Asbestos is known to cause cancer. You must be certified to remove or disturb asbestos.

12.2.0 Plastic Conduit

Plastic conduit may be made of PVC (polyvinyl chloride), PE (polyethylene), or styrene. Since this type of conduit is available in lengths up to 20', fewer couplings are needed than with other types of ducting. Plastic conduit is popular because it is easy to install, requires less labor than other types of conduit, and is inexpensive.

12.3.0 Monolithic Concrete Duct

Monolithic concrete duct is poured at the job site. Multiple duct pathways can be formed using rubber tubing cores on spacers. The cores may be removed after the concrete has set. A die containing steel tubes, known as a boat, can also be used to form ducts. It is pulled slowly through the trench on a track as concrete is poured from the top. Poured concrete ducting made by either method is relatively expensive, but offers the advantage of creating a very clean duct interior with no residue that can decay. The rubber core method is especially useful for forming curves or turns in duct systems.

12.4.0 Controlled Environment Vaults

The controlled environment vault (CEV) is a precast concrete structure consisting of top and bottom sections. It is available in 16' and 24' lengths and is normally placed near a maintenance hole. The vault is designed to house electronic equipment that is sensitive to environmental conditions, and is therefore sealed against gases or moisture that may enter from the outside. The CEV is generally equipped with electrical power, lights, sump pumps, ventilation blowers, heaters, and atmospheric monitors. It may also be air-conditioned.

12.5.0 Pedestals and Cabinets

Pedestals and cabinets are outdoor enclosures used as junction points to provide above-grade access to cables from underground, direct-buried, or aerial sources. There are many types of pedestals; some examples are shown in *Figure 45*.

INSIDE TRACK

Pedestals

Pedestals come in a variety of sizes and perform a variety of functions. This basic pedestal provides the cable TV feed for a single residence.

103SA06.EPS

BD3
- Accepts 25–50 pair cables
- Maximum splice size 100 pairs
- Primary distribution pedestal

BD5
- Accepts 200–600 pair cables
- Maximum splice size 600 pairs
- May contain distribution terminals

UP1248
- Accepts 1200–2400 pair cables
- Maximum splice size 2400 pairs
- Not for distribution

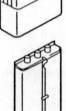

UP900 CROSS-CONNECT
- Primary connection point between feeder and distribution
- Can be configured with X-feeder and X-distribution pairs = 900 total
- Can be pole-mounted

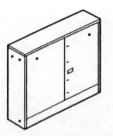

4200 SERIES PEDESTAL
- Provides a cross-connect distribution point for feeder and distribution copper cables or optical fiber cables
- Can also be configured to house electronic equipment

103F45.EPS

Figure 45 ◆ Examples of pedestals.

SINGLE GANG   TWO GANG

THREE GANG   OCTAGONAL

DUAL VOLTAGE   WEATHERPROOF
BOX COVER

103F46.EPS

Figure 46 ◆ Boxes used in raceway systems.

Pedestals may be installed directly on the ground or they may be wall-mounted, pole-mounted, or pad-mounted. Depending on the application, the pedestal may house electronic or optical fiber equipment. Pedestals and cabinets containing electronic equipment may also have environmental control systems, including heating, cooling, and air circulation.

13.0.0 ◆ BOXES

Boxes are made from either metallic or nonmetallic material. The latter are used extensively for low-voltage systems. *Figure 46* shows various boxes used in raceway systems.

13.1.0 Metal Boxes

Metal boxes are made from sheet steel. The surface is galvanized to resist corrosion and provide a continuous ground. Refer to *NEC Section 314.40* for information on thickness and grounding provisions. Metal boxes are made with removable circular sections called pryouts or knockouts. These circular sections are removed to make openings for conduit or cable connections.

13.1.1 Pryouts

In a pryout, a section is cut completely through the metal but only part of the way around, leaving solid metal tabs at two points. A slot is cut in the center of the pryout. To remove the pryout, a screwdriver is inserted into the slot and twisted to break the solid tabs (*Figure 47*).

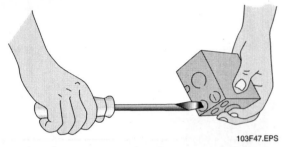

103F47.EPS

Figure 47 ◆ Pryout removal.

13.1.2 Knockouts

Knockouts are pre-punched circular sections that do not include a pryout slot. The knockout is easily removed when sharply hit by a hammer and punch, as shown in *Figure 48*.

Conduit must often enter boxes, cabinets, or panels that do not have pre-cut knockouts. In these cases, a knockout punch can be used to make a hole for the conduit connection. A knockout punch kit is shown in *Figure 49*.

13.2.0 Nonmetallic Boxes

Nonmetallic boxes are made of PVC or Bakelite (a fiber-reinforced plastic). Nonmetallic boxes are often used in corrosive environments. *NEC Section 314.3* covers the use of nonmetallic boxes and the types of conduit, fittings, and grounding requirements for specific applications.

Removing Knockouts

For concentric or eccentric knockouts, first drive down one section of the smallest ring and cut it in half, then drive down the next section of the ring and cut it in half. Finally, twist off the attached portion of the knockout.

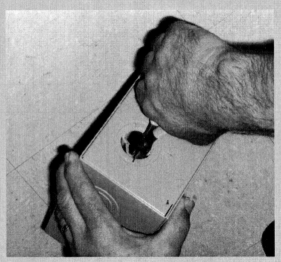

103SA07.EPS

Knockouts

It may be difficult to remove a knockout from a previously installed box without dislodging the box. One way to do it is to drill into the knockout and partially insert a self-tapping screw. Then use diagonal or side-cut pliers to pull the knockout from the box.

Using a Punch

To cut a hole with a knockout punch, first measure for the center and drill a pilot hole large enough to insert the drive screw. Turn the drive nut with a wrench until the punch cuts through the box wall.

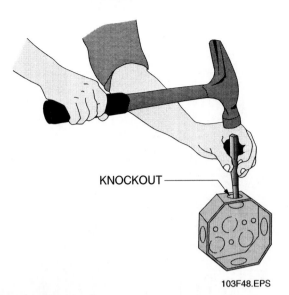

KNOCKOUT

Figure 48 ◆ Knockout removal.

103F48.EPS

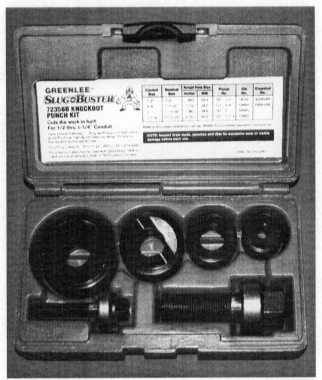

Figure 49 ◆ Knockout punch kit.

103F49.EPS

13.3.0 Low-Voltage Boxes

Low-voltage systems encompass computer networks, telecommunications lines, low-voltage wiring, audio, and video. For that reason, many different types of termination boxes and outlets are required. Several examples are shown in *Figure 50*.

The speaker back box is much larger than the standard outlet box. It is used to mount a speaker and microphone combination such as an intercom.

As shown in *Figure 50*, electrical and telecommunications outlets can reside in the same box, but there must be a partition separating them.

Several types of trim rings are also used. You should note that the term ring does not necessarily mean that the component is circular. The sheetrock (gypsum board) ring fits behind the cover plate and is used to cover up the opening when it is cut too big for the cover plate. The plaster ring is used to build out the box in cases where plaster or similar material is applied over the sheetrock.

14.0.0 ◆ MAKING A CONDUIT-TO-BOX CONNECTION

A proper conduit-to-box connection is shown in *Figure 51*. In order to make a good connection, use the following procedure:

Step 1   Thread the external locknut onto the conduit. Run the locknut to the bottom of the threads.

Step 2   Insert the conduit into the box opening.

Step 3   If an inside locknut or grounding locknut is required, screw it onto the conduit inside the box opening.

Step 4   Screw the bushing onto the threads projecting into the box opening. Make sure the bushing is tightened as much as possible.

Step 5   Tighten the external locknut to secure the conduit to the box.

It is important that the bushings and locknuts fit tightly against the box. For this reason, the conduit must enter straight into the box (*Figure 52*). This may require that a box offset or a kick be made in the conduit.

15.0.0 ◆ CONSTRUCTION PROCEDURES

Procedures for installing conduit and boxes vary according to the structural framework of the building. This section discusses the most common installation procedures.

15.1.0 Masonry and Concrete Flush-Mount Construction

In a reinforced concrete construction environment, the conduit and boxes must be embedded in the concrete to achieve a flush surface. Ordinary boxes may be used, but special concrete

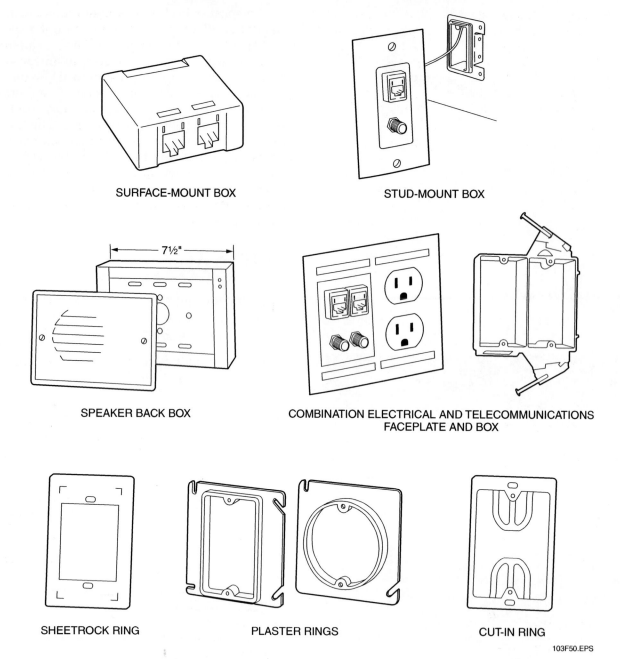

SURFACE-MOUNT BOX

STUD-MOUNT BOX

7½"

SPEAKER BACK BOX

COMBINATION ELECTRICAL AND TELECOMMUNICATIONS
FACEPLATE AND BOX

SHEETROCK RING

PLASTER RINGS

CUT-IN RING

103F50.EPS

Figure 50 ◆ Low-voltage boxes and accessories.

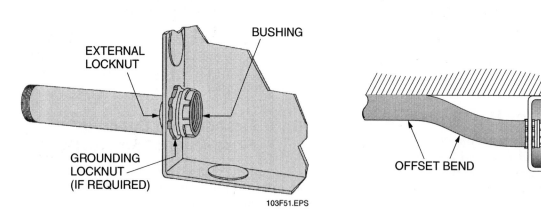

EXTERNAL
LOCKNUT

BUSHING

GROUNDING
LOCKNUT
(IF REQUIRED)

OFFSET BEND

103F51.EPS

103F52.EPS

Figure 51 ◆ Conduit-to-box connection.

Figure 52 ◆ Correct entrance angle.

boxes are preferred and are available in depths up to six inches. These boxes have special ears by which they are nailed to the wooden forms for the concrete. When installing them, stuff the boxes tightly with paper to prevent concrete from seeping in. *Figure 53* shows an installed box.

Flush construction can also be done on existing concrete walls, but this requires chiseling a channel and box opening, anchoring the box and conduit, and then resealing the wall.

To achieve flush construction with masonry walls, the most acceptable method is to work closely with the mason laying the blocks. When the construction blocks reach the convenience outlet elevation, the boxes are made up as shown in *Figure 54*. The figure shows a raised tile ring or box device cover.

103F54.EPS

Figure 54 ◆ Concrete outlet box.

> **NOTE**
>
> Ensure that the box is properly grouted and sealed.

Figure 55 shows the use of a 4-S extension ring installed to bring the box to the masonry surface.

Figure 56 shows a masonry box that needs no extension or deep plaster ring to bring it to the surface.

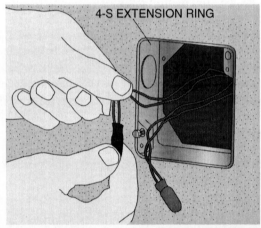

103F55.EPS

Figure 55 ◆ 4-S extension ring used to bring the box to the masonry surface.

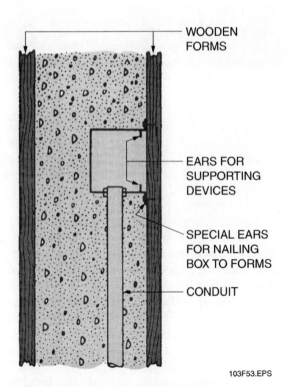

WOODEN FORMS

EARS FOR SUPPORTING DEVICES

SPECIAL EARS FOR NAILING BOX TO FORMS

CONDUIT

103F53.EPS

Figure 53 ◆ Concrete flush-mount installation.

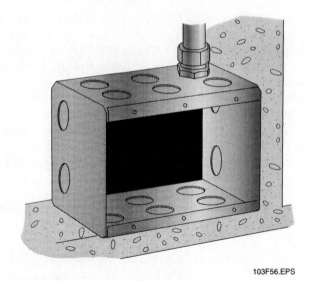

103F56.EPS

Figure 56 ◆ Three-gang switch box.

NOTE

EMT should be installed in the rear knockout of this masonry switch box.

Sections of conduit are then coupled in short (4' or 5') lengths. This is done because it is impractical for the mason to maneuver blocks over 10' sections of conduit.

15.2.0 Metal Stud Environment

Metal stud walls are a popular method of construction for the interior walls of commercial buildings. Metal stud framing consists of relatively thin metal channel studs, usually constructed of galvanized steel and with the same overall dimensions as standard 2 × 4 wooden studs. Wiring in this type of construction is relatively easy when compared to masonry.

EMT conduit is the most common type of raceway specified for metal stud wiring. Metal studs usually have some number of pre-punched holes that can be used to route the conduit. If a pre-punched hole is not located where it needs to be, holes can easily be punched in the metal stud using a hole cutter or knockout punch.

WARNING!

Cutting or punching metal studs can create sharp edges. Avoid contact with these edges, which can result in severe cuts.

Boxes can be secured to the metal stud using self-tapping screws or one of the many types of box supports available. EMT conduit is supported by the metal studs using conduit straps or other approved methods. It is important that the conduit be properly supported to facilitate pulling the conductors through the tubing. Boxes are mounted on the metal studs so that the box will be flush with the finished walls. You must know the finished wall thickness in order to properly secure the boxes to the metal studs. For example, if the finished wall will be ⅝" drywall, then the box must be fastened so that it protrudes ⅝" from the metal stud.

WARNING!

When using a screw gun or cordless drill to mount boxes to studs, keep the hand holding the box away from the gun/drill to avoid injury.

Figure 57 shows several examples of conduit clips, known as caddy-fastening devices, that are used in metal stud environments.

103F57.EPS

Figure 57 ◆ Caddy-fastening devices.

15.3.0 Wood-Frame Environment

At one time, the use of rigid conduit in partitions and ceilings was a laborious and time-consuming operation. Thinwall conduit makes an easier and far quicker job, largely because of the types of fittings that are specially adapted to it.

Figure 58 shows two methods of running thinwall conduit in these locations: boring timbers and notching them. When boring, holes must be drilled large enough for the tubing to be inserted between the studs. The tubing is cut rather short, calling for multiple couplings. EMT can be bowed quite a bit while threading through holes in studs. Boring is the preferred method.

WARNING!

Always wear safety goggles when drilling wood.

NEC Section 300.4 addresses the requirements for preventing physical damage to conductors and cabling in wood members. By keeping the edge of the drilled hole 1¼" from the closest edge of the stud, nails are not likely to penetrate the stud far enough to damage the cables. The building codes provide maximum requirements for bored or notched holes in studs.

The exception in the NEC® permits IMC, RMC, RNC, and EMT to be installed through bored holes or laid-in notches less than 1¼" from the nearest edge without a steel plate or bushing. Also, riser-rated conduit must be used in some applications. Check the specifications for fire ratings when working in a wood-frame environment.

A bearing timber supports floor joists or other weight. Because of its weakening effect upon the structure, notching should be resorted to only where absolutely necessary. Notches should be as narrow as possible and in no case deeper than one-fifth the

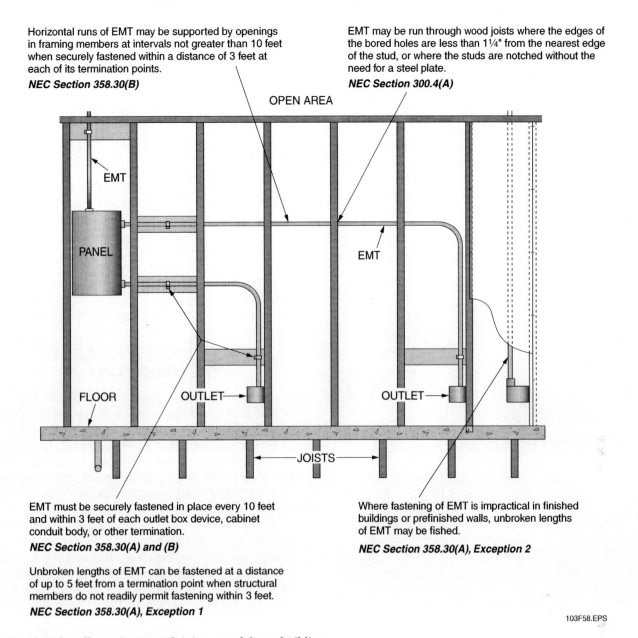

Horizontal runs of EMT may be supported by openings in framing members at intervals not greater than 10 feet when securely fastened within a distance of 3 feet at each of its termination points.
NEC Section 358.30(B)

EMT may be run through wood joists where the edges of the bored holes are less than 1¼" from the nearest edge of the stud, or where the studs are notched without the need for a steel plate.
NEC Section 300.4(A)

OPEN AREA

EMT

PANEL

EMT

FLOOR

OUTLET

OUTLET

JOISTS

EMT must be securely fastened in place every 10 feet and within 3 feet of each outlet box device, cabinet conduit body, or other termination.
NEC Section 358.30(A) and (B)

Unbroken lengths of EMT can be fastened at a distance of up to 5 feet from a termination point when structural members do not readily permit fastening within 3 feet.
NEC Section 358.30(A), Exception 1

Where fastening of EMT is impractical in finished buildings or prefinished walls, unbroken lengths of EMT may be fished.
NEC Section 358.30(A), Exception 2

103F58.EPS

Figure 58 ◆ Installing wire or conduit in a wood-frame building.

stock of the bearing timber. An additional requirement is for the notch to be covered with a steel reinforcement bracket. This bracket aids in retaining the original strength of the timber.

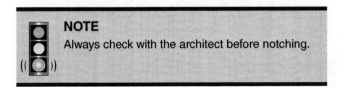

NOTE

Always check with the architect before notching.

15.4.0 Steel Environment

Installations in buildings where steel beams are the structural framework are most often found in industrial buildings and warehouses. This type of construction is typically found in pre-engineered buildings where beams and other supports are pre-cut and pre-drilled so that erection of the building is fast and simple.

The interior of the building will in most cases be unfinished, and the wiring will be supported by the metal beams and **purlins**. Beams and purlins should not be drilled through; consequently, the conduit is supported from the metal beams by anchoring devices designed especially for that purpose. The supports attach to the beams and have clamps to secure the conduit to the structure. All conduit runs should be plumb since they are exposed. Bends should be correct and have a neat and orderly appearance.

Since steel construction usually takes place in warehouses and industrial buildings where load handling and the movement of large and heavy items is common, rigid metal conduit is often required. If several runs of conduit are installed along the same path, strut-type systems are used. These systems are sometimes referred to as Unistrut systems (Unistrut is a manufacturer of these systems). Another manufacturer of strut systems is B-Line. They are very similar. These systems use a channel-type member that can support conduit from the ceiling by using threaded rod supports for the channel, as shown in *Figure 59*. Strut channel can also be secured to masonry walls to support vertical runs of conduit, wireways, and various types of boxes.

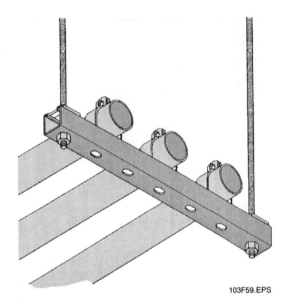

103F59.EPS

Figure 59 ◆ Steel strut system.

15.5.0 Suspended Ceilings

In commercial buildings, it is common to run cabling through the space between the suspended ceiling and the floor or roof above it. Cables may not be laid on the suspended ceiling tiles or its support grid; they must be carried in conduit or wireways approved for the purpose. *Figure 60* shows an example of a cable installation above a suspended ceiling.

If the ceiling space is used as the return air plenum for the air-conditioning system, special requirements apply to the selection of the cable and raceway. For example, only fire-rated (plenum-rated) cable may be used in this application. These requirements are covered in *NEC Section 300.22*.

For a review of the types and construction methods for suspended ceilings, refer to the module entitled *Construction Materials and Methods*.

16.0.0 ◆ OVERVIEW OF CABLE DISTRIBUTION

As previously discussed, the various types of power and low-voltage cable that enter a building commonly come from an underground source such as a maintenance hole or a CEV. Aerial sources, in which the cables are run from utility poles to the building entry point, are also used. *Figure 61* shows an overview of the cable entrance and distribution for a commercial building.

The backbone cable will normally enter a building through pathways made in the exterior wall. In a large commercial building, it is common to have the entrance facility for power and low-voltage cabling in the equipment room (*Figure 62*). From there, it is distributed to the remainder of the

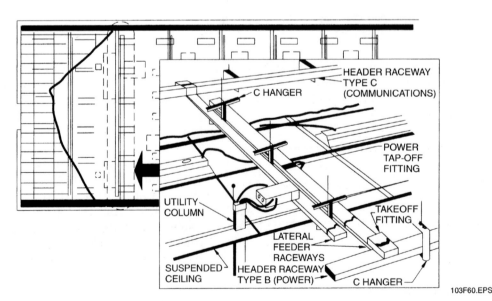

103F60.EPS

Figure 60 ◆ Raceway installed above a suspended ceiling.

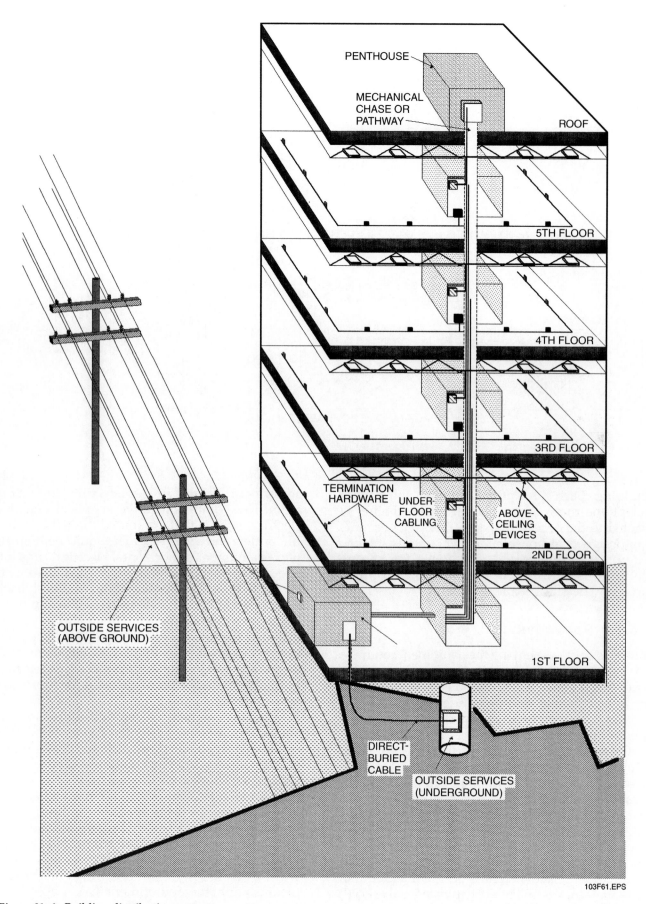

Figure 61 ◆ Building distribution system.

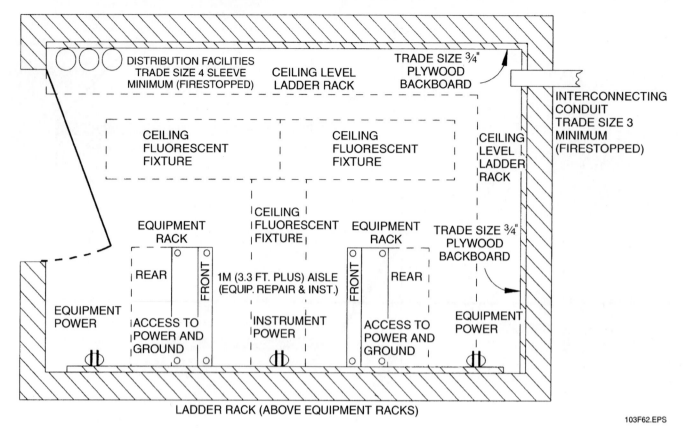

Figure 62 ◆ Telecommunications room layout (top view).

103F62.EPS

building. Each floor of the building will have a telephone room or room from which cabling is routed to the occupied spaces. Equipment rooms are designed to house large components such as equipment cabinets and relay racks, mainframe computers, uninterruptible power supplies, and/or video head-end equipment.

16.1.0 Pathways

Bundles of cables leaving the equipment room are distributed using conduit or wireways, which may travel above a suspended ceiling, through a cellular concrete floor, or under a raised floor. Cables may also be distributed through under-floor or perimeter raceways.

Communication pathways for a typical commercial building are shown in *Figure 63*. Only the first floor and the Nth floor are shown. In actual practice, a separate set of backbone cables would exit the main **cross-connect** in the equipment room in a star fashion and be routed up to an individual telecommunications room on each floor of the building. In this example, two types of backbone cable are shown; one is optical fiber for data and the other is unshielded twisted pair (UTP) cable for voice traffic. For this example, the optical fiber cable is connected to signal conversion

equipment located in the telecommunications room. This equipment converts optical signals to electrical signals that are routed to the horizontal run outlets and vice versa. The equipment **multiplexes** a number of horizontal electrical runs into one pair of fibers due to the high capacity of optical fiber. Thus, the number of fibers in each backbone optical fiber cable depends on the number of multiplexed outlets on each floor plus any fibers included for future system expansion. The number of conductor pairs in the UTP backbone cable depends on the number of outlets on each floor plus any conductor pairs included for future system expansion.

Vertically aligned telecommunications rooms are shown in *Figure 63*. When rooms are aligned one above the other on each floor of a building, sleeves and/or slots are normally used to route vertical backbone cable (*Figure 64*).

In some cases, cable shafts are used when large groups of cables must be routed near the top of the building. In cases where the rooms are not vertically aligned, pathways or conduits are used. Horizontal runs can be through conduits or pathways in walls, floors, and ceilings or through plenums or other environmental air spaces above false ceilings. Elevator shafts are not used for routing communication cables.

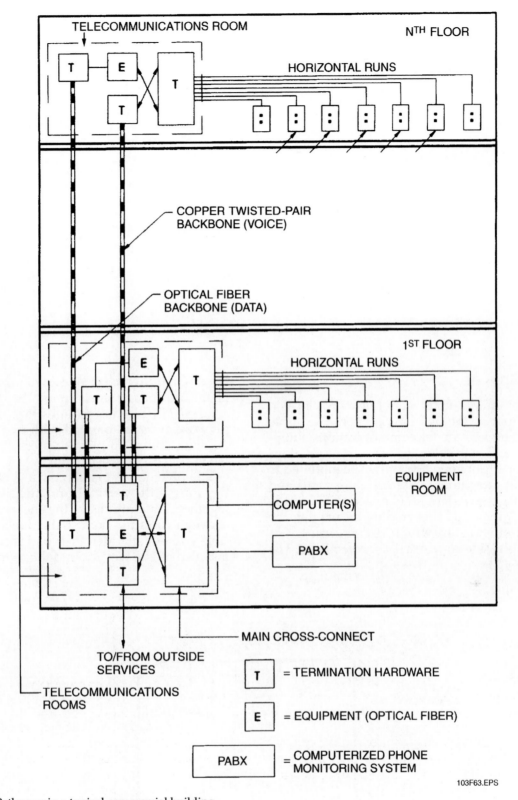

Figure 63 ◆ Pathways in a typical commercial building.

For runs between buildings and other structures, cables that are rated for direct burial should be trench-laid without crossovers and slightly snaked to allow for possible earth settlement, movement, or heaving due to frost action. They should be buried to a depth specified by *NEC Table 300.5* or local code and should be placed on, and covered with, cushions of sand or screened fill to protect the cable jackets from damage due to sharp objects.

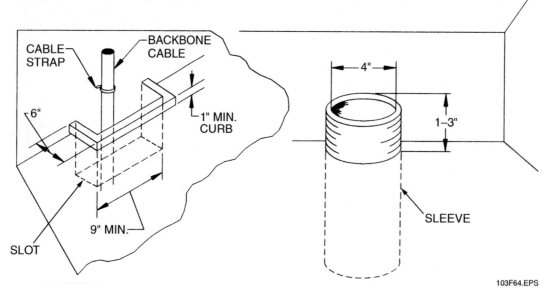

Figure 64 ◆ Typical sleeve and slot sizes.

16.2.0 Spaces

The telecommunications room (*Figure 65*) located on each floor of the building is often a separate room that houses the telecommunications equipment for the floor. Within the telecommunications room, ¾" or 1" plywood boards will be mounted to provide an attachment base for equipment and cable management devices. Plywood with a grade of A/C is preferred. This grading means that the plywood surface on which the equipment is mounted is Grade A, which has no blemishes. The Grade C side, which faces the wall, may have some blemishes and/or small knotholes.

ANSI/TIA/EIA-569 requires that standard A/C plywood must be painted with two coats of fire-resistant paint. Do not use pressure-treated plywood because it resists paint.

The plywood is installed in 4' × 8' sheets, with the long side vertical and the sheets butted together. The bottoms of the sheets are placed 6" above the finished floor so that the tops are accessible without a ladder. Plywood sheets should be installed all the way around the room, if possible.

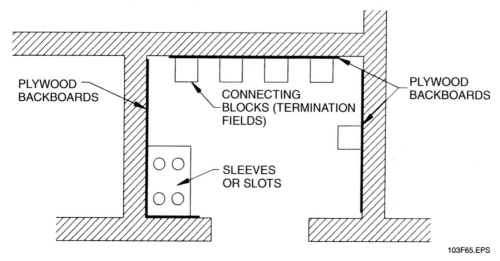

Figure 65 ◆ Typical telecommunications room.

Summary

This module discussed the various types of raceways, boxes, and fittings, including their uses and procedures for installation. The primary purpose of raceways is to house wires and cables used for power distribution, communications, and electronic signal transmission. Raceways provide protection to the wiring and even a means of identifying one type of wire from another when they are run adjacent to each other. This process requires proper planning to allow for current needs, future expansion, and a neat and orderly appearance.

One important lesson to take away from this module is that the NEC® has very specific requirements about the use of conduit, surface raceways, and boxes, including application, bending, fill percentage, and limitations on combining power and low voltage conductors. Never assume anything.

Review Questions

1. In any building exceeding _____ floor(s), ENT must be fire-rated and concealed.
   a. one
   b. two
   c. three
   d. four

2. The lightest duty and most widely used non-flexible metal conduit available for enclosing and protecting cabling and wiring is _____.
   a. electrical metallic tubing
   b. rigid metal conduit
   c. aluminum conduit
   d. plastic-coated GRC

3. Because the wall thickness of _____ is less than that of rigid metal conduit, it is often referred to as thinwall conduit.
   a. intermediate metal conduit
   b. electrical metallic tubing
   c. rigid nonmetallic conduit
   d. galvanized rigid steel conduit

4. The type of conduit that provides the best physical protection for the wire inside is _____.
   a. flexible metal conduit
   b. rigid metal conduit
   c. electrical metallic tubing
   d. intermediate metal conduit

5. Bending IMC is often easier than bending the same size and quantity of rigid metal conduit because IMC has a slightly _____.
   a. larger outside diameter
   b. larger internal diameter
   c. smaller outside diameter
   d. smaller internal diameter

6. Flexible metal conduit _____.
   a. is made from a single strip of steel or aluminum
   b. can be used in wet locations if lead-covered conductors are installed
   c. can be used in underground locations
   d. is available in sizes up to 6" in diameter

7. A Type LB conduit body has the cover on _____.
   a. the left
   b. the right
   c. the back
   d. both sides

8. When conduit is joined to metal boxes, _____ protect the wires from the sharp edges of the conduit.
   a. washers
   b. locknuts
   c. bushings
   d. couplings

9. Sealing fittings are required in conduit runs in locations where the environment contains moisture.
   a. True
   b. False

10. A J-clamp is used to attach _____.
    a. perimeter raceways to a wall
    b. cable to beams
    c. wireway hangers to beams
    d. pancake raceways to a floor

11. Installation specifications for surface metal raceways are covered in _____.
    a. *NEC Article 386*
    b. *NEC Article 388*
    c. *NEC Table 310.16*
    d. *NEC Table 310.18*

12. Surface metal raceway systems are _____.
    a. designed for concealed wiring within walls and partitions
    b. suited for use in wet or damp locations
    c. mainly used for making the transition from a masonry surface to a wood surface
    d. designed for exposed installations on the surface of walls and ceilings

13. Which of the following statements applies when running low-voltage and power conductors?
    a. They may not be run in the same raceway.
    b. They may be run in the same raceway, but must be at least 2" apart.
    c. They may be run in the same raceway, but must be separated by an approved barrier.
    d. If they are run outside a raceway, they must be at least 10' apart.

14. When transporting metal conduit, it is best to _____.
    a. remove your gloves so that you do not contaminate the conduit
    b. remove the thread protection caps so that they do not get lost
    c. place the metal conduit inside a larger raceway to keep it from bending
    d. keep the thread protection caps on to prevent damage to the threads

15. In underground cable installations, a buried conduit through which a cable passes is known as a _____.
    a. maintenance hole
    b. duct
    c. vault
    d. pedestal

16. Pre-punched circular sections that do *not* include a pryout slot are called _____.
    a. concentrics
    b. knockouts
    c. pryouts
    d. pre-cuts

17. Electrical and telecommunications conductors may _____.
    a. never occupy the same box
    b. occupy the same box if they are separated by a partition
    c. occupy the same box if the box is nonmetallic
    d. occupy the same box if the power circuit voltage does not exceed 120 volts

18. In new concrete construction, it is common practice to place the boxes in the forms before the concrete is poured.
    a. True
    b. False

19. When drilling holes in wood studs for cables, the edge of the drilled hole should be _____ from the nearest edge of the stud.
    a. ¾"
    b. 1"
    c. 1¼"
    d. 1½"

20. If you plan to use standard A/C plywood as a backboard in a telecommunications room, it should _____.
    a. be painted with two coats of fire-resistant paint
    b. not be painted
    c. be primed with shellac first
    d. be painted with two coats of latex paint.

Ken Nieto, Installation and Operations Manager

PLA Systems
New Orleans, LA

As a young man, Ken Nieto was fascinated with electronics and communications. He was able to turn this fascination into a rewarding career by starting with a good education. As his career progressed, he maintained a focus on the future and set career goals to get him where he wanted to be.

How did you get started in the electronics industry?
When I was young, I used to build radio kits as a hobby. From this experience, I learned basic electronics, circuit analysis, and soldering. I got involved with the audio-visual club while I was in high school. My electronics knowledge enabled me to troubleshoot and repair the school's A/V equipment. I also obtained a first class FCC license while I was still in community college. A first class license qualifies a person to operate a radio or TV station. Later in life, I was able to get work doing maintenance for radio stations because of my FCC license.

What types of training have you had?
After high school, I attended community college and received an associates degree in electrical engineering. I have taken numerous technical courses offered by industry trade associations and manufacturers. That's the only way to stay current with the technology and expand your knowledge base. I have also taken financial software and accounting courses to help prepare me to take on a management role. I hold the Level IV NICET (National Institute for Certification in Engineering Technologies) certification in Fire Alarm Systems and the Level III NICET certification in Low-Voltage Communications.

What kinds of work have you done in your career?
After I received my associates degree, I went to work for a popular New Orleans hotel as their A/V technician. Among the things I did there was to set up the sound for entertainers in the hotel's night club. I once set up the sound system for B. B. King, as well as other well-known entertainers of the time. I had always wanted to work on large sound systems, so when they built the New Orleans Super Dome, I arranged to get a job as a sound system installer with Educational Electronics. I worked for that company for 20 years, performing all types of work from installer, technician, and system designer to

operations manager. Later, I spent five years at Simplex, where I was manager of installation and service for fire, security, and time recording systems.

In my present job, I am Installation and Operations Manager for PLA systems, which is a technical organization doing integrated electronic systems for life safety, communications, and security in various types of buildings. In this job, I plan and coordinate all the company's installation work and supervise the installers.

What factors have contributed most to your success?
I have a very strong interest in the technology, which I have had pretty much all my life. I think this commitment is necessary to succeed in this business. I am very interested in the growing trend toward system integration, and my company is very involved in system integration, which makes my job more interesting and technically challenging.

What advice would you give to someone just entering the field?
My strongest advice is to maintain a lifelong commitment to education. Decide where you want your career to go and develop a professional growth strategy that will get you there. Also, keep up to date with technology. This will help you be prepared for the exciting changes that will continue to occur in the industry.

Do you have an interesting career-related fact or accomplishment to share?
In 1998, I was one of only four people in the U.S. with NICET Level III Low-Voltage Communications certification. I have also designed professional sound systems for many large entertainment venues in the Gulf Coast area. I mentioned before that I worked on the original sound system for the Super Dome. When the sound system was replaced in 1997, my company partnered with Bose on the project, and I did the sound system design and installation.

Trade Terms Introduced in This Module

Approved: Meeting the requirements of an appropriate regulatory agency.

Bonding conductor: A wire used to make a continuous grounding path between equipment and ground.

Cable trays: Rigid structures used to support wiring and cabling.

Conductors: Wires or cables used to carry current.

Conduit: A round raceway, similar to pipe, that houses conductors.

Continuity: The existence of an uninterrupted circuit.

Cross-connect: A facility for connecting cable runs, subsystems, and equipment using patch cords or jumper cables.

Exposed location: Not permanently closed in by the structure or finish of a building, and able to be installed or removed without damage to the structure.

Fire-rated: Constructed to meet code requirements for fire resistance in hours or fractions of an hour.

Ground: A conducting connection between an electrical circuit or equipment and the earth or another conducting body.

Kick: A bend in a piece of conduit, usually less than 45 degrees, made to change the direction of the conduit.

Multiplex: Combining two or more signals into a single wave from which either of the two original signals can be recovered.

Pathway: A device or group of devices that allow the installation of cables and conductors between building spaces. Also, the vertical and horizontal route of the cable.

Purlin: A horizontal framing member supporting the rafters of a roof.

Raceways: Enclosed channels designed expressly for holding wires, cables, or busbars, with additional functions as permitted in the NEC®.

Splice: The connection of two or more conductors.

Underwriters Laboratories (UL): An agency that evaluates and approves electrical components and equipment.

Additional Resources

This module is intended to be a thorough resource for task training. The following reference works are suggested for further study. These are optional materials for continued education rather than for task training.

Benfield Conduit Bending Manual, 2nd Edition, 1993. Overland Park, KS: EC&M Books.

National Electrical Code® Handbook, Latest Edition. Quincy, MA: National Fire Protection Association.

Telecommunications Cabling Installation Manual, 3rd Edition. Tampa, FL: BiCSi.

Telecommunications Distribution Methods Manual, 10th Edition. Tampa, FL: BiCSi.

Figure Credits

Carlon	103F01, 103F02A
The MaxCell Group	103F02B
Topaz Publications, Inc.	103F05, 103F06, 103F10, 103F14–103F21, 103F26, 103F46, 103F49, 103SA01–103SA04, 103SA06
BICSI	103F32, 103F43–103F45, 103F60, 103F62–103F65
Panduit Corporation	103F33, 103SA05
Tim Ely	103SA07

The NCCER makes every effort to keep these textbooks up-to-date and free of technical errors. We appreciate your help in this process. If you have an idea for improving this textbook, or if you find an error, a typographical mistake, or an inaccuracy in NCCER's Contren® textbooks, please write us, using this form or a photocopy. Be sure to include the exact module number, page number, a detailed description, and the correction, if applicable. Your input will be brought to the attention of the Technical Review Committee. Thank you for your assistance.

Instructors – If you found that additional materials were necessary in order to teach this module effectively, please let us know so that we may include them in the Equipment/Materials list in the Instructor's Guide.

Write: Product Development and Revision
National Center for Construction Education and Research
P.O. Box 141104, Gainesville, FL 32614-1104

Fax: 352-334-0932

E-mail: curriculum@nccer.org

Craft _____ Module Name _____

Copyright Date _____ Module Number _____ Page Number(s) _____

Description _____

_____

_____

_____

(Optional) Correction _____

_____

_____

(Optional) Your Name and Address _____

_____

_____

Fasteners and Anchors

COURSE MAP

This course map shows all of the modules in the first level of the *Electronic Systems Technician* curriculum. The suggested training order begins at the bottom and proceeds up. Skill levels increase as you advance on the course map. The local Training Program Sponsor may adjust the training order.

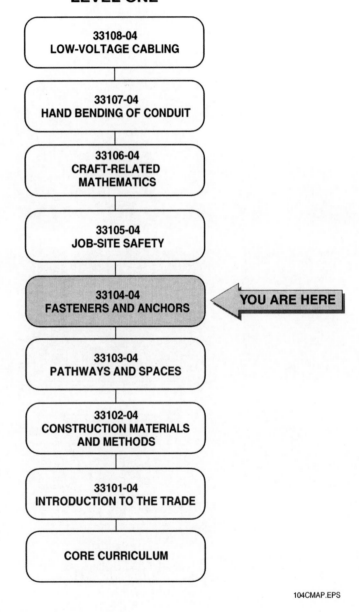

ELECTRONIC SYSTEMS TECHNICIAN
LEVEL ONE

33108-04
LOW-VOLTAGE CABLING

33107-04
HAND BENDING OF CONDUIT

33106-04
CRAFT-RELATED
MATHEMATICS

33105-04
JOB-SITE SAFETY

33104-04
FASTENERS AND ANCHORS

YOU ARE HERE

33103-04
PATHWAYS AND SPACES

33102-04
CONSTRUCTION MATERIALS
AND METHODS

33101-04
INTRODUCTION TO THE TRADE

CORE CURRICULUM

104CMAP.EPS

1.0.0 **INTRODUCTION** 4.1

2.0.0 **THREADED FASTENERS** 4.1

    2.1.0   Thread Standards 4.1

    2.1.1   *Thread Series* 4.2

    2.1.2   *Thread Classes* 4.2

    2.1.3   *Thread Identification* 4.2

    2.1.4   *Grade Markings* 4.3

    2.2.0   Bolt and Screw Types 4.3

    2.2.1   *Machine Screws* 4.3

    2.2.2   *Machine Bolts* 4.4

    2.2.3   *Cap Screws* 4.5

    2.2.4   *Setscrews* 4.6

    2.2.5   *Stud Bolts* 4.6

    2.3.0   Nuts 4.6

    2.3.1   *Jam Nuts* 4.8

    2.3.2   *Castellated, Slotted, and Self-Locking Nuts* 4.8

    2.3.3   *Acorn Nuts* 4.8

    2.3.4   *Wing Nuts* 4.8

    2.4.0   Washers 4.8

    2.4.1   *Lock Washers* 4.9

    2.4.2   *Flat and Fender Washers* 4.9

    2.5.0   Installing Fasteners 4.9

    2.5.1   *Torque Tightening* 4.9

    2.5.2   *Installing Threaded Fasteners* 4.11

3.0.0 **NON-THREADED FASTENERS** 4.13

    3.1.0   Retainer Fasteners 4.13

    3.2.0   Keys 4.14

    3.3.0   Pin Fasteners 4.14

    3.3.1   *Dowel Pins* 4.15

    3.3.2   *Taper and Spring Pins* 4.15

    3.3.3   *Cotter Pins* 4.15

    3.4.0   Blind/Pop Rivets 4.16

    3.5.0   Tie Wraps 4.17

4.0.0 **SPECIAL THREADED FASTENERS** 4.17

    4.1.0   Eye Bolts 4.18

    4.2.0   Anchor Bolts 4.18

    4.3.0   J-Bolts 4.18

5.0.0   **SCREWS** 4.19

    5.1.0   Wood Screws 4.19

    5.2.0   Lag Screws and Shields 4.19

    5.3.0   Concrete/Masonry Screws 4.20

    5.4.0   Thread-Forming and Thread-Cutting Screws 4.20

    5.5.0   Deck Screws 4.21

    5.6.0   Drywall Screws 4.21

    5.7.0   Drive Screws 4.22

6.0.0   **HAMMER-DRIVEN PINS AND STUDS** 4.22

7.0.0   **POWDER-ACTUATED TOOLS AND FASTENERS** 4.22

8.0.0   **MECHANICAL ANCHORS** 4.25

    8.1.0   One-Step Anchors 4.25

    8.1.1   Wedge Anchors 4.25

    8.1.2   Stud Bolt Anchors 4.25

    8.1.3   Sleeve Anchors 4.25

    8.1.4   One-Piece Anchors 4.25

    8.1.5   Hammer-Set Anchors 4.26

    8.1.6   Sammy® Anchors 4.26

    8.2.0   Bolt Anchors 4.26

    8.2.1   Drop-In Anchors 4.26

    8.2.2   Single- and Double-Expansion Anchors 4.26

    8.3.0   Screw Anchors 4.27

    8.4.0   Self-Drilling Anchors 4.27

    8.5.0   Guidelines for Drilling Anchor Holes in
            Hardened Concrete or Masonry 4.28

    8.6.0   Hollow-Wall Anchors 4.28

    8.6.1   Toggle Bolts 4.28

    8.6.2   Sleeve-Type Wall Anchors 4.30

    8.6.3   Wallboard Anchors 4.30

    8.6.4   Metal Drive-In Anchors 4.30

9.0.0   **EPOXY ANCHORING SYSTEMS** 4.30

SUMMARY 4.32

REVIEW QUESTIONS 4.33

PROFILE IN SUCCESS 4.34

GLOSSARY 4.35

APPENDIX, Mechanical Anchors and Their Uses 4.36

REFERENCES & ACKNOWLEDGMENTS 4.37

Figures

Figure 1   Threaded fasteners 4.2

Figure 2   Screw thread designations .4.2

Figure 3   Grade markings for steel bolts and screws 4.4

Figure 4   Machine screws 4.5

Figure 5   Machine bolts 4.5

Figure 6   Cap screws 4.5

Figure 7   Setscrews 4.6

Figure 8   Stud bolt 4.6

Figure 9   Nuts 4.7

Figure 10   Nut finishes 4.7

Figure 11   Jam nut 4.8

Figure 12   Castellated, slotted, and self-locking nuts 4.8

Figure 13   Acorn nut 4.8

Figure 14   Wing nut 4.8

Figure 15   Washers 4.9

Figure 16   Fastener hole guide chart 4.10

Figure 17   Torque wrenches 4.11

Figure 18   Torque value chart 4.12

Figure 19   Safety-wired fasteners 4.13

Figure 20   Retainer fasteners (rings) 4.14

Figure 21   Keys 4.14

Figure 22   Pin fasteners 4.15

Figure 23   Dowel pins 4.15

Figure 24   Taper and spring pins 4.15

Figure 25   Cotter pins 4.16

Figure 26   Blind rivet installation 4.16

Figure 27   Rivet gun 4.16

Figure 28   Joining parts 4.17

Figure 29   Properly installed blind rivets 4.17

Figure 30   Tie wraps 4.17

Figure 31   Eye bolts 4.18

Figure 32   Anchor bolt 4.18

Figure 33   Typical J-bolt 4.18

Figure 34   Wood screws 4.19

Figure 35   Lag screws and shields 4.20

Figure 36   Concrete screws 4.20

Figure 37   Thread-forming screws 4.20

Figure 38   Thread-cutting screws 4.21

Figure 39   Typical deck screws 4.22

Figure 40   Drywall screws 4.22

Figure 41   Drive screws 4.22

Figure 42   Hammer-driven pins and installation tool 4.22

Figure 43   Powder-actuated installation tool and fasteners 4.23

Figure 44   One-step anchors 4.25

Figure 45   Bolt anchors 4.26

Figure 46   Screw anchors and screws 4.27

Figure 47   Self-drilling anchor 4.27

Figure 48   Installing an anchor bolt in hardened concrete 4.28

Figure 49   Toggle bolts 4.29

Figure 50   Sleeve-type, wallboard, and metal
             drive-in anchors 4.30

Figure 51   Fastener anchored in epoxy 4.31

Fasteners and Anchors

Objectives

When you have completed this module, you will be able to do the following:

1. Identify and explain the use of threaded fasteners.
2. Identify and explain the use of non-threaded fasteners.
3. Identify and explain the use of anchors.
4. Demonstrate the correct applications for fasteners and anchors.
5. Install fasteners and anchors.

Recommended Prerequisites

Core Curriculum; Electronic Systems Technician Level One, Modules 33101-04 through 33103-04

Required Trainee Materials

1. Paper and pencil
2. Appropriate personal protective equipment

1.0.0 ◆ INTRODUCTION

Fasteners are used to assemble and install many different types of equipment, parts, and materials. Fasteners include screws, bolts, nuts, pins, clamps, retainers, tie wraps, rivets, and **keys**. You need to be familiar with the many different types of fasteners in order to identify, select, and properly install the correct fastener for a specific application.

The two primary categories of fasteners are threaded fasteners and non-threaded fasteners.

Within each of these two categories, there are many different types and sizes of fasteners. Each type of fastener is designed for a specific application. The kind of fastener used for a job may be listed in the project specifications, or you may have to select an appropriate fastener.

Failure of fasteners can result in a number of different problems. To perform quality work, it is important to use the correct type and size of fastener for the particular job. It is equally important that the fastener be installed properly.

2.0.0 ◆ THREADED FASTENERS

Threaded fasteners are the most commonly used type of fastener. Many threaded fasteners are assembled with nuts and washers. The following sections describe standard threads used on threaded fasteners, as well as different types of bolts, screws, nuts, and washers. *Figure 1* shows several types of threaded fasteners.

2.1.0 Thread Standards

Many different types of threads are used for manufacturing fasteners. The different types of threads are designed to be used for different jobs. Threads used on fasteners are manufactured to industry-established standards for uniformity. The most common **thread standard** is the Unified standard, sometimes referred to as the American standard. Unified standards are used to establish thread series and classes.

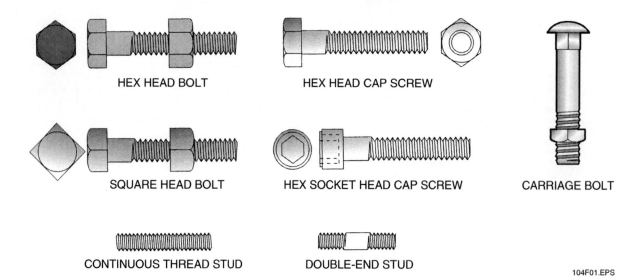

HEX HEAD BOLT   HEX HEAD CAP SCREW

SQUARE HEAD BOLT   HEX SOCKET HEAD CAP SCREW   CARRIAGE BOLT

CONTINUOUS THREAD STUD   DOUBLE-END STUD

104F01.EPS

Figure 1 ◆ Threaded fasteners.

2.1.1 Thread Series

Unified standards are established for three series of threads, depending on the number of threads per inch for a certain diameter of fastener. These three series are:

- *Unified National Coarse (UNC) thread* – Used for bolts, screws, nuts, and other general purposes. Fasteners with UNC threads are commonly used for rapid assembly or disassembly of parts and where corrosion or slight damage may occur.
- *Unified National Fine (UNF) thread* – Used for bolts, screws, nuts, and other applications where a finer thread for a tighter fit is desired.
- *Unified National Extra Fine (UNEF) thread* – Used on thin-walled tubes, nuts, **ferrules**, and couplings.

2.1.2 Thread Classes

The Unified standards also establish **thread classes**. Classes 1A, 2A, and 3A apply to external threads only. Classes 1B, 2B, and 3B apply to internal threads only. Thread classes are distinguished from each other by the amounts of **tolerance** provided. Classes 3A and 3B provide a minimum **clearance** and classes 1A and 1B provide a maximum clearance.

Classes 2A and 2B are the most commonly used. Classes 3A and 3B are used when close tolerances are needed. Classes 1A and 1B are used where quick and easy assembly is needed and a large tolerance is acceptable.

2.1.3 Thread Identification

Thread identification is done using a standard method. *Figure 2* shows how screw threads are designated for a common fastener.

- *Nominal size* – The nominal size is the approximate diameter of the fastener.
- *Number of threads per inch (TPI)* – The TPI is standard for all diameters.
- *Thread series symbol* – The Unified standard thread type (UNC, UNF, or UNEF).
- *Thread class symbol* – The closeness of fit between the bolt threads and nut threads.
- *Left-hand thread symbol* – Specified by the symbol LH. Unless threads are specified with the LH symbol, the threads are right-hand threads.

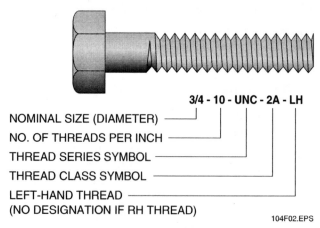

3/4 - 10 - UNC - 2A - LH

NOMINAL SIZE (DIAMETER) ———
NO. OF THREADS PER INCH ———
THREAD SERIES SYMBOL ———
THREAD CLASS SYMBOL ———
LEFT-HAND THREAD ———
(NO DESIGNATION IF RH THREAD)

104F02.EPS

Figure 2 ◆ Screw thread designations.

2.1.4 Grade Markings

Special markings on the head of a bolt or screw can be used to determine the quality of the fastener. The **Society of Automotive Engineers (SAE)** and the **American Society for Testing and Materials (ASTM) International** have developed the standards for these markings. These grade or line markings for steel bolts and screws are shown in *Figure 3*.

Generally, the higher-quality steel fasteners have a greater number of marks on the head. If the head is unmarked, the fastener is usually considered to be made of mild steel (having low carbon content).

2.2.0 Bolt and Screw Types

Bolts and screws are made in many different sizes and shapes and from a variety of materials. They are usually identified by the head type or other special characteristics. The following sections describe several different types of bolts and screws.

2.2.1 Machine Screws

Machine screws are used for general assembly work. They come in a variety of types with slotted or recessed heads. Machine screws are generally available in diameters ranging from 0" (0.060") to ½" (0.500"). The length of machine screws typically varies from ⅛" to 3". Machine screws are also manufactured in metric sizes. *Figure 4* shows different types of machine screws.

As shown, the heads of machine screws are made in different shapes and with slots made to fit various kinds of manual and power tool screwdrivers. Flat-head screws are used in a countersunk hole and tightened so that the head is flush with the surface. Oval-head screws are also used in a countersunk hole in applications where a more decorative finish is desired. Pan and round-head screws are general-purpose fastening screws. Fillister, hex socket, and TORX® socket screws are typically used in confined space applications on

STEEL BOLTS & SCREWS

GRADE MARKING	SPECIFICATION	MATERIAL
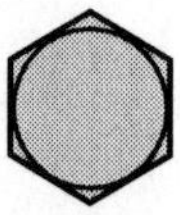	SAE-GRADE 0	STEEL
	SAE-GRADE 1 ASTM-A 307	LOW CARBON STEEL
	SAE-GRADE 2	LOW CARBON STEEL
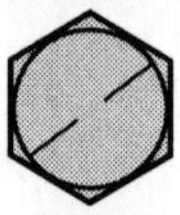	SAE-GRADE 3	MEDIUM CARBON STEEL, COLD WORKED
 A 449	SAE-GRADE 5	MEDIUM CARBON STEEL, QUENCHED AND TEMPERED
	ASTM-A 449	
 A 325	ASTM-A 325	MEDIUM CARBON STEEL, QUENCHED AND TEMPERED
 BB	ASTM-A 354 GRADE BB	LOW ALLOY STEEL, QUENCHED AND TEMPERED
 BC	ASTM-A 354 GRADE BC	LOW ALLOY STEEL, QUENCHED AND TEMPERED
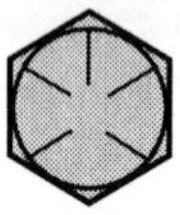	SAE-GRADE 7	MEDIUM CARBON ALLOY STEEL, QUENCHED AND TEMPERED ROLL THREADED AFTER HEAT TREATMENT
	SAE-GRADE 8	MEDIUM CARBON ALLOY STEEL, QUENCHED AND TEMPERED
	ASTM-A 354 GRADE BD	ALLOY STEEL, QUENCHED AND TEMPERED
 A 490	ASTM-A 490	ALLOY STEEL, QUENCHED AND TEMPERED

ASTM SPECIFICATIONS
   A 307 - LOW CARBON STEEL EXTERNALLY AND INTERNALLY THREADED STANDARD FASTENERS.
   A 325 - HIGH STRENGTH STEEL BOLTS FOR STRUCTURAL STEEL JOINTS, INCLUDING SUITABLE
      NUTS AND PLAIN HARDENED WASHERS.
   A 449 - QUENCHED AND TEMPERED STEEL BOLTS AND STUDS.
   A 354 - QUENCHED AND TEMPERED ALLOY STEEL BOLTS AND STUDS WITH SUITABLE NUTS.
   A 490 - HIGH STRENGTH ALLOY STEEL BOLTS FOR STRUCTURAL STEEL JOINTS, INCLUDING
      SUITABLE NUTS AND PLAIN HARDENED WASHERS.
SAE SPECIFICATION
   J 429 - MECHANICAL AND QUALITY REQUIREMENTS FOR THREADED FASTENERS.

104F03.EPS

Figure 3 ◆ Grade markings for steel bolts and screws.

machined assemblies that need a finished appearance. They are often installed in a recessed hole. Truss screws are a low-profile screw generally used without a washer. To prevent damage when tightening and removing machine screws (regardless of head type), make sure to use a screwdriver or power tool bit with the proper tip to drive them.

2.2.2 Machine Bolts

Machine bolts (*Figure 5*) are generally used to assemble parts where close tolerances are not required. Machine bolts have square or hexagonal heads and are generally available in diameters ranging from ¼" to 3". The length of machine bolts typically varies from ½" to 30". Nuts used with

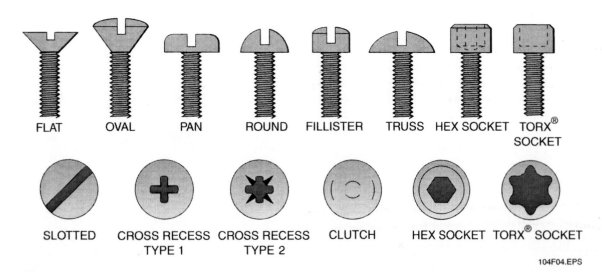

FLAT OVAL PAN ROUND FILLISTER TRUSS HEX SOCKET TORX® SOCKET

SLOTTED CROSS RECESS TYPE 1 CROSS RECESS TYPE 2 CLUTCH HEX SOCKET TORX® SOCKET

104F04.EPS

Figure 4 ◆ Machine screws.

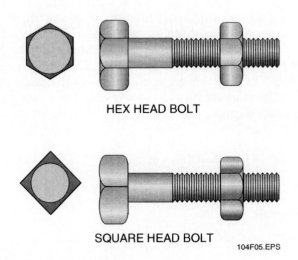

HEX HEAD BOLT

SQUARE HEAD BOLT

104F05.EPS

Figure 5 ◆ Machine bolts.

machine bolts are similar in shape to the bolt heads. The nuts are usually purchased at the same time as the bolts.

2.2.3 Cap Screws

Cap screws are often used on high-quality assemblies requiring a finished appearance. The cap screw passes through a clearance hole in one of the assembly parts and screws into a threaded hole in the other part. The clamping action occurs by tightening the cap screw.

Cap screws (*Figure 6*) are made to close tolerances and are provided with a machined or semi-finished bearing surface under the head. They are normally made in coarse and fine thread series and in diameters from ¼" to 2". Lengths may range from ⅜" to 10". Metric sizes are also available.

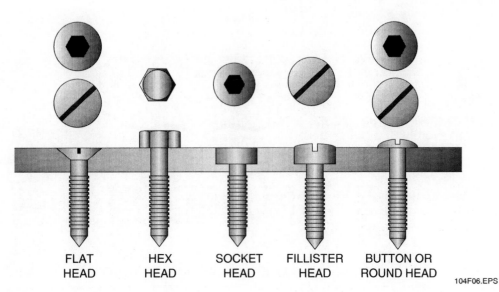

FLAT HEAD HEX HEAD SOCKET HEAD FILLISTER HEAD BUTTON OR ROUND HEAD

104F06.EPS

Figure 6 ◆ Cap screws.

2.2.4 Setscrews

Heat-treated steel is normally used to make set-screws. Common uses of setscrews include preventing pulleys from slipping on shafts, holding collars in place on shafts, and holding shafts in place. The head style and point style are typically used to classify setscrews. *Figure 7* shows several setscrew heads and point styles.

2.2.5 Stud Bolts

Stud bolts (*Figure 8*) are headless bolts that are threaded over the entire length of the bolt or for a length on both ends of the bolt. One end of the stud bolt is screwed into a tapped hole. The part to be clamped is placed over the remaining portion of the stud, and a nut and washer are screwed on to clamp the two parts together. Other stud bolts have machine-screw threads on one end and lag-screw threads on the other so that they can be screwed into wood.

2.3.0 Nuts

Most nuts used with threaded fasteners (*Figure 9*) are hexagonal or square. They are usually used with bolts having the same shape head.

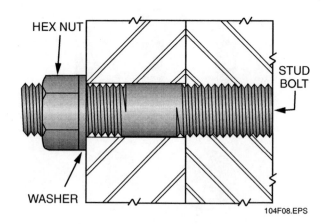

Figure 8 ◆ Stud bolt.

Nuts are typically classified as regular, semi-finished, or finished. The only machining done on regular nuts is to the threads. In addition to the threads, semi-finished nuts are also machined on the bearing face. Machining the bearing face makes a truer surface for fitting the washer. The only difference between semi-finished and finished nuts is that finished nuts are made to closer tolerances.

The standard machine screw nut has a regular finish. Regular and semi-finished nuts are shown in *Figure 10*.

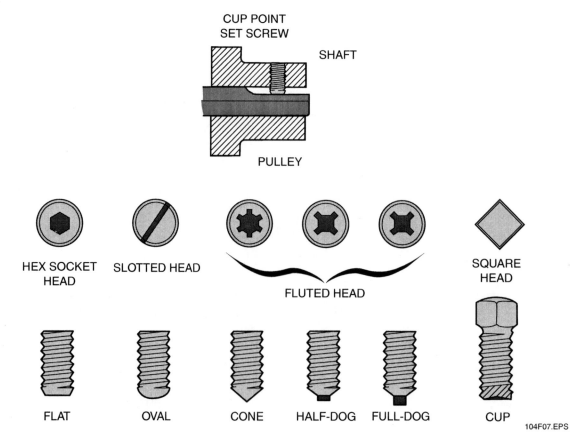

Figure 7 ◆ Setscrews.

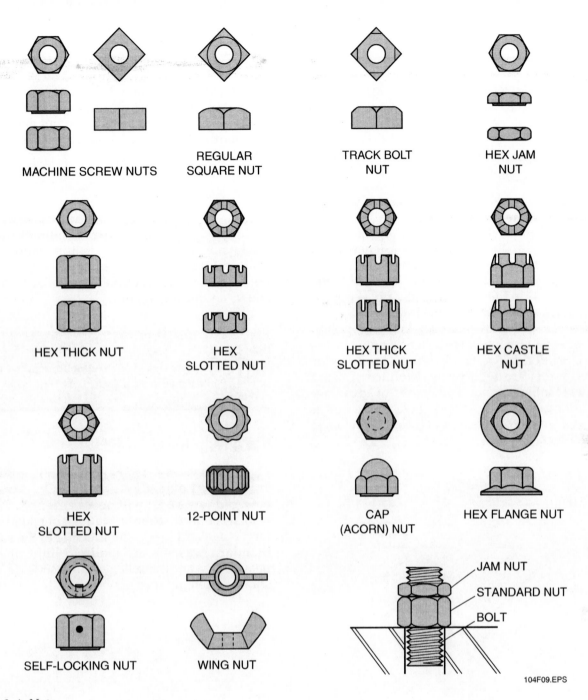

MACHINE SCREW NUTS

REGULAR
SQUARE NUT

TRACK BOLT
NUT

HEX JAM
NUT

HEX THICK NUT

HEX
SLOTTED NUT

HEX THICK
SLOTTED NUT

HEX CASTLE
NUT

HEX
SLOTTED NUT

12-POINT NUT

CAP
(ACORN) NUT

HEX FLANGE NUT

SELF-LOCKING NUT

WING NUT

JAM NUT
STANDARD NUT
BOLT

104F09.EPS

Figure 9 ◆ Nuts.

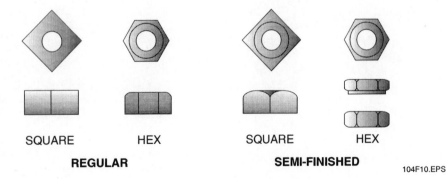

SQUARE

HEX

SQUARE

HEX

REGULAR

SEMI-FINISHED

104F10.EPS

Figure 10 ◆ Nut finishes.

2.3.1 Jam Nuts

A jam nut is used to lock a standard nut in place. A jam nut is a thin nut installed on top of the standard nut. *Figure 11* shows an example of a jam nut installation. Note that a regular nut can also be used as a jam nut.

2.3.2 Castellated, Slotted, and Self-Locking Nuts

Castellated (castle) and slotted nuts are slotted across the flat part of the nut. They are used with specially manufactured bolts in applications where little or no loosening of the fastener can be tolerated. After the nut has been tightened, a cotter pin is fitted in through a hole in the bolt and one set of slots in the nut. The cotter pin keeps the nut from loosening under working conditions.

Self-locking nuts are also used in many applications where loosening of the fastener cannot be tolerated. Self-locking nuts are designed with nylon inserts, or they are deliberately deformed in such a manner that they cannot work loose. An advantage of self-locking nuts is that no hole in the bolt is needed. *Figure 12* shows typical castellated, slotted, and self-locking nuts.

2.3.3 Acorn Nuts

Acorn (cap) nuts are used when appearance is important, or exposed, sharp thread edges on the fastener must be avoided. The acorn nut tightens on the bolt and covers the ends of the threads. The tightening capability of an acorn nut is limited by the depth of the nut. *Figure 13* shows a typical acorn nut.

2.3.4 Wing Nuts

Wing nuts are designed to allow rapid loosening and tightening of the fastener without the need for a wrench. They are used in applications where limited **torque** is required and where frequent adjustments and service are necessary. *Figure 14* shows a typical wing nut.

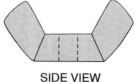

> **NOTE**
> Wing nuts should be used for applications where hand tightening is sufficient.

2.4.0 Washers

There are several different types and sizes of washers. They fit over a bolt or screw to provide an enlarged surface for bolt heads and nuts. Washers also serve to distribute the fastener load over a larger area and to prevent marring of the surfaces. Standard washers are made in light, medium, heavy-duty, and extra heavy-duty series. *Figure 15* shows different types of washers.

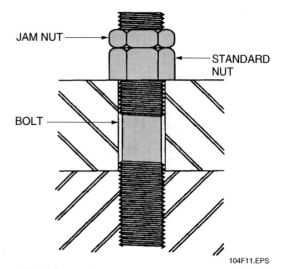

JAM NUT

STANDARD NUT

BOLT

104F11.EPS

Figure 11 ◆ Jam nut.

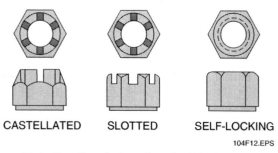

CASTELLATED   SLOTTED   SELF-LOCKING

104F12.EPS

Figure 12 ◆ Castellated, slotted, and self-locking nuts.

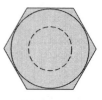 

TOP VIEW   SIDE VIEW

104F13.EPS

Figure 13 ◆ Acorn nut.

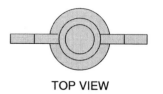

TOP VIEW   SIDE VIEW

104F14.EPS

Figure 14 ◆ Wing nut.

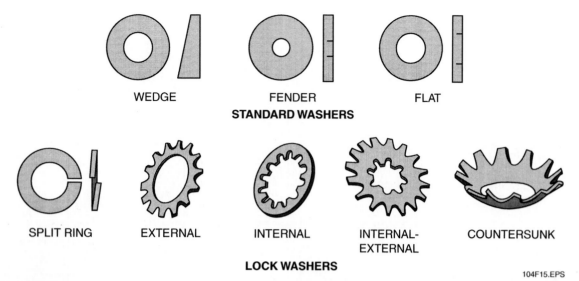

WEDGE   FENDER   FLAT

STANDARD WASHERS

SPLIT RING EXTERNAL INTERNAL INTERNAL- COUNTERSUNK
             EXTERNAL

LOCK WASHERS

104F15.EPS

Figure 15 ◆ Washers.

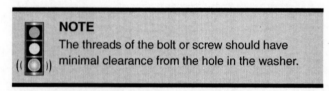

NOTE

The threads of the bolt or screw should have minimal clearance from the hole in the washer.

2.4.1 Lock Washers

Lock washers are designed to keep bolts or nuts from working loose. There are various types of lock washers for different applications.

- *Split-ring* – Commonly used with bolts and cap screws.
- *External (star)* – Used for the greatest resistance.
- *Internal* – Used with small screws.
- *Internal-external* – Used for oversized mounting holes.
- *Countersunk* – Used with flat or oval-head screws.

2.4.2 Flat and Fender Washers

Flat washers are used under bolts or nuts to spread the load over a larger area and protect the surface. Common flat washers are made to fit bolt or screw sizes ranging from No. 6 up to 1" with outside diameters ranging from ⅜" to 2".

Fender washers are wide-surfaced washers made to bridge oversized holes or other wide clearances to keep bolts or nuts from pulling through the material being fastened. They are flat washers that have a larger diameter and surface area than regular washers. They may also be thinner than a regular washer. Fender washers are typically made to fit bolt or screw sizes ranging from ³⁄₁₆" to ½" with outside diameters ranging from ¾" to 2".

2.5.0 Installing Fasteners

Different types of fasteners require different installation techniques. However, all installations require knowing the proper installation methods, tightening sequence, and torque specifications for the type of fastener being used. Some bolts and nuts require that special safety wires or pins be installed to keep them from working loose.

Most fastener manufacturers provide charts that specify the size hole that should be drilled into the base material for use with each of their products. *Figure 16* is an example of such a chart. The charts typically show the proper size drill bit to use if it is necessary to first drill and tap holes for use with machine bolts, screws, or other threaded fasteners. They also show the proper size drill bit to use for drilling pilot holes used with metal and wood screws. Various kinds of screws are described in detail later in this module.

2.5.1 Torque Tightening

To properly tighten a threaded fastener, two primary factors must be considered:

- The strength of the fastener material
- The degree to which the fastener is tightened

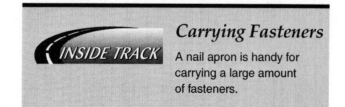

Carrying Fasteners

A nail apron is handy for carrying a large amount of fasteners.

DRILL THIS SIZE HOLE		To Tap For This Size Bolt or Screw	For This Size Wood Screw Pilot in Hard Wood
Drill Size	Dec. Equiv.		
60	.0400		
59	.0410		
58	.0420		
57	.0430		
56	.0465	0 x 80	
3/64	.0469		
55	.0520		
54	.0550	1 x 56	No. 3
53	.0595	1 x 64-72	
1/16	.0625		
52	.0635		No. 4
51	.0670		
50	.0700	2 x 56-64	
49	.0730		No. 5
48	.0760		
5/64	.0781		
47	.0785	3 x 48	No. 6
46	.0810		
45	.0820	3 x 56	
44	.0860	4 x 36	No. 7
43	.0890	4 x 40	
42	.0935	4 x 48	
3/32	.0937		
41	.0960		
40	.0980	5 x 36	No. 8
39	.0995		
38	.1015	5 x 40	
37	.1040	5 x 44	No. 9
36	.1069		
7/64	.1094		
35	.1100	6 x 32	
34	.1110	6 x 36	
33	.1130	6 x 40	No. 10
32	.1160		
31	.1200		No. 11
1/8	.1250	7 x 36	
30	.1285	8 x 30	No. 12
29	.1360	8 x 32-36	
28	.1405	8 x 40	
27	.1440	9 x 30	
26	.1470	3/16 x 24	
25	.1495	10 x 24	No. 14
24	.1520		
23	.1540	10 x 28	
5/32	.1562		
22	.1570	10 x 30	
21	.1590	10 x 32	
20	.1610	3/16 x 32	
19	.1660		
18	.1695		No. 16
11/64	.1719		
17	.1730		
16	.1770	12 x 24	
15	.1800		
14	.1820	12 x 28	
13	.1850	12 x 32	No. 18
3/16	.1875		
12	.1890		

DRILL THIS SIZE HOLE		To Tap For This Size Bolt or Screw	For This Size Wood Screw Pilot in Hard Wood
Drill Size	Dec. Equiv.		
11	.1910		
10	.1935	15 x 20	
9	.1960		
8	.1990		
7	.2010	1/4 x 20	
13/64	.2031		
6	.2040		
5	.2055		
4	.2090	1/4 x 24	No. 20
3	.2130	1/4 x 28	
7/32	.2187	1/4 x 32	
2	.2210		
1	.2280		No. 24
A	.2340		
15/64	.2344		
B	.2380		
C	.2420		
D	.2460		
1/4	.2500		

DRILL THIS SIZE HOLE		To Tap For This Size Bolt or Screw
Drill Size	Dec. Equiv.	
E	.2500	
F	.2570	5/16 x 18
G	.2610	
17/64	.2656	5/16 x 18
H	.2660	
I	.2720	
J	.2770	5/16 x 24-32*
K	.2810	
9/32	.2812	5/16 x 24-32*
L	.2900	
M	.2950	
19/64	.2969	
N	.3020	
5/16	.3125	3/8* x 16-1/8* P
O	.3160	
P	.3230	
21/64	.3281	3/8 x 20-24
Q	.3332	
R	.3390	
11/32	.3437	
S	.3480	
T	.3580	
23/64	.3594	
U	.3680	
3/8	.3750	7/16 x 14
V	.3770	
W	.3860	
25/64	.3906	7/16 x 14
X	.3970	
Y	.4040	
13/32	.4062	
Z	.4130	
27/64	.4219	1/2 x 12-13
7/16	.4375	1/4* Pipe
29/64	.4531	1/2 x 20-24
15/32	.4687	1/2 x 27
31/64	.4844	9/16 x 12
1/2	.5000	

* All tap drill sizes are for 75% full thread except asterisked sizes which are 60% full thread.

104F16.EPS

Figure 16 ◆ Fastener hole guide chart.

A torque wrench is used to control the degree of tightness. The torque wrench measures how much a fastener is being tightened. Torque is the turning force applied to the fastener. Torque is normally expressed in **inch-pounds (in-lbs)** or **foot-pounds (ft-lbs)**. A one-pound force applied to a wrench that is 1-foot-long exerts 1 foot-pound, or 12 inch-pounds, of torque. The torque reading is shown on the indicator on the torque wrench as the fastener is being tightened. *Figure 17* shows two types of torque wrenches.

Different types of bolts, nuts, and screws are torqued to different values depending on the application. Always check the project specifications and the manufacturer's manual to determine the proper torque for a particular type of fastener. *Figure 18* shows selected torque values for various graded steel bolts.

2.5.2 Installing Threaded Fasteners

The following general procedure is used to install threaded fasteners in a variety of applications:

NOTE
When installing threaded fasteners for a specific job, check all installation requirements.

WARNING!
To avoid injury, follow all safety precautions.

Step 1   Select the proper bolts or screws for the job.

Step 2   Check for damaged or dirty internal and external threads.

Step 3   Clean the bolt or screw threads. Do not lubricate the threads if a torque wrench is to be used to tighten the nuts.

Step 4   Insert the bolts through the predrilled holes and tighten the nuts by hand. Or, insert the screws through the holes and start the threads by hand.

NOTE
Turn the nuts or screws several turns by hand and check for cross threading.

DIAL TORQUE TYPE

MICROMETER TYPE

104F17.EPS

Figure 17 ◆ Torque wrenches.

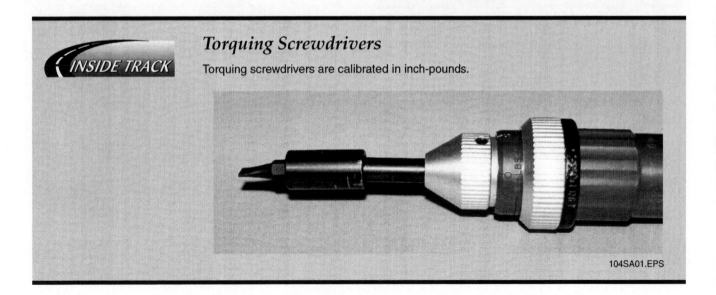

Torquing Screwdrivers

INSIDE TRACK

Torquing screwdrivers are calibrated in inch-pounds.

104SA01.EPS

FASTENER DIAMETER	THREADS PER INCH	MILD STEEL	STAINLESS STEEL 18-8	ALLOY STEEL
1/4	20	4	6	8
5/16	18	8	11	16
3/8	16	12	18	24
7/16	14	20	32	40
1/2	13	30	43	60
5/8	11	60	92	120
3/4	10	100	128	200
7/8	9	160	180	320
1	8	245	285	490

SUGGESTED TORQUE VALUES FOR GRADED STEEL BOLTS

GRADE		SAE 1 OR 2	SAE 5	SAE 6	SAE 8
TENSILE STRENGTH		64,000 PSI	105,000 PSI	130,000 PSI	150,000 PSI
GRADE MARK					
BOLT DIAMETER	THREADS PER INCH	FOOT POUNDS TORQUE			
1/4	20	5	7	10	10
5/16	18	9	14	19	22
3/8	16	15	25	34	37
7/16	14	24	40	55	60
1/2	13	37	60	85	92
9/16	12	53	88	120	132
5/8	11	74	120	169	180
3/4	10	120	200	280	296
7/8	9	190	302	440	473
1	8	282	466	660	714

104F18.EPS

Figure 18 ◆ Torque value chart.

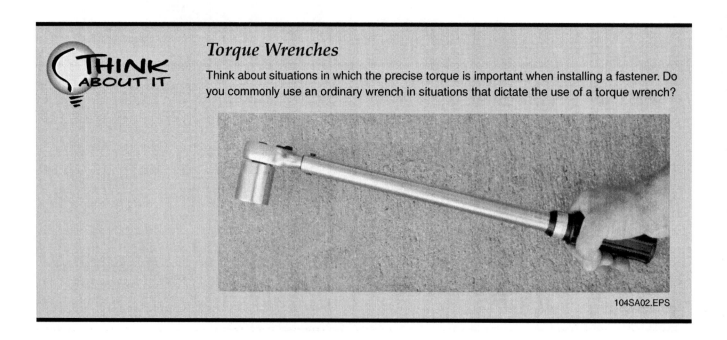

Torque Wrenches

Think about situations in which the precise torque is important when installing a fastener. Do you commonly use an ordinary wrench in situations that dictate the use of a torque wrench?

104SA02.EPS

Step 5 Following the proper tightening sequence, tighten the bolts or screws snugly.

Step 6 Check the torque specification. Following the proper tightening sequence, tighten each bolt, nut, or screw several times, approaching the specified torque. Tighten to the final torque specification.

Step 7 If required to keep the bolts or nuts from working loose, install jam nuts, cotter pins, or safety wire. *Figure 19* shows fasteners with a safety wire installed.

3.0.0 ◆ NON-THREADED FASTENERS

Non-threaded fasteners have many uses. Different types of non-threaded fasteners include retainers, keys, pins, clamps, washers, rivets, and tie wraps.

3.1.0 Retainer Fasteners

Retainer fasteners, also called retaining rings, are used for both internal and external applications. Some retaining rings are seated in grooves in the fastener. Other types of retainer fasteners are self-locking and do not require a groove. Special pliers are used to remove internal and external retainer rings without damaging the ring or the fastener. *Figure 20* shows several types of retainer fasteners.

NOTE

External retainer fasteners are sometimes called clips.

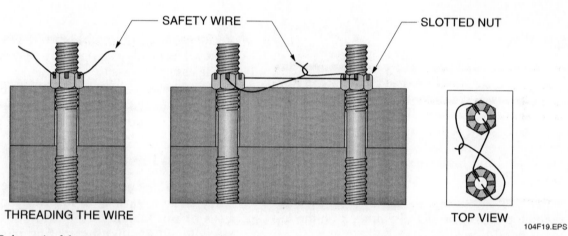

SAFETY WIRE — SLOTTED NUT

THREADING THE WIRE — TOP VIEW

104F19.EPS

Figure 19 ◆ Safety-wired fasteners.

Taps and Dies

Taps and dies are used to cut threads in materials, such as metal, plastic, and hard rubber. Taps are used to cut internal threads in materials, and dies are used to cut external threads on bolts and rods.

Taps and dies can be obtained in complete sets that include various taps and dies, as well as diestocks, tap wrenches, guides, and the screwdrivers and wrenches necessary to loosen and tighten adjusting screws. This photo shows a common tap and die set.

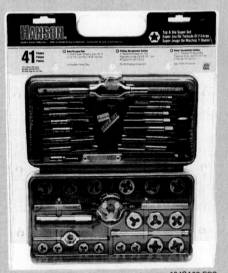

104SA03.EPS

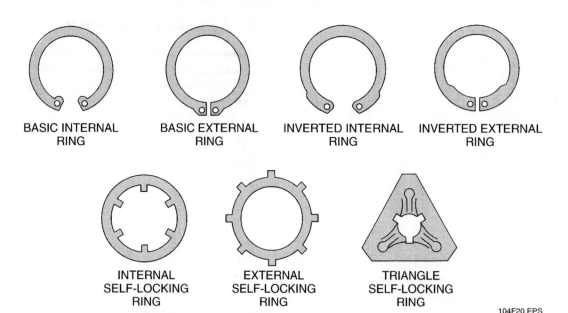

BASIC INTERNAL RING **BASIC EXTERNAL RING** **INVERTED INTERNAL RING** **INVERTED EXTERNAL RING**

INTERNAL SELF-LOCKING RING **EXTERNAL SELF-LOCKING RING** **TRIANGLE SELF-LOCKING RING**

104F20.EPS

Figure 20 ◆ Retainer fasteners (rings).

3.2.0 Keys

Keys are inserted to prevent a gear or pulley from rotating on a shaft. Half of the key fits into a keyseat on the shaft. The other half fits into a **keyway** in the hub of the gear or pulley. The key fastens the two parts together, stopping the gear or pulley from turning on the shaft. *Figure 21* shows several types of keys and their uses. Some different types of keys follow:

- *Square key* – Usually one-quarter of the shaft diameter. It may be slightly tapered on the top for easier fitting.
- *Pratt and Whitney key* – Similar to the square key, but rounded at both ends. It fits into a keyseat of the same shape.

- *Gib head key* – Interchangeable with the square key. The head design allows easy removal from the assembly.
- *Woodruff key* – Semicircular shape that fits into a keyseat of the same shape. The top of the key fits into the keyway of the mating part.

3.3.0 Pin Fasteners

Pin fasteners come in several types and sizes. They have a variety of applications. Common uses of pin fasteners include holding moving parts together, aligning mating parts, fastening hinges, holding gears and pulleys on shafts, and securing slotted nuts. *Figure 22* shows several pin fasteners.

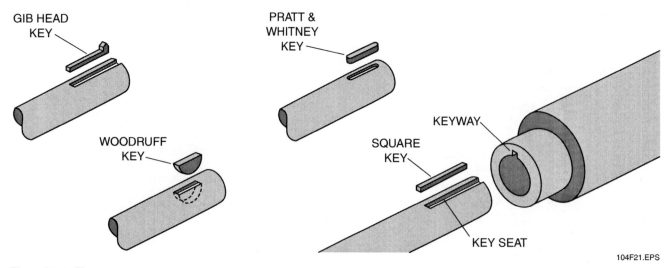

GIB HEAD KEY

PRATT & WHITNEY KEY

WOODRUFF KEY

KEYWAY

SQUARE KEY

KEY SEAT

104F21.EPS

Figure 21 ◆ Keys.

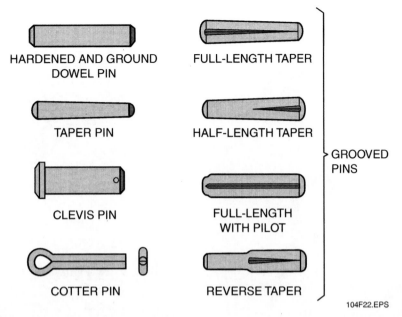

HARDENED AND GROUND
DOWEL PIN

TAPER PIN

CLEVIS PIN

COTTER PIN

FULL-LENGTH TAPER

HALF-LENGTH TAPER

FULL-LENGTH
WITH PILOT

REVERSE TAPER

GROOVED
PINS

104F22.EPS

Figure 22 ◆ Pin fasteners.

3.3.1 Dowel Pins

Dowel pins fit into holes to position mating parts. They may also support a portion of the load placed on the parts. *Figure 23* shows an application of dowel pins used to position mating parts.

3.3.2 Taper and Spring Pins

Taper and spring pins are used to fasten gears, pulleys, and collars to a shaft. *Figure 24* shows how taper and spring pins are used to attach a component to a shaft. The groove in a spring pin allows it to compress against the walls in a springlike fashion.

3.3.3 Cotter Pins

There are several different types of cotter pins used as a locking device for a variety of applications (*Figure 25*). Cotter pins are often inserted through a hole drilled crosswise through a shaft to prevent parts from slipping on or off the shaft. They are also used to keep slotted nuts from working loose. Standard cotter pins are general-use pins. When installed, the extended prong is normally bent back over the nut to provide the locking action. If it is ever removed, throw it away and replace it with a new one. The humped, cinch, and hitch-type cotter pins are self-locking pins. The humped and cinch type should also be thrown away and replaced with a new one if removed. The hitch pin, also called a hair pin, is a reusable pin made to be installed and removed quickly.

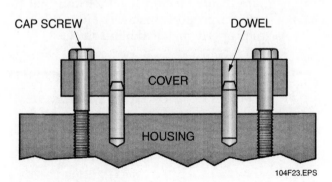

CAP SCREW

DOWEL

COVER

HOUSING

104F23.EPS

Figure 23 ◆ Dowel pins.

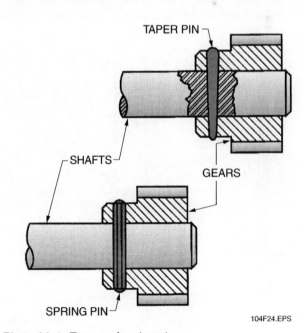

TAPER PIN

SHAFTS

GEARS

SPRING PIN

104F24.EPS

Figure 24 ◆ Taper and spring pins.

FASTENERS AND ANCHORS

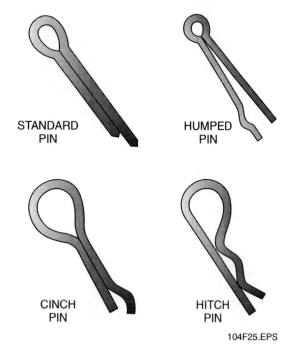

STANDARD PIN

HUMPED PIN

CINCH PIN

HITCH PIN

104F25.EPS

Figure 25 ◆ Cotter pins.

3.4.0 Blind/Pop Rivets

When only one side of a joint can be reached, blind rivets can be used to fasten the parts together. Some applications of blind rivets include fastening light to heavy gauge sheet metal, fiberglass, plastics, and belting. Blind rivets are made of a variety of materials and come in several sizes and lengths. They are installed using special riveting tools. *Figure 26* shows a typical blind rivet installation.

Blind rivets are installed through drilled or punched holes using a special blind (pop) rivet gun. *Figure 27* shows a typical rivet gun.

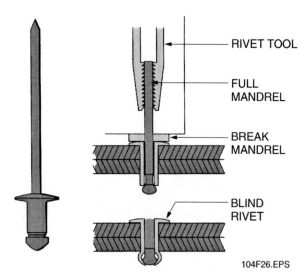

RIVET TOOL

FULL MANDREL

BREAK MANDREL

BLIND RIVET

104F26.EPS

Figure 26 ◆ Blind rivet installation.

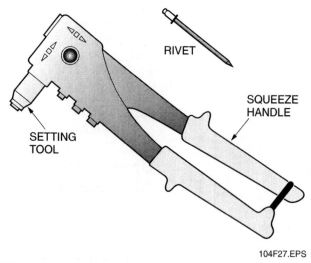

RIVET

SETTING TOOL

SQUEEZE HANDLE

104F27.EPS

Figure 27 ◆ Rivet gun.

Use the following general procedure to install blind rivets:

Step 1 Select the correct length and diameter of blind rivet to be used.

Step 2 Select the appropriate drill bit for the size of rivet being used.

Step 3 Drill a hole through both parts being connected.

Step 4 Inspect the rivet gun for any defects that might make it unsafe for use.

Step 5 Place the rivet mandrel into the proper size setting tool.

Step 6 Insert the rivet end into the predrilled hole.

Step 7 Install the rivet by squeezing the handle of the rivet gun, causing the jaws in the setting tool to grip the mandrel. The mandrel is pulled up, expanding the rivet until it breaks at the shear point. *Figure 28* shows the rivet and tool positioned for joining parts together.

Step 8 Inspect the rivet to make sure the pieces are firmly riveted together and that the rivet is properly installed. *Figure 29* shows a properly installed blind rivet.

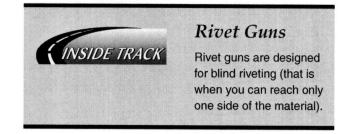

INSIDE TRACK

Rivet Guns

Rivet guns are designed for blind riveting (that is when you can reach only one side of the material).

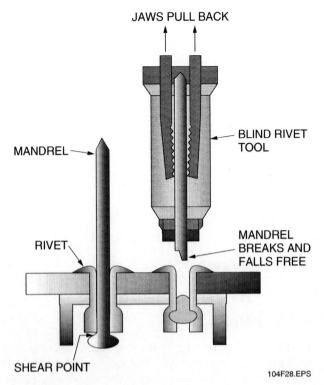

Figure 28 ◆ Joining parts.

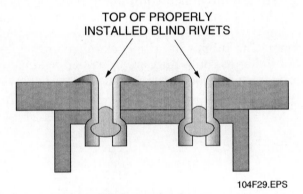

Figure 29 ◆ Properly installed blind rivets.

3.5.0 Tie Wraps

A tie wrap is a one-piece, self-locking cable tie, usually made of nylon, that is used to fasten a bundle of wires and cables together. Tie wraps can be quickly installed either manually or using a special installation tool. Black tie wraps resist ultraviolet light and are recommended for outdoor use.

Tie wraps are made in standard, cable strap and clamp, and identification configurations (*Figure 30*). All types function to clamp bundled wires or cables together. In addition, the cable strap and clamp has a molded mounting hole in the head used to secure the tie with a rivet, screw, or bolt after the tie wrap has been installed around the wires or cable. Identification tie wraps have a

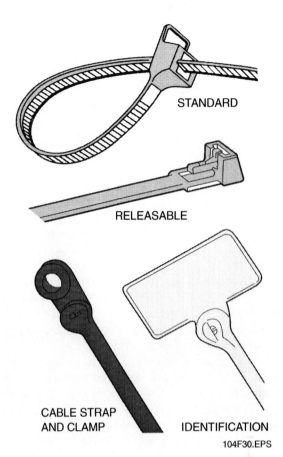

Figure 30 ◆ Tie wraps.

large flat area provided for imprinting or writing cable identification information. There is also a releasable version available. It is a non-permanent tie used for bundling wires or cables that may require frequent additions or deletions. Cable ties are made in various lengths ranging from about 3" to 30", allowing them to be used for fastening wires and cables into bundles with diameters ranging from about ½" to 9", respectively. Tie wraps can also be attached to a variety of adhesive mounting bases made for that purpose.

Tie wraps are available in a wide variety of colors that can be used to color code different cable bundles.

4.0.0 ◆ SPECIAL THREADED FASTENERS

Special threaded fasteners consist of hardware that has been manufactured in several shapes and sizes and designed to perform specific jobs. Certain types of nuts may be considered special threaded fasteners if they are designed especially for a particular application.

The three types of special threaded fasteners described in this section are eye bolts, anchor bolts, and J-bolts.

4.1.0 Eye Bolts

Eye bolts get their name from the eye, or loop, at one end. The other end of an eye bolt is threaded. There are many types of eye bolts. The eye on some eye bolts is formed and welded, while the eye on other types is forged. Shoulder-forged eye bolts are commonly used as lifting devices and guides for wires, cables, and cords. *Figure 31* shows some typical eye bolts.

4.2.0 Anchor Bolts

An anchor bolt is used to fasten parts, machines, and equipment to concrete or masonry foundations, floors, and walls. There are several types of anchor bolts designed for different applications. *Figure 32* shows a type of anchor bolt for use in wet concrete. If the concrete has already hardened, expansion anchor bolts are used. These are covered later in this module.

One common method used to install anchor bolts in wet concrete involves making a wooden template to locate the anchor bolts. The template positions the anchor bolts so that they correspond to those in the equipment to be fastened.

104F32.EPS

Figure 32 ◆ Anchor bolt.

4.3.0 J-Bolts

J-bolts get their name from the curve on one end that gives them a J shape. The other end of a J-bolt is threaded. There are many types of J-bolts. Some J-bolts are used to hold tubing bundles and include a plastic jacket to protect the tubing. Others are used to attach equipment to existing grating. Most J-bolts used in tubing racks are attached using two nuts. The upper nut allows for adjustment. The tubing bundle is clamped firmly, but not flattened. Both nuts are tightened against the tube track for positive holding. *Figure 33* shows a typical J-bolt.

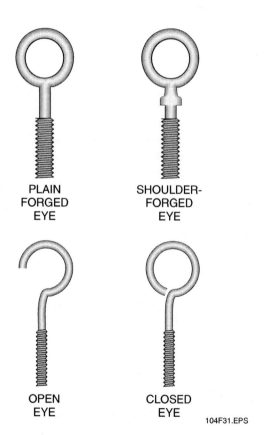

PLAIN
FORGED
EYE

SHOULDER-
FORGED
EYE

OPEN
EYE

CLOSED
EYE

104F31.EPS

Figure 31 ◆ Eye bolts.

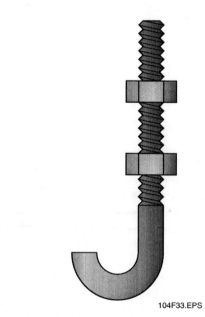

104F33.EPS

Figure 33 ◆ Typical J-bolt.

5.0.0 ◆ SCREWS

Screws are made in a variety of shapes and sizes for different fastening jobs. A screw's finish or coating determines whether the screw is suitable for interior or exterior use, and whether the screw is corrosion resistant. Screws have heads with different shapes and slots similar to those previously described for machine screws. Some have machine threads and are self-drilling. The size or diameter of a screw body or shank is given in gauge numbers ranging from No. 0 to No. 24, and in fractions of an inch for screws with diameters larger than ¼". The higher the gauge number, the larger the diameter of the shank. Screw lengths range from ¼" to 6", measured from the tip to the part of the head that is flush to the surface when driven in. When choosing a screw for an application, you must consider the type and thickness of the materials to be fastened, the size of the screw, the material it is made of, the shape of its head, and the type of driver. Because of the wide diversity in the types of screws and their applications, always follow the manufacturer's recommendation to select the right screw for the job. To prevent damage to the screw head or the material being fastened, always use a screwdriver or power driver bit with the proper size and shape tip to fit the screw.

Some of the more common types of screws are:

- Wood screws
- Lag screws
- Masonry/concrete screws
- Thread-forming and thread-cutting screws
- Deck screws
- Drywall screws
- Drive screws

5.1.0 Wood Screws

Wood screws (*Figure 34*) are typically used to fasten boxes and panel enclosures to wood framing or structures where greater holding power is needed than can be provided by nails. They are also used to fasten equipment to wood in applications where it may occasionally need to be unfastened and removed. Wood screws are commonly made in lengths from ¼" to 4", with shank gauge sizes ranging from 0 to 24. The shank size that is used is normally determined by the size of the hole provided in the box or the panel to be fastened. When determining the length of a wood screw to use, a good rule of thumb is to select screws long enough to allow about two-thirds of the screw length to enter the piece of wood that is being gripped.

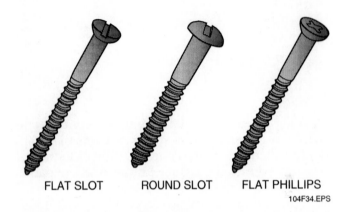

FLAT SLOT   ROUND SLOT   FLAT PHILLIPS

104F34.EPS

Figure 34 ◆ Wood screws.

5.2.0 Lag Screws and Shields

Lag screws (*Figure 35*) or lag bolts are heavy-duty wood screws with square- or hex-shaped heads that provide greater holding power. Lag screws with diameters ranging between ¼" and ½" and lengths ranging from 1" to 6" are common. They are typically used to fasten heavy equipment to wood, but can also be used to fasten equipment to concrete when a lag shield is used.

INSIDE TRACK

Screws

In most applications, either threaded or non-threaded fasteners could be used. However, threaded fasteners are sometimes preferred because they can usually be tightened or removed without damaging the surrounding material.

Driving Wood Screws

To maintain holding power, be careful not to drill your pilot hole too large. It's wise to drill a pilot hole deep enough to equal about two-thirds of the length of the threaded portion of the screw. Additionally, using soap to lubricate screw threads makes the screw easier to drive.

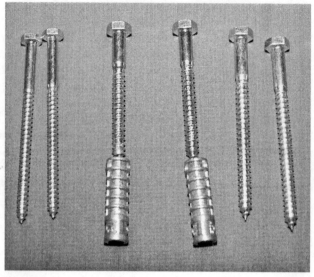

Figure 35 ◆ Lag screws and shields.

PHILLIPS FLAT HEAD   HEX WASHER HEAD

104F36.EPS

Figure 36 ◆ Concrete screws.

A lag shield is a metal tube that is split length-wise but remains joined at one end. It is placed in a predrilled hole in the concrete. When a lag screw is screwed into the lag shield, the shield expands in the hole, firmly securing the lag screw. In hard masonry, short lag shields (typically 1" to 2" long) may be used to minimize drilling time. In soft or weak masonry, long lag shields (typically 1½" to 3" long) should be used to achieve maximum holding strength.

Make sure to use the correct length lag screw to achieve proper expansion. The length of the lag screw used should be equal to the thickness of the component being fastened plus the length of the lag shield. Also, drill the hole in the masonry to a depth approximately ½" longer than the shield being used. If the head of a lag screw rests directly on wood when installed, a flat washer should be placed under the head to prevent the head from digging into the wood as the lag screw is tightened. Be sure to take the thickness of any washers used into account when selecting the length of the screw.

5.3.0 Concrete/Masonry Screws

Concrete/masonry screws (*Figure 36*), commonly called self-threading anchors, are used to fasten a device or fixture to concrete, block, or brick. No anchor is needed. To provide a matched tolerance anchoring system, the screws are installed using specially designed carbide drill bits and installation tools made for use with the screws. These tools are typically used with a standard rotary drill hammer. The installation tool, along with an appropriate drive socket or bit, is used to drive the

screws directly into predrilled holes that have a diameter and depth specified by the screw manufacturer. When being driven into the concrete, the widely spaced threads on the screws cut into the walls of the hole to provide a tight friction fit. Most types of concrete/masonry screws can be removed and reinstalled to allow for shimming and leveling of the fastened device.

5.4.0 Thread-Forming and Thread-Cutting Screws

Thread-forming screws (*Figure 37*), commonly called sheet metal screws, are made of hard metal. They form a thread as they are driven into the work. This thread-forming action eliminates the need to tap a hole before installing the screw. To achieve proper holding, make sure to use the proper size bit when drilling pilot holes for thread-forming screws. The correct drill bit size used for a specific size screw is usually marked on the box containing the screws. Some types of thread-forming screws also drill their own holes, eliminating drilling, punching, and aligning parts. Thread-forming screws are primarily used to fasten light-gauge metal parts together. They are made in the same diameters and lengths as wood screws.

Hardened steel thread-cutting metal screws with blunt points and fine threads (*Figure 38*) are used to join nonferrous metals, heavy-gauge metals, and

STANDARD THREAD-FORMING SCREW   SELF-DRILLING SCREW

104F37.EPS

Figure 37 ◆ Thread-forming screws.

THINK ABOUT IT

Self-Drilling Screws

Can you name an application for self-drilling screws?

104SA04.EPS

metals of different gauges. They are also used to fasten sheet metal to building structural members. These screws are made of hardened steel that is harder than the metal being tapped. They cut threads by removing and cutting a portion of the metal as they are driven into a pilot hole and through the material.

5.5.0 Deck Screws

Deck screws (*Figure 39*) are made in a wide variety of shapes and sizes for different indoor and outdoor applications. Some are made to fasten pressure-treated and other types of wood decking to wood framing. Self-drilling types are made to fasten wood decking to different gauges of metal support structures. Similarly, other self-drilling kinds are made to fasten metal decking and sheeting to different gauges and types of metal structural support members. Because of their wide diversity, it is important to follow the manufacturer's recommendations for selection of the proper screw for a particular application. Many manufacturers make a stand-up installation tool for driving their deck screws. This tool eliminates angle driving, underdriven or overdriven screws, and screw wobble. It also reduces operator fatigue.

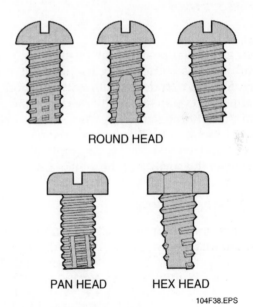

ROUND HEAD

PAN HEAD   HEX HEAD

104F38.EPS

Figure 38 ◆ Thread-cutting screws.

5.6.0 Drywall Screws

Drywall screws (*Figure 40*) are thin, self-drilling screws with bugle-shaped heads. Depending on the type of screw, it cuts through the wallboard and anchors itself into wood and/or metal studs,

---

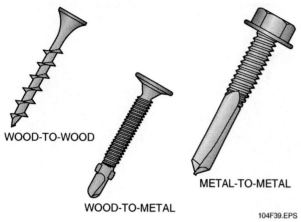

WOOD-TO-WOOD

WOOD-TO-METAL

METAL-TO-METAL

104F39.EPS

Figure 39 ◆ Typical deck screws.

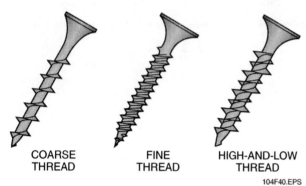

COARSE
THREAD

FINE
THREAD

HIGH-AND-LOW
THREAD

104F40.EPS

Figure 40 ◆ Drywall screws.

holding the wallboard tight to the stud. Coarse thread screws are normally used to fasten wallboard to wood studs. Fine thread and high-and-low thread types are generally used for fastening to metal studs. Some screws are made for use in either wood or metal. A Phillips or Robertson drive head allows the drywall screw to be countersunk without tearing the surface of the wallboard.

5.7.0 Drive Screws

Drive screws do not require the hole to be tapped. They are installed by hammering the screw into a drilled or punched hole of the proper size. Drive screws are mostly used to fasten parts that will not be exposed to much pressure. A typical use of drive screws is to attach permanent name plates on electric motors and other types of equipment. *Figure 41* shows typical drive screws.

6.0.0 ◆ HAMMER-DRIVEN PINS AND STUDS

Hammer-driven pins or threaded studs (*Figure 42*) use a special tool to fasten wood or steel to concrete or block without the need to predrill holes. To

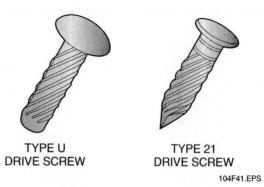

TYPE U
DRIVE SCREW

TYPE 21
DRIVE SCREW

104F41.EPS

Figure 41 ◆ Drive screws.

install these fasteners, insert the pin or threaded stud into the hammer-driven tool point with the washer seated in the recess. Position the pin or stud against the base material to which it is to be fastened and tap the drive rod of the tool lightly until the striker pin contacts the pin or stud. Strike the tool's drive rod using heavy blows with about a two-pound engineer's hammer. The force of the hammer blows transmits through the tool directly to the head of the fastener, causing it to be driven into the concrete or block. For best results, the drive pin or stud should be embedded a minimum of ½" in hard concrete to 1¼" in softer concrete block.

7.0.0 ◆ POWDER-ACTUATED TOOLS AND FASTENERS

Powder-actuated tools (*Figure 43*) can be used to drive a wide variety of specially designed pin and threaded stud-type fasteners into masonry and steel. These tools look and fire like a gun and use the force of a detonated gunpowder load (typically

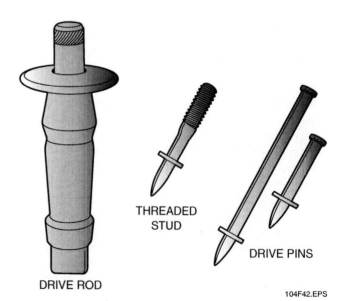

THREADED
STUD

DRIVE PINS

DRIVE ROD

104F42.EPS

Figure 42 ◆ Hammer-driven pins and installation tool.

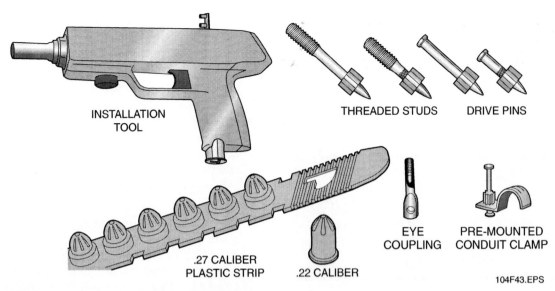

INSTALLATION TOOL

THREADED STUDS

DRIVE PINS

.27 CALIBER PLASTIC STRIP

.22 CALIBER

EYE COUPLING

PRE-MOUNTED CONDUIT CLAMP

104F43.EPS

Figure 43 ◆ Powder-actuated installation tool and fasteners.

.22, .25, or .27 caliber) to drive the fastener into the material. The depth to which the pin or stud is driven is controlled by the density of the base material in which the pin or stud is being installed and by the power level or strength of the powder load.

Powder loads and their cases are designed for use with specific types and/or models of powder-actuated tools and are not interchangeable. Typically, powder loads are made in 12 increasing power or load levels used to achieve the proper penetration. The different power levels are identified by a color-code system and load case types. Note that different manufacturers may use different color codes to identify load strength. Power level 1

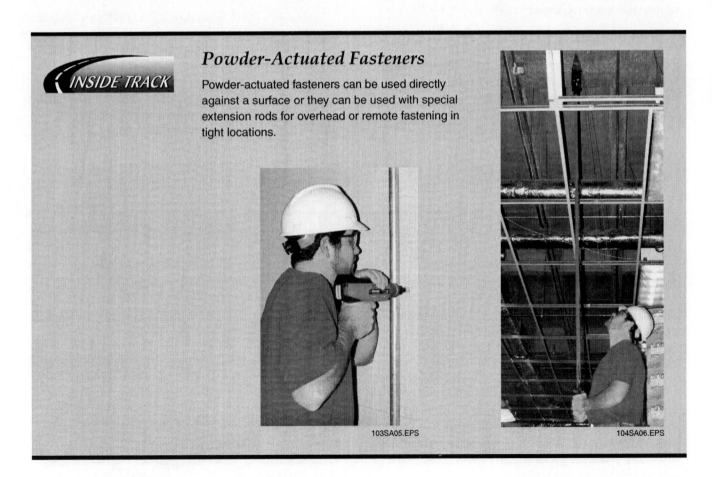

INSIDE TRACK

Powder-Actuated Fasteners

Powder-actuated fasteners can be used directly against a surface or they can be used with special extension rods for overhead or remote fastening in tight locations.

103SA05.EPS

104SA06.EPS

is the lowest power level, while 12 is the highest. Higher number power levels are used when driving into hard materials or when a deeper penetration is needed. Powder loads are available as single-shot units for use with single-shot tools. They are also made in multi-shot strips or disks for semi-automatic tools.

WARNING!
Powder-actuated fastening tools are to be used only by trained and licensed operators and in accordance with the tool operator's manual. You must carry your license with you whenever you are using a powder-actuated tool.

OSHA Standard 29 CFR 1926.302(e) governs the use of powder-actuated tools and states that only those individuals who have been trained in the operation of the particular powder-actuated tool in use be allowed to operate it. Authorized instructors available from the various powder-actuated tool manufacturers generally provide such training and licensing. Trained operators must take precautions to protect both themselves and others in the area when using a powder-actuated driver tool:

- Always use the tool in accordance with the published tool operation instructions. The instructions should be kept with the tool. Never attempt to override the safety features of the tool.
- Never place your hand or other body parts over the front muzzle end of the tool.
- Use only fasteners, powder loads, and tool parts specifically made for use with the tool. Using other materials can cause improper and unsafe functioning of the tool.

- Operators and bystanders must wear eye and hearing protection and hard hats. Other personal safety gear must also be used as required.
- Always post warning signs that state *Powder-Actuated Tool in Use* within 50 feet of the area where tools are used.
- Prior to using a tool, make sure it is unloaded and perform a proper function test. Check the functioning of the unloaded tool as described in the published tool operation instructions.
- Do not guess before fastening into any base material; always perform a center punch test.
- Always make a test firing into a suitable base material with the lowest power level recommended for the tool being used. If this does not set the fastener, try the next higher power level. Continue this procedure until the proper fastener penetration is obtained.
- Always point the tool away from operators or bystanders.
- Never use the tool in an explosive or flammable area.
- Never leave a loaded tool unattended.
- Do not load the tool until you are prepared to complete the fastening.
- Should you decide not to make a fastening after the tool has been loaded, always remove the powder load first, then the fastener. Always unload the tool before cleaning, servicing, or changing parts, prior to work breaks, and when storing the tool.
- Always hold the tool perpendicular to the work surface and use the spall (chip or fragment) guard or stop spall whenever possible.
- Always follow the required spacing, edge distance, and base material thickness requirements.
- Never fire through an existing hole or into a weld area.

Powder-Actuated Tools

A 22-year-old apprentice was killed when he was struck in the head by a nail fired from a powder-actuated tool in an adjacent room. The tool operator was attempting to anchor plywood to a hollow wall and fired the gun, causing the nail to pass through the wall, where it traveled nearly thirty feet before striking the victim. The tool operator had never received training in the proper use of the tool, and none of the employees in the area were wearing personal protective equipment.

The Bottom Line: Never use a powder-actuated tool to secure fasteners into easily penetrated materials; these tools are designed primarily for installing fasteners into masonry. The use of powder-actuated tools requires special training and certification. In addition, all personnel in the area must be aware that the tool is in use and should be wearing appropriate personal protective equipment.

- In the event of a misfire, always hold the tool depressed against the work surface for at least 30 seconds. If the tool still does not fire, follow the published tool instructions. Never carelessly discard or throw unfired powder loads into a trash receptacle.
- Always store the powder loads and the unloaded tool under lock and key.

8.0.0 ◆ MECHANICAL ANCHORS

Mechanical anchors are devices used to give fasteners a firm grip in a variety of materials, where the fasteners by themselves would otherwise have a tendency to pull out. Anchors can be classified in many ways by different manufacturers. In this module, anchors have been divided into five broad categories:

- One-step anchors
- Bolt anchors
- Screw anchors
- Self-drilling anchors
- Hollow-wall anchors

8.1.0 One-Step Anchors

One-step anchors are designed so that they can be installed through the mounting holes in the component to be fastened. This is because the anchor and the hole into which the anchor is installed have the same diameter. They come in various diameters ranging from ¼" to 1¼" with lengths ranging from 1¾" to 12". Wedge, stud, sleeve, one-piece, screw, and nail anchors (*Figure 44*) are common types of one-step anchors.

8.1.1 Wedge Anchors

Wedge anchors are heavy-duty anchors supplied with nuts and washers. The drill bit size used to drill the hole is the same diameter as the anchor. The depth of the hole is not critical as long as it meets the minimum recommended by the manufacturer. Blow the hole clean of dust and other material, insert the anchor into the hole, and drive it with a hammer far enough so that at least six threads are below the top surface of the component. Then, tighten the anchor nut to expand the anchor and secure it in the hole.

8.1.2 Stud Bolt Anchors

Stud bolt anchors are heavy-duty threaded anchors. Because this type of anchor is made to bottom in its mounting hole, it is a good choice to use when jacking or leveling of the fastened component is needed.

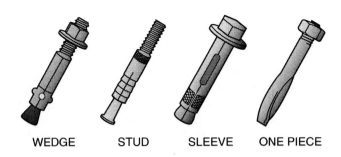

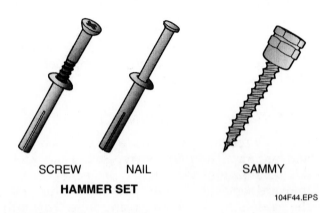

WEDGE STUD SLEEVE ONE PIECE

SCREW NAIL SAMMY

HAMMER SET

104F44.EPS

Figure 44 ◆ One-step anchors.

The depth of the hole drilled in the masonry must be as specified by the manufacturer in order to achieve proper expansion. Blow the hole clean of dust and other material, then insert the anchor in the hole with the expander plug end down. Drive the anchor into the hole with a hammer or setting tool to expand the anchor and tighten it in the hole. The anchor is fully set when it can no longer be driven into the hole. The component is fastened using the correct size and thread bolt for use with the anchor stud.

8.1.3 Sleeve Anchors

Sleeve anchors are multi-purpose anchors. The depth of the anchor hole is not critical as long as the minimum length recommended by the manufacturer is drilled. Blow the hole clean of dust and other material, insert the anchor into the hole, and tap it until it is flush with the component. Tighten the anchor nut or screw to expand the anchor and tighten it in the hole.

8.1.4 One-Piece Anchors

One-piece anchors are multi-purpose anchors. They work on the principle that as the anchor is driven into the hole, the spring force of the expansion mechanism is compressed and flexes to fit the size of the hole. Once set, it tries to regain its original shape. The depth of the hole drilled in the masonry must be at least a half-inch deeper than the required embedment. The proper depth is crucial. Overdrilling is as bad as underdrilling. Blow the hole clean of dust and other material, insert the anchor through the component, and drive it with a hammer into the hole until the head is firmly seated against the component. It is important to make sure that the anchor is driven to the proper embedment depth. Note that manufacturers also make specially designed drivers and manual tools that are used instead of a hammer to drive one-piece anchors. These tools allow the anchors to be installed in confined spaces and they help prevent damage to the component from stray hammer blows.

8.1.5 Hammer-Set Anchors

Hammer-set anchors are made for use in concrete and masonry. There are two types: nail and screw. An advantage of the screw-type anchors is that they are removable. Both types have a diameter the same size as the anchoring hole. For both types, the anchor hole must be drilled to the diameter of the anchor and to a depth at least a quarter-inch deeper than that required for embedment. Blow the hole clean of dust and other material, then insert the anchor into the hole through the mounting holes in the component to be fastened. Drive the screw or nail into the anchor body to expand it. It is important to make sure that the head is seated firmly against the component and is at the proper embedment.

8.1.6 Sammy® Anchors

Sammy® anchors are available for installation in concrete, steel, or wood. The Sammy® anchor is designed to support a threaded rod, which is screwed into the head of the anchor after the anchor is installed. A special nut driver is available for installing the screws.

8.2.0 Bolt Anchors

Bolt anchors are designed to be installed flush with the surface of the base material. They are used in conjunction with threaded machine bolts or screws. In some types, they can be used with threaded rod. Drop-in and single- and double-expansion anchors (*Figure 45*) are commonly used types of bolt anchors.

8.2.1 Drop-In Anchors

Drop-in anchors are typically used as heavy-duty anchors. There are two types of drop-in anchors.

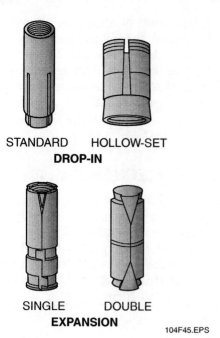

STANDARD   HOLLOW-SET
DROP-IN

SINGLE   DOUBLE
EXPANSION

104F45.EPS

Figure 45 ◆ Bolt anchors.

The first type, made for use in solid concrete and masonry, has an internally threaded expansion anchor with a preassembled internal expander plug. The anchor hole must be drilled to the specific diameter and depth specified by the manufacturer. Blow the hole clean of dust and other material, insert the anchor into the hole, and tap it until it is flush with the surface. Drive the setting tool supplied with the anchor into the anchor to expand it. Position the component to be fastened in place, and fasten it by threading and tightening the correct size machine bolt or screw into the anchor.

The second type, called a hollow set drop-in anchor, is made for use in hollow concrete and masonry base materials. Hollow set drop-in anchors have a slotted, tapered expansion sleeve and a serrated expansion cone. They come in various lengths compatible with the outer wall thickness of most hollow base materials. They can also be used in solid concrete and masonry. The anchor hole must be drilled to the diameter specified by the manufacturer. When installed in hollow base materials, drill the hole into the cell or void. Blow the hole clean of dust and other material, insert the anchor into the hole, and tap it until it is flush with the surface. Position the component to be fastened in place, then thread the proper size machine bolt or screw into the anchor and tighten it to expand the anchor in the hole.

8.2.2 Single- and Double-Expansion Anchors

Single- and double-expansion anchors are made for use in concrete and other masonry. The double-

4.26   ELECTRONIC SYSTEMS TECHNICIAN LEVEL ONE — TRAINEE MODULE 33104-04 expansion anchor is used mainly when fastening into concrete or masonry of questionable strength. For both types, the anchor hole must be drilled to the diameter and depth specified by the manufacturer. Blow the hole clean of dust and other material, then insert the anchor into the hole, threaded cone end first. Tap it until it is flush with the surface. Position the component to be fastened in place, then thread the proper size machine bolt or screw into the anchor and tighten it to expand the anchor in the hole.

8.3.0 Screw Anchors

Screw anchors are lighter-duty anchors made to be installed flush with the surface of the base material. They are used in conjunction with sheet metal, wood, or lag screws. Fiber and plastic anchors are common types of screw anchors (*Figure 46*). The lag shield anchor used with lag screws was described earlier in this module.

Fiber and plastic anchors are typically used in concrete and masonry. Plastic anchors are also commonly used in wallboard and similar base materials. The installation of all types is simple.

The anchor hole must be drilled to the diameter specified by the manufacturer. The minimum depth of the hole must equal the anchor length. Blow the hole clean of dust and other material, insert the anchor into the hole, and tap it until it is flush with the surface. Position the component to be fastened in place, then drive the proper type and size of screw through the component mounting hole and into the anchor to expand the anchor in the hole.

8.4.0 Self-Drilling Anchors

Some anchors made for use in masonry are self-drilling. *Figure 47* is typical of those in common use. This fastener has a cutting sleeve that is first used as a drill bit and later becomes the expandable fastener itself. A rotary hammer is used to drill the hole in the concrete, using the anchor sleeve as the drill bit. After drilling the hole, pull the anchor out and clean the hole. Then insert the anchor's expander plug into the cutting end of the sleeve. Drive the anchor sleeve and expander plug back into the hole with the rotary hammer until they are flush with the surface of the concrete. As

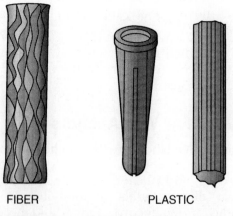

FIBER   PLASTIC

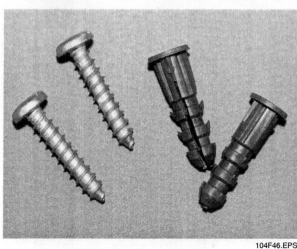

104F46.EPS

Figure 46 ◆ Screw anchors and screws.

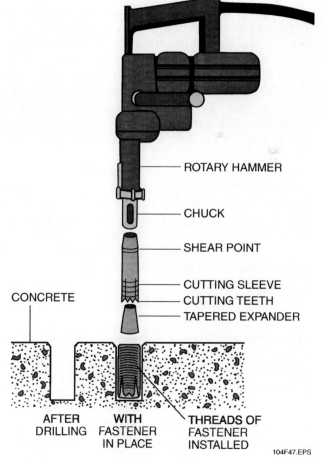

ROTARY HAMMER

CHUCK

SHEAR POINT

CUTTING SLEEVE
CUTTING TEETH
TAPERED EXPANDER

CONCRETE

AFTER DRILLING   WITH FASTENER IN PLACE   THREADS OF FASTENER INSTALLED

104F47.EPS

Figure 47 ◆ Self-drilling anchor.

the fastener is hammered down, it hits the bottom, where the tapered expander causes the fastener to expand and lock into the hole. The anchor is then snapped off at the shear point with a quick lateral movement of the hammer. The component to be fastened can then be attached to the anchor using the proper size bolt.

8.5.0 Guidelines for Drilling Anchor Holes in Hardened Concrete or Masonry

When selecting masonry anchors, regardless of the type, always take into consideration and follow the manufacturer's recommendations pertaining to hole diameter and depth, minimum embedment in concrete, maximum thickness of the material to be fastened, and the pullout and shear load capacities.

When installing anchors and/or anchor bolts in hardened concrete, make sure the area where the equipment or component is to be fastened is smooth so that it will have solid footing. Uneven footing might cause the equipment to twist, warp, not tighten properly, or vibrate when in operation. Before starting, carefully inspect the rotary hammer or hammer drill and the drill bit(s) to ensure they are in good operating condition. Set the drill or hammer tool depth gauge to the depth of the hole needed. Be sure to use the type of carbide-tipped masonry or percussion drill bits recommended by the drill/hammer or anchor manufacturer because these bits are made to take the higher impact of the masonry materials. The trick to using masonry drill bits is not to force them into the material by pushing down hard on the drill. Use a little pressure and let the drill do the work. For large holes, start with a smaller bit, then change to a larger bit.

The methods for installing the different types of anchors in hardened concrete or masonry were briefly described in the sections above. Always install the selected anchors according to the manufacturer's directions. Here is an example of a typical procedure used to install many types of expansion anchors in hardened concrete or masonry. Refer to *Figure 48* as you study the procedure.

WARNING!

Drilling in concrete generates noise, dust, and flying particles. Always wear safety goggles, ear protectors, and gloves. Make sure other workers in the area also wear protective equipment.

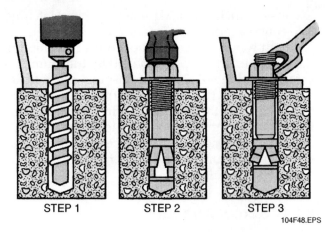

| STEP 1 | STEP 2 | STEP 3 |

104F48.EPS

Figure 48 ◆ Installing an anchor bolt in hardened concrete.

Step 1   Drill the anchor bolt hole the same size as the anchor bolt. The hole must be deep enough for six threads of the bolt to be below the surface of the concrete (*Figure 48, Step 1*). Clean out the hole using a squeeze bulb.

Step 2   Drive the anchor bolt into the hole using a hammer (*Figure 48, Step 2*). Protect the threads of the bolt with a nut that does not allow any threads to be exposed.

Step 3   Put a washer and nut on the bolt, and tighten the nut with a wrench until the anchor is secure in the concrete (*Figure 48, Step 3*).

8.6.0 Hollow-Wall Anchors

Hollow-wall anchors are used in hollow materials such as concrete plank, block, structural steel, wallboard, and plaster. Some types can also be used in solid materials. Toggle bolts, sleeve-type wall anchors, wallboard anchors, and metal drive-in anchors are common anchors used when fastening to hollow materials.

When installing anchors in hollow walls or ceilings, regardless of the type, always follow the manufacturer's recommendations pertaining to use, hole diameter, wall thickness, grip range (thickness of the anchoring material), and the pullout and shear load capacities.

8.6.1 Toggle Bolts

Toggle bolts (*Figure 49*) are used to fasten equipment, hangers, supports, and similar items into hollow surfaces such as walls and ceilings. They consist of a slotted bolt or screw and spring-loaded

WARNING!
Follow all safety precautions to avoid injury.

wings. When inserted through the item to be fastened, then through a predrilled hole in the wall or ceiling, the wings spring apart and provide a firm hold on the inside of the hollow wall or ceiling as the bolt is tightened. Note that the hole drilled in the wall or ceiling should be just large enough for the compressed wing-head to pass through. Once the toggle bolt is installed, be careful not to completely unscrew the bolt because the wings will fall off, making the fastener useless. Screw-actuated plastic toggle bolts are also made. These are similar to metal toggle bolts, but they come with a pointed screw and do not require as large a hole. Unlike the metal version, the plastic wings remain in place if the screw is removed.

Toggle bolts are used to fasten a part to hollow block, wallboard, plaster, panel, or tile. The following procedure can be used to install toggle bolts:

Step 1 Select the proper size drill bit or punch and toggle bolt for the job.

Step 2 Check the toggle bolt for damaged or dirty threads or a malfunctioning wing mechanism.

Step 3 Drill a hole completely through the surface to which the part is to be fastened.

Step 4 Insert the toggle bolt through the opening in the item to be fastened.

Step 5 Screw the toggle wing onto the end of the toggle bolt, ensuring that the flat side of the toggle wing is facing the bolt head.

Step 6 Fold the wings completely back and push them through the drilled hole until the wings spring open.

Step 7 Pull back on the item to be fastened to hold the wings firmly against the inside surface to which the item is being attached.

Step 8 Tighten the toggle bolt with a screwdriver until it is snug.

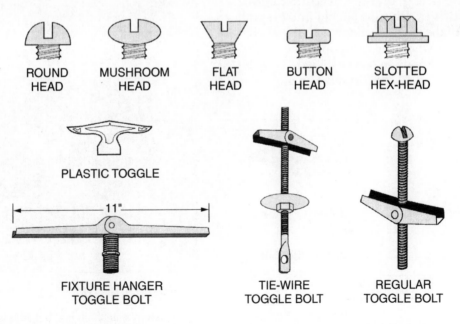

ROUND HEAD   MUSHROOM HEAD   FLAT HEAD   BUTTON HEAD   SLOTTED HEX-HEAD

PLASTIC TOGGLE

11"

FIXTURE HANGER TOGGLE BOLT   TIE-WIRE TOGGLE BOLT   REGULAR TOGGLE BOLT

104F49.EPS

Figure 49 ◆ Toggle bolts.

8.6.2 Sleeve-Type Wall Anchors

Sleeve-type wall anchors (*Figure 50*) are suitable for use in plywood, wallboard, and similar materials. The two types made are standard and drive. The standard type is commonly used in walls and ceilings and is installed by drilling a mounting hole to the required diameter. Insert the anchor into the hole and tap it until the gripper prongs embed in the base material. Tighten the anchor screw to draw the anchor tight against the inside of the wall or ceiling.

The drive-type anchor is hammered into the material without the need for drilling a mounting hole. After the anchor is installed, remove the anchor screw. Position the component being fastened in place, then reinstall the screw through the mounting hole in the component and into the anchor. Tighten the screw into the anchor to secure the component.

8.6.3 Wallboard Anchors

Wallboard anchors (*Figure 50*) are self-drilling medium- and light-duty anchors used for fastening in wallboard. Using a Phillips head manual or cordless screwdriver, drive the anchor into the wall until the head of the anchor is flush with the wall or ceiling surface. Position the component being fastened over the anchor, then secure it by driving the proper size sheet metal screw into the anchor.

8.6.4 Metal Drive-In Anchors

Metal drive-in anchors (*Figure 50*) are used to fasten light to medium loads to wallboard. They have two pointed legs that stay together when the anchor is hammered into a wall and spread out against the inside of the wall when a No. 6 or 8 sheet metal screw is driven in.

9.0.0 ◆ EPOXY ANCHORING SYSTEMS

Epoxy resin compounds can be used to anchor threaded rods, dowels, and similar fasteners in solid concrete, hollow wall, and brick. For one product, a two-part epoxy is packaged in a two-chamber cartridge that keeps the resin and hardener ingredients separated until use. This cartridge is placed into a special tool similar to a caulking gun. When the gun handle is pumped, the epoxy resin and hardener components are mixed within the gun; then the epoxy is ejected from the gun nozzle.

To use epoxy to install an anchor in solid concrete (*Figure 51*), drill a hole of the proper size in the concrete and clean it using a nylon (not metal) brush. Dispense a small amount of epoxy from the gun to make sure that the resin and hardener have mixed properly. This is indicated by the epoxy

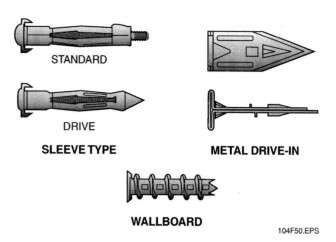

Figure 50 ◆ Sleeve-type, wallboard, and metal drive-in anchors.

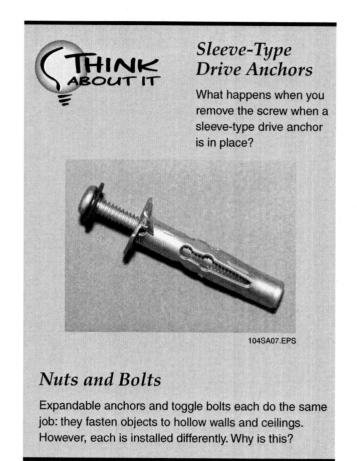

being of a uniform color. Then place the gun nozzle into the hole, and inject the epoxy into the hole until half the depth of the hole is filled. Push the selected fastener into the hole with a slow twisting motion to make sure that the epoxy fills all voids and crevices, then set it to the required plumb (or level) position. After the recommended cure time for the epoxy has elapsed, tighten the fastener nut to secure the component or fixture in place.

The procedure for installing a fastener in a hollow wall or brick when using epoxy is basically the same as the one just described. The difference is that the epoxy is first injected into an anchor screen to fill the screen, then the anchor screen is installed into the drilled hole. Use of the anchor screen is necessary to hold the epoxy intact in the hole until the anchor is inserted into the epoxy.

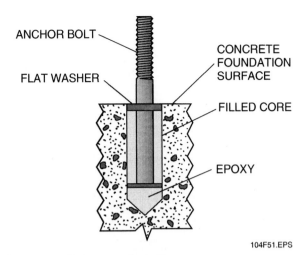

Figure 51 ◆ Fastener anchored in epoxy.

Installation Requirements

In a college dormitory, battery-powered emergency lights were anchored to sheetrock hallway ceilings with sheetrock screws, with no additional support. These fixtures weigh 8–10 pounds each and might easily have fallen out of the ceiling, causing severe injury. When the situation was discovered, the contractor had to remove and replace dozens of fixtures.

The Bottom Line: Incorrect anchoring methods can be both costly and dangerous.

Ceiling Installations

In the dormitory problem discussed above, which of the following fasteners could have been used to safely secure the emergency lights?

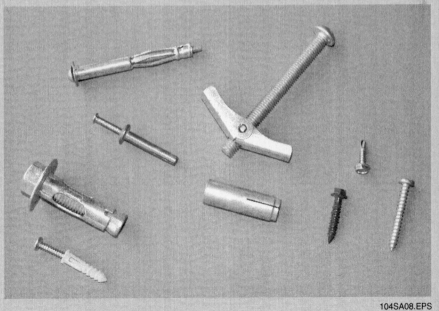

104SA08.EPS

Using Epoxy

Once mixed, epoxy has a limited working time. Therefore, mix exactly what you need and work quickly. After the working time is up, epoxy requires a specific curing time. Always give epoxy its recommended curing time; since epoxy is so strong and sets so quickly, you'll be tempted to stress the bond before it's fully cured.

Use the Proper Tool for the Application

To avoid damaging fasteners, use the correct tool for the job. For example, don't use pliers to install bolts, and don't use a screwdriver that is too large or too small.

Putting It All Together

You are installing a surface-mounted panel. What fasteners would you use in each of the following types of wall construction?

- Sheetrock wall with wood studs
- Sheetrock wall with metal studs
- Concrete masonry units (hollow block)
- Poured concrete

Summary

Fasteners and anchors are used for a variety of tasks. In this module, you learned about various types of fasteners and anchors and their uses. Basic installation procedures were also included. Selecting the correct fastener or anchor for a particular job is required to perform high-quality work. It is important to be familiar with the correct terms used to describe fasteners and anchors. Using the proper technical terms helps avoid confusion and improper selection. Installation techniques for fasteners and anchors may vary depending on the job. Make sure to check the project specifications and manufacturer's information when installing any fastener or anchor.

New fasteners and anchors are being developed every day. Your local distributor or manufacturer is an excellent source of information.

Review Questions

1. The quality of some fasteners can be determined by the _____ on the head of a bolt or screw.
   a. number of grooves cut
   b. number of sides
   c. length of the lines
   d. grade markings

2. The purpose of a jam nut is to _____.
   a. hold a piece of material stationary
   b. lock a standard nut in place
   c. stop rotation of a machine quickly for safety reasons
   d. compress a lock washer in place

3. Washers are used to _____.
   a. distribute the fastener load over a larger area
   b. attach an item to a hollow surface
   c. anchor materials that expand due to temperature changes
   d. allow the bolts to expand with temperature changes

4. Torque is normally expressed in _____.
   a. pounds per square inch (psi)
   b. gallons per minute (gpm)
   c. foot-pounds (ft-lbs)
   d. cubic feet per minute (cpm)

5. When tightening bolts, nuts, or screws, always use the proper _____.
   a. tightening sequence
   b. bolt pattern
   c. ratchet wrench
   d. lubrication

6. What type of fasteners are commonly used as lifting devices?
   a. Toggle bolts
   b. Anchor bolts
   c. J-bolts
   d. Eye bolts

7. When installing a panel in concrete using a lag screw, you would also use a _____.
   a. drop-in anchor
   b. lag shield
   c. caulk-in anchor
   d. double-expansion anchor

8. When fastening a device or fixture to concrete using concrete/masonry screws, the screws _____.
   a. need not be installed in predrilled holes because they are self-tapping
   b. are installed using specially designed carbide drill bits and installation tools made for use with the screws
   c. are installed by hammering them into a drilled or punched hole of the proper size
   d. are installed in a hole drilled with a standard masonry drill bit

9. When using powder-actuated tools and fasteners, _____.
   a. higher-numbered power level loads are used to drive into soft materials
   b. use only powder loads and fasteners that are specifically designed for use with the installation tool
   c. you may use powder loads interchangeably between different tools
   d. you may use standard fasteners

10. Wedge and sleeve anchors are classified as _____ anchors.
    a. bolt
    b. hollow-wall
    c. one-step
    d. screw

Larry Garter, Master Instructor/Consultant
NSCA University

Larry Garter turned a youthful fascination with electronics into a satisfying lifelong career.

How did you get started in the electronics field?
I was interested in electronics at a young age. When I was 16, I was very involved in the school audio-visual program. I also had my own sound and light company to provide music and lights for entertainment venues. After high school, I enrolled in a two-year electronics program while working as a broadcast engineer at a local ABC-affiliate TV station. I ran a video camera, maintained audio equipment, and did the audio recording for local programming, including the news. Later, a friend encouraged me to apply for a job with a local sound and telephone systems contractor, and I was on my way.

What kinds of work have you done in your career?
My career has been heavy in sound system design and installation. However, I have taken training courses and worked as an installer and technician in just about all the EST disciplines, including telephone, nurse call systems, CATV, structured wiring, professional and commercial sound, and CCTV. In fact, the only technical area I haven't worked in is security systems.

What do you do in your current job?
I work part time for NSCA as a master instructor. My job is to conduct EST courses and to develop content for on-line training courses. I also conduct a two-day prep course for NSCA certification at locations around the country. Closer to home, I work as a network administrator for a local consortium of 12 school districts and manage their high-speed, voice, video, and data network. And I have my own consulting business where I do design and management of integrated media systems for schools.

What factors have contributed most to your success?
The biggest thing that contributed to my success is a lifelong interest in electronics, especially video, audio, telephone systems, and computers. The technologies are challenging and interesting. One great thing about it is that the technology is constantly evolving so there's always something new and interesting on the horizon.

What advice would you give to someone just entering the field?
My advice would be to take all the classes you can and get certified in as many specialties as you can. It's important to build a good library and to subscribe to industry publications. You have to be a reader to keep up with changes. Another way to keep up is to get involved with organizations such as NSCA and other industry associations. These organizations are always on the cutting edge of technology and they are helping to set standards for the industry. In addition, by participating you meet people who have common interests and with whom you can exchange knowledge.

Do you have an interesting career-related fact or accomplishment to share?
I produced and directed a children's video program. I also did the sound system design and managed the sound system installation for the Interlochen Arts Academy, which is an internationally known school for music and other performing arts in Michigan.

Trade Terms Introduced in This Module

American Society for Testing and Materials (ASTM) International: An organization that publishes specifications and standards relating to fasteners.

Clearance: The amount of space between the threads of bolts and their nuts.

Ferrule: A mechanical fixture, usually a rigid tube, used to protect and align the stripped end of a wire or fiber.

Foot-pounds (ft-lbs): The normal method used for measuring the amount of torque being applied to bolts or nuts.

Inch-pounds (in-lbs): A method of measuring the amount of torque applied to small bolts or nuts that require measurement in smaller increments than foot-pounds.

Key: A machined metal part that fits into a keyway and prevents parts such as gears or pulleys from rotating on a shaft.

Keyway: A machined slot in a shaft and on parts such as gears and pulleys that accepts a key.

Nominal size: A means of expressing the size of a bolt or screw. It is the approximate diameter of a bolt or screw.

Society of Automotive Engineers (SAE): An organization that publishes specifications and standards relating to fasteners.

Thread classes: Threads are distinguished by three classifications according to the amount of tolerance the threads provide between the bolt and nut.

Thread identification: Standard symbols used to identify threads.

Thread standards: An established set of standards for machining threads.

Tolerance: The amount of difference allowed from a standard.

Torque: The turning force applied to a fastener.

Unified National Coarse (UNC) thread: A standard type of coarse thread.

Unified National Extra Fine (UNEF) thread: A standard type of extra-fine thread.

Unified National Fine (UNF) thread: A standard type of fine thread.

Mechanical Anchors and Their Uses

Anchor Type	Typically Used In	Use with Fastener	Typical Working Load Range*
One-Step Anchors			
Wedge	Concrete **Stone	None	Light, medium, and heavy duty
Stud	Concrete **Stone, solid brick and block	None	Light, medium, and heavy duty
Sleeve	Concrete, solid brick and block **Stone, hollow brick and block	None	Light and medium duty
One-piece	Concrete, solid block **Stone, solid and hollow brick, hollow block	None	Light and medium duty
Hammer-set	Concrete, solid block **Stone, solid and hollow brick, hollow block	None	Light duty
Bolt Anchors			
Drop-in	Concrete **Stone, solid brick	Machine screw or bolt	Light, medium, and heavy duty
Hollow-set drop-in	Concrete, solid brick and block **Stone, hollow brick and block	Machine screw or bolt	Light and medium duty
Single-expansion	Concrete, solid brick and block **Stone, hollow brick and block	Machine screw or bolt	Light and medium duty
Double-expansion	Concrete, solid brick and block **Stone, hollow brick and block	Machine screw or bolt	Light and medium duty
Screw Anchors			
Lag shield	Concrete **Stone, solid and hollow brick and block	Lag screw	Light and medium duty
Fiber	Concrete, stone, solid brick and block **Hollow brick and block, wallboard	Wood, sheet metal, or lag screw	Light and medium duty
Plastic	Concrete, stone, solid brick and block **Hollow brick and block, wallboard	Wood or sheet metal screw	Light duty
Hollow-Wall Anchors			
Toggle bolts	Concrete, plank, hollow block, wallboard, plywood/paneling	None	Light and medium duty
Plastic toggle bolts	Wallboard, plywood/paneling **Hollow block, structural tile	Wood or sheet metal screw	Light duty
Sleeve-type wall	Wallboard, plywood/paneling **Hollow block, structural tile	None	Light duty
Wallboard	Wallboard	Sheet metal screw	Light duty
Metal drive-in	Wallboard	Sheet metal screw	Light duty

*Anchor working loads given in the table are defined below. These are approximate loads only. Actual allowable loads depend on such factors as the anchor style and size, base material strength, spacing and edge distance, and the type of service load applied. Always consult the anchor manufacturer's product literature to determine the correct type of anchor and size to use for a specific application.
  • Light duty—Less than 400 lbs.   • Medium duty—400 to 4,000 lbs.   • Heavy duty—Above 4,000 lbs.
**Indicates use may be suitable depending on the application.

104A01.EPS

Additional Resources

This module is intended to be a thorough resource for task training. The following reference works are suggested for further study. These are optional materials for continued education rather than for task training.

American Electrician's Handbook, 13th Edition. New York: McGraw-Hill.

The Sheet Metal Toolbox Manual, 1991. New York: Prentice Hall.

Figure Credits

Topaz Publications, Inc.   104F35, 104F46 (photo), 104SA01, 104SA02, 104SA04–104SA08

Irwin Industrial Tool Company   104SA03

The NCCER makes every effort to keep these textbooks up-to-date and free of technical errors. We appreciate your help in this process. If you have an idea for improving this textbook, or if you find an error, a typographical mistake, or an inaccuracy in NCCER's Contren® textbooks, please write us, using this form or a photocopy. Be sure to include the exact module number, page number, a detailed description, and the correction, if applicable. Your input will be brought to the attention of the Technical Review Committee. Thank you for your assistance.

Instructors – If you found that additional materials were necessary in order to teach this module effectively, please let us know so that we may include them in the Equipment/Materials list in the Instructor's Guide.

Write: Product Development and Revision
National Center for Construction Education and Research
P.O. Box 141104, Gainesville, FL 32614-1104

Fax: 352-334-0932

E-mail: curriculum@nccer.org

Craft _____ Module Name _____

Copyright Date _____ Module Number _____ Page Number(s) _____

Description _____
_____
_____
_____
_____

(Optional) Correction _____
_____
_____

(Optional) Your Name and Address _____
_____
_____
_____

Job-Site Safety

COURSE MAP

This course map shows all of the modules in the first level of the *Electronic Systems Technician* curriculum. The suggested training order begins at the bottom and proceeds up. Skill levels increase as you advance on the course map. The local Training Program Sponsor may adjust the training order.

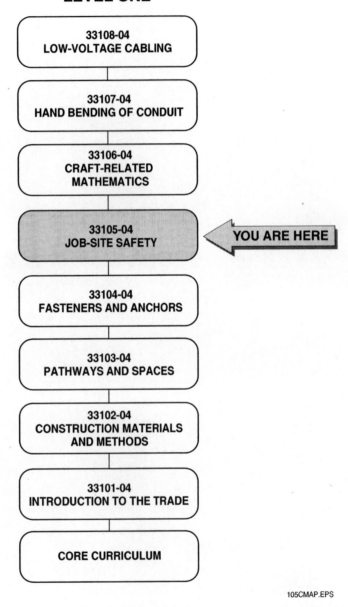

ELECTRONIC SYSTEMS TECHNICIAN
LEVEL ONE

33108-04
LOW-VOLTAGE CABLING

33107-04
HAND BENDING OF CONDUIT

33106-04
CRAFT-RELATED
MATHEMATICS

33105-04
JOB-SITE SAFETY ⟵ YOU ARE HERE

33104-04
FASTENERS AND ANCHORS

33103-04
PATHWAYS AND SPACES

33102-04
CONSTRUCTION MATERIALS
AND METHODS

33101-04
INTRODUCTION TO THE TRADE

CORE CURRICULUM

105CMAP.EPS

1.0.0 **INTRODUCTION** 5.1

2.0.0 **ELECTRICAL SHOCK** .5.2

    2.1.0 The Effect of Current 5.3

    2.1.1 Body Resistance .5.3

    2.1.2 Burns 5.5

3.0.0 **REDUCING YOUR RISK** 5.5

    3.1.0 Protective Equipment 5.6

    3.1.1 Personal Clothing 5.6

    3.1.2 Fuse Pullers 5.7

    3.1.3 Shorting Probes 5.7

    3.1.4 Eye and Face Protection 5.7

    3.2.0 Verify That Circuits Are De-energized 5.7

    3.3.0 Other Precautions 5.7

4.0.0 **OSHA** 5.7

    4.1.0 Safety Standards 5.8

    4.2.0 Safety Philosophy and General Safety Precautions 5.8

    4.3.0 Electrical Regulations 5.10

    4.3.1 OSHA Lockout/Tagout Rule 5.11

    4.4.0 Other OSHA Regulations 5.13

    4.4.1 Testing for Voltage 5.14

5.0.0 **LADDERS AND SCAFFOLDS** 5.15

    5.1.0 Ladders 5.15

    5.1.1 Straight and Extension Ladders 5.15

    5.1.2 Step Ladders .5.16

    5.2.0 Scaffolds 5.16

6.0.0 **LIFTS, HOISTS, AND CRANES** 5.17

7.0.0 **LIFTING** 5.17

8.0.0 **BASIC TOOL SAFETY** 5.17

9.0.0 **CONFINED SPACE ENTRY PROCEDURES** 5.18

    9.1.0 Confined Space Classification 5.19

    9.1.1 Nonpermit-Required Confined Space 5.19

    9.1.2 Permit-Required Confined Space 5.20

    9.2.0 Entry Permits .5.20

    9.3.0 Atmospheric Hazards 5.20

    9.3.1 Oxygen-Deficient or Oxygen-Enriched Atmospheres 5.20

    9.3.2 Combustible Atmospheres 5.23

    9.3.3 Toxic Atmospheres 5.23

    9.3.4 Monitoring the Atmosphere in Confined Spaces 5.24

    9.4.0 Additional Hazards 5.24

9.4.1   *Electric Shock* 5.24

9.4.2   *Purging* 5.24

9.4.3   *Falling Objects* 5.25

9.4.4   *Engulfment* 5.25

9.4.5   *Extreme Temperatures* 5.25

9.4.6   *Noise* 5.25

9.4.7   *Slick or Wet Surfaces* 5.25

9.4.8   *Moving Parts* 5.25

9.5.0   Responsibilities and Duties 5.26

9.5.1   *Entrants* 5.26

9.5.2   *Attendants* 5.26

9.5.3   *Supervisors* 5.26

9.5.4   *Rescue Workers* 5.27

9.6.0   Safeguards 5.27

9.6.1   *Monitoring and Testing* 5.27

9.6.2   *Ventilation* 5.28

9.6.3   *Personal Protective Equipment* .5.28

9.6.4   *Communication* 5.29

9.6.5   *Training* 5.29

10.0.0 FIRST AID 5.29

11.0.0 SOLVENTS AND TOXIC VAPORS .5.29

11.1.0   Precautions When Using Solvents 5.30

11.2.0   Respiratory Protection 5.30

12.0.0 ASBESTOS 5.30

12.1.0   Monitoring 5.31

12.2.0   Regulated Areas 5.31

12.3.0   Methods of Compliance 5.32

13.0.0 BATTERIES 5.32

13.1.0   Acids 5.33

13.2.0   Wash Stations 5.33

14.0.0 PCBs 5.33

15.0.0 FALL PROTECTION 5.33

15.1.0   Fall Protection Procedures 5.33

15.2.0   Types of Fall Protection Systems .5.33

SUMMARY 5.34

REVIEW QUESTIONS 5.34

PROFILE IN SUCCESS 5.35

GLOSSARY 5.37

REFERENCES & ACKNOWLEDGMENTS .5.38

Figures

Figure 1   Body resistance 5.4

Figure 2   Fuse pullers 5.6

Figure 3   Double-insulated electric drill 5.10

Figure 4   Typical GFCI 5.11

Figure 5   Extension cord with a GFCI .5.11

Figure 6   Lockout/tagout device 5.13

Figure 7   Multiple lockout/tagout device 5.13

Figure 8   Straight ladder positioning 5.15

Figure 9   Proper lifting 5.18

Figure 10   Entry permit 5.21–5.22

Figure 11   Detection meters 5.23

Figure 12   Buried alive 5.25

Figure 13   Attendant checks the atmosphere 5.26

Figure 14   Non-entry rescue 5.27

Figure 15   Proper positive ventilation 5.28

Figure 16   Standard personal protective equipment 5.29

Figure 17   Portion of an MSDS 5.31

Tables

Table 1   Current Level Effects on the Human Body 5.2

Table 2   Approach Distances for Qualified
           Employees—Alternating Current 5.5

Job-Site Safety

Objectives

When you have completed this module, you will be able to do the following:

1. Demonstrate safe working procedures in a construction environment.
2. Explain the purpose of OSHA and how it promotes safety on the job.
3. Identify electrical hazards and how to avoid or minimize them in the workplace.
4. Explain safety issues concerning lockout/tagout procedures, personal protection using assured grounding and isolation programs, confined space entry, respiratory protection, and fall protection systems.

Recommended Prerequisites

Core Curriculum; Electronic Systems Technician Level One, Modules 33101-04 through 33104-04

Required Trainee Materials

1. Paper and pencil
2. Copy of the latest edition of the *National Electrical Code®*
3. *OSHA 3075, Controlling Electrical Hazards* (available for free at www.osha.gov/pls/publications/pubindex.list)
4. Appropriate personal protective equipment

1.0.0 ◆ INTRODUCTION

As an electronic systems technician, you will be exposed to many potentially hazardous conditions that will exist on the job site. No training manual, set of rules and regulations, or listing of hazards can make working conditions completely safe. However, it is possible for an EST to work a full career without serious accident or injury. To reach this goal, you need to be aware of potential hazards and stay constantly alert to these hazards. You must take the proper precautions and practice the basic rules of safety. You must be safety-conscious at all times. Safety should become a habit. Keeping a safe attitude on the job will go a long way in reducing the number and severity of accidents. Remember that your safety is up to you.

As an apprentice, you need to be especially careful. You should only work under the direction of experienced personnel who are familiar with the various job site hazards and the means of avoiding them.

The most life-threatening hazards on a construction site are as follows:

- Falls when you are working in high places
- Electrocution caused by coming into contact with live electrical circuits
- The possibility of being crushed by falling materials or equipment
- The possibility of being struck by flying objects or moving equipment/vehicles such as trucks, forklifts, and construction equipment

Note: The designations "*National Electrical Code®*" and "NEC®," where used in this document, refer to the *National Electrical Code®*, which is a registered trademark of the National Fire Protection Association, Quincy, MA. *All National Electrical Code® (NEC®) references in this module refer to the 2002 edition of the NEC®.*

Other hazards include cuts, burns, back sprains, and getting chemicals or objects in your eyes. Most injuries, both those that are life-threatening and those that are less severe, are preventable if the proper precautions are taken.

2.0.0 ◆ ELECTRICAL SHOCK

Electricity can be described as a potential that results in the movement of electrons in a conductor. This movement of electrons is called electrical current. Some substances, such as silver, copper, steel, and aluminum, are excellent conductors. The human body is also a conductor. The conductivity of the human body greatly increases when the skin is wet or moistened with perspiration.

❋ Electrical current flows along the path of least resistance to return to its source. The source return point is called the neutral or ground of a circuit. If the human body contacts an electrically energized point and is also in contact with the ground or another point in the circuit, the human body becomes a path for the current to return to its source. *Table 1* shows the effects of current passing through the human body. One mA is one milliamp, or one one-thousandth of an ampere.

A primary cause of death from electrical shock is when the heart's rhythm is overcome by an electrical current. Normally, the heart's operation uses a very low-level electrical signal to cause the heart to contract and pump blood. When an abnormal electrical signal, such as current from an electrical shock, reaches the heart, the low-level heartbeat signals are overcome. The heart begins twitching in an irregular manner and goes out of rhythm with the pulse. This twitching is called **fibrillation.** Unless the normal heartbeat rhythm is restored using special defibrillation equipment

What's Wrong with This Picture?

105SA01.EPS

Table 1 Current Level Effects on the Human Body

Current Value	Typical Effects
1mA	Perception level. Slight tingling sensation.
5mA	Slight shock. Involuntary reactions can result in serious injuries such as falls from elevations.
6 to 30mA	Painful shock, loss of muscular control.
50 to 150mA	Extreme pain, respiratory arrest, severe muscular contractions. Death is possible.
1000 to 4300mA	Ventricular fibrillation, severe muscular contractions, nerve damage. Typically results in death.

SOURCE: Occupational Safety and Health Administration

105T01.EPS

Electrical Safety in the Workplace

Each year in the U.S., there are approximately 20,000 electricity-related accidents at home and in the workplace. In a recent year, these accidents resulted in 700 deaths. Electrical accidents are the third leading cause of death in the workplace.

Severity of Shock

In *Table 1*, how many milliamps separate a mild shock from a potentially fatal one? What is the fractional equivalent of this in amps? How many amps are drawn by a 60W light bulb?

(paddles), the individual will die. No known case of heart fibrillation has ever been corrected without the use of defibrillation equipment by a qualified medical practitioner. Other effects of electrical shock may include immediate heart stoppage and burns. In addition, the body's reaction to the shock can cause a fall or other accident. Delayed internal symptoms can also result.

2.1.0 The Effect of Current

The amount of current, measured in amperes, that passes through a body determines the outcome of an electrical shock. The higher the voltage, the greater the chance for a fatal shock. In a one-year study in California, the following results were observed by the State Division of Industry Safety:

- Thirty percent of all electrical accidents were caused by contact with conductors. Of these accidents, 66 percent involved low-voltage conductors (those carrying 600 volts [V] or less).

NOTE

Electric shocks or burns are a major cause of accidents in our industry. According to the Bureau of Labor Statistics, electrical shock is the leading cause of death in the electrical industry.

- Portable, electrically operated hand tools made up the second largest number of injuries (15 percent). Almost 70 percent of these injuries happened when the frame or case of the tool became energized. These injuries could have been prevented by following proper safety practices, using **grounded** or **double-insulated/ungrounded tools**, and using ground fault circuit interrupter (GFCI) protection.

In one ten-year study, investigators found 9,765 electrical injuries that occurred in accidents. Over 18 percent of these injuries involved contact with voltage levels of over 600 volts. A little more than 13 percent of these high-voltage injuries resulted in death. These high-voltage totals included limited-amperage contacts, which are often found on electronic equipment. When tools or equipment touch high-voltage overhead lines, the chance that a resulting injury will be fatal climbs to 28 percent. Of the low-voltage injuries, 1.4 percent were fatal.

CAUTION

High voltage, defined as 600 volts or more, is almost ten times as likely to kill as low voltage. However, on the job you spend most of your time working on or near lower voltages. Due to the frequency of contact, most electrocution deaths actually occur at low voltages. Attitudes about the harmlessness of lower voltages undoubtedly contribute to this statistic.

These statistics have been included to help you gain respect for the environment where you work and to stress how important safe working habits really are.

2.1.1 Body Resistance

Electricity travels in closed circuits, and its normal route is through a conductor. Shock occurs when the body becomes part of the electric circuit (*Figure 1*). The current must enter the body at one point and leave at another. Shock normally occurs in one of three ways: the person must come in contact with both wires of the electric circuit, one wire of the electric circuit and the ground, or a metallic part that has become hot by being in contact with

Electrocution

Why can a bird perch safely on an electric wire? Squirrels are a common cause of shorts at substations; why does a squirrel get electrocuted when a bird does not? To fully understand the harm done by electrical shock, we need to understand something about the physiology of certain body parts: the skin, the heart, and muscles

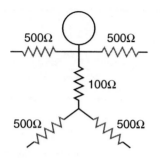

- HAND TO HAND 1000Ω
- 120 VOLT
- FORMULA: I = E/R
- 120/1000 = 0.120 AMPS
  OR 120 MILLIAMPS

105F01.EPS

Figure 1 ◆ Body resistance.

an energized wire while the person is also in contact with the ground.

Skin covers the body and is made up of three layers. The most important layer, as far as electric shock is concerned, is the outer layer of dead cells referred to as the horny layer. This layer is composed mostly of a protein called keratin, and it is the keratin that provides the largest percentage of the body's electrical resistance. When it is dry, the outer layer of skin may have a resistance of several thousand ohms, but when it is moist, there is a radical drop in resistance, as is also the case if there is a cut or abrasion that pierces the horny layer. The amount of resistance provided by the skin will vary widely from individual to individual. A worker with a thick horny layer will have a much higher resistance than a child. The resistance will also vary widely at different parts of the body. For instance, the worker with high-resistance hands may have low-resistance skin on the back of his calf. The skin, like any insulator, has a breakdown voltage at which it ceases to act as a resistor and is simply punctured, leaving only the lower-resistance body tissue to impede the flow of current in the body. The breakdown voltage will vary with the individual, but is in the area of 600V.

The heart is the pump that sends life-sustaining blood to all parts of the body. The blood flow is caused by the contractions of the heart muscle, which is controlled by electrical impulses. The electrical impulses are delivered by an intricate system of nerve tissue with built-in timing mechanisms, which make the chambers of the heart contract at exactly the right time. An outside electric current of as little as 75 milliamperes can upset the rhythmic, coordinated beating of the heart by disturbing the nerve impulses. When this happens, the heart is said to be in fibrillation, and the pumping action stops. Death will occur quickly if the normal beat is not restored. Remarkable as it may seem, what is needed to defibrillate the heart is a shock of an even higher intensity.

The other muscles of the body are also controlled by electrical impulses delivered by nerves. Electric shock can cause loss of muscular control, resulting in the inability to let go of an electrical conductor. Electric shock can also cause injuries of an indirect nature in which involuntary muscle reaction from the electric shock can cause bruises, fractures, and even deaths resulting from collisions or falls.

The severity of shock received when a person becomes a part of an electric circuit is affected by three primary factors: the amount of current flowing through the body (measured in amperes), the path of the current through the body, and the length of time the body is in the circuit. Other factors that may affect the severity of the shock are the frequency of the current, the phase of the heart cycle when shock occurs, and the general health of the person prior to the shock. Effects can range from a barely perceptible tingle to immediate cardiac arrest. Although there are no absolute limits, or even known values that show the exact injury at any given amperage range, *Table 1* lists the general effects of electric current on the body for different current levels. As this table illustrates, a difference of only 100 milliamperes exists between a current that is barely perceptible and one that can kill.

A severe shock can cause considerably more damage to the body than is visible. For example, a person may suffer internal hemorrhages and destruction of tissues, nerves, and muscle. In addition, shock is often only the beginning in a chain of events. The final injury may well be from a fall, cuts, burns, or broken bones.

Bodily Harm

What factors affect the amount of damage to the body during an electric shock?

Dangers of Electricity

Never underestimate the power of electricity. For example, the current through a 25W light bulb is more than enough to kill you.

Emergency Response

If someone near you is receiving an electrical shock, do not touch that person. Instead, immediately turn off the power source. If that is not possible, try using nonconductive material such as a blanket, rope, coat, piece of dry wood, or a belt to separate the person from the electrical source. Never use anything wet or damp. If you touch the person with your body, use a metal object, or use wet or damp material, you could also become a victim.

Once the person has been separated from the shock source, immediately call for medical help. If the victim is not breathing, a trained person should immediately begin artificial respiration.

2.1.2 Burns

The most common shock-related injury is a burn. Burns suffered in electrical accidents may be of three types: electrical burns, arc burns, and thermal contact burns.

Electrical burns are the result of electric current flowing through the tissues or bones. Tissue damage is caused by the heat generated by the current flow through the body. An electrical burn is one of the most serious injuries you can receive, and should be given immediate attention. Because the most severe burning is likely to be internal, what may appear at first to be a small surface wound could, in fact, be an indication of severe internal burns.

Arc burns make up a substantial portion of the injuries from electrical malfunctions. The electric arc between metals can be up to 35,000°F, which is about four times hotter than the surface of the sun. Workers several feet from the source of the arc can receive severe or fatal burns. Because most electrical safety guidelines recommend safe working distances based on shock considerations, workers can be following these guidelines and still be at risk from arc. Electric arcs can occur due to poor electrical contact or failed insulation. Electrical arcing is caused by the passage of substantial amounts of current through the vaporized terminal material (usually metal or carbon).

The third type is a thermal contact burn. It is caused by contact with objects thrown during the blast associated with an electric arc. This blast comes from the pressure developed by the near-instantaneous heating of the air surrounding the arc, and from the expansion of the metal as it is vaporized. Copper, for example, expands by a factor in excess of 65,000 times in boiling. These pressures can be great enough to hurl people, switchgear, and cabinets considerable distances. Another hazard associated with the blast is the hurling of molten metal droplets, which can also cause thermal contact burns and associated damage. A possible beneficial side effect of the blast is that it could hurl a nearby person away from the arc, thereby reducing the effect of arc burns.

CAUTION

The heat of the arc depends on the short circuit current available at the arcing point. Thus, arcs generated on 480V systems can be just as dangerous as those generated at 13,000V.

3.0.0 ◆ REDUCING YOUR RISK

There are many things that you can do to greatly reduce your chances of receiving an electrical shock. Always comply with your company's safety policy and all applicable rules and regulations, including job site rules. In addition, the Occupational Safety and Health Administration (OSHA) publishes the *Code of Federal Regulations (CFR)*. *CFR Part 1910* covers the OSHA standards for general industry and *CFR Part 1926* covers the OSHA standards for the construction industry.

Do not approach any electrical conductors closer than indicated in *Table 2* unless you are sure they are de-energized and your company has designated you as a qualified individual. Also, the values given in the table are minimum safe clearance distances; if you already have standard distances established, these are provided only as supplemental information. These distances are listed in *CFR 1910.333/1926.416*.

Table 2 Approach Distances for Qualified Employees— Alternating Current

Voltage Range (Phase-to-Phase)	Minimum Approach Distance
300V and less	Avoid contact
Over 300V, not over 750V	1 ft 0 in (30.5 cm)
Over 750V, not over 2kV	1 ft 6 in (46 cm)
Over 2kV, not over 15kV	2 ft 0 in (61 cm)
Over 15kV, not over 37kV	3 ft 0 in (91 cm)
Over 37kV, not over 87.5kV	3 ft 6 in (107 cm)
Over 87.5kV, not over 121kV	4 ft 0 in (122 cm)
Over 121kV, not over 140kV	4 ft 6 in (137 cm)

105T02.EPS

3.1.0 Protective Equipment

You should also become familiar with common personal protective equipment. In particular, you should know the voltage rating of each piece of equipment. OSHA addresses the use of protective equipment, apparel, and tools in *CFR 1910.335(a)*. This article is divided into two sections: *Personal Protective Equipment* and *General Protective Equipment and Tools*.

The first section, *Personal Protective Equipment*, includes the following requirements:

- Employees working in areas where there are potential electrical hazards shall be provided with, and shall use, electrical protective equipment that is appropriate for the specific parts of the body to be protected and for the work to be performed.

- Protective equipment shall be maintained in a safe, reliable condition and shall be periodically inspected or tested, as required by *CFR 1910.137/ 1926.95*.

- If the insulating capability of protective equipment may be subject to damage during use, the insulating material shall be protected.

- Employees shall wear nonconductive head protection wherever there is a danger of head injury from electric shock or burns due to contact with exposed energized parts.

- Employees shall wear protective equipment for the eyes and face wherever there is danger of injury to the eyes or face from electric arcs or flashes or from flying objects resulting from an electrical explosion.

The second section, *General Protective Equipment and Tools*, includes the following requirements:

- When working near exposed energized conductors or circuit parts, each employee shall use insulated tools or handling equipment if the tools or handling equipment might make contact with such conductors or parts. If the insulating capability of insulated tools or handling equipment is subject to damage, the insulating material shall be protected.

- Fuse handling equipment, insulated for the circuit voltage, shall be used to remove or install fuses when the fuse terminals are energized.

- Ropes and handlines used near exposed energized parts shall be nonconductive.

- Protective shields, protective barriers, or insulating materials shall be used to protect each employee from shock, burns, or other electrically related injuries while that employee is working near exposed energized parts that might be accidentally contacted or where dangerous electric heating or arcing might occur. When normally enclosed live parts are exposed for maintenance or repair, they shall be guarded to protect unqualified persons from contact with the live parts.

The types of electrical safety equipment, protective apparel, and protective tools available for use are quite varied. We will discuss the most common types of safety equipment. These include the following:

- Personal clothing
- Fuse pullers (*Figure 2*)
- Shorting probes
- Eye and face protection

3.1.1 Personal Clothing

Any individual who will perform work in an electrical environment or in plant substations must dress accordingly. Avoid wearing synthetic-fiber clothing; these types of materials will melt when exposed to high temperatures and will actually increase the severity of a burn. Wear cotton clothing, fiberglass-toe boots or shoes, and hard hats. Use hearing protection where needed. Remove all jewelry.

105F02.EPS

Figure 2 ◆ Fuse pullers.

3.1.2 Fuse Pullers

Use the plastic or fiberglass style of fuse puller for removing and installing low-voltage cartridge fuses. All fuse pulling and replacement operations must be done using fuse pullers.

The best type of fuse puller has a spread guard. A spread guard will prevent a fuse puller from opening if resistance is met when installing fuses.

3.1.3 Shorting Probes

Before working on de-energized circuits that have capacitors installed, you must discharge the capacitors using a safety shorting probe. When using a shorting probe, first connect the test clip to a good ground to make contact. If necessary, scrape the paint from the metal surface. Then, hold the shorting probe by the handle and touch the probe end of the shorting rod to the points to be shorted. The probe end can be hooked over the part or terminal to provide a constant connection to ground. Never touch any metal part of the shorting probe while grounding circuits or components. Whenever possible, especially when working on or near any de-energized high-voltage circuits, shorting probes should be connected and then left attached to the de-energized portion of any circuit for the duration of the work. This action serves as an extra safety precaution against any accidental application of voltage to the circuit.

3.1.4 Eye and Face Protection

NFPA 70-E requires that protective equipment for the eyes and face shall be used whenever there is danger of injury to the eyes or face from electrical arcs or flashes, or from flying or falling objects resulting from an electrical explosion.

3.2.0 Verify That Circuits Are De-energized

You should always assume that all the circuits are energized until you have verified that they are de-energized. Follow these steps to verify that a circuit is de-energized:

Step 1   Ensure that the circuit is properly tagged and locked out (*OSHA 1910.333/1926.417*).

Step 2   Verify the test instrument operation on a known source.

Step 3   Using the test instrument, check the circuit to be de-energized. The voltage should be zero.

Step 4   Using a known power source, verify the test instrument is working.

3.3.0 Other Precautions

There are several other precautions you can take to help make your job safer. For example:

- Always remove all jewelry, such as rings, watches, bracelets, and necklaces, before working on electrical equipment. Most jewelry is made of conductive material and wearing it can result in a shock, as well as other injuries if the jewelry gets caught in moving components.

- When working on energized equipment, it is safer to work in pairs. If one of the workers experiences a harmful electrical shock, the other worker can quickly de-energize the circuit and call for help.

- Plan each job before you begin it. Make sure you understand exactly what it is you are going to do. If you are not sure, ask your supervisor.

- You will need to look over the appropriate prints and drawings to locate isolation devices and potential hazards. Never defeat safety interlocks. Remember to plan your escape route before starting work. Know where the nearest phone is and the emergency number to dial for assistance.

- If you realize that the work will go beyond the scope of what was planned, stop and get instructions from your supervisor before continuing. Do not attempt to plan as you go.

- It is critical that you stay alert. Workplaces are dynamic, and situations relative to safety are always changing. If you leave the work area to pick up material, take a break, or have lunch, reevaluate your surroundings when you return. Remember, plan ahead.

4.0.0 ◆ OSHA

The purpose of OSHA is "to ensure safe and healthful working conditions for working men and women." OSHA is authorized to enforce standards and assist and encourage the states in their efforts to ensure safe and healthful working conditions. OSHA assists states by providing for research, information, education, and training in the field of occupational safety and health.

The law that established OSHA specifies the duties of both the employer and employee with respect to safety. Some of the key requirements are outlined below. This list does not include everything, nor does it override the procedures called for by your employer.

- Employers shall provide a place of employment free from recognized hazards likely to cause death or serious injury.
- Employers shall comply with the standards of the act.
- Employers shall be subject to fines and other penalties for violation of those standards.

NOTE

OSHA states that employees have a duty to follow the safety rules laid down by the employer. Additionally, some states can reduce the amount of benefits paid to an injured employee if that employee was not following known, established safety rules. Your company may also terminate you if you violate an established safety rule.

4.1.0 Safety Standards

OSHA standards are split into several sections. As discussed earlier, the two that affect you the most are *CFR 1926*, which is construction specific, and *CFR 1910*, which is the standard for general industry. Either or both may apply, depending on where you are working and what you are doing. If a job site condition is covered in the *1926* book, then that standard takes precedence. However, if a more stringent requirement is listed in the *1910* standard, it should also be met. An excellent example is the current difference in the two standards on confined spaces; if someone gets hurt or killed, the decision to use the less stringent *1926* standard could be called into question. OSHA's *General Duty Clause* states that an employer should have known all recognized hazards and removed the hazard or protected the employee.

To protect workers from the occupational injuries and fatalities caused by electrical hazards, OSHA has issued a set of design safety standards for electrical utilization systems. These standards are *1926.400–449* and *1910.302–308*. OSHA also recognizes the *National Electrical Code® (NEC®)* for certain installations.

NOTE

OSHA may not recognize the current edition of the NEC®, which can sometimes cause problems; however, OSHA typically will not cite for any differences.

CFR 1910 must be followed whenever the construction standard *CFR 1926* does not address an issue that is covered by *CFR 1910* or for a pre-existing installation. If *CFR 1910* is more stringent than *CFR 1926*, then the more stringent standard should be followed. OSHA does not update their standards in a timely manner. For that reason, there are often differences in similar sections of the two standards. Safety should always be first, and the more protective work rules should always be chosen.

4.2.0 Safety Philosophy and General Safety Precautions

The most important piece of safety equipment required when performing work in an electrical environment is common sense. All areas of electrical safety precautions and practices draw upon common sense and attention to detail. One of the most dangerous conditions in an electrical work area is a poor attitude toward safety.

WARNING

Only qualified individuals may work on electrical equipment. Your employer will determine who is qualified. Remember, your employer's safety rules must always be followed.

As stated in *CFR 1910.333(a)/1926.403*, safety-related work practices shall be employed to prevent electric shock or other injuries resulting from either direct or indirect electrical contact when work is performed near or on equipment or circuits that are or may be energized. The specific safety-related work practices shall be consistent with the nature and extent of the associated electrical hazards. The following are considered some of the basic and necessary attitudes and electrical safety precautions that lay the groundwork for a proper safety program. Before going on any electrical work assignment, these safety precautions should be reviewed and adhered to:

- *All work on electrical equipment should be done with circuits de-energized and cleared or grounded* – It is obvious that working on energized equipment is

much more dangerous than working on equipment that is de-energized. Work on energized electrical equipment should be avoided if at all possible. *CFR 1910.333(a)(1)/1926.403* states that live parts to which an employee may be exposed shall be de-energized before the employee works on or near them, unless the employer can demonstrate that de-energizing introduces additional or increased hazards or is not possible because of equipment design or operational limitations. Live parts that operate at less than 50 volts to ground need not be de-energized if there will be no increased exposure to electrical burns or to explosion due to electric arcs.

- *All conductors, buses, and connections should be considered energized until proven otherwise* – As stated in *1910.333(b)(1)/1926.417*, conductors and parts of electrical equipment that have not been locked out or tagged out in accordance with this section should be considered energized. Routine operation of the circuit breakers and disconnect switches contained in a power distribution system can be hazardous if not approached in the right manner. The following are several basic precautions you should take when operating circuit breakers:

  - Wear proper clothing made of 100 percent cotton or fire-resistant fabric.
  - Eye, face, and head protection should be worn. Turn your head away whenever closing devices.
  - Whenever operating circuit breakers in low-voltage or medium-voltage systems, always stand off to the side of the unit.
  - Always try to operate disconnect switches and circuit breakers under a no-load condition.
  - Never intentionally force an interlock on a system or circuit breaker.

  - Always verify what you are closing a device into; you could violate a lockout or close into a hard fault.

Often, a circuit breaker or disconnect switch is used for providing lockout on an electrical system. To ensure that a lockout is not violated, perform the following procedures when using the device as a lockout point:

- Again, you must lockout and tag breakers whenever you are working on a circuit that is tied to an energized breaker. This applies to breakers that are capable of being opened and racked out to the disconnected position. Afterward, approved safety locks must be installed. The breaker may be removed from its cubicle completely to prevent unexpected mishaps. Always follow the standard rack-out and removal procedures that were supplied with the switchgear. Once removed, a sign must be hung on the breaker identifying its use as a lockout point, and approved safety locks must be installed when the breaker is used for isolation. Breakers equipped with closing springs should be discharged to release all stored energy in the breaker mechanism.

- Some of the circuit breakers used are equipped with keyed interlocks for protection during operation. These locks are generally called kirk locks and are relied upon to ensure proper sequence of operation only. These are not to be used for locking out a circuit or system. Where disconnects are installed for use in isolation, they should never be opened under load. When opening a disconnect manually, it should be done quickly with a positive force. Again, lockouts should be used when the disconnects are open.

- Whenever performing switching or fuse replacements, always use the protective equipment necessary to ensure personnel safety. Never make the assumption that because things have gone fine the last 999 times, they will not go wrong this time. Always prepare yourself for the worst case accident when performing switching.

- Use extreme care whenever re-energizing circuits following maintenance or removal of a faulted component. Always verify that the equipment is in a condition to be re-energized safely. All connections should be insulated and all covers should be installed. Have all personnel stand clear of the area for the initial re-energization. Never assume everything is in perfect condition. Verify the conditions.

The following procedure is provided as a guideline for ensuring that equipment and systems will not be damaged by reclosing low-voltage circuit breakers into faults. If a low-voltage circuit breaker has opened for no apparent reason, perform the following:

Step 1 Verify that the equipment being supplied is not physically damaged and shows no obvious signs of overheating or fire.

Step 2 Make all appropriate tests to locate any faults.

Step 3 Reclose the feeder breaker. Stand off to the side when closing the breaker.

Step 4 If the circuit breaker trips again, do not attempt to reclose the breaker until the cause of the trip can be isolated and repaired.

4.3.0 Electrical Regulations

OSHA has certain regulations that apply to job site electrical safety. These regulations include the following:

- All electrical work shall be in compliance with the latest NEC® and OSHA standards.
- The noncurrent-carrying metal parts of fixed, portable, and plug-connected equipment shall be grounded. It is best to choose grounded tools. However, portable tools and appliances protected by an approved system of double insulation need not be grounded. *Figure 3* shows an example of a double-insulated/ungrounded tool.

- Extension cords shall be the three-wire type, shall be protected from damage, and shall not be fastened with staples or hung in a manner that could cause damage to the outer jacket or insulation. Never run an extension cord through a doorway or window that can pinch the cord. Also, never allow vehicles or equipment to drive over cords.

- Exposed lamps in temporary lights shall be guarded to prevent accidental contact, except where lamps are deeply recessed in the reflector. Temporary lights shall not be suspended, except in accordance with their listed labeling.

- Receptacles for attachment plugs shall be of an approved type and properly installed. Installation of the receptacle will be in accordance with the listing and labeling for each receptacle and shall be GFCI-protected if the setting is a temporarily wired construction site. If permanent receptacles are used with extension cords, then you must use GFCI protection.

- Each disconnecting means for motors and appliances and each service feeder or branch circuit at the point where it originates shall be legibly marked to indicate its purpose and voltage.

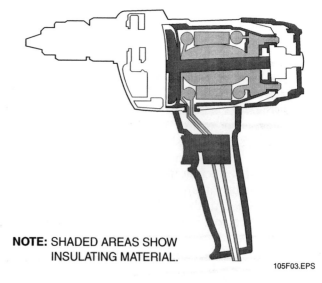

NOTE: SHADED AREAS SHOW INSULATING MATERIAL.

105F03.EPS

Figure 3 ◆ Double-insulated electric drill.

Working on Energized Systems

Some technicians commonly work on energized systems because they think it's too much trouble to turn off the power. What practices have you seen around your home or workplace that could be deadly?

- Flexible cords shall be used in continuous lengths (no splices) and shall be of a type listed in *NEC Table 400.4*.
- Ground fault protection is required when supplying temporary power to equipment used by personnel during any repair, remodel, maintenance, construction, and demolition activities. There are two methods for accomplishing this: an assured grounding program (limited to use in certain industrial applications only per *NEC Section 527.6*), or ground fault protection receptacles or breakers. Each employer will set the standard and method to be used. *Figure 4* shows a typical ground-fault circuit interrupter. *Figure 5* shows an extension cord with a GFCI.

4.3.1 OSHA Lockout/Tagout Rule

OSHA released the *29 CFR 1926* lockout/tagout rule in December 1991. This rule covers the specific procedure for the servicing and maintenance of machines and equipment where the "unexpected energization or startup of the machines or equipment, or releases of stored energy, could cause injury to employees."

The purpose of the OSHA procedure is to ensure that equipment is isolated from all potentially hazardous energy, including electrical, mechanical, hydraulic, chemical, or thermal, and tagged and locked out before employees perform any servicing or maintenance activities. All employees must be instructed in the lockout/tagout procedure.

 WARNING
Although 99 percent of your work may be electrical, be aware that you may also need to lock out mechanical equipment.

The following is an example of a lockout/tagout procedure. Make sure to use the procedure that is specific to your employer or job site.

105F04.EPS

Figure 4 ◆ Typical GFCI.

 WARNING
This procedure is provided for your information only. The OSHA procedure provides only the minimum requirements for lockouts/tagouts. Consult the lockout/tagout procedure for your company and the plant or job site at which you are working. Remember that your life could depend on the lockout/tagout procedure. It is critical that you use the correct procedure for your site. The NEC® requires that remote-mounted motor disconnects be permanently equipped with a lockout feature.

I. *Introduction*
   A. This lockout/tagout procedure has been established for the protection of personnel from potential exposure to hazardous energy sources during construction, installation, service, and maintenance of electrical energy systems.
   B. This procedure applies to, and must be followed by, all personnel who may be potentially exposed to the unexpected startup or release of hazardous energy, including electrical, mechanical, pneumatic, hydraulic, chemical, or thermal energy.

   Exception: This procedure does not apply to process and/or utility equipment or systems with cord and plug power supply systems when the cord and plug are the only source of hazardous energy, are removed from the source, and remain under the exclusive control of the authorized employee.

   Exception: This procedure does not apply to troubleshooting (diagnostic) procedures and installation of electrical equipment and systems when the energy source cannot be de-energized because continuity of service is essential or shutdown of the system is impractical. Additional personal protective

105F05.EPS

Figure 5 ◆ Extension cord with a GFCI.

equipment for such work is required and the safe work practices identified for this work must be followed.

II. *Definitions*

- *Affected employee* – Any person working on or near equipment or machinery when maintenance or installation tasks are being performed by others during lockout/tagout conditions.
- *Appointed authorized employee* – Any person appointed by the job site supervisor to coordinate and maintain the security of a group lockout/tagout condition.
- *Authorized employee* – Any person authorized by the job site supervisor to use lockout/tagout procedures while working on electrical equipment.
- *Authorized supervisor* – The assigned job site supervisor who is in charge of coordinating procedures and maintenance of security for all lockout/tagout operations at the job site.
- *Energy isolation device* – An approved electrical disconnect switch capable of accepting approved lockout/tagout hardware for the purpose of isolating and securing a hazardous electrical source in an open or safe position.
- *Lockout/tagout hardware* – A combination of padlocks, danger tags, and other devices designed to attach to and secure electrical isolation devices.

III. *Training*

A. Each authorized supervisor, authorized employee, and appointed authorized employee shall receive initial and as-needed user-level training in lockout/tagout procedures.

B. Training is to include recognition of hazardous energy sources, the type and magnitude of energy sources in the workplace, and the procedures for energy isolation and control.

C. Retraining will be conducted on an as-needed basis whenever lockout/tagout procedures are changed or there is evidence that procedures are not being followed properly.

IV. *Protective Equipment and Hardware*

A. Lockout/tagout devices shall be used exclusively for controlling hazardous electrical energy sources.

B. All padlocks must be numbered and assigned to one employee only.

C. No duplicate or master keys will be made available to anyone other than the site supervisor.

D. A current list with the lock number and authorized employee's name must be maintained by the site supervisor.

E. Danger tags must be of the standard white, red, and black *DANGER—DO NOT OPERATE* design and shall include the authorized employee's name, the date, and the appropriate network company (use permanent markers).

F. Danger tags must be used in conjunction with padlocks, as shown in *Figure 6*.

V. *Procedures*

A. Preparation for lockout/tagout:
1. Check the procedures to ensure that no changes have been made since you last used a lockout/tagout.
2. Identify all authorized and affected employees involved with the pending lockout/tagout.

B. Sequence for lockout/tagout:
1. Notify all authorized and affected personnel that a lockout/tagout will be performed and explain the reason why.
2. Shut down the equipment or system using the normal OFF or STOP procedures.
3. Lock out energy sources and test disconnects to be sure they cannot be moved to the ON position and open the control cutout switch. If there is no cutout switch, block the magnet in the switch open position before working on electrically operated equipment/apparatus such as motors and relays. Remove the control wire.
4. Lock and tag the required switches in the open position. Each authorized employee must affix a separate lock and tag. An example is shown in *Figure 7*.

Potential Hazards

A self-employed buider was using a metal cutting tool on a metal carport roof and was not using GFCI protection. The male and female plugs of his extension cord partially separated, and the active pin touched the metal roofing. When the builder grounded himself on the gutter of an adjacent roof, he received a fatal shock.

The Bottom Line: Always use GFCI protection and be on the lookout for potential hazards.

Figure 6 ♦ Lockout/tagout device.

105F06.EPS

5. Dissipate any stored energy by attaching the equipment or system to ground.
6. Verify that the test equipment is functional via a known power source.
7. Confirm that all switches are in the open position and use test equipment to verify that all parts are de-energized.
8. If it is necessary to leave the area temporarily, retest upon returning to ensure that the equipment or system is still de-energized.

C. Restoration of energy:
1. Confirm that all personnel and tools, including shorting probes, are accounted for and removed from the equipment or system.
2. Completely reassemble and secure the equipment or system.
3. Replace and/or reactivate all safety controls.
4. Remove locks and tags from isolation switches. Authorized employees must remove their own locks and tags.
5. Notify all affected personnel that the lockout/tagout has ended and the equipment or system is energized.
6. Operate or close isolation switches to restore energy.

VI. *Emergency Removal Authorization*
A. In the event a lockout/tagout device is left secured, and the authorized employee is absent, or the key is lost, the authorized supervisor can remove the lockout/tagout device.

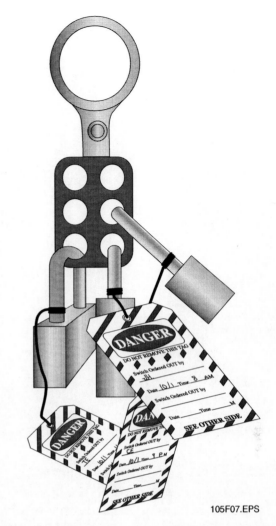

105F07.EPS

Figure 7 ♦ Multiple lockout/tagout device.

B. The authorized employee must be informed that the lockout/tagout device has been removed.
C. Written verification of the action taken, including informing the authorized employee of the removal, must be recorded in the job journal.

4.4.0 Other OSHA Regulations

There are other OSHA regulations that you need to be aware of on the job site:

• OSHA requires the posting of hard hat areas. Be alert to those areas and always wear your hard hat properly, with the bill in front. Hard hats should be worn whenever overhead hazards exist, or there is the risk of exposure to electric shock or burns.

• You should wear safety shoes on all job sites. Keep them in good condition.

What's Wrong with This Picture?

105SA03.EPS

- Do not wear clothing with exposed metal zippers, buttons, or other metal fasteners. Avoid wearing loose-fitting or torn clothing.
- Protect your eyes. Your eyesight is threatened by many activities on the job site. Always wear safety glasses with full side shields. In addition, the job may also require protective equipment, such as face shields or goggles.

4.4.1 Testing for Voltage

OSHA also requires that you inspect or test existing conditions before beginning work on electrical equipment or lines. Usually, you will need a voltmeter or voltage tester to do this. You should assume that all electrical equipment and lines are energized until you have determined that they are not. Do not work on or near energized parts until the operating voltage is determined.

After the electrical equipment has been locked and tagged out, the equipment must be verified as de-energized before work can proceed. This section sets the requirements that must be met before any circuits or equipment can be considered de-energized. First, and most importantly, only qualified persons may verify that a circuit or piece of equipment is de-energized. Before approaching the equipment to be worked on, the qualified person shall operate the equipment's normal operating controls to check that the proper energy sources have been disconnected.

Upon opening a control enclosure, the qualified person shall note the presence of any components that may store electrical energy. Initially, these components should be avoided.

To verify that the lockout was adequate and the equipment is indeed de-energized, a qualified person must use appropriate test equipment to

Lockout/Tagout Dilemma

In Georgia, workers found energized switches after the lockout of a circuit panel in an older system that had been upgraded several times. The existing wiring did not match the current site drawings. A subsequent investigation found many such situations in older facilities.

The Bottom Line: Never rely solely on drawings. It is mandatory that the circuit be tested after lockout to verify that it is de-energized.

Lockout/Tagout—Who Does It and When?

What situations are likely to require lockout/tagout? Who is responsible for performing the lockout/tagout? When would more than one person be responsible?

check for power, paying particular attention to induced voltages and unrelated feedback voltage.

Ensure that your testing equipment is working properly by performing the live-dead-live check before each use. To do this, perform the following steps:

Step 1 Check your voltmeter on a known live voltage source. This known source must be in the same range as the electrical equipment you will be working on.

Step 2 Without changing scales on your voltmeter, check for the presence of power in the equipment you have locked out.

Step 3 To ensure that your voltmeter did not malfunction, check it again on the known live source.

Performing this test will assure you that your voltage testing equipment is reliable.

According to *OSHA Section 1910.333(b)(2)(iv)/ 1926.417(d)(4)(ii)*, if the circuit to be tested normally operates at more than 600 volts, the live-dead-live check must be performed.

Once it has been verified that power is not present, stored electrical energy that might endanger personnel must be released. A qualified person must use the proper devices to release the stored energy, such as using a shorting probe to discharge a capacitor.

5.0.0 ◆ LADDERS AND SCAFFOLDS

Ladders and scaffolds account for about half of the injuries from workplace electrocutions. The involuntary recoil that can occur when a person is shocked can cause the person to be thrown from a ladder or high place.

5.1.0 Ladders

Many job site accidents involve the misuse of ladders. Make sure to follow these general rules every time you use any ladder. Following these rules can prevent serious injury or even death.

- Before using any ladder, inspect it. Look for loose or missing rungs, cleats, bolts, or screws, and check for cracked, broken, or badly worn rungs, cleats, or side rails.
- If you find a ladder in poor condition, do not use it. Report it and tag it for repair or disposal.
- Never modify a ladder by cutting it or weakening its parts.
- Do not set up ladders where they may be run into by others, such as in doorways or walkways. If it is absolutely necessary to set up a ladder in such a location, protect the ladder with barriers.

- Do not increase a ladder's reach by standing it on boxes, barrels, or anything other than a flat surface.
- Check your shoes for grease, oil, or mud before climbing a ladder. These materials could make you slip.
- Always face the ladder and hold on with both hands when climbing up or down.
- Never lean out from the ladder. Center yourself between the rails. If something is out of reach, get down and move the ladder.

WARNING

When performing electrical work, always use ladders made of nonconductive material.

5.1.1 Straight and Extension Ladders

There are some specific rules to follow when working with straight and extension ladders:

- Always place a straight ladder at the proper angle. The distance from the ladder feet to the base of the wall or support should be about one-fourth the working height of the ladder (see *Figure 8*).
- Secure straight ladders to prevent slipping. Use ladder shoes or hooks at the top and bottom. Another method is to secure a board to the floor against the ladder feet. For brief jobs, someone can hold the straight ladder.
- Side rails should extend above the top support point by at least 36 inches.

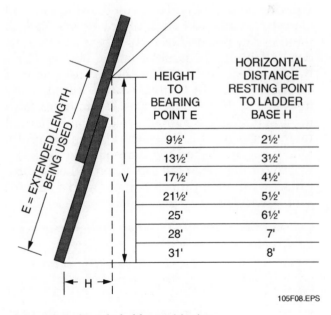

	HEIGHT TO BEARING POINT E	HORIZONTAL DISTANCE RESTING POINT TO LADDER BASE H
	9½'	2½'
	13½'	3½'
	17½'	4½'
	21½'	5½'
	25'	6½'
	28'	7'
	31'	8'

105F08.EPS

Figure 8 ◆ Straight ladder positioning.

- It takes two people to safely extend and raise an extension ladder. Extend the ladder only after it has been raised to an upright position.
- Never carry an extended ladder.
- Never use two ladders spliced together.
- Ladders should not be painted because paint can hide defects.

5.1.2 Step Ladders

There are also a few specific rules for using a step ladder:

- Always open the step ladder all the way and lock the spreaders to avoid collapsing the ladder accidentally.
- Use a step ladder that is high enough for the job so that you do not have to reach. Get someone to hold the ladder if it is more than 10 feet high.
- Never use a step ladder as a straight ladder.
- Never stand on or straddle the top two rungs of a step ladder.
- Do not use a ladder as a shelf.

 WARNING
Do not leave tools or materials on a step ladder.

Sometimes you will need to move or remove protective equipment, guards, or guardrails to complete a task using a ladder. Always replace what you moved or removed before leaving the area.

5.2.0 Scaffolds

Working on scaffolds also involves being safe and alert to hazards. Keep scaffold platforms clear of unnecessary material or scrap. These can become deadly tripping hazards or falling objects. Carefully inspect each part of the scaffold as it is erected. Makeshift scaffolds have caused many injuries and deaths on job sites. Use only scaffolding and planking materials designed and marked for their specific use. When working on a scaffold, follow the established specific requirements set by OSHA for the use of fall protection. When appropriate, wear an approved harness with a lanyard properly anchored to the structure.

 NOTE
The following requirements represent a compilation of the more stringent requirements of both *CFR 1910* and *CFR 1926*.

What's Wrong with This Picture?

105SA04.EPS

The following are some of the basic OSHA rules for working safely on scaffolds:

- Scaffolds must be erected on sound, rigid footing that can carry the maximum intended load.
- Guardrails and toe boards must be installed on the open sides and ends of platforms that are higher than six feet above the ground or floor.
- There must be a screen of half-inch maximum openings between the toe board and the midrail where persons are required to work or pass under the scaffold.
- Scaffold planks must extend over their end supports not less than six inches nor more than 12 inches and must be properly blocked.
- If the scaffold does not have built-in ladders that meet the standard, then it must have an attached ladder access.
- All employees must be trained to erect, dismantle, and use scaffold(s).
- Unless it is impossible, fall protection must be worn while building or dismantling all scaffolding.
- Work platforms must be completely decked for use by employees.

- Your hard hat is the first line of protection from falling objects. Your hard hat, however, cannot protect your shoulders, arms, back, or feet from the danger of falling objects. The person working below depends on those working above. When you are working above the ground, be careful so that material, including your tools, cannot fall from your work site. Use trash containers or other similar means to keep debris from falling and never throw or sweep material from above.

6.0.0 ◆ LIFTS, HOISTS, AND CRANES

On the job, you may be working in the operating area of lifts, hoists, or cranes. The following safety rules are for those who are working in the area with overhead equipment but are not directly involved in its operation.

- Stay alert and pay attention to the warning signals from operators.
- Never stand or walk under a load, regardless of whether it is moving or stationary.
- Always warn others of moving or approaching overhead loads.
- Never attempt to distract signal persons or operators of overhead equipment.
- Obey warning signs.
- Do not use equipment that you are not qualified to operate.

7.0.0 ◆ LIFTING

Back injuries cause many lost working hours every year. That is in addition to the misery felt by the person with the hurt back! Learn how to lift properly and size up the load. To lift, first stand close to the load. Then, squat down and keep your back straight. Get a firm grip on the load and keep the load close to your body. Lift by straightening your

What's Wrong with This Picture?

105SA05.EPS

legs. Make sure that you lift with your legs and not your back. Do not be afraid to ask for help if you feel the load is too heavy. See *Figure 9* for an example of proper lifting.

8.0.0 ◆ BASIC TOOL SAFETY

When using any tools for the first time, read the operator's manual to learn the recommended safety precautions. If you are not certain about the operation of any tool, ask the advice of a more experienced worker. Before using a tool, you should know its function and how it works.

Always use the right tool for the job. Incorrectly using tools is one of the leading causes of job site injury. Using a hammer as a pry bar or using a screwdriver as a chisel can cause damage to the tool and injure you in the process.

Scaffolds and Electrical Hazards

Remember that scaffolds are excellent conductors of electricity. Recently, a maintenance crew needed to move a scaffold and although time was allocated in the work order to dismantle and rebuild the scaffold, the crew decided to push it instead. They did not follow OSHA recommendations for scaffold clearance and did not perform a job site survey. During the move, the five-tier scaffold contacted a 12,000V overhead power line. All four members of the crew were killed and the crew chief received serious injuries.

The Bottom Line: Never take shortcuts when it comes to your safety and the safety of others. Trained safety personnel should survey each job site prior to the start of work to assess potential hazards. Safe working distances should be maintained between scaffolding and power lines.

Lifting

If you bend from the waist to pick up a 50-pound object, you are applying 10 times the amount of pressure (500 pounds) to your lower back. Lower back injuries are one of the most common workplace injuries because it's so easy to be careless about lifting, especially when you are in a hurry. Remember, it is much easier to ask for help than it is to nurse an injured back.

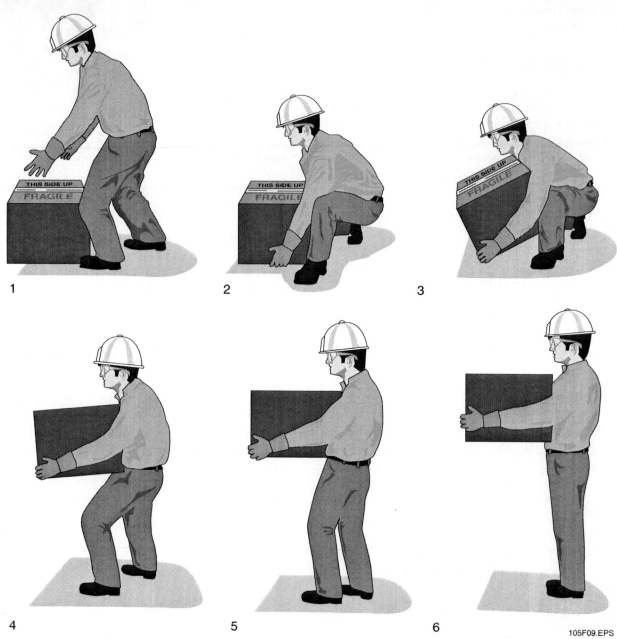

1 2 3

4 5 6

105F09.EPS

Figure 9 ◆ Proper lifting.

9.0.0 ◆ CONFINED SPACE ENTRY PROCEDURES

Occasionally, you may be required to do your work in a maintenance hole or vault. If this is the case, there are some special safety considerations that you need to be aware of. For details on the subject of working in maintenance holes and vaults, refer to *1910.146/1926.21(a)(6)(i)* and *(ii)* and the *National Electrical Safety Code.* The general precautions are listed in the following paragraphs.

Culvert Check Saves a Life

One lucky worker checked out a culvert before entering it and found a nest of rattlesnakes.

The Bottom Line: Always be sure to look inside the confined space before entering.

Spaces on a job site are considered confined when their size and shape restrict the movement of anyone who must enter, work in, and exit the space. **Confined spaces** often have poor ventilation and are difficult to enter and exit. For example, employees who work in process vessels generally must squeeze in and out through narrow openings and perform their tasks while in a cramped or awkward position. In some cases, confinement itself creates a hazard.

In a confined space, hazards such as poor air quality, toxins, explosions, fire, and moving machinery parts tend to be far more deadly. In fact, over an 8-year period in the 1990s an average of 38 workers per year were killed in confined spaces.

Confined spaces may contain unforeseeable hazards. In one instance, a worker was lowered into a 21-foot-deep maintenance hole on a looped chain seat. Twenty seconds after entering the maintenance hole, he started gasping for air and fell. He landed face down in the water at the bottom of the maintenance hole. An autopsy determined that he died from lack of oxygen. The amount of oxygen cannot be determined by simply looking into a confined space; however, there is a specific test that you may perform to determine the amount of oxygen in a confined space. This test is explained later in this module.

Most confined spaces have restricted entrances and exits. Workers are often injured as they enter or exit through small doors and hatches. It can also be difficult to move around in a confined space and workers can be struck by moving equipment. Escapes and rescues are much more difficult in confined spaces than they are elsewhere.

Confined spaces are entered for inspection, equipment testing, repair, cleaning, or emergencies. They should only be entered for short periods of time.

Some of the confined spaces you may work in include the following:

- Maintenance holes
- Boilers
- Trenches
- Tunnels
- Sewers
- Underground utility vaults
- Pipelines
- Pits
- Air ducts

A written confined-space entry program can protect you. It will identify the hazards and specify the equipment or support that is needed to avoid injury. All industrial and some construction sites have written confined-space entry programs. You need to know and follow your company's policy.

9.1.0 Confined Space Classification

Confined spaces must be inspected before work can begin. This helps to identify possible hazards. After an inspection by a company-authorized person, the confined space is classified based on any hazards that are present. The two classifications are **nonpermit-required** and **permit-required confined spaces**.

9.1.1 Nonpermit-Required Confined Space

A nonpermit-required confined space is a work space free of any mechanical, physical, electrical, and **atmospheric hazards** that can cause death or injury. After a space has been classified as a nonpermit-required space, workers can enter using the appropriate personal protective equipment for the type of work to be performed. Always check with your supervisor if it is unclear what personal protective equipment is required. A space is considered a nonpermit-required confined space if it:

- Is large enough and so configured that an employee can bodily enter and perform assigned work
- Has a limited or restricted means of entry or exit (such as tanks, vessels, silos, storage bins, hoppers, vaults, and pits)
- Is not designed for continuous employee occupancy

9.1.2 Permit-Required Confined Space

A permit-required confined space is a confined space that has real or possible hazards. These hazards can be atmospheric, physical, electrical, or mechanical. OSHA *CFR 1910.146* defines a permit-required confined space as a confined space that:

- Contains or has the potential to contain a hazardous atmosphere
- Contains a material that has the potential for engulfing an entrant
- Has an internal configuration such that an entrant could be trapped or asphyxiated by inwardly converging walls or by a floor that slopes downward and tapers to a small cross-section
- Contains any other recognized serious safety or health hazard

An entry permit must be issued and signed by the job-site supervisor before the confined space is entered. No one is allowed to enter a confined space unless there is a valid entry permit. The permit is to be kept at the confined space while work is being performed. Always check with your supervisor if it is unclear whether or not you need a permit to enter a confined space.

WARNING

All permit-required confined spaces must be identified, and the associated permit must be posted.

9.2.0 Entry Permits

Confined spaces can be extremely dangerous. Entry into the space begins when any part of your body passes the entrance or opening of a confined space. Before entering a permit-required confined space, you must have an entry permit (*Figure 10*).

An entry permit is a job checklist that verifies that the space has been inspected. It also lets everyone on the site know about the hazards of the job. All entry permits must be filled out and signed by the supervisor before anyone enters the space. The permit must also be posted at the entrance to the site and be available for workers to review. Entry permits must include the following information:

- A description of the space and the type of work that will be done
- The date the permit is valid and how long it lasts
- Test results for all atmospheric testing including oxygen, toxin, and flammable material levels
- The name and signature of the person who did the tests
- The name and signature of the entry supervisor
- A list of all workers, including supervisors, who are authorized to enter the site
- The means by which workers and supervisors will communicate with each other
- Special equipment and procedures that are to be used during the job
- Other permits needed for work done in the space, such as welding
- The contact information for the emergency response rescue team

NOTE

Some confined spaces require both a permit to enter and a permit to work in the space.

9.3.0 Atmospheric Hazards

Atmospheric hazards are the most common hazards in a confined space. In a hazardous atmosphere, the air can have either too little or too much oxygen, be explosive or flammable, or contain toxic gases. Special meters are used to detect these atmospheric hazards (*Figure 11*).

9.3.1 Oxygen-Deficient or Oxygen-Enriched Atmospheres

A confined space that does not have enough oxygen is called an **oxygen-deficient** atmosphere; a confined space that has too much oxygen is called an **oxygen-enriched** atmosphere. For safe working conditions, the oxygen level in a confined space must range between 19.5 percent and 23.5 percent by volume, with 21 percent being considered the normal level. Oxygen concentrations below 19.5 percent by volume are considered oxygen deficient; those above 23.5 percent by volume are considered oxygen enriched.

Attachment 16 – 2
Confined-Space Entry Permit

Master Card / Safe Work Ticket No. _____

---

1. Work Description: _____

Equip. Name / Number & Location or Area _____

Purpose of Entry _____

Valid Start Date _____   Duration Time _____ to _____

---

2. Hazardous Materials:

What did the equipment last contain? _____

Will the work generate a hazardous atmosphere? ☐ Yes ☐ No If yes, specify hazards and controls.

_____

---

3. Rescue Requirements:

☐ External, by attendant   ☐ Complex Rescue, by rescue team at point of entry

☐ Non-IDLH and/or Simple Rescue, by rescue team on-site   ☐ IDLH, by rescue team at point of entry

Has the rescue team been notified of the entry?   ☐ Yes   ☐ N/A Time of notification _____

How will the rescue team be summonsed for an emergency?   ☐ Radio Channel: _____ ☐ Other: _____

---

4. Gas Test Requirements:

LEL/0_2 - Instrument Mfg./No. _____/_____   Bump Check Time/Gas Tester - _____/_____

Toxicity - Instrument Mfg./No. _____/_____   Bump Check Time/Gas Tester - _____/_____

Frequency of Testing: ☐ Continuous ☐ Other - Specify - _____

∞   Continuous monitoring results must be recorded every three hours

Acceptable Levels	Results								
Oxygen: 19.5% - 23.5%									
Combustible Gas: %LEL - <10%									
Other _____ < PEL* _____									
Other _____ < PEL* _____									
Other _____ < PEL* _____									

∞   Entry in excess of the PEL will require appropriate PPE.

---

5. Ventilation / Exhaust Equipment:

☐ None required, natural ventilation adequate   ☐ Forced air ventilation   ☐ Exhaust ventilation

Equipment Type: ☐ Air powered horn   ☐ Electric blower   Volume Required - _____ cfm

---

6. Personal Protection:

☐ Gloves (type) _____   ☐ Respirator (type) _____

☐ Goggles or face shield   ☐ Self Contained Breathing Equipment

☐ Lifelines Attached to Harness   ☐ Other, specify: _____

☐ Chemical Resistant Suit, Specify Type _____

---

7. Fire Protection: ☐ None required   ☐ Portable Fire Extinguisher – type and size:_____

☐ Fire Watch   ☐ Other, specify: _____

105F10A.EPS

Figure 10 ◆ Entry permit. (1 of 2)

8. Condition of Area and Equipment:

Required Yes	N/A		THESE KEY POINTS MUST BE CHECKED
		a.	Equipment locked and tagged out?
		b.	Piping is disconnected, capped or plugged and/or blinded.
		c.	Equipment emptied, washed, purged & ventilated?
		d.	Low voltage or GFCI protected equipment provided?
		e.	Explosion proof electrical equipment provided?
		f.	Provisions are made to barricade or post signs at entry points when attendant is not on duty.

Other Requirements: _____

9. Special Instructions: ☐ None ☐ Check with issuer before starting work

10. Approval

	Permit			Permit Acceptance		
	Supt. / Area Supv.	Date	Time	Maint. Supv. / Engineer / Contractor Supv.	Date	
Issued by						
Endorsed by						
Endorsed by						

11. Individual Review / Entrant Roster: I have been instructed in the proper Work Permit, Confined Space Entry, Lockout/Tagout Procedures, associated physical and atmospheric hazards and have reviewed the gas testing results.

Entrants	Date	Time In / Out	Time In / Out	Time In / Out	Time In / Out	Time In / Out

I have been informed of the duties and responsibilities for an attendant, the associated physical and atmospheric hazards, and have reviewed the gas testing results.

Attendants	Date	Time On / Off	Time On / Off	Time On / Off

12. Job Completion:
☐ Yes ☐ N/A Has the rescue team been notified?
☐ Yes ☐ No Is the work on equipment complete & the confined space ready to return to service?
☐ Yes ☐ No Has the worksite been cleaned and made safe?
Workers answering above questions: _____

13. Post Job Review: Were any hazards encountered or created during entry operations?
☐ Yes ☐ No If yes, describe: _____
Possible solutions: _____

Forward to job file within 7 days of job completion.

105F10B.EPS

Figure 10 ◆ Entry permit. (2 of 2)

105F11.EPS

Figure 11 ◆ Detection meters.

 WARNING
Never enter a confined space if you are not sure how safe it is.

Many of the processes that occur in a confined space use oxygen and may reduce the percentage of oxygen to an unsafe level. These processes include the following:

• Burning
• Rusting of metal
• Breaking down of plants or garbage
• Oxygen mixing with other gases

WARNING
Normal breathing in a confined space can also create an oxygen deficiency.

When the oxygen in a confined space is reduced, breathing becomes more difficult. The symptoms of insufficient oxygen happen in the following order:

1. Fast breathing and heartbeat
2. Impaired mental judgment
3. Extreme emotional reaction
4. Unusual fatigue
5. Nausea and vomiting
6. Inability to move your body freely
7. Loss of consciousness
8. Death

Too much oxygen in a confined space is a fire hazard and can cause explosions. Materials like clothing and hair are highly flammable and will burn rapidly in oxygen-enriched atmospheres. Fires can start easily in a confined space with oxygen-enriched air.

9.3.2 Combustible Atmospheres

Air in a confined space becomes **combustible** when chemicals or gases reach a certain concentration. Flammable gases can be trapped in confined spaces. These include acetylene, butane, propane, methane, and others. Dust and work byproducts from spray painting or welding can also form a combustible atmosphere.

Some flammable gases are lighter than air and have a higher concentration at the top of a confined space. Vapors from fuels are generally heavier than air and will form a greater concentration at the bottom of the space.

A spark or flame will cause an explosion in a combustible atmosphere.

WARNING
Explosion-proof lights, motors, exhaust fans, and other equipment must be used to prevent fires and explosions in any combustible area.

9.3.3 Toxic Atmospheres

Toxic gases and vapors come from many sources. They can be deadly when they are inhaled or absorbed through the skin above certain concentration levels. In spaces with no ventilation, high concentrations can gather and quickly become toxic. Even in lower doses, some chemicals can seriously affect your breathing and brain functions.

The harmful effects of toxic gases and vapors vary. Many toxic gases, such as carbon monoxide, cannot be detected by sight or smell. Some toxic gases have harmful effects that may not show up until years after contact. Others, such as nitric oxide, can kill quickly.

9.4.0 Additional Hazards

In addition to atmospheric hazards, there are several other physical and environmental hazards in confined spaces. These hazards include the following:

- Electric shock
- Purging
- Falling objects
- Engulfment
- Extreme temperatures
- Noise
- Slick or wet surfaces
- Moving parts

9.3.4 Monitoring the Atmosphere in Confined Spaces

The air inside a permit-required confined space must be tested before anyone is allowed to enter. Atmospheric tests must be done in this order:

1. Oxygen content
2. Flammable gases and vapors
3. Potential toxic contaminants

The test for oxygen must be performed first because most combustible gas meters are oxygen dependent and will not provide reliable readings in an oxygen-deficient atmosphere. The test for combustible gases is performed next because the threat of fire or explosion is usually more urgent and more life threatening than exposure to toxic gases and vapors.

Various instruments are used to test and monitor confined-space atmospheres. Portable, battery-operated gas detection meters can measure oxygen levels by changing the sensor in the detection meter. Gas detection meters must be calibrated and operated according to the manufacturer's instructions. The meter must be able to detect oxygen and combustible gases at the levels specified in *OSHA 29 CFR 1910.146.*

9.4.1 Electric Shock

Electric shock can occur when power tools and line cords are used in an area where there are wet floors or surfaces. Tools and equipment should be grounded or a ground fault circuit interrupter should be used when working in a confined space.

9.4.2 Purging

Purging happens when toxic, corrosive, or natural gases enter and mix with the air in a confined space. Purging is most often experienced when working in pipes. Purging gases are used to clean pipelines. These gases can create an oxygen imbalance in the space that will suffocate workers almost immediately. Once purging is complete, appropriate ventilation must be established to render the atmosphere safe. Air monitoring is necessary to verify air quality.

Added Oxygen Causes Lost Life

A welder entered a 24"-diameter steel pipe to grind a bad weld on a valve about 30' from the entry point. Before he entered, other crew members decided to add oxygen to the pipe near the bad weld to make sure the air was safe. The welder had been grinding off and on for about five minutes when a fire broke out. The fire covered his clothing. He was pulled from the pipe and the fire was put out. The burns were so serious that the welder died the next day.

The Bottom Line: This accident could have been avoided. It happened because of poor communication between workers and unsafe work practices.

Source: The Occupational Safety and Health Administration (OSHA)

9.4.3 Falling Objects

Materials or equipment can fall into confined spaces and strike workers. This usually happens when another worker enters or exits a confined space with a top-side opening, such as a maintenance hole. Vibrations can also cause materials or tools to fall and strike workers.

9.4.4 Engulfment

Engulfment occurs when a worker is buried alive by a liquid or material that enters a confined space (*Figure 12*). Small, loose material stored in bins and hoppers, such as grain, sand, or coal, can engulf and suffocate a worker. Heavier materials or liquids that enter a confined space can crush or strangle a worker.

105F12.EPS

Figure 12 ◆ Buried alive.

9.4.5 Extreme Temperatures

Confined spaces that are too hot or too cold can be hazardous to workers. Spaces that are too hot can cause heat stroke or heat exhaustion, while spaces that are too cold can cause **hypothermia**. Another temperature-related hazard in a confined space is steam. Steam is extremely hot and can cause serious or deadly burns.

9.4.6 Noise

Noise in a confined space can be very loud. This happens because the size of the space is small and sound bounces off the walls. Too much noise, or noise that is too loud, can permanently damage hearing. It can also prevent workers from communicating. If this happens, an evacuation warning could be missed.

9.4.7 Slick or Wet Surfaces

Workers can get seriously hurt by slips and falls on slick or wet surfaces. Wet surfaces also add to the chance of electrocution from electrical circuits, equipment, and power tools.

9.4.8 Moving Parts

Workers can get struck or trapped by moving parts such as augers or belts. This usually happens when a worker slips or falls. It also can happen if the operator of the moving machinery is wearing loose clothing or jewelry.

Four Die in Confined Space

A project involved the upgrade/replacement of a sewer pumping station and the contractor prepared a confined-space entry permit for the work. One employee was disconnecting a sewer bypass connection in a maintenance hole while three others were at the maintenance hole entrance. The maintenance hole filled with sewage and gases from the sewer line, and the employee was overcome by a lack of oxygen. The other three employees tried to help. Each entered the maintenance hole one at a time, apparently to attempt rescue. Each was overcome by the sewer gases and died.

The Bottom Line: Asphyxiation (lack of oxygen) is not like what you see in the movies. You can't go in unprotected, stagger around awhile, save a couple of lives, then exit coughing and unharmed. Reality is quite different. Upon your first breath you pass out. If a retrieval system is not in place, anyone who enters the space to rescue you will die. Many workers have died simply by putting their heads in maintenance holes to assess a situation. Even without fully entering the confined space, these workers were immediately incapacitated.

Source: The Occupational Safety and Health Administration (OSHA)

9.5.0 Responsibilities and Duties

Everyone involved in confined-space work must have special training. This includes entrants doing work in a confined space, attendants at the opening of the space, entry supervisors, and rescue workers.

9.5.1 Entrants

Entrants are people who enter a confined space to do the work. They must be aware of the dangers of the job and know how to protect themselves. The duties of an entrant are as follows:

- Make sure they have a valid entry permit.
- Know the atmospheric, fire, and toxic contamination hazards.
- Use the specified personal protective equipment, including face and eye protection, gloves, aprons, and coveralls as required.
- Stay in contact with the attendant to make sure they are being monitored and can be told to evacuate, if needed.
- Alert the attendant when warning signs or symptoms of exposure exist.
- Know how to escape when necessary.
- Exit the space immediately upon hearing an evacuation alarm or if an uncontrolled hazard is detected within the space.

> **NOTE**
>
> Retrieval methods should be part of an emergency procedure. However, exercise caution when using retrieval devices in situations where the device may cause worker entanglement.

9.5.2 Attendants

An attendant stays outside of the confined space and communicates directly with the entrant. The attendant has constant contact with the entrant though telephone, radio, visual, or other means. An attendant's basic responsibility is to protect the entrant. To do this, the attendant must do the following:

- Set up a station at the exit of the confined space.
- Keep count of the personnel inside.
- Know what work is allowed or disallowed in the space.
- Know how to monitor for safety.

- Test the atmosphere remotely using a probe (*Figure 13*) and recognize safe and unsafe levels.
- Maintain contact with entrants and be able to recognize symptoms of physical distress.
- Order evacuation when problems occur.
- Know how to call rescuers and use the alarm system.
- Refuse entry to unauthorized personnel.
- Never enter the space for rescue attempts.

9.5.3 Supervisors

The entry supervisor is the person responsible for safe confined-space entry operations. This means that he or she is responsible for the lives of all workers involved in the operation. The entry supervisor must do the following:

- Authorize and oversee entry.
- Be well trained in entry procedures.
- Know the hazards of the confined space.

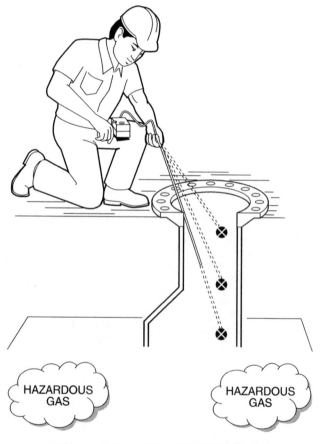

TEST ALL AREAS OF A CONFINED SPACE.

105F13.EPS

Figure 13 ◆ Attendant checks the atmosphere.

- Make sure all entry permits are correct and complete.
- Make sure that proper lockout/tagout procedures are performed.
- Make sure that all equipment required for entry is available and understand how it works.
- Make sure that workers understand the job.
- Know rescue plans and rescue workers.
- Be responsible for canceling entry authorization and terminating entry when unacceptable conditions are present or when the job is completed.
- Evaluate problems and recognize when re-entry is safe.
- Ensure that explosion-proof equipment is used.
- Notify all workers in the area or facility that work is being done in a confined space.

9.5.4 Rescue Workers

There are two types of rescues: non-entry rescues and entry rescues.

A non-entry rescue can be done by anyone outside of the confined space. It is usually done by the attendant. In this type of rescue, winches and tripods can be used to pull the entrant out of the space without endangering other workers (*Figure 14*).

Rescue workers have a responsibility to do the following:

- Know the hazards of the confined space.
- Know the proper use of personal protective and rescue equipment, including respirators.
- Practice rescue operations and know how to perform rescues.
- Be trained in first aid and CPR.
- Know the company's confined-space rescue program.

Entry rescues can be extremely hazardous. Only trained rescue workers are allowed to enter a confined space during an emergency. More rescue workers are killed in confined-space accidents than the workers they are trying to rescue.

9.6.0 Safeguards

It is important to understand how to protect yourself and your co-workers when working in a confined space. In order to do this, everyone must be aware of what is happening on the site and understand how to work safely. These are the most common safeguards that should be used during confined-space operations.

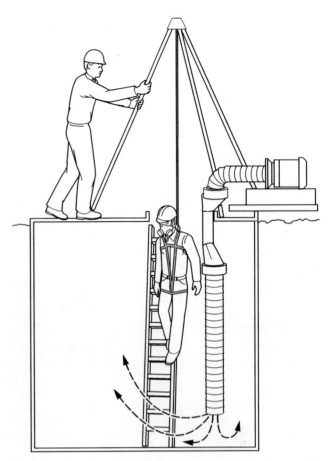

105F14.EPS

Figure 14 ◆ Non-entry rescue.

- Monitoring and testing
- Ventilation
- Personal protective equipment
- Communications
- Training

9.6.1 Monitoring and Testing

The air in a confined space must be tested before any workers enter it. Testing must be done by a properly trained, qualified person. This person must be a company-approved or otherwise designated individual. He or she is referred to as the confined-space attendant. The air is tested for oxygen content, explosive gases or vapors, and toxic chemicals. This can be done by inserting a wand attached to a gas meter into the confined space.

NOTE

Entrants and attendants have the right to witness or review the gas testing results and may request additional tests if deemed necessary.

The atmosphere in a confined space may need to be monitored during the entire job. This is done by attaching monitors to entrants or by using outside devices. When the atmosphere is monitored, workers can be assured that the air quality is good and that they will immediately know about changes in the atmosphere that would require them to leave.

9.6.2 Ventilation

If the air in a confined space is hazardous or has the potential of becoming dangerous, the space must be ventilated immediately to remove toxic gases or vapors and to replace lost oxygen. Ventilators blow clean air into the space, as shown in *Figure 15*. They must stay on as long as workers are in the space.

It's important to remember that just because there is air being blown into or being removed from the space, it doesn't mean that the air is being ventilated. Toxic gases can hide in confined spaces. Make sure the attendant has carefully tested the entire space before entering it.

9.6.3 Personal Protective Equipment

Every job requires some type of personal protective equipment. Standard personal protective equipment (*Figure 16*) includes safety goggles and glasses, hard hats, gloves, and boots. On a confined-space job site, the following items may be needed in addition to the standard equipment:

- Full body harness
- Lifelines
- Air-purifying respirator
- Air-supplying respirator

NOTE

Always check the entry permit to make sure you have the personal protective equipment needed to enter a confined space.

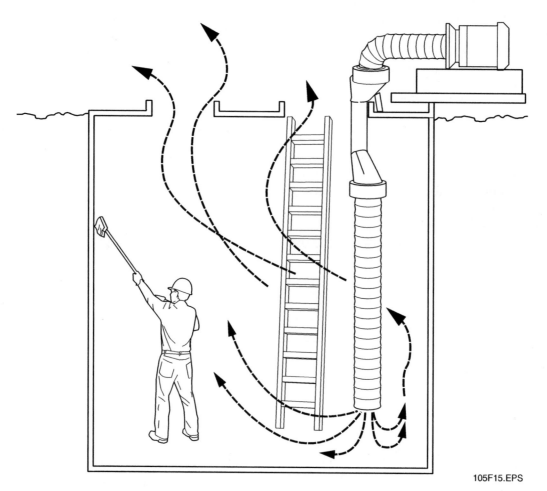

105F15.EPS

Figure 15 ◆ Proper positive ventilation.

9.6.4 Communication

All workers on a site must be able to communicate with one another. It is especially important for attendants and entrants to be able to communicate. This allows attendants to warn entrants about dangers and order an evacuation when necessary. Communication between workers is another way to monitor the confined space.

9.6.5 Training

Entering a confined space requires specialized training. In fact, no one is allowed to enter a confined space unless they have been properly trained and authorized by the site supervisor to enter the space. Training gives workers the knowledge needed to complete their jobs safely and efficiently. If you have not been properly trained, do not enter any confined space.

10.0.0 ◆ FIRST AID

You should be prepared in case an accident does occur on the job site or anywhere else. First aid training that includes certification classes in CPR and artificial respiration could be the best insurance you and your fellow workers ever receive. Make sure that you know where first aid is available at your job site. Also, make sure you know the accident reporting procedure. Each job site should also have a first aid manual or booklet giving easy-to-find emergency treatment procedures for various types of injuries. Emergency first aid telephone numbers should be readily available to everyone on the job site. Refer to *CFR 1910.151/1926.23* and *1926.50* for specific requirements.

11.0.0 ◆ SOLVENTS AND TOXIC VAPORS

Solvents may give off vapors that are toxic enough to make people temporarily ill or even cause permanent injury. Many solvents are skin and eye irritants. Solvents can also be systemic poisons when they are swallowed or absorbed through the skin.

105F16.EPS

Figure 16 ◆ Standard personal protective equipment.

DID YOU KNOW?
Digital Cameras for Safety

Industrial hygiene personnel, supervisors, and planners can use digital cameras with a 20X zoom and flash to capture data on equipment located inside confined spaces. The camera can be used from outside the confined space to capture information such as data on tags, part numbers, and equipment configurations. In some cases, this eliminates the need for entry altogether, which in turn eliminates potential accidents and injuries.

Source: The Occupational Safety and Health Administration (OSHA)

Solvents in spray or aerosol form are dangerous in another way. Small aerosol particles or solvent vapors mix with air to form a combustible mixture with oxygen. The slightest spark could cause an explosion in a confined area because the mix is perfect for fast ignition. There are procedures and methods for using, storing, and disposing of most solvents and chemicals. These procedures are normally found in the material safety data sheets (MSDSs) available at your facility.

An MSDS is required for all materials that could be hazardous to personnel or equipment. These sheets contain information on the material, such as the manufacturer and chemical makeup. As much information as possible is kept on the hazardous material to prevent a dangerous situation; or, in the event of a dangerous situation, the information is used to rectify the problem in as safe a manner as possible. See *Figure 17* for an example of MSDS information you may find on the job.

11.1.0 Precautions When Using Solvents

It is always best to use a nonflammable, nontoxic solvent whenever possible. However, any time solvents are used, it is essential that your work area be adequately ventilated and that you wear the appropriate personal protective equipment:

- A chemical face shield with chemical goggles should be used to protect the eyes and skin from sprays and splashes.

- A chemical apron should be worn to protect your body from sprays and splashes. Remember that some solvents are acid-based. If they come into contact with your clothes, solvents can eat through your clothes to your skin.

- A paper filter mask does not stop vapors; it is used only for nuisance dust. In situations where a paper mask does not supply adequate protection, chemical cartridge respirators might be needed. These respirators can stop many vapors if the correct cartridge is selected. In areas where ventilation is a serious problem, a self-contained breathing apparatus (SCBA) must be used.

- Make sure that you have been given a full medical evaluation and that you are properly trained in using respirators at your site.

11.2.0 Respiratory Protection

Protection against high concentrations of dust, mist, fumes, vapors, gases, and/or oxygen deficiency is provided by appropriate respirators. Appropriate respiratory protective devices should be used for the hazardous material involved and the extent and nature of the work performed.

An air-purifying respirator is, as its name implies, a respirator that removes contaminants from air inhaled by the wearer. The respirators may be divided into the following types: particulate-removing (mechanical filter), gas- and vapor-removing (chemical filter), and a combination of particulate-removing and gas- and vapor-removing.

Particulate-removing respirators are designed to protect the wearer against the inhalation of particulate matter in the ambient atmosphere. They may be designed to protect against a single type of particulate, such as pneumoconiosis-producing and nuisance dust, toxic dust, metal fumes or mist, or against various combinations of these types.

Gas- and vapor-removing respirators are designed to protect the wearer against the inhalation of gases or vapors in the ambient atmosphere. They are designated as gas masks, chemical cartridge respirators (nonemergency gas respirators), and self-rescue respirators. They may be designed to protect against a single gas, such as chlorine; a single type of gas, such as acid gases; or a combination of types of gases, such as acid gases and organic vapors.

If you are required to use a respiratory protective device, you must be evaluated by a physician to ensure that you are physically fit to use a respirator. You must then be fitted and thoroughly instructed in the respirator's use.

Any employee whose job entails having to wear a respirator must keep his face free of facial hair in the seal area.

Respiratory protective equipment must be inspected regularly and maintained in good condition. Respiratory equipment must be properly cleaned on a regular basis and stored in a sanitary, dustproof container.

 WARNING

Do not use any respirator unless you have been fitted for it and thoroughly understand its use. As with all safety rules, follow your employer's respiratory program and policies.

12.0.0 ◆ ASBESTOS

Asbestos is a mineral-based material that is resistant to heat and corrosive chemicals. Depending on the chemical composition, asbestos fibers may range in texture from coarse to silky. The properties that make asbestos fibers so valuable to industry

Section VII — Precautions for Safe Handling and Use

Steps to Be Taken in Case Material is Released or Spilled

Isolate from oxidizers, heat, sparks, electric equipment, and open flames.

Waste Disposal Method

Recycle or incinerate observing local, state and federal health, safety

and pollution laws.

Precautions to Be Taken in Handling and Storing

Store in a cool dry place. Observe label cautions and instructions.

Other Precautions

SEE ATTACHMENT PARA #3

Section VIII — Control Measures

Respiratory Protection (Specify Type)

Suitable for use with organic solvents

Ventilation	Local Exhaust	preferable	Special	none
	Mechanical (General)	acceptable	Other	none
Protective Gloves	recommended (must not dissolve in solvents)		Eye Protection	goggles
Other Protective Clothing or Equipment	none			
Work/Hygenic Practices	Use with adequate ventilation. Observe label cautions.			

Figure 17 ◆ Portion of an MSDS.

105F17.EPS

are its high tensile strength, flexibility, heat and chemical resistance, and good frictional properties.

Asbestos fibers enter the body by inhalation of airborne particles or by ingestion. They can become embedded in the tissues of the respiratory or digestive systems. Years of exposure to asbestos can cause numerous disabling or fatal diseases. Among these diseases are asbestosis, an emphysema-like condition; lung cancer; mesothelioma, a cancerous tumor that spreads rapidly in the cells of membranes covering the lungs and body organs; and gastrointestinal cancer. The use of asbestos was banned in 1978.

12.1.0 Monitoring

Employers who have a workplace or work operation covered by *OSHA 3096* (*Asbestos Standard for the Construction Industry*) must perform initial monitoring to determine the airborne concentrations of asbestos to which employees may be exposed. If employers can demonstrate that employee exposures are below the action level and/or excursion limit by means of objective or historical data, initial monitoring is not required. If initial monitoring indicates that employee exposures are below the

action level and/or excursion limit, then periodic monitoring is not required. Within regulated areas, the employer must conduct daily monitoring unless all workers are equipped with supplied-air respirators operated in the positive-pressure mode. If daily monitoring by statistically reliable measurements indicates that employee exposures are below the action level and/or excursion limit, then no further monitoring is required for those employees whose exposures are represented by such monitoring. Employees must be given the chance to observe monitoring, and affected employees must be notified as soon as possible following the employer's receipt of the results.

12.2.0 Regulated Areas

The employer must establish a regulated area where airborne concentrations of asbestos exceed or can reasonably be expected to exceed the locally determined exposure limit, or when certain types of construction work are performed, such as cutting asbestos-cement sheets and removing asbestos-containing floor tiles or insulation. Only authorized personnel may enter regulated areas. All persons entering a regulated area must be supplied with an appropriate respirator. No smoking, eating, drinking, or applying cosmetics is permitted in regulated areas. Warning signs must be displayed at each regulated area and must be posted at all approaches to regulated areas. These signs must bear the following information:

DANGER
ASBESTOS
CANCER AND LUNG DISEASE HAZARD
AUTHORIZED PERSONNEL ONLY
RESPIRATORS AND PROTECTIVE CLOTHING
ARE REQUIRED IN THIS AREA

Where feasible, the employer shall establish negative-pressure enclosures before commencing asbestos removal, demolition, and renovation operations. The setup and monitoring requirements for negative-pressure enclosures are as follows:

- A competent person shall be designated to set up the enclosure and ensure its integrity and supervise employee activity within the enclosure.

- Exemptions are given for small-scale, short-duration maintenance or renovation operations.

- The employer shall conduct daily monitoring of the exposure of each employee assigned to work in a regulated area. Short-term monitoring is required whenever asbestos concentrations will not be uniform throughout the workday and where high concentrations of asbestos may be expected to be released or created in excess of the local limit.

In addition, warning labels must be affixed on all asbestos products and to all containers of asbestos products, including waste containers, that may be in the workplace. The label must include the following information:

DANGER
CONTAINS ASBESTOS FIBERS
AVOID CREATING DUST
CANCER AND LUNG DISEASE HAZARD

12.3.0 Methods of Compliance

To the extent feasible, engineering and work practice controls must be used to reduce employee exposure to within the permissible exposure limit (PEL). The employer must use one or more of the following control methods to achieve compliance:

- Local exhaust ventilation equipped with high-efficiency particulate air (HEPA) filter dust collection systems

- General ventilation systems

- Vacuum cleaners equipped with HEPA filters

- Enclosure or isolation of asbestos dust-producing processes

- Use of wet methods, wetting agents, or removal encapsulants during asbestos handling, mixing, removal, cutting, application, and cleanup

- Prompt disposal of asbestos-containing wastes in leak-tight containers

Prohibited work practices include the following:

- The use of high-speed abrasive disc saws that are not equipped with appropriate engineering controls

- The use of compressed air to remove asbestos-containing materials, unless the compressed air is used in conjunction with an enclosed ventilation system

Where engineering and work practice controls have been instituted but are insufficient to reduce employee exposure to a level that is at or below the PEL, respiratory protection must be used to supplement these controls.

13.0.0 ◆ BATTERIES

Working around wet cell batteries can be dangerous if the proper precautions are not taken. Batteries often give off hydrogen gas as a byproduct. When hydrogen mixes with air, the mixture can be explosive in the proper concentration. For this reason, smoking is strictly prohibited in battery rooms, and only insulated tools should be used.

Altered Respiratory Equipment

A self-employed man applied a solvent-based coating to the inside of a tank. Instead of wearing the proper respirator, he used nonstandard air supply hoses and altered the face mask. All joints and the exhalation slots were sealed with tape. He collapsed and was not discovered for several hours.

The Bottom Line: Never alter or improvise safety equipment.

Proper ventilation also reduces the chance of explosion in battery areas. Follow your company's procedures for working near batteries. Also, ensure that your company's procedures are followed for lifting heavy batteries. Do not connect or disconnect batteries without proper supervision.

13.1.0 Acids

Batteries also contain acid, which will eat away human skin and many other materials. Personal protective equipment for battery work includes chemical aprons, sleeves, gloves, face shields, and goggles to prevent acid from contacting skin and eyes. Follow your site procedures for dealing with spills of these materials. Also, know the location of first aid when working with these chemicals.

13.2.0 Wash Stations

Because of the chance that battery acid may contact someone's eyes or skin, wash stations are located near battery rooms. Everyone who works in the area should know where the nearest wash station is and how to use it. Battery acid should be flushed from the skin and eyes with large amounts of water or with a neutralizing solution.

14.0.0 ◆ PCBs

Polychlorinated biphenyls (PCBs) are chemicals that were marketed under various trade names as a liquid insulator/cooler in older transformers. In addition to being used in older transformers, PCBs are also found in some large capacitors and in the small ballast transformers used in street lighting and ordinary fluorescent light fixtures. Disposal of these materials is regulated by the Environmental Protection Agency (EPA) and must be done through a regulated disposal company; use extreme caution and follow your facility procedures.

WARNING
Do not come into contact with PCBs. They present a variety of serious health risks, including lung damage and cancer.

15.0.0 ◆ FALL PROTECTION

Electronic systems technicians sometimes install or service equipment located in high places or six feet or more above a lower level. In these situations, fall protection procedures and systems can protect against injury or death.

15.1.0 Fall Protection Procedures

Fall protection must be used when employees are on a walking or working surface that is six feet or more above a lower level and has an unprotected edge or side. The areas covered include, but are not limited to the following:

- Finished and unfinished floors or mezzanines
- Temporary or permanent walkways/ramps
- Finished or unfinished roof areas
- Elevator shafts and hoist-ways
- Floor, roof, or walkway holes
- Areas six feet or more above dangerous equipment

Exception: If the dangerous equipment is unguarded, fall protection must be used at all heights regardless of the fall distance.

NOTE
Walking/working surfaces do not include ladders, scaffolds, vehicles, or trailers. Also, an unprotected edge or side is an edge/side where there is no guardrail system at least 39 inches high.

Fall protection is not required during inspection, investigation, or assessment of job site conditions before or after construction work.

Fall protection must be selected in order of preference as listed below. Selection of a lower-level system, such as a safety net, must be based only on feasibility of protection. The list includes, but is not limited to, the following:

- Guardrail systems and hole covers
- Personal fall arrest systems
- Safety nets

These fall protection procedures are designed to warn, isolate, restrict, or protect workers from a potential fall hazard.

15.2.0 Types of Fall Protection Systems

The type of system selected depends on the fall hazards associated with the work to be performed. First, a hazard analysis must be conducted by the job site supervisor prior to the start of work. Based on the hazard analysis, the job site supervisor and project manager, in consultation with the safety manager, will select the appropriate fall protection system. All employees must be instructed in the use of the fall protection system before starting work.

Summary

Safety must be your concern at all times so that you do not become either the victim of an accident or the cause of one. Safety requirements and safe work practices are provided by OSHA and your employer. It is essential that you adhere to all safety requirements and follow your employer's safe work practices and procedures. Also, you must be able to identify the potential safety hazards of your job site. The consequences of unsafe job site conduct can often be expensive, painful, or even deadly. Report any unsafe act or condition immediately to your supervisor. Also report all work-related accidents, injuries, and illnesses to your supervisor immediately. Remember, proper techniques, common sense, and a good safety attitude will help to prevent accidents, injuries, and fatalities.

Review Questions

1. The most life-threatening hazards on a construction site include all of the following *except* _____.
   a. falls
   b. electrocution
   c. being crushed or struck by falling or flying objects
   d. chemical burns

2. If a person's heart begins to fibrillate due to an electrical shock, the solution is to _____.
   a. leave the person alone until the fibrillation stops
   b. administer heart massage
   c. use the Heimlich maneuver
   d. have a qualified person use emergency defibrillation equipment

3. The majority of injuries due to electrical shock are caused by _____.
   a. electrically operated hand tools
   b. contact with low-voltage conductors
   c. contact with high-voltage conductors
   d. operating electric hand tools outside in wet weather

4. The best way to remove a cartridge fuse is to pry it out with a screwdriver.
   a. True
   b. False

5. Before working on de-energized circuits that have capacitors installed, discharge the capacitors using a _____.
   a. safety shorting probe
   b. fuse puller
   c. spread guard
   d. kirk lock

6. Which of these statements correctly describes a double-insulated power tool?
   a. There is twice as much insulation on the power cord.
   b. It can safely be used in place of a grounded tool.
   c. It is made entirely of plastic or other non-conducting material.
   d. The entire tool is covered in rubber.

7. Which of the following applies in a lockout/tagout procedure?
   a. Only the supervisor can install lockout/tagout devices.
   b. If several employees are involved, the lockout/tagout equipment is applied only by the first employee to arrive at the disconnect.
   c. Lockout/tagout devices applied by one employee can be removed by another employee as long as it can be verified that the first employee has left for the day.
   d. Lockout/tagout devices are installed by every authorized employee involved in the work.

8. The proper distance from the feet of a straight ladder to the wall is _____.
   a. one-fourth the working height of the ladder
   b. one-half the height of the ladder
   c. three feet
   d. one-fourth of the square root of the height of the ladder

9. What are the minimum and maximum distances (in inches) that a scaffold plank can extend beyond its end support?
   a. 4; 8
   b. 6; 10
   c. 6; 12
   d. 8; 12

10. A confined-space entry permit must contain all of the following information *except* _____.
    a. the atmospheric test results
    b. the name of the entry supervisor
    c. emergency contact information
    d. the name of the building owner

Jerry Budge, Manager – Systems Engineering Department
Blonder Tongue Laboratories, Inc.

You could say that Jerry Budge was overtaken by the future. He didn't start out looking for a career in electronic systems, but once he got into it, he realized that it was intended to be his life's work.

How did you choose a career in the EST field?
The career actually chose me. It all started in college with my need to earn money for living expenses. I held several jobs, but one of the jobs I liked was installing satellite dishes. I eventually partnered up with my boss at the time. After competing with the cable TV company, and losing for several years, we decided to start sub-contracting for them. We learned the business of cable TV by contracting for them for two years, and decided that we could do the same thing they were doing. This brought us to the point of building and managing our own private cable TV systems.

What types of training have you been through?
I studied literature in college, and was trained by the Army as a combat medic. All my education in the electronics field has been in the school of hard knocks, learning by making mistakes. After I made the mistake, I had to find people more experienced than me to learn what I did wrong, and more importantly, how to correct it.

What kinds of work have you done in your career?
If it has something to do with RF (radio frequency) technology, I have been involved with it. My current position at Blonder Tongue enables me to be involved with every type of RF technology used in moving voice, video, or data from point A to point B.

Tell us about your present job.
Currently I am the manager of the systems engineering department for Blonder Tongue Laboratories, Inc. In

this position I manage six field service engineers who provide technical support, both by telephone and on site. The department has to be expert in antennas, head end, cable modem, fiber optics, satellite, microwave, distribution, and interdiction, as well as test equipment and procedures. The second hat I wear is as Director of Operations for BDR Broadband, a private cable operator that operates about 20 systems over several states. This job keeps me in touch with what is really going on in the field and in contact with all the new technologies.

What factors have contributed most to your success?
Knowing what I don't know, and learning how to find the answer. Remember that doctors and lawyers don't have all the answers and they don't know everything. They do know where to go and find the answers and that is the difference between a professional and an amateur in my opinion.

What advice would you give to those new to EST field?
Always ask questions of those who are more experienced than you are. All of my knowledge has been gained by directly asking others. Never forget that knowledge is power and power is money!

Do you have an interesting career-related fact or accomplishment to share?
I am a decorated Desert Storm veteran. I'm currently working towards U.S. Coast Guard captain's papers. I am also the founding partner of a leading industry hardware distributor.

Trade Terms Introduced in This Module

Atmospheric hazard: A potential danger in the air or a condition of poor air quality.

Combustible: Air or materials that can explode and cause a fire.

Confined space: Spaces on a job site are considered confined when their size and shape get in the way of anyone who must enter, work in, and exit the space.

Double-insulated/ungrounded tool: An electrical tool that is constructed so that the case is insulated from electrical energy. The case is made of a nonconductive material.

Fibrillation: Very rapid irregular contractions of the muscle fibers of the heart that result in the heartbeat and pulse going out of rhythm with each other.

Grounded tool: An electrical tool with a three-prong plug at the end of its power cord or some other means to ensure that stray current travels to ground without passing through the body of the user. The ground plug is bonded to the conductive frame of the tool.

Hypothermia: A life-threatening condition caused by exposure to very cold temperatures.

Nonpermit-required confined space: A work space free of any atmospheric, physical, electrical, and mechanical hazards that can cause death or injury.

Oxygen-deficient: An atmosphere in which there is not enough oxygen. This is usually considered less than 19.5% oxygen by volume.

Oxygen-enriched: An atmosphere in which there is too much oxygen. This is usually considered more than 23.5% oxygen by volume.

Permit-required confined space: A confined space that has real or possible hazards. These hazards can be atmospheric, physical, electrical, or mechanical.

Polychlorinated biphenyls (PCBs): Toxic chemicals that may be contained in liquids used to cool certain types of large transformers and capacitors.

Additional Resources

This module is intended to be a thorough resource for task training. The following reference works are suggested for further study. These are optional materials for continued education rather than for task training.

29 CFR Parts 1900–1910, Standards for General Industry. Occupational Safety and Health Administration, U.S. Department of Labor.

29 CFR Part 1926, Standards for the Construction Industry. Occupational Safety and Health Administration, U.S. Department of Labor.

National Electrical Code® Handbook, Latest Edition. Quincy, MA: National Fire Protection Association.

National Electrical Safety Code, Latest Edition. Quincy, MA: National Fire Protection Association.

Figure Credits

Gardner Bender, Actuant Inc.	105F02
Topaz Publications, Inc.	105F04, 105F06, 105SA03, 105F16 (boot)
Coleman Cable, Inc.	105F05
Draeger Safety, Inc.	105F11 (top)
RAE Systems, Inc.	105F11 (bottom)
Bacou-Dalloz	105F16 (safety glasses)
Bullard Classic Head Protection	105F16 (hard hat)
North Safety Products	105F16 (gloves)
Mike Powers	105SA01, 105SA02, 105SA04–105SA06

The NCCER makes every effort to keep these textbooks up-to-date and free of technical errors. We appreciate your help in this process. If you have an idea for improving this textbook, or if you find an error, a typographical mistake, or an inaccuracy in NCCER's Contren® textbooks, please write us, using this form or a photocopy. Be sure to include the exact module number, page number, a detailed description, and the correction, if applicable. Your input will be brought to the attention of the Technical Review Committee. Thank you for your assistance.

Instructors – If you found that additional materials were necessary in order to teach this module effectively, please let us know so that we may include them in the Equipment/Materials list in the Instructor's Guide.

Write: Product Development and Revision
National Center for Construction Education and Research
P.O. Box 141104, Gainesville, FL 32614-1104

Fax: 352-334-0932

E-mail: curriculum@nccer.org

Craft _____ Module Name _____

Copyright Date _____ Module Number _____ Page Number(s) _____

Description _____

_____

_____

_____

(Optional) Correction _____

_____

_____

(Optional) Your Name and Address _____

_____

_____

Craft-Related Mathematics

COURSE MAP

This course map shows all of the modules in the first level of the *Electronic Systems Technician* curriculum. The suggested training order begins at the bottom and proceeds up. Skill levels increase as you advance on the course map. The local Training Program Sponsor may adjust the training order.

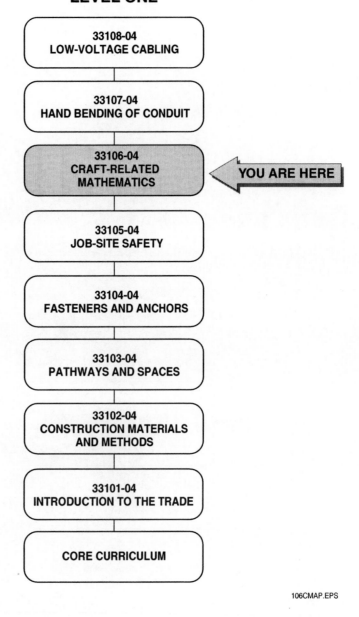

ELECTRONIC SYSTEMS TECHNICIAN
LEVEL ONE

33108-04
LOW-VOLTAGE CABLING

33107-04
HAND BENDING OF CONDUIT

33106-04
CRAFT-RELATED
MATHEMATICS ◁ YOU ARE HERE

33105-04
JOB-SITE SAFETY

33104-04
FASTENERS AND ANCHORS

33103-04
PATHWAYS AND SPACES

33102-04
CONSTRUCTION MATERIALS
AND METHODS

33101-04
INTRODUCTION TO THE TRADE

CORE CURRICULUM

106CMAP.EPS

1.0.0 **INTRODUCTION** 6.1

2.0.0 **CONVERTING DECIMAL FEET AND FEET AND INCHES** 6.1

   2.1.0 Converting Decimal Feet to Feet and Inches 6.1

   2.2.0 Converting Feet and Inches to Decimal Feet 6.2

3.0.0 **THE METRIC SYSTEM** 6.2

   3.1.0 Fundamental Units 6.2

   3.2.0 Length, Area, and Volume 6.4

   3.2.1 *The Meter* 6.4

   3.2.2 *Length* 6.4

   3.2.3 *Area* 6.5

   3.2.4 *Volume* 6.6

   3.2.5 *Wet Volume Measurements* 6.9

   3.3.0 Mass Versus Weight 6.9

   3.3.1 *Mass* 6.9

   3.3.2 *Weight (Force)* 6.9

   3.4.0 Pressure (Force) and Acceleration 6.11

   3.5.0 Temperature 6.13

   3.5.1 *Temperature Scales* 6.13

   3.5.2 *Temperature Conversions* .6.14

4.0.0 **SCIENTIFIC NOTATION** 6.14

   4.1.0 Addition and Subtraction of Powers of Ten 6.16

   4.2.0 Multiplication and Division of Powers of Ten 6.16

   4.3.0 Using Scientific Notation with a Calculator 6.16

5.0.0 **ENGINEERING NOTATION** 6.16

6.0.0 **DECIBELS** 6.17

7.0.0 **LOGARITHMS** 6.18

8.0.0 **POWERS AND ROOTS** 6.18

   8.1.0 Square and Square Roots 6.19

   8.2.0 Other Powers and Roots 6.19

9.0.0 **INTRODUCTION TO ALGEBRA** 6.19

   9.1.0 Definition of Terms 6.19

   9.1.1 *Mathematical Operators* 6.19

   9.1.2 *Equations* 6.20

   9.1.3 *Variables* 6.20

   9.1.4 *Constants* 6.20

   9.1.5 *Coefficients* 6.20

   9.2.0 Sequence of Operations 6.20

   9.3.0 Solving Algebraic Equations .6.21

10.0.0 INTRODUCTION TO GEOMETRY 6.22

    10.1.0 Points and Lines 6.23

    10.2.0 Circles 6.23

    10.3.0 Angles 6.24

    10.4.0 Polygons 6.24

    10.5.0 Triangles 6.25

11.0.0 WORKING WITH RIGHT TRIANGLES 6.27

    11.1.0 Right Triangle Calculations Using
            the Pythagorean Theorem 6.27

    11.2.0 Right Triangle Calculations Using Trigonometry 6.28

SUMMARY 6.29

REVIEW QUESTIONS 6.30

PROFILE IN SUCCESS 6.31

GLOSSARY 6.33

APPENDIX A, Conversion Factors 6.34

APPENDIX B, Temperature Conversion Table 6.35

REFERENCES & ACKNOWLEDGMENTS 6.36

Figures

Figure 1   Basic measurement units 6.4

Figure 2   Comparison of inches to centimeters 6.5

Figure 3   Measuring the area of a square and rectangle 6.6

Figure 4   Measuring the area of a circle 6.6

Figure 5   Conversion of units for a square 6.7

Figure 6   Conversion of units for a rectangle 6.7

Figure 7   Conversion of units for a circle 6.7

Figure 8   Volume of a rectangle 6.7

Figure 9   Volume of a cylindrical tank 6.8

Figure 10   Conversion of units for a box 6.8

Figure 11   Conversion of units for a cylindrical tank 6.8

Figure 12   Common metric prefixes used with volumes 6.9

Figure 13   Equal forces applied to different surface areas 6.10

Figure 14   Known forces applied to known surface areas 6.10

Figure 15   Comparison of temperature scales 6.13

Figure 16   Sample temperature unit conversions 6.14

Figure 17   Lines 6.23

Figure 18   Perpendicular and parallel lines 6.23

Figure 19   Circle 6.23

Figure 20   Angle 6.24

Figure 21   Right, straight, acute, and obtuse angles 6.25

Figure 22   Adjacent, complementary, and
            supplementary angles 6.25

Figure 23   Common polygons 6.26

Figure 24   Equilateral, isosceles, and scalene triangles 6.26

Figure 25   Right, obtuse, and acute triangles 6.27

Figure 26   Common labeling of angles and sides
            in a right triangle 6.27

Figure 27   Angle/side relationships in a right triangle 6.28

Tables

Table 1   Fundamental Units 6.2

Table 2   Common Units in the English System 6.3

Table 3   Metric System Prefixes 6.3

Table 4   Length Conversion Multipliers 6.5

Table 5   Volume Relationships 6.9

Table 6   Mass and Weight Equivalences 6.10

Table 7   Force Conversion Factors 6.12

Table 8   Pressure Conversion Factors 6.12

Table 9   Common Powers of Ten 6.15

Craft-Related Mathematics

Objectives

When you have completed this module, you will be able to do the following:

1. Identify similar units of measurement in both the English and metric systems and know which units are larger.
2. Convert measured values in the English system to equivalent metric values and vice versa.
3. Express numbers as powers of ten.
4. Determine the powers and roots of numbers.
5. Solve basic algebraic equations.
6. Recognize various geometric figures.
7. Use the Pythagorean theorem and trigonometry to make calculations involving right triangles.
8. Convert decimal feet to feet and inches and vice versa.

Recommended Prerequisites

Core Curriculum; Electronic Systems Technician Level One, Modules 33101-04 through 33105-04

Required Trainee Materials

1. Paper and pencil
2. Scientific calculator

1.0.0 ◆ INTRODUCTION

This module expands on the materials covered in *Basic Math* in *Core Curriculum*. In the *Basic Math* module, you studied whole numbers, fractions, decimals, percentages, and the metric system. If necessary, you may want to review all or part of the material covered in *Basic Math* before proceeding with the material covered here.

2.0.0 ◆ CONVERTING DECIMAL FEET AND FEET AND INCHES

When using trigonometric functions to calculate numerical values for **lengths**, distances, and angles, the answers obtained are normally expressed as a decimal. Construction drawings and plot plans often express similar measurements in feet and inches. For this reason, it is often necessary to convert between these two measurement systems. Conversion tables are available in many trade-related reference books. However, in case conversion tables are not readily available, you should become familiar with the methods for making such conversions mathematically.

2.1.0 Converting Decimal Feet to Feet and Inches

To convert values given in decimal feet into equivalent feet and inches, use the following procedure. We will convert 45.3646 feet to feet and inches.

Step 1 Subtract 45' from 45.3646' = 0.3646'.

Step 2 Convert 0.3646' to inches by multiplying 0.3646' by 12 = 4.3752".

Step 3 Subtract 4" from 4.3752" = 0.3752".

Step 4 Convert 0.3752" into eighths of an inch by multiplying 0.3752" by 8 = 3.0016 eighths or, when rounded off, ⅜. Therefore, 45.3646' = 45'-4⅜".

2.2.0 Converting Feet and Inches to Decimal Feet

To convert values given in feet and inches (and inch-fractions) into equivalent decimal feet values, use the following procedure. For our example, we will convert 45'-4⅜" to decimal feet:

Step 1   Convert the inch-fraction ⅜" to a decimal. This is done by dividing the numerator of the fraction (top number) by the denominator of the fraction (bottom number). For example, ⅜" = 0.375.

Step 2   Add 0.375" to 4" to obtain 4.375".

Step 3   Divide 4.375" by 12 to obtain 0.3646'.

Step 4   Add 0.3646' to 45' to obtain 45.3646'. Therefore, 45'-4⅜" = 45.3646'.

3.0.0 ◆ THE METRIC SYSTEM

The metric system was introduced in the *Basic Math* module. Because of its global use in construction documents and specifications, the metric system is covered here in more detail. Included in the coverage of the metric system are some related fundamental concepts of physics and geometry.

If you have not used the metric system on the job, you most certainly will use it in the near future.

3.1.0 Fundamental Units

Most work in science and engineering is based on the exact measurement of physical quantities. A measurement is simply a comparison of a quantity to some definite standard measure of dimension called a **unit**. When a physical quantity is described, the units of the standard to which the quantity was compared must be specified. A number alone is insufficient to describe a physical quantity.

The importance of specifying the units of measurement for a number used to describe a physical quantity is clearly seen when you note that the same physical quantity may be measured using a variety of different units. For example, length may be measured in inches, feet, yards, miles, centimeters, meters, kilometers, and so on. All physical quantities can ultimately be expressed in terms of the following three fundamental units:

- *Length* – The distance from one point to another
- *Mass* – The quantity of matter
- *Time* – The period during which an event occurs

The following are the three most widely used systems of measurement:

- Meter-kilogram-second (MKS) system
- Centimeter-gram-second (CGS) system
- English system

Table 1 shows the fundamental units of length, mass, and time in each of these three systems. The MKS and CGS units are both part of the metric system of measure. The English system is probably most familiar to you. Notice that time is measured in the same units (seconds) in all systems.

The existence of different sets of fundamental units contributes to a considerable amount of confusion in many calculations. Today, both the English and metric systems are widely employed in engineering and construction calculations. Therefore, it is necessary to have some degree of understanding of both systems of units.

The metric system is actually much simpler to use than the English system because it is a decimal system in which prefixes are used to denote powers of ten. The older English system requires the use of

Table 1 Fundamental Units

Unit	MKS	CGS	English
Length	Meter (m)	Centimeter (cm)	Foot (ft)
Mass	Kilogram (km)	Gram (g)	Pound (lb)
Time	Second (sec)	Second (sec)	Second (sec)

106T01.EPS

The French Connection

The official name of the metric system is Système International d' Unités and metric units are commonly known as SI units. It was first adopted by the French revolutionary assembly in 1795. At first, there was considerable resistance to the system.

The first countries to actually require the use of the metric system were Belgium, the Netherlands, and Luxembourg, in 1820. The use of the metric system was legalized in the United States by an act of Congress in 1866, but was not made mandatory.

It was adopted by all industrialized countries in 1875. Twenty countries, including the United States, signed the *Treaty of the Meter*. As a result, the International Bureau of Weights and Measures (Bureau International des Poids et Mésures, BIPM) was established in Paris.

The Big and Small of It

The largest number in the world was invented by an eight-year-old boy. According to the story, in 1938, an American mathematician, Kasner, asked his nephew what name he would give to a really large number, and a googol became the quantity equal to 10^{100} (1 followed by 100 zeroes). Kasner also defined the googolplex, equal to 10^{GOOGOL}, that is, 1 followed by a googol of zeroes.

The metric system has standard measures. To make larger or smaller numbers you only need to add a different prefix. Periodically, the International Bureau of Weights and Measures adds new prefixes. In 1991, they extended the list of metric prefixes to include the yotta- at 10^{24} (one septillion) to yocto- at 10^{-24} (one septillionth).

conversion factors that must be memorized and are not categorized as logically as powers of ten. For example, 1 mile is 5,280 feet, and 1 foot is 12 inches. *Table 2* lists some of the more common units in the English system.

The metric system prefixes are listed in *Table 3*. From this table, you can see that the use of the metric system is logically arranged, and that the name of the unit will also represent an order of magnitude (via the prefix) that foot and pound cannot.

Transferring the American engineering practices and equipment to the metric system was a very expensive transition for most industries. Manufacturers are currently publishing their technical manuals and instrument data sheets displaying all values, as in the past, in the English system units, but also putting the metric equivalents in parentheses

Table 2 Common Units in the English System

Unit	Equivalent
12 inches (in)	1 foot (ft)
1 yard (yd)	3 ft
1 mile (mi)	5,280 ft
16 ounces (oz)	1 pound (lb)
1 ton	2,000 lbs
1 minute (min)	60 seconds (sec)
1 hour (hr)	3,600 sec
1 U.S. gallon (gal)	0.1337 cubic foot (ft³)

106T02.EPS

behind the English units. In the future, you may only find the metric units listed, so it is a good time to become familiar with both and understand how to convert from one to the other.

Table 3 Metric System Prefixes

Prefix	Symbol	Amount	American Standard
yotta-	Y	10^{24}	1 septillion
zetta-	Z	10^{21}	1 sextillion
exa-	E	10^{18}	1 quintillion
peta-	P	10^{15}	1 quadrillion
tera-	T	10^{12}	1 trillion
giga-	G	10^{9}	1 billion
mega-	M	10^{6}	1 million
kilo-	k	10^{3}	1 thousand
hecto-	h	10^{2}	1 hundred
deka-	da	10	ten
deci-	d	10^{-1}	1 tenth
centi-	c	10^{-2}	1 hundredth
milli-	m	10^{-3}	1 thousandth
micro-	μ	10^{-6}	1 millionth
nano-	n	10^{-9}	1 billionth
pico-	p	10^{-12}	1 trillionth
femto-	f	10^{-15}	1 quadrillionth
atto-	a	10^{-18}	1 quintillionth
zepto-	z	10^{-21}	1 sextillionth
yocto-	y	10^{-24}	1 septillionth

NOTE: Prefixes for other multiples, such as 10^{5}, 10^{-4}, and 10^{-5} were never generally accepted.

The most common metric system prefixes are mega- (m), kilo- (k), centi- (c), milli- (m), and micro- (μ). Even though these prefixes may seem difficult to understand at first, you are probably already using them regularly. For example, you have probably seen the terms megawatts, kilometers, centimeters, millivolts, and microamps.

There are four basic parameters used to describe different quantities: **weight**, length, **volume**, and temperature. *Figure 1* references the familiar English unit for each of these parameters and the metric unit that is becoming more and more common.

The most common measurements encountered by electronic systems technicians can be classified into four categories:

- Dimensional measurements (lengths, **levels**, **areas**, and volumes)
- Mass and weight measurements
- Pressure measurements
- Temperature measurements

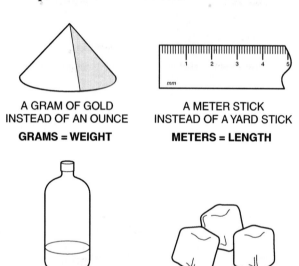

A GRAM OF GOLD
INSTEAD OF AN OUNCE
GRAMS = WEIGHT

A METER STICK
INSTEAD OF A YARD STICK
METERS = LENGTH

A 1-LITER
BOTTLE OF SODA
INSTEAD OF
A QUART
LITERS = VOLUME

ICE CUBES FREEZE
AT 0° CELSIUS
VERSUS 32°
FAHRENHEIT
CELSIUS = TEMPERATURE

106F01.EPS

Figure 1 ◆ Basic measurement units.

3.2.0 Length, Area, and Volume

In the *Basic Math* module, you were concerned primarily with the development of mathematical skills which enable you to solve problems. It is important to realize that in the field, numbers usually represent physical quantities. In order to give meaning to these quantities, we must assign measurement units to the numbers.

3.2.1 The Meter

To say that the length of a room is 17 is completely meaningless unless we indicate the units into which the room is divided. With regard to length, a unit is simply a standard distance.

In the English system, the standard of distance is called the foot. When seeking to define a new standard for length in developing the metric system, scientists wanted to select a reference that would be more precise and less likely to ever change. They selected the meter, which was originally defined as $\frac{1}{10,000,000}$ of the Earth's meridional quadrant (the distance from the north pole to the equator). Today, the length of a meter is defined based on the speed of light. For our purposes, 39.37" is equal to one meter.

3.2.2 Length

Length typically refers to the long side of an object or surface. Length can be expressed in either English or metric units (for example, inches or centimeters).

When working in construction, instructions or plans can be in either system of measurement. It is important that you know the relationships so you can convert from one system to the other. *Table 4* shows the relationships of the most common units of length. *Figure 2* shows the comparison of inches directly to centimeters.

You may be called upon to convert a measurement in one system into the other system's units. The multipliers in *Table 4* may be used to make these conversions.

Table 4 Length Conversion Multipliers

Unit	CM	IN	FT	M	KM
1 millimeter	0.1	0.03937	0.003281	0.001	0.000001
1 centimeter	1	0.3937	0.03281	0.01	0.00001
1 inch	2.54	1	0.08333	0.0254	0.0000254
1 foot	32.81	12	1	0.3048	0.0003048
1 meter	100	39.37	3.281	1	1,000
1 kilometer	100,000	39,370	3,281	1,000	1

106T04.EPS

106F02.EPS

Figure 2 ◆ Comparison of inches to centimeters.

Example 1: An installation plan calls for a telephone jack to be mounted within three meters of a workstation. What is the maximum distance in feet that the jack can be located from the workstation?

$$1 \text{ m} = 39.37 \text{ in}$$
$$3 \times 1 \text{ m} = 3 \times 39.37 \text{ in}$$
$$3 \text{ m} = 118.11 \text{ in}$$

Then convert to feet from inches:

$$3 \text{ m} = \frac{118.11 \text{ in}}{12 \text{ in/ft}}$$
$$3 \text{ m} = 9.843 \text{ in}$$

You can also convert directly to feet:

$$1 \text{ m} = 3.281 \text{ ft}$$
$$3 \times 1 \text{ m} = 3 \times 3.281 \text{ ft}$$
$$3 \text{ m} = 9.843 \text{ ft}$$

Example 2: An installation plan calls for an instrument having a range of measurement of 150 inches. However, the manufacturer lists the instrument range on the faceplate and in the instrument panels in meters. Which of the three instruments below would be most appropriate?

- Two-meter range
- Three-meter range
- Four-meter range

$$39.37 \text{ in} = 1 \text{ m}$$
$$\frac{150 \text{ in}}{39.37 \text{ in/m}} = 3.81 \text{ meters}$$

Therefore, only the four-meter range instrument would be appropriate.

NOTE

Appendix A contains listings of common conversion factors in construction. Also, some scientific calculators have the capability of converting English units to metric units and vice versa.

3.2.3 Area

The area of a square or rectangular surface is the product of two lengths. It has units of length times length, or length squared. In the familiar English system, the units of area are square feet (ft^2) or square inches (in^2). *Figure 3* shows the application of this concept.

NOTE

The area of any rectangle is equal to the length multiplied by the width.

Square Millimeters

The area of a computer chip is measured in square millimeters. Current chips average 80 to 300 mm^2. Over the next decades, the average chip is expected to grow to 200 to 300 mm^2, as developers find ways to pack more transistors on a single chip. At its introduction in 2000, Intel's Pentium 4 chip at 217 mm^2 was more than double the size of its predecessor, the Pentium III, which only took up about 100 square millimeters.

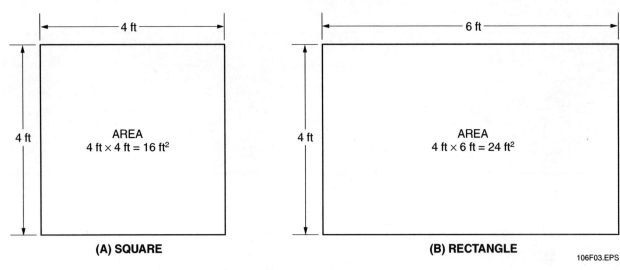

(A) SQUARE

(B) RECTANGLE

106F03.EPS

Figure 3 ◆ Measuring the area of a square and rectangle.

The area of a circle (*Figure 4*) may be found using the following formula:

Area = πr^2

Where:

A = the area of the circle

π = a **constant** of 3.14159 (often rounded off to 3.14)

r = the radius (distance from the center to the edge of the circle)

When converting areas from one measurement system to the other, we must remember that every dimension must be converted. So, for converting the dimensions of the square shown previously in *Figure 3A*, we must convert both the length and the width, as shown in *Figure 5*.

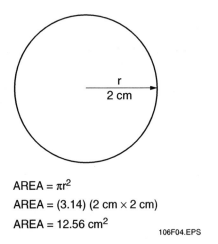

AREA = πr^2

AREA = (3.14) (2 cm × 2 cm)

AREA = 12.56 cm²

106F04.EPS

Figure 4 ◆ Measuring the area of a circle.

For converting the dimensions of the rectangle shown in *Figure 3B*, we must convert both the length and the width, as shown in *Figure 6*.

When converting the dimensions of a circle, only the radius has a measured dimension that must be converted. In the example shown in *Figure 7*, centimeters must be converted into inches.

3.2.4 Volume

The volume of a square or rectangle is the product of three lengths. It has units of length × length × length, or length cubed. In the familiar English system, the most common units of volume are cubic feet (ft³) or cubic inches (in³).

Figure 8 shows the three-dimensional measurement of a rectangle. Its volume is calculated by multiplying length × width × height.

This will suffice for finding the volume of box-shaped containers. The second common shape is that of a tank or other cylindrical object, as shown in *Figure 9*.

Since the volume of the box can be considered the area of any side times the height, likewise, the volume of a cylindrical tank can be simplified by considering it as the area of the circle times its depth (or height).

When converting these two volumes from one measurement system to the other, again, we must remember that every dimension must be independently converted. So, for converting the dimensions of the box, we must convert the length, width, and height, as shown in *Figure 10*.

In the example of the cylindrical tank, the same rule applies, as shown in *Figure 11*.

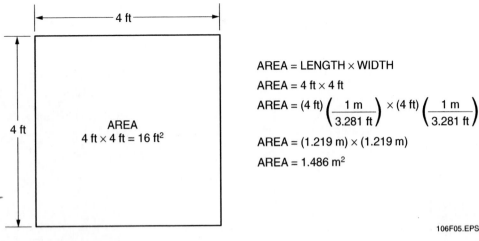

AREA = LENGTH × WIDTH

AREA = 4 ft × 4 ft

AREA = (4 ft) $\left(\dfrac{1\ m}{3.281\ ft}\right)$ × (4 ft) $\left(\dfrac{1\ m}{3.281\ ft}\right)$

AREA = (1.219 m) × (1.219 m)

AREA = 1.486 m²

106F05.EPS

Figure 5 ◆ Conversion of units for a square.

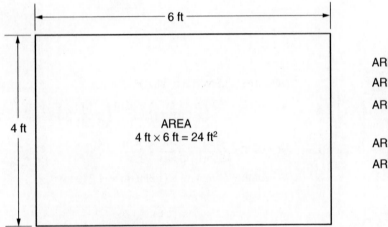

AREA = LENGTH × WIDTH

AREA = 4 ft × 6 ft

AREA = (4 ft) $\left(\dfrac{1\ m}{3.281\ ft}\right)$ × (6 ft) $\left(\dfrac{1\ m}{3.281\ ft}\right)$

AREA = (1.219 m) × (1.829 m)

AREA = 2.229 m²

106F06.EPS

Figure 6 ◆ Conversion of units for a rectangle.

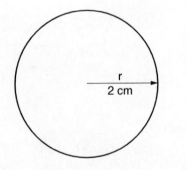

AREA = πr²

AREA = (3.14) [(2 cm) (0.3937 in/cm)] [(2 cm) (0.3937 in/cm)]

AREA = (3.14) (0.7874 in) (0.7874 in)

AREA = (3.14) (0.6200 in)

AREA = 1.95 in²

106F07.EPS

Figure 7 ◆ Conversion of units for a circle.

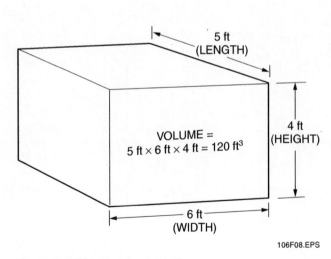

106F08.EPS

Figure 8 ◆ Volume of a rectangle.

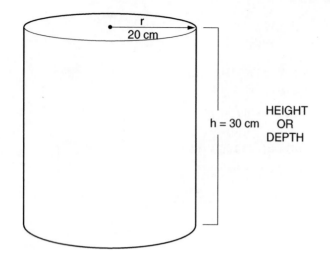

VOLUME = $(\pi r^2) \times h$ *or* AREA OF THE CIRCLE $\times$ HEIGHT

$$\text{VOLUME} = \overbrace{\{(3.14)\,[(20\text{ cm})\,(20\text{ cm})]\}}^{\text{AREA}} \times \overbrace{(30\text{ cm})}^{\text{HEIGHT}}$$

VOLUME = $[(3.14)\,(400\text{ cm}^2)] \times (30\text{ cm})$

VOLUME = $(1{,}256\text{ cm}^2) \times (30\text{ cm})$

VOLUME = $37{,}680\text{ cm}^3$

106F09.EPS

Figure 9 ◆ Volume of a cylindrical tank.

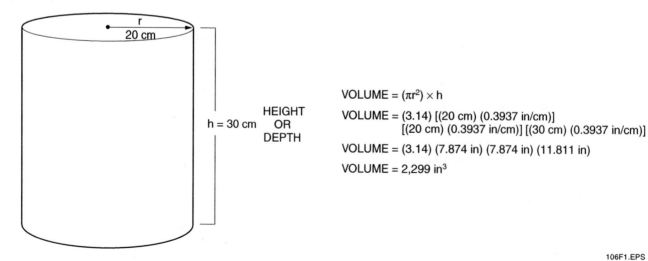

VOLUME = LENGTH $\times$ WIDTH $\times$ HEIGHT

VOLUME = $(5\text{ ft})\left(\dfrac{1\text{ m}}{3.281\text{ ft}}\right) \times (6\text{ ft})\left(\dfrac{1\text{ m}}{3.281\text{ ft}}\right) \times (4\text{ ft})\left(\dfrac{1\text{ m}}{3.281\text{ ft}}\right)$

VOLUME = $\dfrac{5\text{ m}}{3.281} \times \dfrac{6\text{ m}}{3.281} \times \dfrac{4\text{ m}}{3.281}$

VOLUME = $(1.524\text{ m}) \times (1.829\text{ m}) \times (1.219\text{ m})$

VOLUME = 3.398 m^3

106F10.EPS

Figure 10 ◆ Conversion of units for a box.

VOLUME = $(\pi r^2) \times h$

VOLUME = $(3.14)\,[(20\text{ cm})\,(0.3937\text{ in/cm})]$
$[(20\text{ cm})\,(0.3937\text{ in/cm})]\,[(30\text{ cm})\,(0.3937\text{ in/cm})]$

VOLUME = $(3.14)\,(7.874\text{ in})\,(7.874\text{ in})\,(11.811\text{ in})$

VOLUME = $2{,}299\text{ in}^3$

106F1.EPS

Figure 11 ◆ Conversion of units for a cylindrical tank.

3.2.5 Wet Volume Measurements

In our discussion of volume measurements, we have been using the shape of the container to calculate the volume. This is referred to as a dry measure. In practice, we are much more used to dealing with wet measures, or the amount of a fluid that would fill the volume. Common wet measures in the English system include the pint, quart, and gallon.

The metric system also uses wet measuring units. The **liter** is the most common and is about five percent greater than a quart.

By definition, one liter is one cubic decimeter. In other words, a cube with each side equal to one decimeter (or ten centimeters) will hold one liter of fluid. Knowing the wet measures for a substance allows easy handling and measuring of fluids, since the fluid will conform to the shape of the container. If you had to recalculate the amount each time you moved a fluid, you would soon see the advantage of using wet measures.

Table 5 shows the volume relationships between the liter and the dry volume of the cubic meter in the metric system and the pint and gallon in the English system.

Figure 12 shows that the same metric prefixes that apply to the meter can be used with the liter.

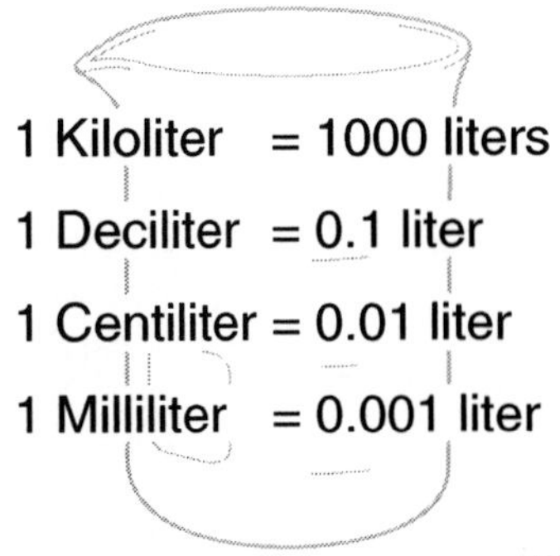

3.3.0 Mass Versus Weight

Mass is defined as the quantity of matter present. We often use the term weight to mean mass, but this is technically incorrect. Weight is actually the **force** on an object that is due to the pull of the Earth's gravity. As a body gets further away from the Earth, the effect of the Earth's gravity decreases. Therefore, as you climb a mountain, your actual weight decreases with the increasing altitude. However, the mass of your body has not changed at all. These two terms are used interchangeably because they are proportionally the same anywhere. However, if you are measuring very small amounts or are trying to be extremely accurate, it will be necessary to compensate for the altitude (the distance above or below sea level). For example, Denver is almost a mile above sea level. This

1 Kiloliter	= 1000 liters
1 Deciliter	= 0.1 liter
1 Centiliter	= 0.01 liter
1 Milliliter	= 0.001 liter

106F12.EPS

Figure 12 ◆ Common metric prefixes used with volumes.

could cause a slight error in the measurement of weights. Since we most often use weight to determine mass, it could also be measured inaccurately.

3.3.1 Mass

Since mass is a term used more often by scientists, it is not surprising that the most common units of mass are the metric system units. The basic unit of mass is the gram. A gram (g) is a relatively small amount of matter. It is equivalent to about 1 milliliter of water. The same prefixes used with the meter and the liter in the metric system are used with the gram. The most common units are the milligram (mg), gram (g), and kilogram (kg).

3.3.2 Weight (Force)

Since weight is actually force, it is the push we exert on the surface of the Earth due to our mass and the pull of the Earth's gravity. Force is a **vector quantity** that has both magnitude and direction.

Weight is a force with its direction always assumed to be downward. In the English system, the most common units for weight are the pound (lb) and the ounce (oz). The English system also uses these units to represent mass, such as pounds-mass (lb-m) or pounds force (lb-f).

Table 6 shows the relationships between mass and weight units in both systems. For most instances, they are interchangeable for both mass or weight.

Table 5 Volume Relationships

Unit	Cubic Meter	Gallon	Liter	Pint
Cubic meter (m³)	1	0.003785	0.001	0.0004732
U.S. gallon (gal)	264.2	1	0.264	0.125
Liter (L)	1,000	3.785	1	0.4732
U.S. pint (pt)	2,113	8	2.113	1

106T05.EPS

Table 6 Mass and Weight Equivalences

Unit	Kilogram	Pound	Ounce	Gram
1 kilogram (kg)	1	2.205	35.27	1,000
1 pound (lb)	0.4536	1	16	453.6
1 ounce (oz)	0.02835	0.0625	1	28.35
1 gram (g)	0.001	0.002205	0.03527	1

106T06.EPS

The metric system uses the **newton (n)** as the basic unit of force. Sir Isaac Newton discovered the true importance of gravity, created the field of mathematics known as calculus, and defined the properties of matter and bodies in motion.

Newton's First Law of Motion states that every body persists in its state of rest, or of uniform motion in a straight line, unless it is compelled to change that state by forces impressed on it. In other words, a body at rest stays at rest and a body in motion stays in motion at a constant velocity, unless something acts to influence it. That something is force.

With respect to the body in Newton's First Law, a force can be applied in a direction that aids the moving body to increase its velocity. Conversely, a force can be applied in a direction that opposes the moving body to decrease its velocity. **Acceleration** is the term used to represent a change in velocity with respect to time. Notice that a body at rest can be viewed as having a velocity equal to zero. If a force applied to the body causes motion at some velocity, it can be said that the body was accelerated from rest.

Figure 13 shows equal forces applied to two different bodies, which are viewed as two different surface areas.

The surface area that Body A presents to Force A is four times larger than the surface area that Body B presents to Force B. Another way of describing this is to say that Force A is spread over a larger area than Force B. As a result, the force per unit area applied to Body A is one-fourth of the force per unit area applied to Body B. *Figure 14* shows the same two bodies with the surface areas and forces specified.

Pounds per square inch (psi) is the most common unit of pressure in the English system. Pressure is measured in newtons per square meter (N/m^2) in the metric system. One N/m^2 is also referred to as one pascal, after Blaise Pascal, a seventeenth-century French philosopher who contributed greatly to mathematics and engineering. The pascal, or Pa, is equal to a force of one newton exerted on an area of one square meter.

One pascal is not really very much pressure—not nearly as much as one psi. You can get an idea of its size if you spread half a cup (about 100 grams) of sugar evenly over the top of a table that is one meter on each side. The pressure or force exerted at any one point on the table would be approximately one pascal. It would take 200,000 pascals (N/m^2) to inflate an ordinary automobile tire to about 28 psi.

A second common metric unit of pressure is the bar (b), which is equal to 100,000 Pa. The bar is used by weather forecasters. You are probably familiar with barometric pressure readings from watching the weather information on the evening news. You will also see the term millibar, which is 0.001 bar (b).

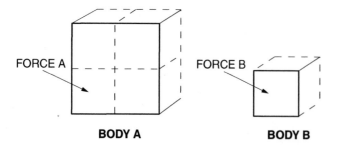

FRONT OF BODY A = 4 UNITS OF SURFACE AREA
FRONT OF BODY B = 1 UNIT OF SURFACE AREA
FORCE A = FORCE B

106F13.EPS

Figure 13 ◆ Equal forces applied to different surface areas.

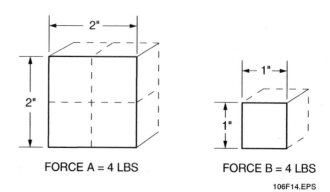

FORCE A = 4 LBS   FORCE B = 4 LBS

106F14.EPS

Figure 14 ◆ Known forces applied to known surface areas.

Occasionally, you will see the metric unit of a dyne to represent very small forces (one newton = 1,000 dynes).

In the next section, we will relate these metric units to the more familiar pressure units of the English system and review the concept of pressure measurement at the same time.

3.4.0 Pressure (Force) and Acceleration

Pressure is a quantity that is also closely related to force, but is probably more familiar to you. In a service station, you may ask the attendant for 28 pounds of air in the tires of your car. What you really want is an amount of air put into the tires that can exert 28 more pounds of force per square inch on the inside of the tires than the air pressure of the atmosphere exerts on the outside of the tires.

To cause a specified amount of acceleration, a force must have sufficient magnitude and must be applied in such a direction that it overcomes any opposing forces that are present. The mass of a body has a direct effect on the magnitude of force required.

Newton's Second Law of Motion states that if a body is acted upon by a force, the body will be accelerated at a rate directly proportional to that force, and inversely proportional to the body's mass. In other words, a body with a large mass requires more force to obtain a specified amount of acceleration than does a body with less mass. Mass can simply be described as the amount of matter contained in a body. The relationship of force, mass, and acceleration is expressed as follows:

$$\text{Acceleration} = \frac{\text{force}}{\text{mass}}$$

or

$$\text{Force} = \text{mass} \times \text{acceleration}$$

Two bodies of the same size but made of different materials can have different masses. Two bodies can also have different masses if one body has been made larger by adding more of the material to it.

The basic unit of force in the metric system, the newton (N), can now be defined as the amount of force required to accelerate 1 kilogram at the rate of one meter per second per second. Expressed mathematically:

$$\text{Force (1 newton)} = \text{mass (1 kilogram)} \times \text{acceleration (1 meter/sec/sec)}$$

or

$$\text{1 newton} = \text{1 kilogram} \times \text{1 meter/sec}^2$$

The definition of pressure is force per unit area, or:

$$\text{Pressure} = \frac{\text{force}}{\text{area}}$$

The force per unit area that is applied to Body A (shown in *Figure 14*) is:

$$\text{Pressure} = \frac{4 \text{ lbs}}{4 \text{ in}^2} = 1 \text{ lb per in}^2$$

The force per unit area that is applied to Body B (shown in *Figure 14*) is:

$$\text{Pressure} = \frac{4 \text{ lbs}}{1 \text{ in}^2} = 4 \text{ lb per in}^2$$

Pressure represents the force applied perpendicular to a surface. The pressure applied to Body A in *Figure 14* is one pound per square inch (1 psi). The pressure applied to Body B is four pounds per square inch (4 psi).

As shown, applying equal forces to bodies of different surface areas results in applying different pressures to the bodies.

When converting these two pressures to their metric system equivalents, remember that each dimension must be converted. As we deal with more complex measurements, it becomes much easier to use conversion factors directly for the more common units of measure. *Table 7* shows the more common conversion factors used to convert

Table 7 Force Conversion Factors

Unit	Kilogram-Force	Pound-Force	Gram-Force
Newton	9.807	4.448	0.009807
Dyne	980,665	444,822	980.7

106T07.EPS

the newton or dyne directly for general forces. *Table 8* shows the conversion factors used to convert the pascal or newton/meter^2 or dyne/cm^2 for very small pressures. Since the pascal is such a small unit and it takes so many pascals to define even a low pressure, the pascal is normally represented in kilopascals (kPa).

To convert the 1 psi for Body A in *Figure 14*:

1 psi × 6,895 Pa = 6,895 Pa

To convert the 4 psi for Body B in *Figure 14*:

4 psi × 6,895 Pa = 27,580 Pa or 27.580 kPa

As you can see, the pascal is indeed small in comparison to the psi.

For example, a person weighing 160 pounds is wearing ice skates. The total surface area of the two skate blades that are in contact with the ice is as follows:

Total area = length × width × 2 blades

Total area = 12 in × ⅛ in × 2

Total area = 3 in^2

Therefore, the person exerts a pressure on the surface of the ice equal to the following:

$$\text{Pressure} = \frac{\text{force}}{\text{unit area}}$$

$$\text{Pressure} = \frac{160 \text{ lbs}}{3 \text{ in}^2}$$

Pressure = 53.3333 psi or 367,733 Pa

Now suppose that the person weighing 160 pounds is wearing snow skis. The total surface area of the two skis that are in contact with the ice is as follows:

Total area = 6 ft × 3 in × 2 skis

Total area = 72 in × 3 in × 2

Total area = 432 in^2

Therefore, the person exerts a pressure on the surface of the ice equal to the following:

$$\text{Pressure} = \frac{160 \text{ lbs}}{432 \text{ in}^2}$$

Pressure = 0.3703 psi or 2,553 Pa

Suppose you are the person weighing 160 pounds and you see a friend break through the ice and fall into the lake. You should immediately lay down flat on the ice to distribute your weight over as large a surface area as possible. For example, if you are approximately 6 feet (72 inches) in height and on average 18 inches wide, the surface area now becomes the following:

Total area = 72 in × 18 in

Total area = 1,296 in^2

You would exert a pressure on the surface of the ice equal to:

$$\text{Pressure} = \frac{160 \text{ lbs}}{1,296 \text{ in}^2}$$

Pressure = 0.1234 psi or 851 Pa

Table 8 Pressure Conversion Factors

Unit	Kilogram-Force per cm^2	Pound-Force per in^2	Pound-Force per ft^2	Kilogram-Force per m^2
1 kilopascal (kPa)	98.067	6.895	0.04788	0.009807
Pascal (Pa)	98,067	6,895	47.99	9.807
Newton/meter^2 (n/m^2)	98,067	6,895	47.88	9.807
Dyne/cm^2	980,665	68,947	478.8	98.07

106T08.EPS

That is a reduction in pressure of over 2,000 times your pressure when standing upright wearing ice skates.

3.5.0 Temperature

The temperature of a substance is normally thought of in relation to its surroundings. If the temperature of an object is greater than body temperature, it is considered hot. If its temperature is lower than body temperature, it is considered cold. The hotness or coldness of an object is a result of molecular activity; the greater the activity, the greater the temperature. The activity is an indication of the kinetic energy of the atoms that make up molecules. Temperature, therefore, is a measure of the atomic kinetic energy of an object.

3.5.1 Temperature Scales

Temperature is measured in degrees on a temperature scale. In order to establish the scale, a substance is needed that can be placed in reproducible conditions. The substance used is water. The point at which water freezes at atmospheric pressure is one reproducible condition and the point at which water boils at atmospheric pressure is another. The four temperature scales commonly used today are the Fahrenheit scale, Celsius scale, Rankine scale, and Kelvin scale (see *Figure 15*). On the Fahrenheit scale, the freezing temperature of water is 32°F and the boiling temperature is 212°F. On the Celsius scale, the freezing temperature of water is 0°C and the boiling temperature is 100°C. The temperatures at which these fixed points occur were arbitrarily chosen by the inventors of the scales.

The Rankine scale and the Kelvin scale are based on the theory that at some extremely low temperature, no molecular activity occurs. The temperature at which this condition occurs is called absolute zero, the lowest temperature possible. Both the Rankine and Kelvin scales have their zero degree points at absolute zero. On the Rankine scale, the freezing point of water is 491.7°R and the boiling point is 671.7°R. The increments on the Rankine scale correspond in size to

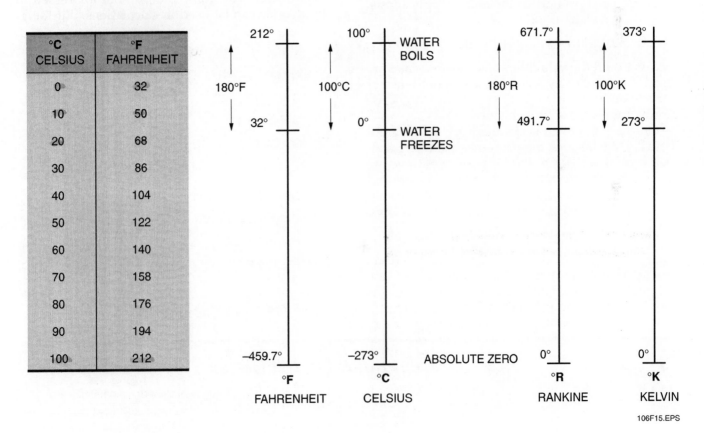

Figure 15 ◆ Comparison of temperature scales.

the increments on the Fahrenheit scale; for this reason, the Rankine scale is sometimes referred to as the absolute Fahrenheit scale. Both the Rankine and Fahrenheit scales are part of the English system of measurement.

On the Kelvin scale, the freezing point of water is 273°K and the boiling point is 373°K. The increments on the Kelvin scale correspond to the increments on the Celsius scale; for this reason, the Kelvin scale is sometimes referred to as the absolute Celsius scale. Both the Kelvin and Celsius scales are part of the metric system of measurement.

 NOTE
Because there are 100 degrees on a standard portion of the Celsius scale, Celsius temperature measurements are sometimes referred to as degrees centigrade.

In the construction industry, the scales of primary importance are the Fahrenheit scale and the Celsius scale. The Rankine scale and the Kelvin scale are used primarily in scientific applications.

3.5.2 Temperature Conversions

Because both the Fahrenheit and Celsius scales are used in our industry, it sometimes becomes necessary to convert between the two. You should be familiar with these conversions.

On the Fahrenheit scale, there are 180 degrees between the freezing temperature and boiling temperature of water. On the Celsius scale, there are 100 degrees between the freezing temperature and the boiling temperature of water. The relationship between the two scales can be expressed as follows:

$$\frac{\text{Fahrenheit range (freezing to boiling)}}{\text{Celsius range (freezing to boiling)}} = \frac{180°}{100°} = \frac{9}{5} \quad \text{✻}$$

Therefore, one degree Fahrenheit is ⅝ of one degree Celsius and conversely, one degree Celsius is ⅝ of one degree Fahrenheit. Thus to convert a

Fahrenheit temperature to a Celsius temperature, it is necessary to subtract 32°, since 32°F corresponds to 0°C, then multiply by ⅝. To convert a Celsius temperature to a Fahrenheit temperature, it is necessary to multiply by ⅝, then add 32°C.

$$°C = \tfrac{5}{9}\,(°F - 32°)$$
$$°F = (\tfrac{9}{5} \times °C) + 32° \quad \text{✻}$$

You will need to practice these calculations to become more comfortable with using them. *Figure 16* shows two examples.

 NOTE
Appendix B contains a temperature conversion chart.

4.0.0 ◆ SCIENTIFIC NOTATION

The mathematics related to electronics commonly uses numbers in the millions and larger, as well as numbers of less than one on down to a millionth or even lower. The complete number expressed in basic units can be used in calculations, but this is

EXAMPLE: 77°F to °C

$$°C = \tfrac{5}{9}\,(77° - 32°)$$
$$°C = \tfrac{5}{9}\,(45°)$$
$$°C = 25°C$$

EXAMPLE: 90°C to °F

$$°F = (\tfrac{9}{5} \times 90°) + 32°$$
$$°F = 162° + 32°$$
$$°F = 194°F$$

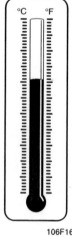

106F16.EPS

Figure 16 ◆ Sample temperature unit conversions.

 *Extreme Temperature Electronics*

Applications for electronics are expanding into hostile environments where temperatures are extremely high or low, such as outer space, the ocean floor, and even automobile engines. Most electronic components operate best at close to room temperature. Heaters are sometimes used to maintain proper operating temperatures for electronic equipment exposed to extreme cold. In 2003, Motorola introduced a microcontroller that operates in the range of −55°C to +125°C. This device is designed to meet a growing need for microcontrollers that tolerate the low temperatures encountered on aircraft and spacecraft without the need for a nearby heater.

very cumbersome and increases the chance for error. For example, suppose we want to multiply 10 megohms times 50 picofarads in order to find the time constant of a circuit. The calculation would be:

$$10,000,000 \times 0.00000000005 = 0.0005$$

A method called scientific notation can be used to simplify calculations by expressing all numbers as a power of ten. In scientific notation, numbers are expressed as a base number times ten raised to some power (or **exponent**). The base number, also called the mantissa, consists of an integer (equal to or greater than one and less than 10) followed by a decimal. For example, in the base number 3.6099, 3 is the integer and 0.6099 is the decimal. The power of ten is the exponent; it tells how many times ten is used as a factor in multiplying. For example, 10^2 indicates 10×10; 10^3 is $10 \times 10 \times 10$, and so on. *Table 9* shows a list of the powers of ten that occur most often.

There are two basic rules for converting numbers to powers of ten:

Rule 1: For a number larger than one, move the decimal point to the left until the number is between one and ten. Then count the number of places the decimal was moved, and use that number as a positive (+) power of ten. For example:

725	$= 7.25 \times 10^2$
3,000	$= 3 \times 10^3$
500,000	$= 5 \times 10^5$
10,000,000	$= 10 \times 10^6$

Rule 2: For a number smaller than one, move the decimal point to the right until the number is between one and ten. Then count the number of

Table 9 Common Powers of Ten

Unit	Unit
$10^0 = 1$	$10^{-1} = 0.1$
$10^1 = 10$	$10^{-2} = 0.01$
$10^2 = 100$	$10^{-3} = 0.001$
$10^3 = 1,000$	$10^{-4} = 0.0001$
$10^4 = 10,000$	$10^{-5} = 0.00001$
$10^5 = 100,000$	$10^{-6} = 0.000001$
$10^6 = 1,000,000$	$10^{-7} = 0.0000001$

106T09.EPS

places the decimal was moved, and use that number as a negative (–) power of ten. For example:

0.005	$= 5 \times 10^{-3}$
0.000008	$= 8 \times 10^{-6}$
0.00000000005	$= 5 \times 10^{-11}$

The process is reversed by performing opposite actions. The power of ten exponent tells you where the decimal point would be if you were to write the number longhand. A positive exponent tells you how many places the decimal point is moved to the right. A negative exponent tells you how many places the decimal is moved to the left. In both instances, zeros are added as needed. For example:

7.25×10^2	$= 725$
3×10^3	$= 3,000$
5×10^5	$= 500,000$
10×10^6	$= 10,000,000$
5×10^{-3}	$= 0.005$
8×10^{-6}	$= 0.000008$
5×10^{-11}	$= 0.00000000005$

Other Power

It is commonly understood that a gigabyte is one billion bytes as giga is the metric prefix for billion. However, the metric system is a decimal system based on a unit of ten. Computers are not based in the decimal system; they are binary systems based on a unit of 2. One billion is not a round number for a computer. A one-gig computer memory actually has 1,073,741,824 bytes or 2^{30}. This has led to confusion within the industry.

In 1998, the International Electrotechnical Commission decided that the metric prefixes should be used in computing just as they are used in other fields. Thus, 5 gigabytes should mean exactly 5,000,000,000 bytes. They created new prefixes for the binary system, including:

- kibi for $2^{10} = 1,024$
- mebi for $2^{20} = 1,048,576$
- gibi for $2^{30} = 1,073,741,824$

However, once again people are resisting change. Few people are using the new binary prefixes. For the most part, when they are referenced, it is in a complaint by someone who doesn't want to use them.

4.1.0 Addition and Subtraction of Powers of Ten

To add and subtract powers of ten, all the numbers must be converted to the same power of ten. Then the numbers can be added or subtracted in the normal way and the same power of ten retained in the answer.

Example 1: Add, $(4.32 \times 10^4) + (6.68 \times 10^3) + (142 \times 10^0)$:

Convert the numbers to the same power of ten:

$4.32 \times 10^4 = 4.320 \times 10^4$

$6.68 \times 10^3 = 0.668 \times 10^4$

$142 \times 10^0 = 0.014 \times 10^4$

Then add:

$$\begin{array}{r} 4.320 \times 10^4 \\ 0.668 \times 10^4 \\ + \ 0.014 \times 10^4 \\ \hline 5.002 \times 10^4 \end{array}$$

Example 2: Subtract, $(2.88 \times 10^4) - (0.65 \times 10^3)$:

Convert the numbers to the same power of ten:

$2.88 \times 10^4 = 2.880 \times 10^4$

$0.65 \times 10^3 = 0.065 \times 10^4$

Then subtract:

$$\begin{array}{r} 2.880 \times 10^4 \\ - \ 0.065 \times 10^4 \\ \hline 2.815 \times 10^4 \end{array}$$

4.2.0 Multiplication and Division of Powers of Ten

To multiply numbers expressed as powers of ten, multiply the numbers together, then add the exponents. Three rules to remember when multiplying follow:

Rule 1: If both powers of ten are positive, add them. For example:

$4,500 \times 400 = (4.5 \times 10^3)(4 \times 10^2)$

$4,500 \times 400 = (4.5 \times 4)(10^{3+2})$

$4,500 \times 400 = 18 \times 10^5$

Rule 2: If both powers of ten are negative, add them. For example:

$0.045 \times 0.005 = (4.5 \times 10^{-2})(5 \times 10^{-3})$

$0.045 \times 0.005 = (4.5 \times 5)(10^{-2+-3})$

$0.045 \times 0.005 = 22.5 \times 10^{-5}$

Rule 3: If the exponents have different signs, the difference between the signs is calculated. For example:

$7,500 \times 0.0004 = (7.5 \times 10^3)(4 \times 10^{-4})$

$7,500 \times 0.0004 = (7.5 \times 4)(10^{3+-4})$

$7,500 \times 0.0004 = 30 \times 10^{-1}$

$7,500 \times 0.0004 = 3.0$

To divide numbers involving powers of ten, divide the numbers and then subtract the exponent of the divisor from the exponent of the number being divided. Note that when dividing, the power of ten exponent in the divisor can be moved to the numerator by changing the sign of the exponent. For example:

$64 \times 10^5 \div 4 \times 10^3 = \dfrac{64 \times 10^5}{4 \times 10^3}$

$64 \times 10^5 \div 4 \times 10^3 = \dfrac{64 \times 10^5 \times 10^{-3}}{4}$

$64 \times 10^5 \div 4 \times 10^3 = 16 \times 10^2$

$64 \times 10^5 \div 4 \times 10^3 = 1,600$

4.3.0 Using Scientific Notation with a Calculator

Scientific calculators are capable of performing calculations using data entered in scientific notation. Some calculator manufacturers refer to this capability as the scientific or engineering display format. The procedure for entering calculation data using the scientific notation format may differ depending on the calculator being used and should be done according to the instructions for the specific calculator.

The procedure for entering a number in scientific notation using one popular type of calculator is done by entering the base or mantissa number, then pressing the [+/−] key if the number is negative. Following this, the enter exponent [EE] key is pressed, then the power of ten is entered. If negative, the [+/−] key is also pressed. Addition, subtraction, multiplication, and division of the numbers entered in scientific notation are all performed in the usual manner.

5.0.0 ◆ ENGINEERING NOTATION

Like scientific notation, engineering notation is a method of expressing very large and very small numbers as a base number times 10 raised to some power (or exponent). However, with engineering notation the exponent of 10 is always a factor of 3.

Because the exponent is a factor of 3, the number can be expressed using the prefixes discussed earlier under the metric system. You may have noticed that the prefix of kilo- was equal to 10^3, while mega- was 10^6 and milli- was 10^{-3}.

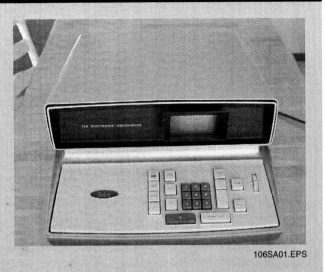
The rules for proper engineering notation differ from those for scientific notation. First, as mentioned before, the exponent of 10 will always be a factor of 3, such as 3, 6, 9, 12 or –3, –6, –9, –12, and so on. Secondly, the base number (or mantissa) will be a number greater than or equal to 1 and less than 1,000. Normally, only three digits will be shown in the base number, although that is not a hard and fast rule.

A number like 1,250,000V would be shown in engineering notation as 1.25×10^6 or expressed as 1.25 megavolts (MV). Likewise a very small number such as 0.0000008 ohms would be shown as 800×10^{-9} or 800 nano-ohms (nΩ). While some people might think you could express the previous number as 0.8×10^{-6} or 0.8 micro-ohms ($\mu\Omega$), that would be improper engineering notation, since 0.8 is <1.

All the features of addition, subtraction, multiplication, and division discussed under scientific notation also apply to engineering notation. However, any answers are always presented with the base number > = 1 and <1,000 and with an exponent of 10 as a factor of 3 or using the proper engineering prefix.

6.0.0 ◆ DECIBELS

The **decibel (dB)** is one of the most fundamental elements in our business. The unit of gain or loss was originally defined as the bel, which was the logarithmic comparison of output power to input power in a transmission line. The original formula for the bel was as follows:

$$Bel = \log(P_{out} / P_{in})$$

However the bel turned out to be too large of a unit to easily work with, so the decibel (which is one-tenth of a bel) has been adopted as the unit of choice when measuring gains or losses in a transmission line or amplification system. The formula for the decibel follows:

$$dB = 10 \log(P_{out} / P_{in})$$

By comparing the output power to the input power of an amplification stage logarithmically, we can describe the gain of the amplifier stage with a single numerical unit in decibels.

For example, if a given amplifier has an output of 100 watts when its input is driven with 1mW (1mW = 0.001W), the gain can be calculated as follows:

$$dB_{gain} = 10 \log(100/0.001)$$
$$dB_{gain} = 10 \log100,000$$
$$dB_{gain} = 50$$

NOTE

The factor of 10 before the log function is due to the units being decibels instead of bels.

The unit of a decibel in its relative form is only a comparison between two quantities. However, when a standard measure is part of the equation, the standard or reference is applied to the denominator of the ratio and a suffix is usually applied to the unit of dB. For example, in the equation above, the 1mW input is the reference power for the unit of dBm, so the above amplifier output could have been stated as 50dBm and you would have known that the input was 1mW by reference.

Many other references can be attached to the dB indicating a particular type of reference level for the equation. These will be defined further in future modules.

Although the decibel shown above is a comparison of output power to input power, the decibel is also used to compare voltages, pressures, and even distances.

It should be noted that when the decibel is used to describe differences in voltage, instead of power, the formula changes. Because of the relationship of power to voltage and resistance is $P = E^2/R$, when comparing voltage the resistance can be cancelled out leaving just the voltage:

$$dB = 10 \log[(E^2/R)_{out}/(E^2/R)_{in}]$$

Mathematically we can move the exponent to be a multiplier, thus simplifying the equation:

$$dB = 10 \log(E^2_{out}/E^2_{in})$$
$$dB = 2 \times 10 \log(E_{out}/E_{in})$$
or
$$dB = 20 \log(E_{out}/E_{in})$$

Thus the two forms of the formula are as follows:

$$dB = 10 \log(P_{out}/P_{in})$$
and
$$dB = 20 \log(E_{out}/E_{in})$$

A truly unique tool, the decibel gives us an easy way to compare gains or losses through almost any medium or system. You will see the decibel expanded upon in many other modules to come, as it is used to indicate gains or losses in many types of the systems in which we work. Some examples are audio amplification and transmission systems, optical fiber transmission systems and RF transmission systems.

7.0.0 ◆ LOGARITHMS

In the previous section on decibels, we introduced the mathematical operator called a logarithm. Note that logarithms are usually expressed with a base notation. However, when expressed the way we use the term, the base is understood to be 10 or $\log_{10}$ and is not expressly written.

Using the logarithmic expression of the ratio, we can express very large numbers with a much smaller value. A case in point is the example given of comparing an output of 100 watts to an input of 1mW. The difference is a factor of 100,000, but it is easily expressed as 50dB, a much easier number to work with.

The logarithm of a number is the inverse operation to raising 10 (the base) to some power. In fact, the logarithm of a number is the value you would use as an exponent of 10 to equal the original number. For example, the log of $5 \approx 0.69897$ and the value of $10^{0.69897} \approx 5$, shows that one operation is the inverse of the other.

Early mathematicians went to great efforts to create tables of logarithms, so you could look up the value for any number. However, we have it easy and are able to use the "log" function on a scientific calculator to produce the correct answer instantly. When we write the equation $dB = 10 \log(100/0.001)$, we mean to find the value of the log of 100,000 and multiply it by a factor of 10. Even though a multiplication sign is not included between the 10 and the log function, it should be understood that the values are to be multiplied together.

A thorough understanding of logarithms is not needed for an EST to use the function appropriately. However, you need to understand the relationship between the $\log X$ and 10^X. Let's take a look at the previous problem again, and this time, let's have our unknown be the final output power of the amplifier.

Step 1   Start by dividing both sides by 10:
$$50dB = 10 \log(P_{out}/0.001)$$

Step 2   To remove the log function, express 5dBm as an exponent of 10:
$$5 = \log(P_{out}/0.001)$$
$$10^5 = P_{out}/0.001$$

Step 3   Now multiply each side by 0.001 to reach the answer in watts:
$$100,000 = P_{out}/0.001$$
$$100 \text{ watts} = P_{out}$$

When finding a logarithm with most scientific calculators, enter the value first and then press the [log] function key to obtain the log value. Some calculators will have you press [log] and then the value. Make sure you know how your calculator works to avoid errors.

When the value for a logarithm is an operation, such as 100/0.001, it is necessary to complete that operation first, or if brackets are available, place brackets around the division operation to indicate to the calculator that it must be accomplished before the logarithm is found.

8.0.0 ◆ POWERS AND ROOTS

Many mathematical formulas used in electronics and construction require that the power or root of a number be found. As in scientific notation, a power (or exponent) is a number written above and to the right of another number, which is called the base. For example, the expression y^x means to take the value of y and multiply it by itself x number of times. The xth root of a number y is another number that when multiplied by itself x times returns a value of y. Expressed mathematically:

$$\sqrt[x]{y^x} = y$$

8.1.0 Square and Square Roots

The need to find squares and square roots is common in trade mathematics. A square is the product of a number or quantity multiplied by itself. For example, the square of 6 means 6×6. To denote a number as squared, simply place the exponent 2 above and to the right of the base number. For example:

$$6^2 = 6 \times 6 = 36$$

The square root of a number is the divisor which, when multiplied by itself (squared), gives the number as a product. Extracting the square root refers to a process of finding the equal factors which, when multiplied together, return the original number. The process is identified by the radical symbol [√]. This symbol is a shorthand way of stating that the equal factors of the number under the radical sign are to be determined.

For example, $\sqrt{16}$ is read as the square root of 16. The number consists of the two equal factors 4 and 4. Thus, when 4 is raised to the second power or squared, it is equal to 16. The term squaring a number simply means multiplying the number by itself.

The number 16 is also a perfect square. Numbers that are perfect squares have whole numbers as the square roots. For example, the square roots of perfect squares 4, 25, 36, 121, and 324 are the whole numbers 2, 5, 6, 11, and 18, respectively.

Squares and square roots can be calculated by hand, but the process is very time-consuming and subject to error. Most people find squares and square roots of numbers using a calculator. To find the square of a number, the calculator's square key [x^2] is used. When pressed, it takes the number shown in the display and multiplies it by itself. For example, to square the number 4.235, you would enter 4.235, press the [x^2] key, then read 17.935225 on the display.

Similarly, to find the square root of a number, the calculator's square root key [√] or [√x] is used. When pressed, it calculates the square root of the number shown in the display. For example, to find the square root of the number 17.935225, enter 17.935225, press the [√] or [√x] key, then read 4.235 on the display. Note that on some calculators, the [√] or [√x] key must be pressed before entering the number.

8.2.0 Other Powers and Roots

It is sometimes necessary to find powers and roots other than squares and square roots. This can easily be done with a calculator. The powers key [y^x] raises the displayed value to the xth power. The order of entry must be y, [y^x], then x. For example, to find the power $2.86^{-.42}$ you would enter 2.86, press the [y^x] key, enter 0.42, press the [+/−] key, press the [=] key, then read 0.643170721 on the display.

The root key [$^x\sqrt{y}$] is used to find the xth root of the displayed value y. The order of entry is y [INV] [$^x\sqrt{y}$]. The [INV] or [2nd F] key, when pressed before any other key that has a dual function, will cause the second function of the key to be operated. For example, to find the cube root of 1,500, you would enter 1,500, press the [INV] [$^x\sqrt{y}$] keys, enter 3, press the [=] key, then read 11.44714243 on the display. Note that on some calculators, the [$^x\sqrt{y}$] key must be pressed before entering the number.

Remembering that the xth root of a number y is another number that when multiplied by itself x times returns the value of y, you can easily check your answer by using the [y^x] function to raise the answer on the display to a power of 3. For example, $11.44714243^3 = 1,500$.

9.0.0 ◆ INTRODUCTION TO ALGEBRA

Algebra is the mathematics of defining and manipulating equations containing symbols instead of numbers. The symbols may be either constants or **variables**. They are connected to each other with mathematical operators such as +, −, ×, and ÷.

As in all fields of mathematics, an understanding of algebra requires the knowledge of some basic rules and definitions. These definitions and rules will be introduced where required to promote the understanding necessary to become proficient in algebra.

9.1.0 Definition of Terms

This section defines basic algebraic terms, including operators, equations, variables, constants, and **coefficients**.

9.1.1 Mathematical Operators

Mathematical operators define the required action using a symbol. Common operators follow:

    +   Addition
    −   Subtraction
    ×   Multiplication
    •   Multiplication
    ÷   Division

9.1.2 Equations

An equation is a collection of numbers, symbols, and mathematical operators connected by an equal sign (=). The following are some examples of equations:

2 + 3 = 5

P = EI

Volume = L × W × H

9.1.3 Variables

A variable is an element of an equation that may change in value. For example, let's examine the simple equation for the area of a rectangle:

Area = L × W

If the area is 12 and the length (L) is 6, the equation would read as follows:

12 = 6 × W

In this case, it is easy enough to see that the width (W) is equal to 2 because 12 = 6 × 2. What is the width if the length is equal to 3?

12 = 3 × W

In this case, the width is equal to 4 because 12 = 3 × 4. Therefore, in these two equations (12 = 6 × W and 12 = 3 × W), W is a variable because it is dependent on the value of L.

Brackets/symbols

9.1.4 Constants

A constant is an element of an equation that does not change in value. For example, consider the following equation:

2 + 5 = 7

In this equation, 2, 5, and 7 are constants. The number 2 will always be 2, 5 will always be 5, and 7 will always be 7, no matter what the equation. Constants also refer to accepted values that represent one element of an equation and do not change from situation to situation. One of the most common constants that you will be dealing with is Pi (π). It has an approximate value of 3.14 and represents the ratio of the circumference to the diameter in a circle.

9.1.5 Coefficients

A coefficient is a multiplier. Consider the following equation:

Area = L × W

In this equation, L is the coefficient of W. It can also be written as LW, without the multiplication sign. No multiplication symbol is required when the intended relationship between symbols and letters is clear:

- 2L means two times L (2 is the coefficient of L)
- IR means I times R (I is the coefficient of R)

Equations often include grouping symbols, such as parentheses ( ), brackets [ ], or braces { } that have a plus (+) or minus (−) coefficient which must be multiplied by each term in the group. If there is no numerical coefficient outside of the grouping symbol, it means that +1 or −1 is the coefficient.

The following rules apply to the removal of grouping symbols:

- *Positive coefficient* – When the grouping symbol is preceded by a plus (+) sign, simply drop the symbol. This is the same as multiplying each term within the group by +1.

  3 + (2 − 1) = 3 + 2 − 1

- *Negative coefficient* – When the grouping symbol is preceded by a minus (−) sign, multiply each term within the group by −1, then drop the symbol. Remember that a negative number multiplied by a negative number becomes positive.

  3 − (2 − 1) = 3 − 2 + 1

- *Positive numerical coefficient* – When the grouping symbol is preceded by a positive numerical coefficient, multiply each term within the group by the coefficient and its sign, then drop the symbol:

  3 + 2(2 − 1) = 3 + 4 − 2

- *Negative numerical coefficient* – When the grouping symbol is preceded by a negative numerical coefficient, multiply each term within the group by the coefficient and its sign, then drop the symbol:

  3 − 2(2 − 1) = 3 − 4 + 2

9.2.0 Sequence of Operations

Complicated equations must be solved by performing the indicated operations in a prescribed sequence. This sequence is: multiply, divide, add, and subtract (MDAS). For example, the following equation can result in a number of answers if the MDAS sequence is not followed:

3 + 3 × 2 − 6 ÷ 3 = ?

To come up with the correct result, this equation must be solved in the following order:

Step 1 Multiply:

$$3 + \underline{3 \times 2} - 6 \div 3$$

Step 2 Divide:

$$3 + 6 - \underline{6 \div 3}$$

Step 3 Add:

$$\underline{3 + 6} - 2$$

Step 4 Subtract:

$$9 - 2$$

Result:

7

9.3.0 Solving Algebraic Equations

Some equations may include several variables. Solving these equations means to simplify them as much as possible and, if necessary, to separate the desired variable so that it is on one side by itself, with everything else on the other side. Problems such as these are known as algebraic expressions. When an algebraic expression appears in an equation, the MDAS sequence also applies. For example:

$$P = R - [5(3A + 4B) + 40L]$$

The parentheses represent multiplication, so they are worked on first. When working with multiple sets of parentheses or brackets, always begin by eliminating the innermost symbols first, then working your way to the outermost symbols. Thus, in the above equation, the expressions within parentheses (3A + 4B) with the coefficient of 5 are multiplied first:

$$P = R - [15A + 20B + 40L]$$

The brackets also represent multiplication, so they are worked on next. The minus sign is the same as a coefficient of –1, so each term within the brackets is multiplied by –1:

$$P = R - 15A - 20B - 40L$$

At this point, the equation has been simplified as much as possible. However, we will see what happens when we apply this same equation to a real-life situation. Suppose you have just installed cable in five identical apartments in a complex, and you want to determine the profit on the job. If we wrote this equation out longhand, it would look like the following:

Profit (P) is equal to the payment received (R) minus five apartments times three pieces of one type of cable in each apartment at a certain cost per piece (A) plus four pieces of a second type of cable in each apartment at a certain cost per piece (B) plus forty hours of labor times an hourly rate (L).

It makes a lot more sense to simply write it algebraically:

$$P = R - [5(3A + 4B) + 40L]$$

or

$$P = R - 15A - 20B - 40L$$

Now, we will plug in numbers for the known values. Say that R = $1,500, A = $10, B = $15, and L = $12. This results in the following:

$$P = 1,500 - (15 \times 10) - (20 \times 15) - (40 \times 12)$$

Multiplying, we get:

$$P = 1,500 - 150 - 300 - 480$$

$$P = \$570$$

There are a few simple rules that, once memorized, will help you to simplify and solve almost any equation you encounter as an electronic systems technician:

Rule 1: If the same value is added to or subtracted from both sides of an equation, the resulting equation is valid. For example, consider the following equation:

$$5 = 5$$

If 3 is added to each side of the equation, the resulting equation remains valid (both sides are still equal to one another):

$$5 + 3 = 5 + 3$$
$$8 \quad = 8$$

In the same way, if we subtract the same number from both sides of an equation, the resulting equation is valid. For example, consider the following equation:

$$5 = 5$$

If 4 is subtracted from both sides of the equation, the resulting equation remains valid.

$$5 - 4 = 5 - 4$$
$$1 \quad = 1$$

Moving variables from one side of an equation to another is done in the same way as when moving constants. Recall that when an equation is solved for one particular variable, that means that the variable should be on one side of the equation by itself. For example, consider the following pressure equation:

Absolute pressure = gauge pressure + 14.7

To solve this equation for gauge pressure, 14.7 must be moved to the other side of the equation with absolute pressure. To do so, we will subtract 14.7 from both sides of the equation:

Absolute pressure − 14.7 = gauge pressure + 14.7
− 14.7

It should be clear that the +14.7 and −14.7 on the right cancel each other out and we are left with:

Absolute pressure − 14.7 = gauge pressure

or

Gauge pressure = absolute pressure − 14.7

The equation has been solved for gauge pressure. If we wanted to take this new equation and solve it for absolute pressure again, we would simply add 14.7 to each side:

Gauge pressure + 14.7 = absolute pressure − 14.7
+ 14.7

Again, the +14.7 and −14.7 on the right cancel each other out and we are left with:

Gauge pressure + 14.7 = absolute pressure

or

Absolute pressure = gauge pressure + 14.7

Rule 2: If both sides of an equation are multiplied or divided by the same value, the resulting equation is valid. For this rule, we will examine the equation for Ohm's Law, which you will use often in your work as an electronic systems technician. This equation is as follows:

E = IR

Where:

E = voltage

I = current

R = resistance

If you know the voltage (E) and the current (I), but need to find the resistance (R), how do you rearrange the equation? To solve this equation for R, I must be moved to the other side of the equation with E. To do so, we will divide both sides by I:

$$\frac{E}{I} = \frac{IR}{I}$$

The two I's on the right cancel each other out, and we are left with:

$$\frac{E}{I} = R \qquad or \qquad R = \frac{E}{I}$$

The equation has been solved for resistance. If we wanted to take this new equation and solve it for E again, we would simply multiply each side by I:

$$I \times R = \frac{E}{I} \times I$$

The two I's on the right cancel each other out and we are left with:

IR = E   *or*   E = IR

Rule 3: Like terms may be added and subtracted in a manner similar to constant numbers. For example, given the equation:

2A + 3A = 15

The like terms (2A and 3A) may be added directly:

5A = 15

Dividing both sides of the equation by 5, we have:

$$\frac{5A}{5} = \frac{15}{5}$$

A = 3

These rules may be used repeatedly until an equation is in the desired form. For example, take a look at the following pressure equation:

$$P = \frac{hd}{144}$$

Where:

P = pressure

h = height

d = density

Solve the equation for density (d):

Step 1   Remove the fraction by multiplying both sides by 144.

$$P \times 144 = \frac{hd}{144} \times 144$$

144P   = hd

Step 2   Divide both sides by h.

$$\frac{144P}{h} = d \qquad or \qquad d = \frac{144P}{h}$$

The equation has been solved for density (d).

10.0.0 ◆ INTRODUCTION TO GEOMETRY

Geometry is the study of various figures. It consists of two main fields: plane and solid geometry.

Plane geometry is the study of two-dimensional figures such as squares, rectangles, triangles, circles, and polygons. Solid geometry is the study of figures that occupy space, such as cubes, spheres, and other three-dimensional objects. The focus of this section is on the elements of plane geometry.

10.1.0 Points and Lines

A geometric point represents a position only. It has no dimensions such as length, width, or height. A point is an origin or beginning, such as a starting place for a circle. Two points are necessary to define a line and three points may define a flat surface or plane.

A line has one dimension: length (*Figure 17*). A straight line is defined as the shortest distance between two points. A line with no end points has an unlimited (infinite) length. A line that begins at one point and ends at another has a fixed (finite) length and is called a line segment. Note that the word line is commonly used to mean line segment. A line having the same direction throughout its length is called a straight line. A broken line is a series of connected straight line segments extending in different directions. A line that continuously changes direction is a curved line.

A line that forms a right angle (90 degrees) with one or more lines is said to be perpendicular to those lines (*Figure 18*). The distance from a point to a line is the measure of the perpendicular line

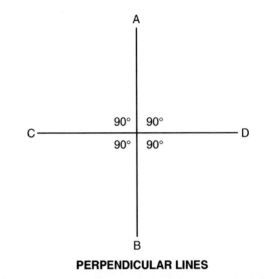

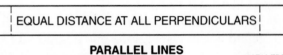

PERPENDICULAR LINES

EQUAL DISTANCE AT ALL PERPENDICULARS

PARALLEL LINES

106F18.EPS

Figure 18 ◆ Perpendicular and parallel lines.

drawn from that point to the line. Two or more straight lines that are the same distance apart at all perpendiculars are said to be parallel. Note that parallel lines do not intersect.

10.2.0 Circles

As shown in *Figure 19*, a circle is a finite curved line that connects with itself and has these properties:

- All points on a circle are the same distance (equidistant) from the point at the center.
- The distance from the center to any point on the curved line, called the radius (r), is always the same.
- The shortest distance from any point on the curve through the center to a point directly opposite is called the diameter (d). The diameter is equal to twice the radius (d = 2r).

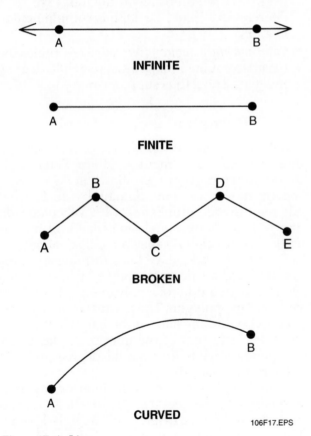

INFINITE

FINITE

BROKEN

CURVED

106F17.EPS

Figure 17 ◆ Lines.

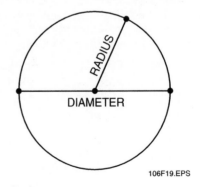

DIAMETER

106F19.EPS

Figure 19 ◆ Circle.

- The distance around the outside of the circle is called the circumference. It can be determined by using the equation: circumference = πd, where π is a constant equal to approximately 3.14 and d is the diameter.

- A circle is divided into 360 parts with each part called a *degree*; therefore, one degree = 1/360 of a circle. The degree is the unit of measurement commonly used in construction layout for measuring the size of angles.

- The total measure of all the angles formed by all consecutive radii equals 360 degrees.

10.3.0 Angles

Two straight lines meeting at a point, called the vertex, form an angle (*Figure 20*). The two lines are the sides of the angle. These lines are called the rays of the angle. The angle is the amount of opening that exists between the rays and is measured in degrees. There are two ways commonly used to identify angles. One is to assign a letter to the angle, such as angle D shown in *Figure 20*. This is written: ∠D. The other way is to name the two end points of the rays and put the vertex letter between them (∠ABC). When you show the angle measure in degrees, it should be written inside the angle, if possible. If the angle is too small to show the measurement, you may put it outside of the angle and draw an arrow to the inside.

There are several types of angles, as shown in *Figures 21* and *22*:

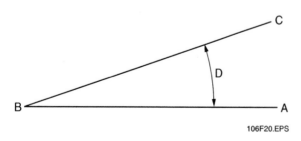

106F20.EPS

Figure 20 ◆ Angle.

- *Right angle* – This angle has rays that are perpendicular to one another (*Figure 21*). The measure of this angle is always 90 degrees.

- *Straight angle* – This angle does not look like an angle at all. The rays of a straight angle lie in a straight line, and the angle measures 180 degrees.

- *Acute angle* – An angle less than 90 degrees.

- *Obtuse angle* – An angle greater than 90 degrees, but less than 180 degrees.

- *Adjacent angles* – When three or more rays meet at the same vertex, the angles formed are said to be *adjacent* (next to) one another. In *Figure 22*, the angles ∠ABC and ∠CBD are adjacent angles. The ray BC is said to be common to both angles.

- *Complementary angles* – Two adjacent angles that have a combined total measure of 90 degrees. In *Figure 22*, ∠DEF is complementary to ∠FEG.

- *Supplementary angles* – Two adjacent angles that have a combined total measure of 180 degrees. In *Figure 22*, ∠HIJ is supplementary to ∠JIK.

10.4.0 Polygons

A polygon is formed when three or more straight lines are joined in a regular pattern. Some of the most familiar polygons are shown in *Figure 23*. As shown, they have common names which generally refer to their number of sides. When all sides of a polygon have equal length and all internal angles are equal, it is called a regular polygon.

Each of the boundary lines forming the polygon is called a side of the polygon. The point at which any two sides of a polygon meet is called a vertex of the polygon. The perimeter of any polygon is equal to the sum of the lengths of each of the sides. The sum of the interior angles of any polygon is equal to (n − 2) × 180 degrees, where n is the number of sides.

For example, the sum of the interior angles for a square is 360 degrees [(4 − 2) × 180 degrees = 360 degrees] and for a triangle is 180 degrees [(3 − 2) × 180 degrees = 180 degrees].

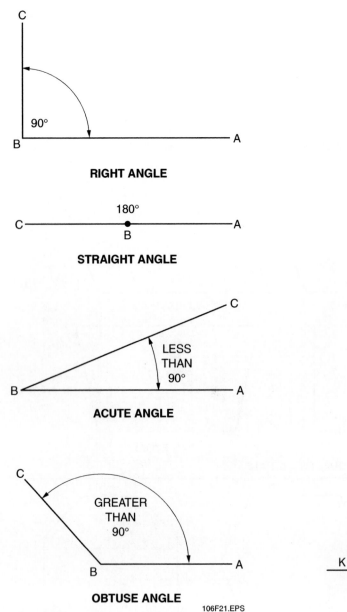

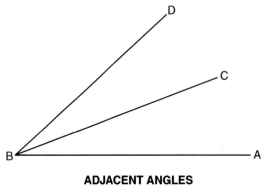

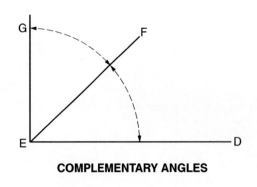

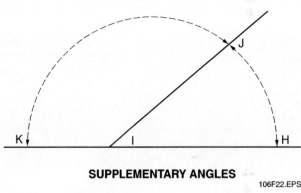

Figure 21 ◆ Right, straight, acute, and obtuse angles.

Figure 22 ◆ Adjacent, complementary, and supplementary angles.

10.5.0 Triangles

As mentioned previously, triangles are three-sided polygons. *Figure 24* shows three different types of triangles. A regular polygon with three equal sides is called an equilateral triangle. Two types of irregular triangles are the isosceles (having two sides of equal length) and the scalene (having all sides of unequal length). An important fact to remember about triangles is that the sum of the three angles of any triangle equals 180 degrees. As shown, all three sides of an equilateral triangle are equal. In such a triangle, the three angles are also equal. The isosceles triangle has two equal sides with the angles opposite the equal sides also being equal.

Triangles are also classified according to their interior angles (*Figure 25*). If one of the three interior angles is 90 degrees, the triangle is called a right triangle. If one of the three interior angles is greater than 90 degrees, the triangle is called an obtuse triangle. If each of the interior angles is less than 90 degrees, the triangle is called an acute triangle. The sum of the three interior angles of any triangle is always equal to 180 degrees. This is helpful to remember whenever you know two angles of a triangle and need to calculate the third.

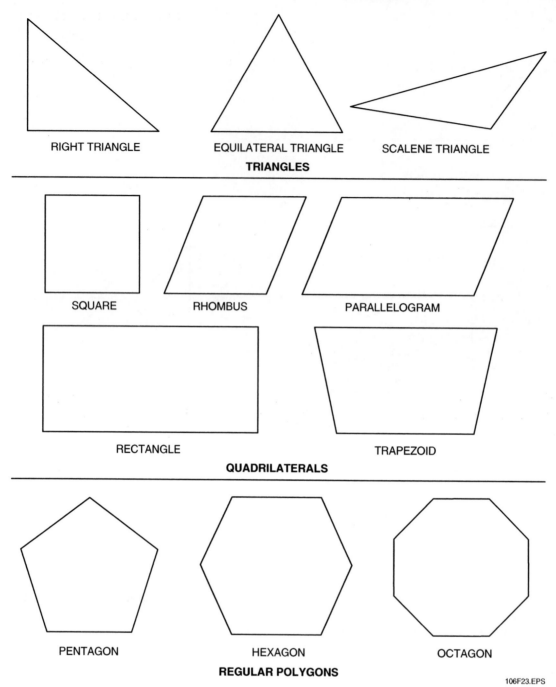

Figure 23 ◆ Common polygons.

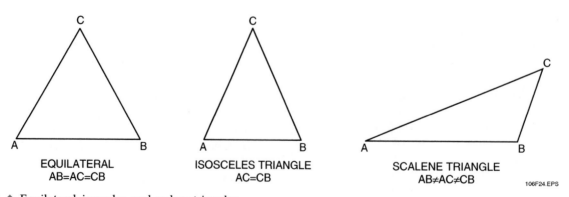

Figure 24 ◆ Equilateral, isosceles, and scalene triangles.

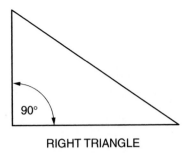

RIGHT TRIANGLE

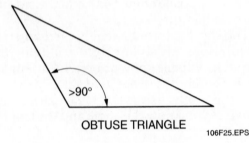

ACUTE TRIANGLE

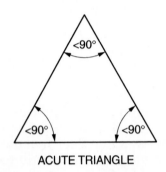

OBTUSE TRIANGLE

106F25.EPS

Figure 25 ◆ Right, obtuse, and acute triangles.

11.0.0 ◆ WORKING WITH RIGHT TRIANGLES

One of the most common triangles used in electronics and construction is the right triangle. Since it has one right angle, the other two angles are acute angles. They are also complementary angles, the sum of which equals 90 degrees. The right triangle has two sides perpendicular to each other, thus forming the right angle. To aid in writing equations, the sides and angles of a right triangle are labeled as shown in *Figure 26*. Normally, capital (uppercase) letters are used to label the angles and lowercase letters are used to label the sides. The third side, which is always opposite the right angle (C), is called the hypotenuse. It is always longer than either of the other two sides. The other sides can be remembered as *a* for altitude and *b* for base. Note that the letters that label the sides and angles are opposite each other. For example, side a is opposite angle A, and so forth.

11.1.0 Right Triangle Calculations Using the Pythagorean Theorem

If you know the length of any two sides of a right triangle, you can calculate the length of the third side using a rule called the Pythagorean theorem. It states that the square of the hypotenuse (c) is equal to the sum of the squares of the remaining two sides (a and b). Expressed mathematically:

$$c^2 = a^2 + b^2$$

You may rearrange to solve for the unknown side as follows:

$$a = \sqrt{c^2 - b^2}$$
$$b = \sqrt{c^2 - a^2}$$
$$c = \sqrt{a^2 + b^2}$$

For example, assume you had a right triangle with an altitude (side a) equal to 8' and a base (side b) equal to 12'. To find the length of the hypotenuse (side c), proceed as follows:

$$c = \sqrt{a^2 + b^2}$$
$$c = \sqrt{(8')^2 + (12')^2}$$
$$c = \sqrt{64 + 144}$$
$$c = \sqrt{208}$$
$$c = 14.422'$$

To determine the actual length of the hypotenuse using the formula above, it is necessary to calculate the square root of the sum of the sides squared. Fortunately, this is easy to do using a scientific calculator. On many calculators, you simply key in the number and press the square root [√] key. On some calculators, the square root does not have a separate key. Instead, the square root function is the inverse of the [x²] key, so you have to press [INV] or [2nd F], depending on your calculator, followed by [x²], to obtain the square root.

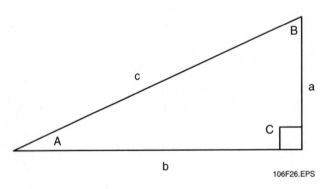

106F26.EPS

Figure 26 ◆ Common labeling of angles and sides in a right triangle.

11.2.0 Right Triangle Calculations Using Trigonometry

The Pythagorean theorem can be used in solving for the lengths of the sides of a right triangle, but it gives no information about the size of the angles. This is where the use of trigonometric functions are necessary. Trigonometry recognizes that there is a relationship between the size of an angle and the length of the sides in a right triangle.

The sides of a triangle are referred to as side opposite, side adjacent, and hypotenuse with respect to either of the acute angles. As shown for the angle A relationships in *Figure 27*, the side opposite angle A is labeled *a* and the side adjacent to angle A is labeled *b*. A scientific calculator contains the keys for sine (SIN), cosine (COS), and tangent (TAN) functions, all of which represent relationships between the sides of a right triangle.

As shown in *Figure 27*, these relationships for angle A are expressed as follows:

$$SIN\ A = \frac{(a)\ length\ of\ side\ opposite\ A\ (O)}{(c)\ length\ of\ hypotenuse\ \ \ \ \ \ (H)}$$

$$COS\ A = \frac{(b)\ length\ of\ side\ adjacent\ to\ A\ (A)}{(c)\ length\ of\ hypotenuse\ \ \ \ \ \ \ \ \ \ \ (H)}$$

$$TAN\ A = \frac{(a)\ length\ of\ side\ opposite\ A\ \ \ \ (O)}{(b)\ length\ of\ side\ adjacent\ to\ A\ (A)}$$

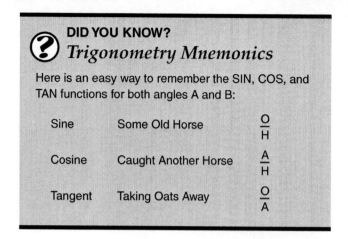

DID YOU KNOW?
Trigonometry Mnemonics

Here is an easy way to remember the SIN, COS, and TAN functions for both angles A and B:

Sine	Some Old Horse	$\frac{O}{H}$
Cosine	Caught Another Horse	$\frac{A}{H}$
Tangent	Taking Oats Away	$\frac{O}{A}$

As shown in *Figure 27*, the same relationships exist for angle B as shown for angle A. However, you must substitute *B* for *A* in the SIN, COS, and TAN formulas and make sure to substitute the correct labeling for the sides in the formulas (e.g., the side opposite angle B is *b* and the side adjacent to angle B is *a*).

The specific formula that is used when making calculations involving right triangles is determined by what is known about the triangle. If you know the lengths of any two sides, you can calculate the angle using the basic formulas given above. If you know the angle and the length of one

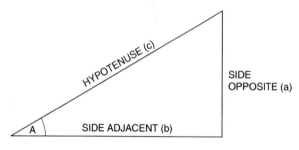

ANGLE A RELATIONSHIPS

$$SIN\ A = \frac{SIDE\ OPPOSITE\ (a)}{HYPOTENUSE\ (c)}$$

$$COS\ A = \frac{SIDE\ ADJACENT\ (b)}{HYPOTENUSE\ (c)}$$

$$TAN\ A = \frac{SIDE\ OPPOSITE\ (a)}{SIDE\ ADJACENT\ (b)}$$

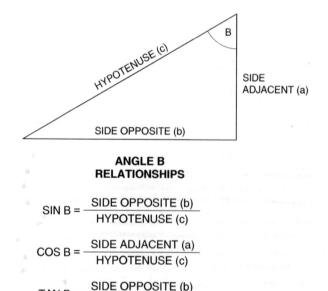

ANGLE B RELATIONSHIPS

$$SIN\ B = \frac{SIDE\ OPPOSITE\ (b)}{HYPOTENUSE\ (c)}$$

$$COS\ B = \frac{SIDE\ ADJACENT\ (a)}{HYPOTENUSE\ (c)}$$

$$TAN\ B = \frac{SIDE\ OPPOSITE\ (b)}{SIDE\ ADJACENT\ (a)}$$

106F27.EPS

Figure 27 ◆ Angle/side relationships in a right triangle.

side, you can calculate the lengths of the other sides using the appropriate SIN, COS, or TAN formulas given above after they have been rearranged to solve for the unknown. For angle A, these relationships are as follows:

Length of side a = c SIN A *or* b TAN A *or* c COS B

Length of side b = c COS A *or* c SIN B *or* a TAN B

Length of side c = a/SIN A *or* b/COS A *or* a/COS B
or b/SIN B

Example 1: Assume that you want to determine the size of angle A for a right triangle that has an adjacent side (side b) of 280' and an opposite side (side a) of 210'. In this case, we know the length of the two sides, so the tangent (TAN) formula can be used to find angle A as follows:

$$\text{TAN A} = \frac{\text{(a) length of side opposite A} \quad \text{(O)}}{\text{(b) length of side adjacent to A (A)}}$$

TAN A = 210' ÷ 280' = 0.75

To convert the numerical tangent value (0.75) to its corresponding angle in degrees, you can either use the *Tables of Trigonometric Functions* (published in engineering reference books or math textbooks) or you can use a scientific calculator. The calculator is normally used by electronic systems technicians. The process of finding the angle is basically the inverse or opposite of computing a trigonometric function. For this reason, the name inverse trig function is used. The ARC trigonometric functions arcsine, arccosine, and arctangent are trigonometric functions in reverse. The term arcsine (often written $\sin^{-1}$) means the angle whose sine is a given number. The result of an arc calculation is an angle value in degrees. With a scientific calculator, it is a simple matter to determine the value of an unknown angle. To convert the numerical tangent value for this example (0.75) to its corresponding angle, enter the value of 0.75, press the inverse [INV] or second function [2nd F] key, then press TAN to obtain the angle, which is 36.8699 degrees. It should be pointed out that on some calculators, the number to be entered (numerical tangent value for this example) must be keyed in before pressing the [INV] or [2nd F] and TAN keys; on other calculators, the number is keyed in after the [INV] or [2nd F] and [TAN] keys have been pressed. Also, you must be sure that the calculator is in the degree mode.

Example 2: Assume you have a right triangle with an angle A that is equal to 36.8699 degrees and a hypotenuse (side c) of 350', and you want to know the length of the side opposite angle A (side a). Since we know the value of angle A (in degrees) and the length of the hypotenuse, you would use the formula for the sine [SIN] function because it contains the known and unknown elements involved.

$$\text{SIN A} = \frac{\text{(a) length of side opposite A} \quad \text{(O)}}{\text{(c) length of hypotenuse} \quad \text{(H)}}$$

To solve for the unknown side (side a) you need to use a variation of the formula above. It becomes:

Length of side a = c SIN A = hypotenuse × SIN A
Length of side a = 350' × SIN A

To convert the angle of 36.8699 degrees into its corresponding sine numerical value using a calculator, press the [SIN] key and enter the angle (36.8699 degrees), which yields a sine of 0.5999. Substituting this value in the formula, the length of the opposite side (side a) is calculated to be 210', as follows:

Length of side a = 350' × 0.5999

Length of side a = 209.96' = approx. 210'

Example 3: Based on the calculations in *Examples 1* and *2*, you can calculate the size of angle B as 53.13 degrees. This can be done by subtracting the sum of angles A and C from 180 degrees (180 degrees − [36.8699 degrees + 90 degrees]) = 53.1301 degrees. To check this answer, you can also calculate the size of the angle by using the TAN function for angle B as follows:

$$\text{TAN B} = \frac{\text{(b) length of side opposite A} \quad \text{(O)}}{\text{(c) length of side adjacent to A (A)}}$$

TAN B = 280' ÷ 210' = 1.3333

Converting the tangent value of 1.3333 to its corresponding angle using the [INV] or [2nd F] function key and [TAN] key of the calculator shows that angle B is equal to 53.13 degrees.

Summary

This module built on the knowledge gained in the *Basic Math* module. It covered mathematics important to the electronic systems technician, with an emphasis placed on the metric system. It also introduced basic concepts concerning scientific notation, powers and roots, algebra, geometry, and trigonometry.

There are many aspects of electronic systems work that require the use of mathematics. The design and installation of audio systems is only one example.

Review Questions

1. Convert 6.875 feet to feet and inches.
   a. 6'-2¼"
   b. 6'-8¼"
   c. 6'-10½"
   d. 6'-11½"

2. One meter is equal to _____.
   a. 0.3937'
   b. 39.37'
   c. 3.281'
   d. 3,281'

3. A room has a length of 3.568 meters and a width of 2.438 meters. The area of this room in square feet is _____.
   a. 20 ft²
   b. 71.36 ft²
   c. 93.64 ft²
   d. 384 ft²

4. A 55-gallon drum can hold _____ liters of fluid.
   a. 55
   b. 110
   c. 175
   d. 208

5. A crate containing an electronic assembly is marked as weighing 175 pounds. What does it weigh in kilograms?
   a. 68.5 kilograms
   b. 79.37 kilograms
   c. 96.33 kilograms
   d. 125 kilograms

6. A temperature of 68°F is equal to _____.
   a. 20°C
   b. 36°C
   c. 41°C
   d. 100°C

7. Express the number 7.32×10^5 as a number without a power of ten.
   a. 0.0000732
   b. 0.00732
   c. 73,200
   d. 732,000

8. Express the number 0.000064 as a number between 1 and 10, times a power of ten.
   a. 6.4×10^{-3}
   b. 6.4×10^{-4}
   c. 6.4×10^{-5}
   d. 6.4×10^{-6}

9. The square root of 12,500, which is expressed mathematically as $\sqrt{12,500}$ is equal to _____.
   a. 1.11803
   b. 11.1803
   c. 111.803
   d. 1118.03

10. The power of the number 3.21413^3 is equal to _____.
    a. 3.3203993
    b. 33.203993
    c. 333.20993
    d. 3332.0993

11. Given the equation $P = E^2/R$, solve for R.
    a. $R = E^2/P$
    b. $R = E^2 \times P$
    c. $R = P/E^2$
    d. $R = \sqrt{PE}$

12. The distance from the center of a circle to any point on the curved line is called the _____.
    a. circumference
    b. radius
    c. diameter
    d. cord

13. A triangle in which all sides are of unequal length is called a(n) _____ triangle.
    a. equilateral
    b. isosceles
    c. right
    d. scalene

14. Each of the following is a form of the Pythagorean theorem *except* _____.
    a. $c^2 = a^2 + b^2$
    b. $a = \sqrt{c^2 - b^2}$
    c. $b = \sqrt{c^2 - a^2}$
    d. $c = \sqrt{a^2 - b^2}$

15. The sine [SIN] function of an angle is determined by dividing the _____.
    a. side adjacent by the hypotenuse
    b. side opposite by the hypotenuse
    c. hypotenuse by the side adjacent
    d. side opposite by the side adjacent

Michael Friedman, Education and Training Consultant
Lutherville, MD

If this story had a moral, it would be that you never know where life will take you. Mike Friedman laid the foundation for his career by getting a good education. Then he embarked on a successful career in the chemical industry that took him to a key management position with a major company. Despite his success in the corporate world, Mike had the desire to run his own business and be his own boss. Instead of just thinking about it, he acted on it, and went on to create a very successful fire sprinkler and alarm business.

How did you get your start in the fire protection industry?
I approached it in a sort of roundabout way. After high school, I studied engineering and received a bachelor's degree in chemical engineering. I then took a master's degree in chemical and nuclear engineering at MIT. I worked as an engineer at the Oak Ridge Tennessee nuclear facility, and then went to work for Monsanto Chemical. Later, I was hired by the Clairol division of Bristol Meyers as a plant manager. During that time, I supervised the construction of a large manufacturing facility where I was exposed to all aspects of construction, including fire protection, security, and safety.

What happened then?
I guess the entrepreneurial spirit overtook me. I decided that I wanted to be in business for myself, but it couldn't be just any business. I didn't want to own a donut shop; I wanted to be in a technical business where I could use my engineering background. An opportunity came up to buy into a fire sprinkler business, and I jumped on it. As long as there is construction going on, there is a need for this business. Both business owners and insurance companies recognize the value of fire alarm and fire suppression systems. From an owner's standpoint, these systems protect their businesses and their employees by limiting the damage from fire. Of course, the insurance companies like these systems, and reward those who use them, because the systems reduce their cost risk.

What did your company do?
We installed sprinkler systems, as well as fire extinguishing systems using halon and other gases. We also installed and serviced fire alarm systems. My engineering background was valuable for doing system design. A few years ago, I sold the business to Grinnell, which later became SimplexGrinnell. At that time, I became an education and training consultant focusing on fire alarm and suppression systems.

What do you do as a consultant?
One of the important things I do is help in developing the NCCER EST curriculum by serving on the development committee with other subject matter experts. I also serve on the NCCER Craft Training Committee, which assists NCCER in developing training plans and strategies for the future. I serve as a consultant to SimplexGrinnell as well as the National Fire Sprinkler Association. In that role, I create and deliver training programs on fire sprinkler systems, fire alarm systems, construction practices, and project management. I also do design work for other clients and I am sometimes called upon to testify as an expert witness in court cases.

What advice would you give someone just starting out?
Get a good education. If you are going to be in this field, then you need a good technical background with plenty of math. When you start work, look for a company that focuses on education and training. If the company has a tuition reimbursement program and internal training programs, that is a good sign. It means they are committed to the idea that having highly skilled, well-trained employees is the way to success for both the company and the employees. Not all companies are like that. Some employers have the idea that training their employees just makes the employees more attractive to their competitors, so they provide few, if any, training opportunities. Working for an employer with that kind of attitude is a good way to find your career at a dead end.

Do you have an interesting experience or accomplishment that you would like to share?
In 2002, I received the golden Sprinkler Award from the National Fire Sprinkler Association for lifetime achievement in fire protection. In the 1980s and 1990s, I served as the first chairman of a consortium of industry, fire service, and the federal government called Operation Life Safety. The work of that organization led to the requirements for residential sprinkler systems that exist in many communities throughout the U.S.

Trade Terms Introduced in This Module

Acceleration: The rate of change of velocity; also, the process by which a body at rest becomes a body in motion.

Area: The amount of surface in a given plane or two-dimensional shape.

Coefficient: A multiplier, such as the numeral 2 in the expression 2b.

Constant: In an equation, an element with a fixed value.

Decibel (dB): One-tenth of a bel. The bel, named for Alexander Graham Bell, is a unit signifying a logarithmic ratio of two quantities. The decibel is most commonly used to quantify a relationship of output power to input power, although it can be applied to other units as well. The decibel is the unit of gain and/or loss in a transmission or amplification system.

Exponent: A small figure or symbol placed above and to the right of another figure or symbol to show how many times the latter is to be multiplied by itself, such as $b^3 = b \times b \times b$.

Force: A push or pull on a surface. In this module, force is considered to be the weight of an object or fluid. This is a common approximation.

Length: The distance from one point to another; typically refers to a measurement of the long side of an object or surface.

Level: A measured height or value. With liquids, the measurement of the level of fluid in a tank is a measurement of length from the surface of the fluid to the bottom of the tank.

Liter: A standard unit of volume in the metric system. It is equal to one cubic decimeter.

Mass: The quantity of matter present.

Newton (n): The amount of force required to accelerate one kilogram at a rate of one meter per second.

Unit: A definite standard measure of a dimension.

Variable: An element of an equation that may change in value.

Vector quantity: A quantity that has both magnitude and direction. Force is a vector quantity. Weight is a force with its direction always assumed to be downward.

Volume: The amount of space contained in a given three-dimensional shape.

Weight: The force exerted on an object due to the pull of the Earth's gravity.

Conversion Factors

Length Units				
MULTIPLY		BY		TO OBTAIN
Centimeters	×	0.3937	=	Inches
Fathoms	×	6.0	=	Feet
Feet	×	12.0	=	Inches
Feet	×	0.3048	=	Meters
Inches	×	2.54	=	Centimeters
Kilometers	×	0.6214	=	Miles
Meters	×	3.281	=	Feet
Meters	×	39.37	=	Inches
Meters	×	1.094	=	Yards
Miles	×	5280.0	=	Feet
Miles	×	1.609	=	Kilometers
Rods	×	5.5	=	Yards
Yards	×	0.9144	=	Meters

Area				
Acres	×	43560.0	=	Sq feet
Acres	×	4840.0	=	Sq yards
Circular mils	×	7.854×10^{-7}	=	Sq inches
Circular mils	×	0.7854	=	Sq mils
Sq centimeters	×	0.155	=	Sq inches
Sq feet	×	144.0	=	Sq inches
Sq feet	×	0.0929	=	Sq meters
Sq inches	×	6.452	=	Sq centim.
Sq meters	×	1.196	=	Sq yards
Sq miles	×	640.0	=	Acres
Sq mils	×	1.273	=	Circular mils
Sq yards	×	0.8361	=	Sq meters

Volume				
Cubic feet	×	0.0283	=	Cubic meters
Cubic feet	×	7.481	=	Gallons
Cubic inches	×	0.5541	=	Ounces (fluid)
Cubic meters	×	35.31	=	Cubic feet
Cubic meters	×	1.308	=	Cubic yards
Cubic yards	×	0.7646	=	Cubic meters
Gallons	×	0.1337	=	Cubic feet
Gallons	×	3.785	=	Liters
Liters	×	0.2642	=	Gallons
Liters	×	1.057	=	Quarts (fluid)
Ounces (fluid)	×	1.805	=	Cubic inches
Quarts (fluid)	×	0.9463	=	Liters

106A01.EPS

Force and Weight				
MULTIPLY		BY		TO OBTAIN
Grams	×	0.0353	=	Ounces
Kilograms	×	2.205	=	Pounds
Newtons	×	0.2248	=	Pounds (force)
Onces	×	28.35	=	Grams
Pounds	×	453.6	=	Grams
Pounds (force)	×	4.448	=	Newtons
Tons (short)	×	907.2	=	Kilograms
Tons (short)	×	2000.0	=	Pounds

Torque				
Gram-centim.	×	0.0139	=	Ounce-inches
Newton-meters	×	0.7376	=	Pound-feet
Newton-meters	×	8.851	=	Pound-inches
Ounce-inches	×	72.0	=	Gram-centim.
Pound-feet	×	1.3558	=	Newton-meters
Pound-inches	×	0.113	=	Newton-meters

Energy or Work				
Btu	×	778.2	=	Foot-pounds
Btu	×	252.0	=	Gram-calories

Power				
Btu per hour	×	0.293	=	Watts
Horsepower	×	33000.0	=	Ft-lbs/minute
Horsepower	×	550.0	=	Ft-lbs/second
Horsepower	×	746.0	=	Watts
Kilowatts	×	1.341	=	Horsepower

Plane Angle				
Degrees	×	0.0175	=	Radians
Minutes	×	0.01667	=	Degrees
Minutes	×	2.9×10^{-4}	=	Radians
Quadrants	×	90.0	=	Degrees
Quadrants	×	1.5708	=	Radians
Radians	×	57.3	=	Degrees

Pounds are U.S. avoirdupois.
Gallons and quarts are U.S.

106A02.EPS

Temperature Conversion Table

Locate the known temperature in the °C/°F column.
Read the converted temperature in the °C or °F column.

°C	°C/°F	°F	°C	°C/°F	°F
−45.4	−50	−58	46.1	115	239
−42.7	−45	−49	48.9	120	248
−40	−40	−40	51.6	125	257
−37.2	−35	−31	54.4	130	266
−34.4	−30	−22	57.1	135	275
−32.2	−25	−13	60	140	284
−29.4	−20	−4	62.7	145	293
−26.6	−15	5	65.5	150	302
−23.8	−10	14	68.3	155	311
−20.5	−5	23	71	160	320
−17.8	0	32	73.8	165	329
−15	5	41	76.5	170	338
−12.2	10	50	79.3	175	347
−9.4	15	59	82.1	180	356
−6.7	20	68	85	185	365
−3.9	25	77	87.6	190	374
−1.1	30	86	90.4	195	383
1.7	35	95	93.2	200	392
4.4	40	104	96	205	401
7.2	45	113	98.8	210	410
10	50	122	101.6	215	419
12.8	55	131	104.4	220	428
15.5	60	140	107.2	225	437
18.3	65	149	110	230	446
21.1	70	158	112.8	235	455
23.9	75	167	115.6	240	464
26.6	80	176	118.2	245	473
29.4	85	185	120.9	250	482
32.2	90	194	123.7	255	491
35	95	203	126.5	260	500
37.8	100	212	129.3	265	509
40.5	105	221	132.2	270	518
43.4	110	230	136	275	527

$°F = (\frac{9}{5} \times °C) + 32$
$°C = \frac{5}{9}(°F − 32)$

106A03.EPS

Additional Resources

This module is intended to be a thorough resource for task training. The following reference work is suggested for further study. This is optional material for continued education rather than for task training.

Fundamentals of Mechanical and Electrical Mathematics, 1996. Upper Saddle River, NJ: Prentice Hall.

The NCCER makes every effort to keep these textbooks up-to-date and free of technical errors. We appreciate your help in this process. If you have an idea for improving this textbook, or if you find an error, a typographical mistake, or an inaccuracy in NCCER's Contren® textbooks, please write us, using this form or a photocopy. Be sure to include the exact module number, page number, a detailed description, and the correction, if applicable. Your input will be brought to the attention of the Technical Review Committee. Thank you for your assistance.

Instructors – If you found that additional materials were necessary in order to teach this module effectively, please let us know so that we may include them in the Equipment/Materials list in the Instructor's Guide.

Write: Product Development and Revision
National Center for Construction Education and Research
P.O. Box 141104, Gainesville, FL 32614-1104

Fax: 352-334-0932

E-mail: curriculum@nccer.org

Craft

Module Name

Copyright Date

Module Number

Page Number(s)

Description

(Optional) Correction

(Optional) Your Name and Address

Hand Bending of Conduit

COURSE MAP

This course map shows all of the modules in the first level of the *Electronic Systems Technician* curriculum. The suggested training order begins at the bottom and proceeds up. Skill levels increase as you advance on the course map. The local Training Program Sponsor may adjust the training order.

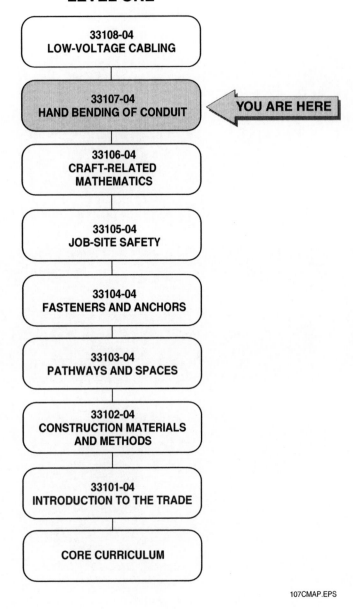

ELECTRONIC SYSTEMS TECHNICIAN
LEVEL ONE

33108-04
LOW-VOLTAGE CABLING

33107-04
HAND BENDING OF CONDUIT   ◄ YOU ARE HERE

33106-04
CRAFT-RELATED
MATHEMATICS

33105-04
JOB-SITE SAFETY

33104-04
FASTENERS AND ANCHORS

33103-04
PATHWAYS AND SPACES

33102-04
CONSTRUCTION MATERIALS
AND METHODS

33101-04
INTRODUCTION TO THE TRADE

CORE CURRICULUM

107CMAP.EPS

1.0.0 INTRODUCTION 7.1

2.0.0 CUTTING, REAMING, AND THREADING CONDUIT 7.1

    2.1.0   Cutting Conduit with a Hacksaw 7.1

    2.2.0   Cutting Conduit with a Pipe Cutter 7.2

    2.3.0   Reaming Conduit 7.3

    2.4.0   Threading Conduit 7.3

    2.5.0   Cutting and Joining PVC Conduit 7.4

3.0.0 HAND BENDING EQUIPMENT 7.5

    3.1.0   Geometry Required to Make a Bend 7.7

    3.2.0   Making a 90-Degree Bend 7.8

    3.3.0   Gain 7.10

    3.4.0   Back-to-Back 90-Degree Bends 7.10

    3.5.0   Offsets 7.10

    3.5.1   *Offset Calculations* 7.11

    3.5.2   *Making an Offset* 7.12

    3.6.0   Parallel Offsets 7.12

    3.7.0   Saddle Bends 7.14

    3.8.0   Four-Bend Saddles 7.15

SUMMARY 7.17

REVIEW QUESTIONS 7.17

PROFILE IN SUCCESS 7.19

GLOSSARY 7.21

APPENDIX A, Using Trigonometry to Determine Offset
              Angles and Multipliers 7.22

APPENDIX B, Bending Radius Table 7.24

REFERENCES & ACKNOWLEDGMENTS 7.25

Figures

Figure 1   Conduit ends after cutting 7.2
Figure 2   Cutter rotation 7.2
Figure 3   Rigid conduit reamer 7.3
Figure 4   Reamer rotation 7.3
Figure 5   Hand-operated ratchet threader 7.3
Figure 6   Hand benders 7.5
Figure 7   Pushing down on the bender to finish the bend 7.6
Figure 8   Hickeys 7.6
Figure 9   Typical PVC heating units 7.6
Figure 10   Typical plug set 7.7
Figure 11   Right triangle and offset bend 7.7
Figure 12   Circles and 90-degree bends 7.8
Figure 13   Bender markings 7.9
Figure 14   Bending an 18" stub-up 7.9
Figure 15   Gain 7.10
Figure 16   Back-to-back bends 7.11
Figure 17   Offsets 7.11
Figure 18   Incorrect parallel offsets 7.13
Figure 19   Center of first bend 7.13
Figure 20   Successive centerlines 7.13
Figure 21   Parallel offset pipes 7.14
Figure 22   Saddle measurement 7.14
Figure 23   Measurement locations 7.15
Figure 24   Location of bends 7.15
Figure 25   Typical four-bend saddle 7.15
Figure 26   Four-bend saddle 7.15
Figure 27   Four-bend saddle measurements 7.16
Figure 28   Bend and offset measurements 7.16

Tables

Table 1   Typical Bender Take-Up Distances 7.8
Table 2   Shrinkage Calculation 7.11
Table 3   Common Offset Factors (in Inches) 7.12
Table 4   Shrinkage Chart for Saddle Bends with a
          45° Center Bend and Two 22½° Bends 7.15

Hand Bending of Conduit

Objectives

When you have completed this module, you will be able to do the following:

1. Identify the methods of hand bending conduit.
2. Identify the various methods used to install conduit.
3. Use math formulas to determine conduit bends.
4. Make 90-degree bends, back-to-back bends, offsets, kicks, and saddle bends using a hand bender.
5. Cut, ream, and thread conduit.

Recommended Prerequisites

Core Curriculum; Electronic Systems Technician Level One, Modules 33101-04 through 33106-04

Required Trainee Materials

1. Paper and pencil
2. Copy of the latest edition of the *National Electrical Code®*
3. Appropriate personal protective equipment
4. Scientific calculator

1.0.0 ◆ INTRODUCTION

Practice, knowledge, and training will help you gain the skills necessary for proper conduit bending and installation. You will practice conduit bending in the lab and in the field under the supervision of instructors and experienced co-workers. This module covers the techniques for using hand-operated and step conduit benders, such as the hand bender and the hickey. This module will also explain the process of hand bending conduit and cutting, reaming, and threading conduit.

2.0.0 ◆ CUTTING, REAMING, AND THREADING CONDUIT

Rigid metal conduit (RMC), intermediate metal conduit (IMC), and electrical metallic tubing (EMT) are available in standard 10-foot lengths. When installing conduit, a length is cut to fit the job requirements.

2.1.0 Cutting Conduit with a Hacksaw

Conduit is normally cut using a hacksaw. To cut conduit with a hacksaw:

Step 1 Inspect the blade of the hacksaw and replace it, if needed. A blade with 18, 24, or 32 cutting teeth per inch is recommended for conduit. Use a higher tooth count for EMT and a lower tooth count for rigid conduit and IMC. If the blade needs to be replaced, point the teeth toward the front of the saw when installing the new blade.

Step 2 Secure the conduit in a pipe vise.

Step 3 Rest the middle of the hacksaw blade on the conduit where the cut is to be made. Position the saw so the end of the blade is pointing slightly down and the handle is pointing slightly up. Push forward gently until the cut is started. Make even strokes until the cut is finished.

Note: The designations *"National Electrical Code®"* and "NEC®," where used in this document, refer to the *National Electrical Code®*, which is a registered trademark of the National Fire Protection Association, Quincy, MA. *All National Electrical Code® (NEC®) references in this module refer to the 2002 edition of the NEC®.*

Using Your Bender Head to Secure Conduit

To secure conduit while cutting, insert the conduit into one of the holes in the bender head, brace your knee against the bender to secure it, then proceed to cut the conduit.

WARNING!

To avoid bruising your knuckles on the newly cut pipe, use gentle strokes for the final cut.

Step 4 Check the cut. The end of the conduit should be straight and smooth. *Figure 1* shows correct and incorrect cuts. Ream the conduit.

2.2.0 Cutting Conduit with a Pipe Cutter

A pipe cutter can also be used to cut RMC and IMC. To use a pipe cutter, proceed as follows:

Step 1 Secure the conduit in a pipe vise and mark a place for the cut.

Step 2 Open the cutter and place it over the conduit with the cutter wheel on the mark.

Step 3 Tighten the cutter by rotating the screw handle.

CAUTION

Do not overtighten the cutter. Overtightening can break the cutter wheel and distort the wall of the conduit.

Step 4 Rotate the cutter counterclockwise to start the cut. *Figure 2* shows the proper way to rotate the cutter.

Step 5 Tighten the cutter handle one-quarter turn for each full turn around the conduit. Again, make sure that you do not overtighten it.

Step 6 Add a few drops of cutting oil to the groove and continue cutting. Avoid skin contact with the oil.

Step 7 When the cut is almost finished, stop cutting and snap the conduit to finish the cut. This reduces the ridge that can be formed on the inside of the conduit.

Step 8 Clean the conduit and cutter with a shop towel rag.

Step 9 Ream the conduit.

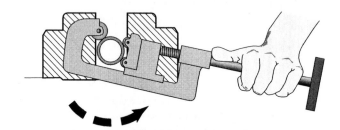

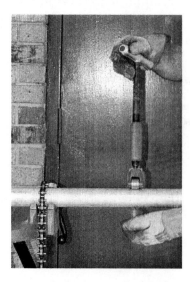

107F02.EPS

Figure 2 ◆ Cutter rotation.

INCORRECT   CORRECT

107F01.EPS

Figure 1 ◆ Conduit ends after cutting.

Using Tape

Use a piece of tape as a guide for marking your cutting lines around the conduit. This ensures a straight cut.

2.3.0 Reaming Conduit

When the conduit is cut, the inside edge is sharp. This edge will damage the insulation of the wire when it is pulled through. To avoid this damage, the inside edge must be smoothed or reamed using a reamer (*Figure 3*). To ream the inside edge of a piece of conduit using a hand reamer, proceed as follows:

Step 1   Place the conduit in a pipe vise.

Step 2   Insert the reamer tip in the conduit.

Step 3   Apply light forward pressure, and start rotating the reamer. *Figure 4* shows the proper way to rotate the reamer. It should be rotated using a downward motion and can be damaged if you rotate it in the wrong direction. The reamer should bite as soon as you apply the proper pressure.

Step 4   Remove the reamer by pulling back on it while continuing to rotate it. Check the progress, and then reinsert the reamer. Rotate the reamer until the inside edge is smooth. You should stop when all burrs have been removed.

NOTE

If a conduit reamer is not available, use a half-round file (the tang of the file must have a handle attached). EMT may be reamed using the nose of diagonal cutters or small hand reamers.

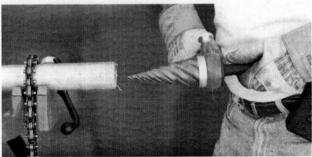
107F03.EPS

Figure 3 ◆ Rigid conduit reamer.

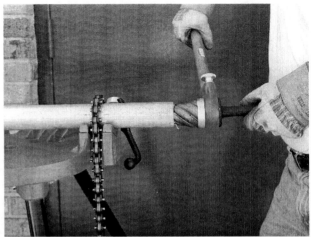
107F04.EPS

Figure 4 ◆ Reamer rotation.

2.4.0 Threading Conduit

After conduit is cut and reamed, it is usually threaded so it can be properly joined. Only RMC and IMC have walls thick enough for threading.

The tool used to cut threads in conduit is called a die. Conduit dies are made to cut a taper of ¾ inch per foot. The number of threads per inch varies from 8 to 18, depending upon the diameter of the conduit. A thread gauge is used to measure how many threads per inch are cut.

The threading dies are contained in a die head. The die head can be used with a hand-operated ratchet threader (*Figure 5*) or with a portable power drive. To thread conduit using a hand-operated threader, proceed as follows:

Step 1   Insert the conduit in a pipe vise. Make sure the vise is fastened to a strong surface. Place supports, if necessary, to help secure the conduit.

Step 2   Determine the correct die and head. Inspect the die for damage such as broken teeth. Never use a damaged die.

107F05.EPS

Figure 5 ◆ Hand-operated ratchet threader.

Step 3   Insert the die securely in the head. Make sure the proper die is in the appropriately numbered slot on the head.

Step 4   Determine the correct thread length to cut for the conduit size used (match the manufacturer's thread length).

Step 5   Lubricate the die with cutting oil at the beginning and throughout the threading operation. Avoid skin contact with the oil.

Step 6   Cut threads to the proper length. Make sure that the conduit enters the tapered side of the die. Apply pressure and start turning the head. You should back off the head each one-quarter turn to clear away chips.

Step 7   Remove the die when the proper cut is made. Threads should be cut only to the length of the die. Overcutting will leave the threads exposed to corrosion.

Step 8   Inspect the threads to make sure they are clean, sharp, and properly made. Use a thread gauge to measure the threads. The finished end should allow for a wrench-tight fit with one or two threads exposed.

NOTE

The conduit should be reamed again after threading to remove any burrs and edges. Cutting oil must be swabbed from the inside and outside of the conduit. Use a sandbox or drip pan under the threader to collect drips and shavings.

Die heads can also be used with portable power drives. You will follow the same steps when using a portable power drive. Threading machines are often used on larger conduit and where frequent threading is required. Threading machines hold and rotate the conduit while the die is fed onto the conduit for cutting. When using a threading machine, make sure you secure the legs properly and follow the manufacturer's instructions.

2.5.0 Cutting and Joining PVC Conduit

PVC (polyvinyl chloride) conduit may be easily cut with a fine-tooth handsaw. To ensure square cuts, a miter box or similar device is recommended for cutting 2" and larger PVC. You can deburr the cut ends using a pocket knife. Smaller diameter PVC conduit, up to 1½", may be cut using a PVC cutter.

Use the following steps to join PVC conduit sections or attachments to plastic boxes:

Oiling the Threader

For smoother operation, oil the threader often while threading the conduit.

107SA01.EPS

Threading Conduit

The key to threading conduit is to start with a square cut. If you don't get it right the first time, the fitting won't thread properly.

Step 1   Wipe all the contacting surfaces clean and dry.

Step 2   Apply a coat of cement (a brush or aerosol can is recommended) to the male end to be attached.

Step 3   Press the conduit and fitting together, and rotate about a half-turn to evenly distribute the cement.

NOTE

Cementing the PVC must be done quickly. The aerosol spray cans of cement or the cement/brush combination are usually provided by the PVC manufacturer. Make sure you use the recommended cement.

WARNING!

Solvents and cements used with PVC are hazardous. Wear gloves, and follow the product instructions.

Forming PVC in the field requires a special tool called a hot box or other specialized methods. PVC may not be threaded when it is used for electrical applications.

3.0.0 ◆ HAND BENDING EQUIPMENT

Figure 6 shows a hand bender. Hand benders are convenient because they are portable and no electrical power is required. Hand benders have a shape that supports the walls of the conduit being bent.

These benders are used to make various bends in smaller size conduit (½" to 1¼"). Most hand benders are sized to bend rigid conduit and electrical metallic tubing (EMT) of corresponding sizes. For example, a single hand bender can bend either ¾" EMT or ½" rigid conduit. The next larger size of hand bender will bend either 1" EMT or ¾" rigid conduit. This is because the corresponding sizes of conduit have nearly equal outside diameters.

The first step in making a good bend is familiarizing yourself with the bender. The manufacturer of the bender will typically provide documentation indicating starting points, distance between **offsets**, **gains**, and other important values associated with that particular bender. There is no substitute for taking the time to review this information. It will make the job go faster and will result in better bends.

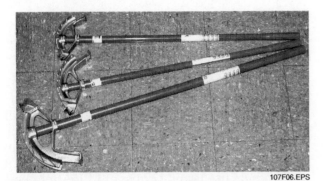

Figure 6 ◆ Hand benders.

107F06.EPS

> **WARNING!**
> When making bends, be sure you have a firm grip on the handle to avoid slippage and possible injury.

When performing a bend, it is important to keep the conduit on a stable, firm, flat surface for the entire duration of the bend. Hand benders are designed to have force applied using one foot and the hands. See *Figure 7*. It is important to use constant foot pressure as well as force on the handle

PVC Cutters

A nylon string can be used to cut PVC in place in awkward locations. However, it is best to use a PVC cutter to cut smaller trade sizes of PVC.

107SA02.EPS

Working with Conduit

Unprotected electrical cable is susceptible to moisture and physical damage; therefore, protect the wiring with conduit.

Bending Conduit

A good way to practice bending conduit is to use a piece of No. 10 or No. 12 solid wire and bend it to resemble the bends you need. This gives you some perspective on how to bend the conduit and it will also help you to anticipate any problems with the bends.

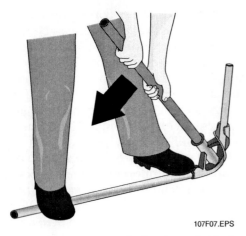

Figure 7 ◆ Pushing down on the bender to finish the bend.

to achieve uniform bends. Allowing the conduit to rise up or performing the bend on soft ground can result in distorting the conduit outside the bender.

NOTE

Bends should be made in accordance with the guidelines of *NEC Article 342* (IMC), *Article 344* (RMC), *Article 352* (RNC), or *Article 358* (EMT).

A hickey should not be confused with a hand bender. The hickey, which is used for RMC and IMC only, functions quite differently (*Figure 8*).

When you use a hickey to bend conduit, you are forming the bend as well as the radius. When using a hickey, be careful not to flatten or kink the conduit. Hickeys should only be used with RMC and IMC because very little support is given to the walls of the conduit being bent. A hickey is a **segment bending** device. First, a small bend of about 10 degrees is made. Then, the hickey is moved to a new position and another small bend is made. This process is continued until the bend is completed. A hickey can be used for conduit **stub-ups** in slabs and decks.

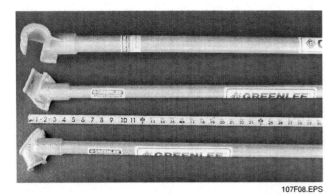

Figure 8 ◆ Hickeys.

PVC conduit is bent using a heating unit (*Figure 9*). The PVC must be rotated regularly while it is in the heater so that it heats evenly. Once heated, the PVC is removed, and the bending is performed by hand. Some units use an electric heating element, while others use liquid propane (LP). After bending, a damp sponge or cloth is often used to wipe down and cool off the PVC so that it sets up faster.

WARNING!

Avoid contact with the case of the heating unit; it can become very hot and cause burns. Also, to avoid a fire hazard, ensure that the unit is cool before storage. If using an LP unit, keep a fire extinguisher nearby.

When bending PVC that is 2" or larger in diameter, there is risk of wrinkling or flattening the bend. A plug set eliminates this problem (*Figure 10*). A plug is inserted into each end of the piece of PVC being bent. Then a hand pump is used to pressurize the conduit before bending it. The pressure is about 3 to 5 psi (pounds per square inch).

Figure 9 ◆ Typical PVC heating units.

Figure 10 ◆ Typical plug set.

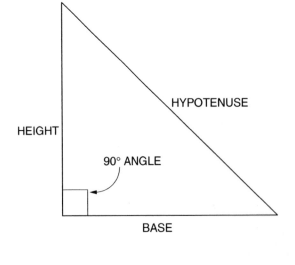

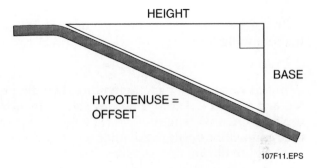

Figure 11 ◆ Right triangle and offset bend.

107F11.EPS

107F10.EPS

NOTE

The plugs must remain in place until the pipe is cooled and set.

3.1.0 Geometry Required to Make a Bend

Bending conduit requires that you use some basic geometry. You may already be familiar with most of the concepts needed; however, here is a review of the concepts directly related to this task.

A right triangle is defined as any triangle with a 90-degree angle. The side directly opposite the 90-degree angle is called the hypotenuse, and the side on which the triangle sits is the base. The vertical side is called the height. On the job, you will apply the relationships in a right triangle when making an offset bend. The offset forms the hypotenuse of a right triangle (*Figure 11*).

NOTE

There are reference tables for sizing offset bends based on these relationships (*Appendix A*).

A circle is defined as a closed curved line whose points are all the same distance from its center. The distance from the center point to the edge of the circle is called the radius. The length from one edge of the circle to the other edge through the center point is the diameter. The distance around the circle is called the circumference. A circle can be divided into four equal quadrants. Each quadrant accounts for 90 degrees, making a total of 360 degrees. When you make a **90-degree bend**, you will use one-quarter of a circle, or one quadrant. Concentric circles are circles that have a common center but different radii. The concept of concentric circles can be applied to **concentric bends** in conduit. The angle of each bend is 90 degrees. Such bends have the same center point, but the radius of each is different. See *Figure 12*.

Practical Bending

INSIDE TRACK

When making offset bends of 45 degrees to step conduit up to another level, square floor tiles make a convenient grid to gauge the distance and angles.

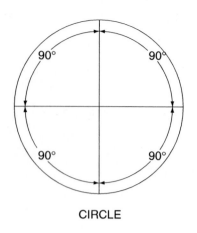
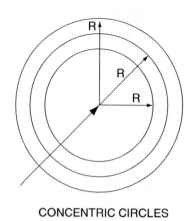
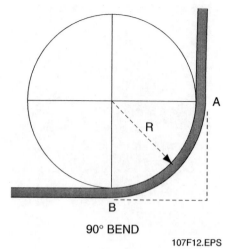

CIRCLE   CONCENTRIC CIRCLES

90° BEND

107F12.EPS

Figure 12 ◆ Circles and 90-degree bends.

To calculate the circumference of a circle, use the following formula:

$$C = \pi \times D \text{ or } C = \pi D$$

In this formula, C = circumference, D = diameter, and π = 3.14. Another way of stating the formula for circumference is $C = 2\pi R$, where R equals the radius or one-half the diameter.

To figure the arc of a quadrant use:

$$\text{Length of arc} = (0.25) \, 2\pi R = 1.57R$$

For this formula, the arc of a quadrant equals one-quarter the circumference of the circle or 1.57 times the radius.

A bending radius table is included in *Appendix B*.

3.2.0 Making a 90-Degree Bend

The 90-degree stub bend is probably the most basic bend of all. The stub bend is used much of the time regardless of the type of conduit being installed.

Before beginning to make the bend, you need to know two measurements:

- Desired **rise** or stub-up
- **Take-up** distance of the bender

The desired rise is the height of the stub-up. The take-up is the amount of conduit the bender will use to form the bend. Take-up distances are usually listed in the manufacturer's instruction manual. Typical bender take-up distances are shown in *Table 1*.

Once you have determined the take-up, subtract it from the stub-up height. Mark that distance on the conduit (all the way around) at that distance from the end. The mark will indicate the point at which you will begin to bend the conduit. Line up the starting point on the conduit with the starting

Table 1 Typical Bender Take-Up Distances

EMT	Rigid/IMC	Take-Up
½"	—	5"
¾"	½"	6"
1"	¾"	8"
1¼"	1"	11"

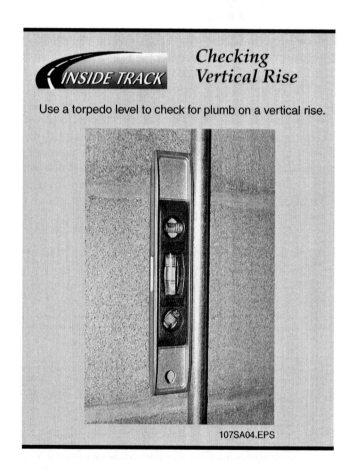

INSIDE TRACK

Checking Vertical Rise

Use a torpedo level to check for plumb on a vertical rise.

107SA04.EPS

point on the bender. Most benders have a mark, like an arrow, to indicate this point (*Figure 13*). *Figure 14* shows the take-up required to achieve an 18" stub-up on a piece of ½" EMT.

Once you have lined up the bender, use one foot to hold the conduit steady. Keep your heel on the floor for balance. Apply pressure on the bender foot pedal with your other foot. Make sure you hold the bender handle straight and as far up as possible in order to get maximum leverage. Then, bend the conduit in one smooth motion, pulling as steadily as possible. Avoid overstretching.

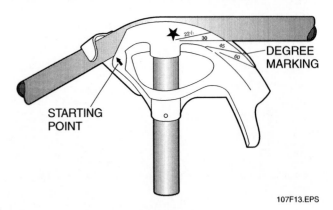

Figure 13 ◆ Bender markings.

NOTE

When bending conduit using the take-up method, always place the bender on the conduit and make the bend facing the hook of the conduit from which the measurements were taken.

After finishing the bend, check to make sure you have the correct angle and measurement. Use the following steps to check a 90-degree bend:

Step 1 With the back of the bend on the floor, measure to the end of the conduit stub-up to make sure it is the right length.

Step 2 Check the 90-degree angle of the bend with a square or at the angle formed by the floor and a wall. A torpedo level may also be used.

NOTE

If you slightly overbend or underbend the conduit, you can use the bender to bend the conduit to the correct angle.

The above procedure will produce a 90-degree one-shot bend. That means that it took a single bend to form the conduit bend. A segment bend is any bend that is formed by a series of bends of a few degrees each, rather than a single one-shot bend. A shot is actually one bend in a segment

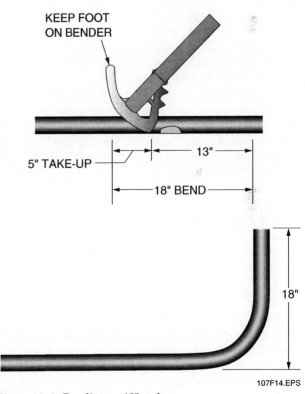

Figure 14 ◆ Bending an 18" stub-up.

bend. Sweep bends are required when pulling optical fiber cable. This type of cable requires a larger radius to prevent kinking during the cable pull. Segment or sweep bends must conform to the provisions of the NEC®.

Smooth Bends

Why are smooth bends so important?

Gain

What is the difference between the gain and the take-up of a bend?

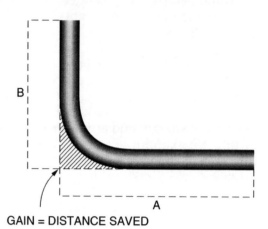

GAIN = DISTANCE SAVED

3.3.0 Gain

The gain is the distance saved by the arc of a 90-degree bend. Knowing the gain can help you precut, ream, and prethread both ends of the conduit before you bend it. This will make your work go more quickly because it is easier to work with conduit while it is straight. *Figure 15* shows that the overall **developed length** of a piece of conduit with a 90-degree bend is less than the sum of the horizontal and vertical distances when measured square to the corner. This is shown by the following equation:

Developed length = (A + B) − gain

An example of a manufacturer's gain table is also shown in *Figure 15*. These tables are used to determine the gain for a certain size conduit.

Conduit Size	NEC® Radius	90° Gain
½"	4"	2⅝"
¾"	5"	3¼"
1"	6"	4"
1¼"	8"	5⅝"

TYPICAL GAIN TABLE

107F15.EPS

Figure 15 ◆ Gain.

3.4.0 Back-to-Back 90-Degree Bends

A **back-to-back bend** consists of two 90-degree bends made on the same piece of conduit and placed back-to-back (*Figure 16*).

To make a back-to-back bend, first cut and ream your piece of conduit to its developed length:

Developed length = (X − gain) + L + (Y − gain)

Make your first 90-degree bend (labeled X in *Figure 16*) in the usual manner. Make sure you have the correct angle and measurement. Now reverse the conduit and make another 90-degree bend. Again, make sure you have the correct angle and measurement.

NOTE

While making your second 90-degree bend, you must make sure that the first 90-degree bend is properly aligned.

3.5.0 Offsets

Many situations require that the conduit be bent so that it can pass over objects such as beams and other conduits, or enter racks and junction boxes. Bends used for this purpose are called offsets (kicks). To produce an offset, two equal bends of less than 90 degrees are required, a specified distance apart, as shown in *Figure 17*.

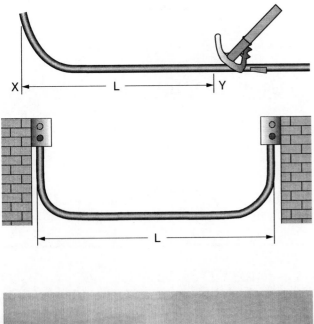

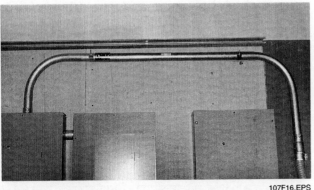

Figure 16 ◆ Back-to-back bends.

107F16.EPS

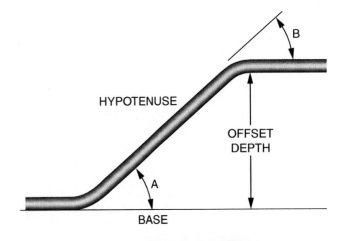

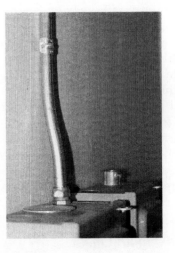

Figure 17 ◆ Offsets.

107F17.EPS

3.5.1 Offset Calculations

Offsets are a trade-off between space and the effort it will take to pull the wire. The larger the degree of bend, the harder it will be to pull the wire. The smaller the degree of bend, the easier it will be to pull the wire. Use the shallowest degree of bend that will still allow the conduit to bypass the obstruction and fit in the given space.

When conduit is offset, some of the conduit length is used. If the offset is made into the area, an allowance must be made for this shrinkage. If the offset angle is away from the obstruction, the shrinkage can be ignored. *Table 2* shows the amount of shrinkage per inch of rise for common offset angles.

Developed length = distance of base + shrinkage

The formula for figuring the distance between bends is as follows:

Distance between bends = depth of offset × multiplier

Table 2 Shrinkage Calculation

Offset Angles	Multiplier	Shrinkage (per inch of rise)
10° × 10°	6	1/16"
22½° × 22½°	2.6	3/16"
30° × 30°	2	1/4"
45° × 45°	1.4	3/8"
60° × 60°	1.2	1/2"

The distance between the offset bends can generally be found in the manufacturer's documentation for the bender. *Table 3* shows the distance between bends for the most common offset angles.

Calculations related to offsets are derived from the branch of mathematics known as trigonometry, which deals with triangles. The multipliers shown in *Table 2* represent the cosecant (CSC) of the related offset angle. The multiplier is determined by dividing the depth of the offset by the hypotenuse of the triangle created by the offset (*Figure 17*).

Table 3 Common Offset Factors (in Inches)

Offset Depth	22½°		30°		45°		60°	
	Between Bends	Shrinkage	Between Bends	Shrinkage	Between Bends	Shrinkage	Between Bends	Shrinkage
2	5¼	⅜	—	—	—	—	—	—
3	7¾	9/16	6	¾	—	—	—	—
4	10½	¾	8	1	—	—	—	—
5	13	1 5/16	10	1¼	7	1⅞	—	—
6	15½	1⅛	12	1½	8½	2¼	7¼	3
7	18¼	1 5/16	14	1¾	9¾	2⅝	8⅜	3½
8	20¾	1½	16	2	11¼	3	9⅝	4
9	23½	1¾	18	2¼	12½	3⅜	10⅞	4½
10	26	1⅞	20	2½	14	3¾	12	5

Basic trigonometry (trig) functions are briefly covered in *Appendix A*. As you will see in the next section, the tangent (TAN) of the offset angle is also used in calculating parallel offsets. Understanding trig functions will help you understand how offsets are determined. If you have a scientific calculator and understand these functions, you can calculate offset angles when you know the dimensions of the triangle created by the offset and the obstacle.

3.5.2 Making an Offset

An offset consists of two bends made to route conduit over an obstruction. The procedure for making an offset bend is as follows:

Step 1 Determine the depth of the offset.

Step 2 Determine the required distance between bends.

Step 3 Determine the developed length.

Step 4 Cut the conduit to the required developed length. Ream the conduit ends.

NOTE
If the developed length will be too short to work properly in the bender, it may be easier to cut the conduit after making the bend.

Step 5 Mark the first bend (depth of the offset).

Step 6 Mark the second bend (distance between bends).

Step 7 Line up the first bend. Use the side of the bender that shows the multipliers.

Step 8 Make the first bend to the point shown by the correct multiplier on the bender.

Step 9 Line up the second bend by reversing the conduit in the bender so that the handle is on the floor and the bender is raised with the first bend facing straight down.

Step 10 Place your foot against the handle of the bender to prevent it from slipping. Bend the conduit partially around the bender.

Step 11 Reposition the conduit and bender to the normal position. Do not to lose your mark.

Step 12 Finish the bend to the multiplier mark.

NOTE
A magnetic torpedo level can also be used to determine the end of the second bend. Bend the conduit until the level shows that it is parallel to the first bend.

3.6.0 Parallel Offsets

Often, multiple pieces of conduit must be bent around a common obstruction. In this case, parallel offsets are made. Because the bends are laid out along a common radius, an adjustment must be made to ensure that the ends do not come out uneven, as shown in *Figure 18*.

The center of the first bend of the innermost conduit is found first (*Figure 19*). Each successive conduit must have its centerline moved farther away from the end of the pipe (*Figure 20*). The amount to add is calculated as follows:

Amount added = center-to-center spacing × tangent (TAN) of ½ offset angle

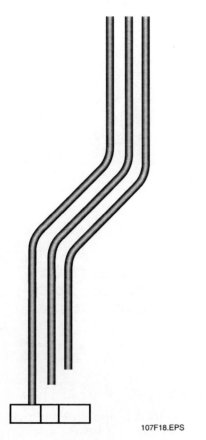

Figure 18 ◆ Incorrect parallel offsets.

107F18.EPS

THINK ABOUT IT

Calculating Shrinkage

You're making a 30-degree by 30-degree offset to clear a 6" obstruction. What will be the distance between bends? What will be the developed length shrink? Make the same calculations for a 10" offset with 45-degree bends.

Tangents can be found using the trig tables provided in *Appendix A*. For example, *Figure 21* shows three pipes laid out as parallel and offset. The angle of the offset is 30 degrees. The center-to-center spacing is 3". The start of the innermost pipe's first bend is 12".

The starting point of the second pipe will be:

12" + [center-to-center spacing × TAN (½ offset angle)]

12" + (3" × TAN 15 degrees) = 12" + (3" × 0.2679) = 12" + 0.8037" ≈ 12¹³⁄₁₆"

The starting point for the outermost pipe is:

12¹³⁄₁₆" + ¹³⁄₁₆" = 13⅝"

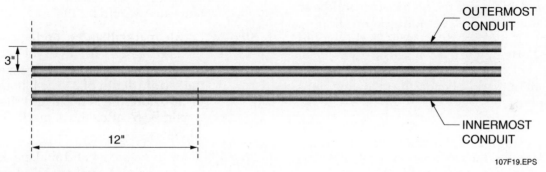

OUTERMOST CONDUIT

3"

INNERMOST CONDUIT

12"

107F19.EPS

Figure 19 ◆ Center of first bend.

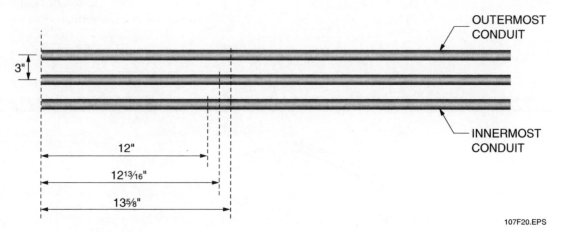

OUTERMOST CONDUIT

3"

INNERMOST CONDUIT

12"

12¹³⁄₁₆"

13⅝"

107F20.EPS

Figure 20 ◆ Successive centerlines.

Equal Angles

Why is it important that the angles be identical when making an offset bend?

Calculating Parallel Offsets

You're making parallel offsets of 45 degrees, and the lengths of conduit are spaced 4" center to center. If the offset starts 12" down the pipe, what is the starting point for the bend on the second pipe?

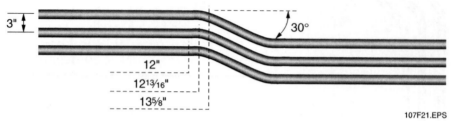

Figure 21 ◆ Parallel offset pipes.

3.7.0 Saddle Bends

A saddle bend is used to go around obstructions. *Figure 22* illustrates an example of a saddle bend that is required to clear a pipe obstruction. Making a saddle bend will cause the center of the saddle to shorten 3/16" for every inch of saddle depth (*Table 4*). For example, if the pipe diameter is 2", this would cause a 3/8" shortening of the conduit on each side of the bend.

When making saddle bends, the following steps should apply:

Step 1 Locate the center mark A on the conduit by using the size of the obstruction (pipe diameter, for example) and calculate the shrink rate of the obstruction. For example, if the pipe diameter is 2", 3/8" of conduit will be lost on each side of the bend for a total shrinkage of 3/4". This figure will be added to the measurement from the end of the conduit to the centerline of the obstruction. For example, if the distance measured from the conduit end and the obstruction centerline was 15", the distance to A would be 15 3/8".

Step 2 Locate marks B and C on the conduit by measuring 2½" for every 1" of saddle depth from the A mark. For example, for the saddle depth of 2", the B mark would be 5" before the A mark and the C mark would be 5" after the A mark. See *Figure 23*.

Step 3 Refer to *Figure 24* and make a 45-degree bend at point A, make a 22½-degree bend at point B, and make a 22½-degree bend at point C. Be sure to check the manufacturer's specifications.

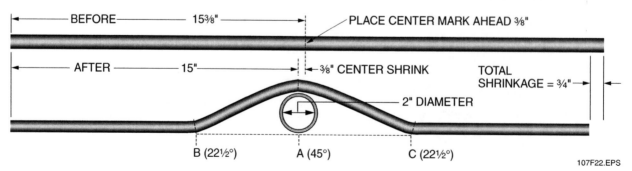

Figure 22 ◆ Saddle measurement.

Table 4 Shrinkage Chart for Saddle Bends with a 45° Center Bend and Two 22½° Bends

Obstruction Depth	Shrinkage Amount (Move Center Mark Forward)	Make Outside Marks from New Center Mark
1	³⁄₁₆"	2½"
2	³⁄₈"	5"
3	⁹⁄₁₆"	7½"
4	¾"	10"
5	¹⁵⁄₁₆"	12½"
6	1⅛"	15"
For each additional inch, add	³⁄₁₆"	2½"

3.8.0 Four-Bend Saddles

Four-bend saddles can be difficult. The reason is that four bends must be aligned exactly on the same plane. Extra time spent laying it out and performing the bends will pay off in not having to scrap the whole piece and start over.

Figure 25 illustrates that the four-bend saddle is two offsets formed back-to-back. Working left to right, the procedure for forming this saddle follows:

Step 1   Determine the height of the offset.

Step 2   Determine the correct spacing for the first offset and mark the conduit.

Step 3   Bend the first offset.

Step 4   Mark the start point for the second offset at the trailing edge of the obstruction.

Step 5   Mark the spacing for the second offset.

Step 6   Bend the second offset.

Using *Figure 26* as an example, a four-bend saddle using ½" EMT is laid out as follows:

- Height of the box = 6"
- Width of the box = 8"
- Distance to the obstruction = 36"

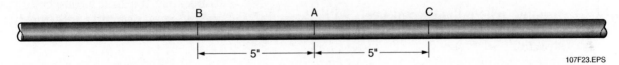

Figure 23 ◆ Measurement locations.

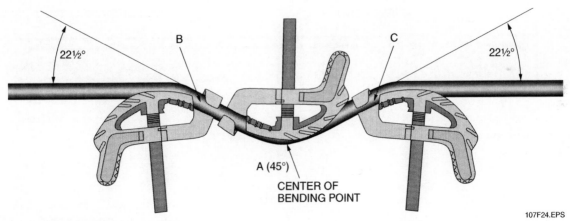

Figure 24 ◆ Location of bends.

Figure 25 ◆ Typical four-bend saddle.

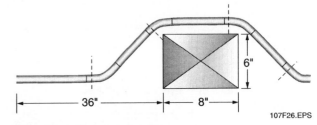

Figure 26 ◆ Four-bend saddle.

Planning Bends

The more bends you make, the more difficult it is to pull the wires through the conduit. Therefore, plan your bends in advance, avoid sharp bends, and make as few bends as possible. The NEC® allows the bends in a single run of conduit to total 360 degrees; however, 360 degrees is not as much as you might think. For example, if you bend the conduit 90 degrees for two corners of a room, with two 45-degree offsets where the conduit connects to a panelboard and junction box, you've used up your 360 degrees.

Two 30-degree offsets will be used to form the saddle. It is created as follows:

Step 1 See *Figure 27*. Working from left to right, calculate the start point for the first bend. The distance to the obstruction is 36", the offset is 6", and the 30-degree multiplier from *Table 2* is 2.00:

Distance to the obstruction − (offset × constant for the angle) + shrinkage = distance to the first bend

36" − (6" × 2.00) + 1½" = 25½"

Step 2 Determine where the second bend will end to ensure the conduit clears the obstruction. See *Figure 28*.

Distance to the first bend + distance to second bend + shrinkage = total length of the first offset

25½" + 12" + 1½" = 39"

Step 3 Determine the start point of the second offset. The width of the box is 8"; therefore, the start point of the second offset should be 8" beyond the end of the first offset:

8" + 39" = 47"

Step 4 Determine the spacing for the second offset. Because the first and second offsets have the same rise and angle, the distance between bends will be the same, or 12".

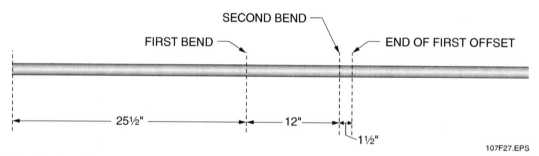

Figure 27 ◆ Four-bend saddle measurements.

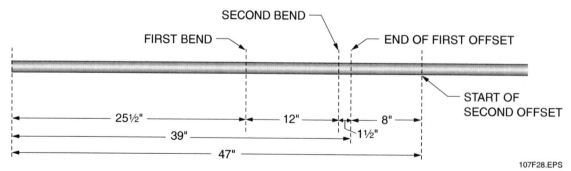

Figure 28 ◆ Bend and offset measurements.

Summary

This module covered conduit cutting and bending. Conduit is normally cut using a hacksaw. However, RMC and IMC conduit can be cut with a pipe cutter, and PVC can be cut using a PVC cutter. RMC and IMC have thick walls and can be threaded. When conduit is cut or threaded it must be reamed to remove burrs that could damage wiring.

You must choose a conduit bender to suit the kind of conduit being installed and the type of bend to be made. Some knowledge of the geometry of right triangles and circles is required to make the necessary calculations. You must be able to calculate, lay out, and perform bending operations on a single run of conduit and also on two or more parallel runs of conduit. At times, data tables for the figures may be consulted for the calculations. All work must conform to the requirements of the NEC®.

Review Questions

1. When using a pipe cutter, always rotate the cutter _____ to start the cut.

   a. clockwise
   b. with the grain
   c. counterclockwise
   d. against the grain

2. You would use _____ to smooth the sharp inside edge of metal conduit after it has been cut.

   a. a flat file
   b. rough sandpaper
   c. a reamer
   d. a pocket knife

3. What tool is used to cut threads in RMC or IMC?

   a. Thread gauge
   b. Cutter
   c. Tap
   d. Die

4. The field bending of PVC requires a _____.

   a. hickey
   b. heating unit
   c. segmented bender
   d. one-shot bender

5. After bending PVC, the bend can be set by using _____.

   a. a damp sponge or cloth
   b. dry ice
   c. ice-cold water
   d. a blow dryer

6. A hickey is used for bending _____.

   a. RMC and IMC
   b. EMT
   c. PVC
   d. RMC, EMT, IMC, and PVC conduit

7. A plug set is typically used to prevent _____ PVC when bending it.

   a. overpressurizing
   b. flattening
   c. corroding
   d. cutting

8. What is the key to uniform bending with a hand bender?

   a. Correct size and length of handle
   b. Constant foot pressure on the back piece
   c. Using only the correct brand of bender
   d. Correct inverting of the conduit bender

9. In a right triangle, the side directly opposite the 90-degree angle is called the _____.

   a. right side
   b. hypotenuse
   c. altitude
   d. base

10. The formula for calculating the circumference of a circle is _____.

    a. $\pi \times R^2$
    b. $2\pi \times R^2$
    c. $\pi \times D$
    d. $2\pi \times D$

11. Prior to making a 90-degree bend, what two measurements must be known?

    a. Length of conduit and size of conduit
    b. Desired rise and length of conduit
    c. Size of bender and size of conduit
    d. Stub-up distance and take-up distance

12. A back-to-back bend consists of _____.

    a. a two-shot 90-degree bend
    b. two 90-degree bends
    c. an offset with four bends
    d. a segmented bend

13. To ensure the conduit enters straight into the junction box, a(n) _____ may be required.

    a. back-to-back bend
    b. saddle bend
    c. offset
    d. take-up

14. To prevent the ends of the conduit from being staggered, what additional information must be used when making parallel offset bends?

    a. Center-to-center spacing and tangent of ½ the offset angle

    b. Length of conduit and size of conduit

    c. Stub-up distance and take-up distance

    d. Offset angle and length of conduit

15. When making a saddle bend, the center of the saddle will cause the conduit to shrink _____ for every inch of saddle depth.

    a. ⅜"

    b. ³⁄₁₆"

    c. ¾"

    d. ³⁄₃₂"

Paul Salyers, Vice President, Sales and Engineering
Copp Systems Integrator

Paul Salyers received his training in basic electronics in the U.S. Navy. This training, combined with his Navy experience and his lifelong commitment to education, launched him on a successful career in the corporate electronics industry.

How did you choose a career in the EST field?
I began my career in the U.S. Navy as an electronics warfare technician. I received extensive training in electronics and systems during my six years in the Navy. After my discharge, I attended Ohio University for four years, and then moved into the broadcast field as a senior broadcast engineer for public television. While in the PBS job, I attended classes in networking technology and computer based design and drafting on my own time. This coursework led to a position in corporate information technology at another company where I designed and developed digital video production facilities, an Avid editing suite, and cross platform networks for graphics, prepress, and printing facility needs.

What types of technical training have you been through?
I received three years of electronics and systems training in the Navy. In addition to the four years I spent at Ohio University, I have taken training in Novell® networking and servers, Windows® networking and servers, and Apple® networking, servers, and prepress publishing.

What kinds of work have you done in your career?
I once serviced a radar system atop a 200-foot mast on a ship while it was underway near Iceland. While in the Navy, I led a team of technicians who maintained the radar, communications, and electronic countermeasures systems aboard a ship. I have also maintained radio and TV production and transmitter facilities and designed networks for prepress and digital video facilities.

Tell us about your present job.
As vice president for sales and engineering, I wear two hats. I'm responsible for directing the company's sales efforts, which includes developing sales strategies and searching out new and better business opportunities that fit who we are as a company. When I'm wearing the engineering hat, I'm responsible for overseeing the process of system design and installation, as well as service. One of the key things I do is to see that the technology and the manufacturers meet our needs as well as those of our customers. We're always looking for the best fit of function, quality, and support.

What factors have contributed most to your success?
I have always remained focused on the future because it is important in this industry to keep up with emerging technologies. I have looked for industry trends and then leveraged my existing knowledge and skills to move in directions that interest me. Most importantly, I have taken responsibility for my own education and training. Along the way, there will be people that won't always support your efforts. Never give in, never say I can't.

What advice would you give to someone new to the EST field?
Take the initiative on the job and in your life. Don't wait around for someone to tell you what you need to learn. Figure it out for yourself, or ask people who should know. If they don't, keep asking until you get answers that make sense to you. Then, go and get the training you need to do your job effectively and to advance your career. The industry changes constantly, and technology moves from the lab to the marketplace so fast that it is easy to be left behind if you don't make a conscious effort to keep abreast of changes. The only person that can hold back your career or success is you. Invest in yourself.

Trade Terms Introduced in This Module

90-degree bend: A bend that changes the direction of the conduit by 90 degrees.

Back-to-back bend: Any bend formed by two 90-degree bends with a straight section of conduit between the bends.

Concentric bends: Making 90-degree bends in two or more parallel runs of conduit and increasing the radius of each conduit from the inside of the run toward the outside.

Developed length: The actual length of the conduit that will be bent.

Gain: Because a conduit bends in a radius and not at right angles, the length of conduit needed for a bend will not equal the total determined length. Gain is the distance saved by the arc of a 90-degree bend.

Offsets: An offset (kick) is two bends placed in a piece of conduit to change elevation to go over or under obstructions or for proper entry into boxes, cabinets, etc.

Rise: The length of the bent section of conduit measured from the bottom, centerline, or top of the straight section to the end of the bent section.

Segment bend: A large bend formed by multiple short bends or shots.

Stub-up: Another name for the rise in a section of conduit. Also, a term used for conduit penetrating a slab or the ground.

Take-up: The amount of conduit used to form a bend.

Using Trigonometry to Determine Offset Angles and Multipliers

You do not have to be a mathematician to use trigonometry. Understanding the basic trig functions and how to use them can help you calculate unknown distances or angles. Assume that the right triangle below represents a conduit offset. If you know the length of one side and the angle, you can calculate the length of the other sides. If you know the length of any two of the sides of the triangle, you can then find the offset angle using one or more of these trig functions. You can use a trig table like that shown on the following pages or a scientific calculator to determine the offset angle. For example, if the cosecant of angle A is 2.6, the trig table tells you that the offset angle is 22½ degrees.

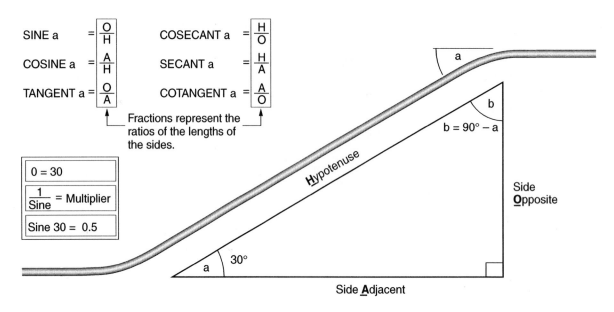

SINE a $= \dfrac{O}{H}$ COSECANT a $= \dfrac{H}{O}$

COSINE a $= \dfrac{A}{H}$ SECANT a $= \dfrac{H}{A}$

TANGENT a $= \dfrac{O}{A}$ COTANGENT a $= \dfrac{A}{O}$

Fractions represent the ratios of the lengths of the sides.

O = 30

$\dfrac{1}{\text{Sine}}$ = Multiplier

Sine 30 = 0.5

b = 90° − a

Side **O**pposite

Side **A**djacent

Hypotenuse

30°

To determine the multiplier for the distance between bends in an offset:

1. Determine the angle of the offset: 30°

2. Find the sine of the angle: 0.5

3. Find the inverse (reciprocal) of the sine: $\dfrac{1}{0.5}$ = 2. This is also listed in trig tables as the cosecant of the angle.

4. This number multiplied by the height of the offset gives the hypotenuse of the triangle, which is equal to the distance between bends.

107A01.EPS

ANGLE	SINE	COSINE	TANGENT	ANGLE	SINE	COSINE	TANGENT
1°	0.0175	0.9998	0.0175	46°	0.7193	0.6947	1.0355
2°	0.0349	0.9994	0.0349	47°	0.7314	0.6820	1.0724
3°	0.0523	0.9986	0.0524	48°	0.7431	0.6691	1.1106
4°	0.0698	0.9976	0.0699	49°	0.7547	0.6561	1.1504
5°	0.0872	0.9962	0.0875	50°	0.7660	0.6428	1.1918
6°	0.1045	0.9945	0.1051	51°	0.7771	0.6293	1.2349
7°	0.1219	0.9925	0.1228	52°	0.7880	0.6157	1.2799
8°	0.1392	0.9903	0.1405	53°	0.7986	0.6018	1.3270
9°	0.1564	0.9877	0.1584	54°	0.8090	0.5878	1.3764
10°	0.1736	0.9848	0.1763	55°	0.8192	0.5736	1.4281
11°	0.1908	0.9816	0.1944	56°	0.8290	0.5592	1.4826
12°	0.2079	0.9781	0.2126	57°	0.8387	0.5446	1.5399
13°	0.2250	0.9744	0.2309	58°	0.8480	0.5299	1.6003
14°	0.2419	0.9703	0.2493	59°	0.8572	0.5150	1.6643
15°	0.2588	0.9659	0.2679	60°	0.8660	0.5000	1.7321
16°	0.2756	0.9613	0.2867	61°	0.8746	0.4848	1.8040
17°	0.2924	0.9563	0.3057	62°	0.8829	0.4695	1.8807
18°	0.3090	0.9511	0.3249	63°	0.8910	0.4540	1.9626
19°	0.3256	0.9455	0.3443	64°	0.8988	0.4384	2.0503
20°	0.3420	0.9397	0.3640	65°	0.9063	0.4226	2.1445
21°	0.3584	0.9336	0.3839	66°	0.9135	0.4067	2.2460
22°	0.3746	0.9272	0.4040	67°	0.9205	0.3907	2.3559
23°	0.3907	0.9205	0.4245	68°	0.9272	0.3746	2.4751
24°	0.4067	0.9135	0.4452	69°	0.9336	0.3584	2.6051
25°	0.4226	0.9063	0.4663	70°	0.9397	0.3420	2.7475
26°	0.4384	0.8988	0.4877	71°	0.9455	0.3256	2.9042
27°	0.4540	0.8910	0.5095	72°	0.9511	0.3090	3.0777
28°	0.4695	0.8829	0.5317	73°	0.9563	0.2924	3.2709
29°	0.4848	0.8746	0.5543	74°	0.9613	0.2756	3.4874
30°	0.5000	0.8660	0.5774	75°	0.9659	0.2588	3.7321
31°	0.5150	0.8572	0.6009	76°	0.9703	0.2419	4.0108
32°	0.5299	0.8480	0.6249	77°	0.9744	0.2250	4.3315
33°	0.5446	0.8387	0.6494	78°	0.9781	0.2079	4.7046
34°	0.5592	0.8290	0.6745	79°	0.9816	0.1908	5.1446
35°	0.5736	0.8192	0.7002	80°	0.9848	0.1736	5.6713
36°	0.5878	0.8090	0.7265	81°	0.9877	0.1564	6.3138
37°	0.6018	0.7986	0.7536	82°	0.9903	0.1392	7.1154
38°	0.6157	0.7880	0.7813	83°	0.9925	0.1219	8.1443
39°	0.6293	0.7771	0.8098	84°	0.9945	0.1045	9.5144
40°	0.6428	0.7660	0.8391	85°	0.9962	0.0872	11.4301
41°	0.6561	0.7547	0.8693	86°	0.9976	0.0698	14.3007
42°	0.6691	0.7431	0.9004	87°	0.9986	0.0523	19.0811
43°	0.6820	0.7314	0.9325	88°	0.9994	0.0349	28.6363
44°	0.6947	0.7193	0.9657	89°	0.9998	0.0175	57.2900
45°	0.7071	0.7071	1.0000	90°	1.0000	0.0000	

107A02.EPS

Bending Radius Table

Radius (Inches)	Radius Increments (Inches)									
	0	1	2	3	4	5	6	7	8	9
0	0.00	1.57	3.14	4.71	6.28	7.85	9.42	10.99	12.56	14.13
10	15.70	17.27	18.84	20.41	21.98	23.85	25.12	26.69	28.26	29.83
20	31.40	32.97	34.54	36.11	37.68	39.25	40.82	42.39	43.96	45.83
30	47.10	48.67	50.24	51.81	53.38	54.95	56.52	58.09	59.66	61.23
40	62.80	64.37	65.94	67.50	69.03	70.65	72.22	73.79	75.36	76.93
50	87.50	80.07	81.64	83.21	84.78	86.35	87.92	89.49	91.06	92.63
60	94.20	95.77	97.34	98.91	100.48	102.05	103.62	105.19	106.76	108.33
70	109.90	111.47	113.04	114.61	116.18	117.75	119.32	120.89	122.46	124.03
80	125.60	127.17	128.74	130.31	131.88	133.45	135.02	136.59	138.16	139.73
90	141.30	142.87	144.44	146.01	147.58	149.15	150.72	–	–	–

Developed length for following angles use fraction of 90° chart.

For	15°	22½°	30°	45°	60°	67½°	75°	90°
Take	⅙	¼	⅓	½	⅔	¾	⅚	See Chart

For any other degrees: Developed length = 0.01744 × radius × degrees.

107A03.EPS

Additional Resources

This module is intended to be a thorough resource for task training. The following reference works are suggested for further study. These are optional materials for continued education rather than for task training.

Benfield Conduit Bending Manual, 2nd Edition. Overland Park, KS: EC&M Books.

National Electrical Code® Handbook. Quincy, MA: National Fire Protection Association.

Tom Henry's Conduit Bending Package (includes video, book, and bending chart). Winter Park, FL: Code Electrical Classes, Inc.

Figure Credits

Topaz Publications, Inc.   107F02B, 107F03, 107F04B, 107F05, 107F06, 107F08–107F10, 107F16B, 107F17B, 107SA01–107SA04

CONTREN® LEARNING SERIES — USER UPDATE

The NCCER makes every effort to keep these textbooks up-to-date and free of technical errors. We appreciate your help in this process. If you have an idea for improving this textbook, or if you find an error, a typographical mistake, or an inaccuracy in NCCER's Contren® textbooks, please write us, using this form or a photocopy. Be sure to include the exact module number, page number, a detailed description, and the correction, if applicable. Your input will be brought to the attention of the Technical Review Committee. Thank you for your assistance.

Instructors – If you found that additional materials were necessary in order to teach this module effectively, please let us know so that we may include them in the Equipment/Materials list in the Instructor's Guide.

Write: Product Development and Revision
    National Center for Construction Education and Research
    P.O. Box 141104, Gainesville, FL 32614-1104

Fax: 352-334-0932

E-mail: curriculum@nccer.org

Craft _____ Module Name _____

Copyright Date _____ Module Number _____ Page Number(s) _____

Description _____

_____

_____

_____

_____

(Optional) Correction _____

_____

_____

(Optional) Your Name and Address _____

_____

_____

_____

Low-Voltage Cabling

COURSE MAP

This course map shows all of the modules in the first level of the *Electronic Systems Technician* curriculum. The suggested training order begins at the bottom and proceeds up. Skill levels increase as you advance on the course map. The local Training Program Sponsor may adjust the training order.

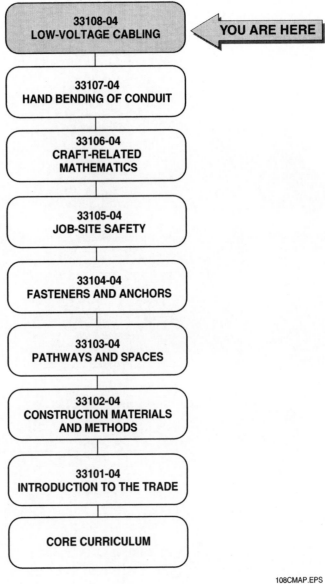

**ELECTRONIC SYSTEMS TECHNICIAN
LEVEL ONE**

33108-04
LOW-VOLTAGE CABLING

YOU ARE HERE

33107-04
HAND BENDING OF CONDUIT

33106-04
CRAFT-RELATED
MATHEMATICS

33105-04
JOB-SITE SAFETY

33104-04
FASTENERS AND ANCHORS

33103-04
PATHWAYS AND SPACES

33102-04
CONSTRUCTION MATERIALS
AND METHODS

33101-04
INTRODUCTION TO THE TRADE

CORE CURRICULUM

108CMAP.EPS

1.0.0 INTRODUCTION 8.1

2.0.0 LOW-VOLTAGE CABLE CONDUCTORS AND INSULATION 8.2

2.1.0 Conductor Wire Size 8.2

2.2.0 Conductor Material 8.2

2.3.0 Insulation 8.3

2.4.0 Conductor Voltage Drop 8.3

3.0.0 LOW-VOLTAGE AND OPTICAL FIBER CABLES 8.4

3.1.0 NEC® Classifications and Ratings 8.4

3.2.0 PTLC, Fire Alarm, and Class 2/3 Cable
       Styles and Construction 8.10

3.3.0 Communication Cable Styles and Construction 8.13

3.3.1 Unshielded Twisted-Pair Cable (UTP) 8.13

3.3.2 Unshielded Twisted-Pair Patch Cords 8.14

3.3.3 Undercarpet Telecommunication Cable (UTC) 8.14

3.3.4 Screened Twisted-Pair (ScTP) Cable and Patch Cord 8.15

*3.3.5 Shielded Twisted-Pair (STP) Cable, Enhanced Shielded
       Twisted-Pair (STP-A) Cable, and STP Patch Cord* 8.15

3.3.6 Coaxial Cable 8.16

3.4.0 Optical Fiber Cable 8.18

4.0.0 COMMERCIAL CABLE INSTALLATION 8.20

4.1.0 Fish Tapes 8.20

4.2.0 Power Conduit Fishing Systems .8.21

4.3.0 Wire Grips 8.22

4.4.0 Pull Lines 8.22

4.5.0 Safety Precautions 8.23

4.6.0 Pulling Equipment 8.24

4.7.0 Planning the Installation 8.25

4.7.1 Pulling Location 8.26

4.7.2 Pathway Cable Pull Operations 8.26

4.8.0 Setting Up for Cable Pulling 8.27

4.8.1 Setting Up the Cable Reels or Boxes 8.27

4.8.2 Preparing Conduit Pathways for Cables 8.29

4.8.3 Installing a Pull Line in Conduit or Inner Duct 8.30

4.8.4 Installing a Pull Line in Open Ceilings 8.31

4.8.5 Preparing Cable Ends for Pulling 8.32

4.8.6 Types of Pulling Lines 8.32

4.9.0 Using Cable Pulling Equipment .8.35

4.10.0 Pulling Safety 8.36

4.11.0 Vertical and Horizontal Pathway Cable Pulls 8.36

4.11.1 Vertical Backbone Cable Pulls from the Top Down 8.37

4.11.2 Vertical Backbone Cable Pulls from the Bottom Up 8.39

4.11.3 *Horizontal Backbone Cable Pulls* 8.41

4.11.4 *Optical Fiber Backbone Cable Pulls* .8.45

4.12.0 Horizontal Work Area Cable Pulls .8.47

4.13.0 Conduit Fill for Backbone Cable .8.48

5.0.0 **RESIDENTIAL LOW-VOLTAGE CABLE INSTALLATION** 8.49

5.1.0 Residential Unit Communication/Data Cabling Requirements and Grades .8.49

5.1.1 *Residential Unit Grade 1 Service Cabling* 8.49

5.1.2 *Residential Unit Grade 2 Service Cabling* 8.49

5.1.3 *Residential Unit Communication/Data Cable Types* 8.50

5.2.0 Understanding the Job 8.50

5.3.0 Residential Cable Installation Requirements/Considerations 8.50

5.4.0 Drilling and Fishing Cable in Existing Construction 8.53

6.0.0 **INTERIOR LOW-VOLTAGE CABLING INSTALLATION REQUIREMENTS** 8.53

6.1.0 Class 1 Circuits 8.53

6.1.1 *Conductors of Different Circuits in the Same Cable, Enclosure, or Raceway* 8.53

6.2.0 Class 2 and 3 Circuits 8.54

6.2.1 *Separation of Class 2 and 3 Circuits from Power Circuits* 8.54

6.2.2 *Separation in Hoistways* 8.54

6.2.3 *Separation in Other Applications* .8.54

6.2.4 *Support of Conductors* 8.55

6.2.5 *Installation in Plenums, Risers, Cable Trays, and Hazardous Locations* 8.55

6.3.0 Instrumentation Tray Cable Circuits 8.55

6.4.0 Nonpower-Limited Fire Alarm Circuits 8.55

6.4.1 *Conductors of Different Circuits in the Same Cable, Enclosure, or Raceway* 8.55

6.5.0 Power-Limited Fire Alarm Circuits 8.56

6.5.1 *Separation of Power-Limited Fire Alarm Circuits from Power Circuits* 8.56

6.5.2 *Separation in Hoistways* 8.57

6.5.3 *Separation in Other Applications* .8.57

6.5.4 *Current-Carrying Continuous Line-Type Fire Detectors* 8.57

6.5.5 *Plenums and Risers* 8.57

6.6.0 Optical Fiber Cable 8.57

6.7.0 Hybrid Cable 8.58

6.8.0 Communication Circuits within Buildings 8.58

6.8.1 *Separation of Communication Circuits from Power Circuits* . . .8.58

6.8.2 *Separation in Other Applications* .8.58

6.8.3   Support of Conductors 8.59

6.8.4   Cable Trays 8.59

6.8.5   Plenums and Risers 8.59

6.8.6   Plenums, Risers, and General-Purpose Raceways 8.59

6.9.0   Coaxial CATV Cable Installation within Buildings 8.59

6.9.1   Separation in Raceways and Boxes .8.59

6.9.2   Separation in Other Applications 8.59

6.9.3   Support of Conductors 8.59

6.10.0   Network-Powered Broadband Communication
System Installation within Buildings 8.59

6.10.1   Separation in Raceways and Boxes .8.60

6.10.2   Separation in Other Applications 8.60

6.10.3   Support of Conductors 8.60

7.0.0   TELEPHONE SYSTEMS 8.60

7.1.0   Basic Telephone Operation 8.61

7.2.0   Multiplexing 8.61

7.3.0   Key Systems and Private Branch Exchanges (PBXs) 8.62

7.4.0   Premises Cable 8.63

7.5.0   Installation Standards 8.65

7.5.1   Outside Plant 8.65

7.5.2   Commercial Premises Wiring 8.66

7.5.3   Residence Premises Wiring 8.69

7.6.0   Grounding and Bonding 8.71

8.0.0   ELECTROMAGNETIC INTERFERENCE CONSIDERATIONS 8.72

8.1.0   EMI Guidelines 8.72

SUMMARY 8.73

REVIEW QUESTIONS 8.73

PROFILE IN SUCCESS 8.75

GLOSSARY 8.77

APPENDIX A, Installing Cable in Unfinished Areas
of Commercial Construction 8.79

APPENDIX B, Installing Cable in Residential and Finished
Areas of Commercial Construction 8.83

APPENDIX C, Tool Illustrations and Descriptions 8.91

REFERENCES & ACKNOWLEDGMENTS 8.107

Figures

Figure 1   Wire sizes (enlarged) showing increasing wire
            diameter versus decreasing AWG numbers 8.2

Figure 2   Standard wire gauge 8.2

Figure 3   Permitted communication, Class 2, and
            Class 3 cable substitutions 8.11

Figure 4   Permitted communication and power-limited
            fire alarm cable substitutions 8.11

Figure 5   Permitted optical fiber cable substitutions 8.12

Figure 6   Typical PLTC, fire alarm, and Class 2/3 cables 8.12

Figure 7   Cable with messenger 8.13

Figure 8   Typical UTP cable 8.13

Figure 9   Typical undercarpet cable and support device 8.15

Figure 10   Typical undercarpet ribbon cable 8.15

Figure 11   Typical screened twisted-pair (ScTP) cable 8.16

Figure 12   Typical enhanced shielded twisted-pair
            (STP-A) cable 8.16

Figure 13   Typical shielded coaxial cables 8.17

Figure 14   Typical simplex optical fiber cable 8.19

Figure 15   Single-mode core fiber 8.19

Figure 16   Multi-mode core fiber 8.19

Figure 17   Tight-buffered optical multi-fiber cable 8.20

Figure 18   Loose-tube optical multi-fiber cable 8.20

Figure 19   Fish tape installation 8.21

Figure 20   Power fishing system 8.22

Figure 21   Power fishing system (blower mode) 8.23

Figure 22   Basket grip 8.23

Figure 23   Manual wire puller 8.24

Figure 24   Power puller 8.24

Figure 25   Cable caddy 8.24

Figure 26   Staggered reels for a multiple cable pull 8.25

Figure 27   Cable pulling equipment checklist 8.27

Figure 28   Transporting cable reels 8.27

Figure 29   Proper and improper ways of transporting
            cable reels 8.28

Figure 30   Typical reel stands 8.29

Figure 31   Devices used to inspect, clean, and
            lubricate raceway systems 8.29

Figure 32   Faults that may be detected with
            a conduit mandrel 8.30

Figure 33   Obtaining the greatest possible cable
             sweep in a pull box 8.30

Figure 34   Conduit with inner duct installed 8.30

Figure 35   Types of pistons in common use 8.31

Figure 36   Typical pulling grip and clevis used during
             cable installation 8.33

Figure 37   Rolling hitch knot 8.33

Figure 38   Core hitches 8.34

Figure 39   Connection to optical fiber strength member 8.34

Figure 40   Basic parts of a power cable tugger 8.35

Figure 41   Typical reel brake for cable reel 8.38

Figure 42   Typical bullwheel 8.38

Figure 43   Rolling hitch knot used to snub cable in
             vertical pulls 8.39

Figure 44   Typical support channel with straps 8.39

Figure 45   Power tugger positioned and secured to
             a concrete floor 8.41

Figure 46   Beam clamps and J-hooks .8.42

Figure 47   Typical cable tray pulling arrangement 8.43

Figure 48   Arrangements of cable bullwheels and pulleys 8.43

Figure 49   Support points for right-angle turns and
             existing cable placement 8.44

Figure 50   Typical support points for a cable tray
             vertical offset 8.44

Figure 51   Flexible nonmetallic conduit in wood
             stud construction 8.51

Figure 52   Municipal telephone system 8.62

Figure 53   Frequency division multiplexing 8.63

Figure 54   Two-wire twisted pair circuit 8.64

Figure 55   Two-wire to four-wire hybrid 8.65

Figure 56   Telecommunications room 8.67

Figure 57   Premises wiring 8.68

Figure 58   Combination NID auxiliary disconnect 8.69

Figure 59   Auxiliary disconnect removed 8.70

Figure 60   Backfeed installation 8.70

Figure 61   Looped installation 8.71

Figure 62   Homerun installation 8.71

Figure 63   Plug wiring for residential termination 8.71

Tables

Table 1   Wire Size Selection for Load Current at 12V 8.3

Table 2   Wire Size Selection for Load Current at 24V 8.4

Table 3   Cable Classifications, Ratings, and Usages 8.5–8.10

Table 4   Typical Color Codes for Wire Pairs
            and Binder Groups 8.14

Table 5   Typical Color Codes for UTP Patch Cords 8.15

Table 6   Optical Multi-Fiber Cable Strand Color Code 8.20

Table 7   Cable Pulling Lubricants Suitable for
            Most Applications 8.35

Table 8   Typical Pulling Forces for Various Wraps 8.36

Table 9   Conduit Fill Requirements for Backbone Cable 8.48

Table 10   Residential Grades Versus Services Supported 8.49

Table 11   Entrance Facility Room Size 8.67

Low-Voltage Cabling

Objectives

When you have completed this module, you will be able to do the following:

1. Explain the various sizes and gauges of wire in accordance with the American Wire Gauge (AWG) standards and determine the proper gauge for an application.
2. Read and identify markings on conductors and cables.
3. Describe the different materials from which conductors are made.
4. Describe the different types of conductor insulation.
5. Describe the color coding of insulation.
6. Identify selected NEC® low-voltage cable classifications.
7. Plan and set up for a cable pull.
8. Properly install a pull line for a cable pulling operation.
9. Prepare the ends of conductors for pulling.
10. Safely pull cable through conduit in vertical and horizontal pathways.
11. Wrap, tie, fasten, label, and protect cable, and explain the importance of maintaining the proper slack.
12. Describe the installation of cables in cable trays.
13. Describe and/or demonstrate a residential low-voltage cable installation.
14. State the restrictions imposed by the NEC® on the uses of various types of cable.

Recommended Prerequisites

Core Curriculum; Electronic Systems Technician Level One, Modules 33101-04 through 33107-04

Required Trainee Materials

1. Paper and pencil
2. Appropriate personal protective equipment
3. Copy of the latest edition of the *National Electrical Code®*

1.0.0 ◆ INTRODUCTION

As an electronic systems technician, you will be required to pull various types of cable through conduit and wireways, or run it through walls, over ceilings, and under floors in order to terminate it at desired locations for a particular job. In some instances, you may be required to select the proper type of cabling to be used for the job. This module covers the general procedures for installing cable in residential and commercial structures. It also covers the various types and ratings of common low-voltage cable, as well as optical fiber cable used for nonpower-limited, power-limited, remote control, signaling, fire alarm, and communication circuits.

Manufacturers produce a wide variety of cables that meet the requirements for various types of installations. The cable construction and rating of each manufacturer may differ, even though the cables may meet the classification type established by the NEC® or other standards. The man-

Note: The designations "*National Electrical Code®*" and "*NEC®*," where used in this document, refer to the *National Electrical Code®*, which is a registered trademark of the National Fire Protection Association, Quincy, MA. *All National Electrical Code® (NEC®) references in this module refer to the 2002 edition of the NEC®.*

ufacturer's specifications and installation recommendations must always be followed when selecting or installing cable.

2.0.0 ◆ LOW-VOLTAGE CABLE CONDUCTORS & INSULATION

The term conductor is used two ways. It is usually used to describe individual insulation-covered wires within a cable. It is also used to define the current-carrying material of a wire, either insulated or uninsulated. In this module, it will be used to describe individual insulation-covered wires, unless otherwise stated. Conductors are identified by size and insulation material. The size refers to the physical American Wire Gauge (AWG) size of the current-carrying wire of the conductor.

2.1.0 Conductor Wire Size

The AWG system uses numbers to identify different sizes of drawn, solid wire. The numbers represent the number of progressively smaller dies that the wire must be drawn through to reach a desired size. The larger the number, the smaller the cross-sectional area of the wire (*Figure 1*). The smaller the cross-sectional area, the smaller the current that the wire can conduct. The AWG numbers range from 50 (smallest) to 1; then 0, 00, 000, and 0000 (largest). Low-voltage cable typically contains conductors with solid wire sizes ranging anywhere from No. 26 to No. 12 AWG. Stranded wire of the same gauge as solid wire is somewhat larger in diameter, but has the same cross-sectional conducting material area as its solid counterpart. Unfortunately, its DC resistance per foot is higher and at high data transfer frequencies, stranding can cause up to 20 percent more signal **attenuation**. Most manufacturers mark the size on the insulation jacket. For smaller

size conductors, a standard wire gauge (*Figure 2*) can be used to check the size of the solid wires.

2.2.0 Conductor Material

The standard material used for the current-carrying wire of conductors used in low-voltage cable is annealed (soft) solid copper. In some cases, copper-coated (copper-clad) steel or copper alloys such as cadmium-chromium copper or zirconium copper are used to increase the strength of the conductors. Unfortunately, copper-clad steel or copper alloys have inferior current-carrying ability.

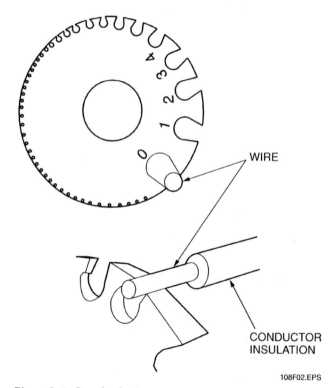

Figure 2 ◆ Standard wire gauge.

| 26 | 24 | 22 | 20 | 18 | 16 | 14 | 12 | 10 | 8 |

108F01.EPS

Figure 1 ◆ Wire sizes (enlarged) showing increasing wire diameter versus decreasing AWG numbers.

2.3.0 Insulation

Thermoplastics are widely used for conductor insulation materials and cable jackets. Some of the most popular and effective types include the following:

- *Polyvinyl chloride (PVC)* – The most common material used for conductor insulation and cable jackets. Available only as non-plenum rated.
- *Polyethylene (PE)* – An excellent weatherproofing material used primarily for insulation of control and communication wiring and for underground cabling.
- *Fluorinated ethylene propylene (FEP) or ethylene chlorotrifluoroethylene (ECTFE)* – Provides better smoke and flame resistance and improved transmission performance for high-performance cable.
- *Cross-linked polyethylene (XLP)* – An improved PE with superior heat and moisture resistance.
- *Nylon* – Primarily used as cable jacketing material.
- *Teflon®* – A high-temperature insulation that is widely used for communication wiring in plenum-rated cable.
- *Rubber compounds* – Typically used for outdoor cabling.
- *Ceramic fiber* – Used for high-temperature applications.
- *Glass bead* – Used for high-temperature applications.

2.4.0 Conductor Voltage Drop

In installations where cabling or wiring for fire alarm circuits or other types of control or communications circuits may be required to supply current over long distances, excessive voltage drop may occur due to the conductor sizes selected. Normally, the maximum voltage drop allowable at the load end of the wiring run should be no more than 3 percent of the source voltage. Either one of the following equations may be used to determine the DC or single-phase AC voltage drop for a specific size of copper conductor:

$$VD = \frac{2 \times L \times K \times I}{CM} \quad or \quad VD = \frac{2 \times L \times R \times I}{1,000}$$

Where:

VD = voltage drop

L = one-way length of wiring run

K = constant for copper (12.9)

I = current in amperes required by the load at the rated source voltage

CM = cross-sectional area of the conductor in circular mils

R = DC resistance of the conductor per 1,000'

For conductors that are No. 18 AWG or larger, the circular mil area or DC resistance of the conductor can be found in tables included in the NEC®.

To select conductors with light loads over long distances at low voltages, load current wire selection tables similar to *Tables 1* and *2* are very common and can save calculation time. The numbers within the 12V or 24V tables at the intersection of various wire lengths and current requirements represent the AWG conductor size that can support the current load with no more than a 3 percent voltage drop.

For example, to select a wire size adequate for a 24V control circuit to a load requiring 1A at 150', refer to *Table 2* and scan down the 1A column to the 150' row. At the intersection of the column and row, note that a No. 16 AWG wire is specified for the stated distance and load.

Table 1 Wire Size Selection for Load Current at 12V

Total One Way Length of Wire Run	¼A	½A	¾A	1A	1¼A	1½A	2A	3A
100'	20	18	16	14	14	12	12	10
150'	18	16	14	12	12	12	10	—
200'	16	14	12	12	10	10	—	—
250'	16	14	12	10	10	10	—	—
300'	16	12	12	10	10	—	—	—
400'	14	12	10	—	—	—	—	—
500'	14	10	10	—	—	—	—	—
750'	12	10	—	—	—	—	—	—
1,000'	10	—	—	—	—	—	—	—
1,500'	10	—	—	—	—	—	—	—

108T01.EPS

Wire Resistance

The resistance of a wire is inversely proportional to its diameter. That is, the smaller the wire, the greater the resistance. AWG 26 wire, for example, has a resistance of about 41 ohms per thousand feet at 68°F. The resistance of AWG 20 wire at the same temperature is about 10 ohms per thousand feet. Stranded wire has roughly 10 percent more resistance than solid wire.

Table 2 Wire Size Selection for Load Current at 24V

Total One Way Length of Wire Run	¼A	½A	¾A	1A	1¼A	1½A	2A	3A
100'	24	20	18	18	16	16	14	12
150'	22	18	16	16	14	14	12	10
200'	20	18	16	14	14	12	12	10
250'	18	16	14	14	12	12	12	10
300'	18	16	14	12	12	12	10	—
400'	18	14	12	12	10	10	—	—
500'	16	14	12	10	10	—	—	—
750'	14	12	10	10	—	—	—	—
1,000'	14	10	10	—	—	—	—	—
1,500'	12	20	—	—	—	—	—	—

108T02.EPS

3.0.0 ◆ LOW-VOLTAGE AND OPTICAL FIBER CABLES

It is necessary to select the proper type and rating of low-voltage and optical fiber cables to meet NEC® safety requirements, local codes, and equipment manufacturer requirements for the system being installed. With the exception of optical fiber or communication cables that enter a structure and are terminated in an enclosure within 50' of the entrance, the NEC® requires that low-voltage and optical fiber cables used for installation be listed and marked with an appropriate classification code. Various styles of cables are available that meet the various classification codes. The NEC® classification codes, along with a description of the typical cable styles available, are provided in the following paragraphs.

3.1.0 NEC® Classifications and Ratings

Low-voltage and optical fiber cables are type-classified, rated, and listed for use in various areas of a structure in accordance with the following:

- *NEC Article 725*, Remote Control, Signaling, and Power-Limited Circuits (Class 1, 2, and 3 Circuits)

- *NEC Article 727*, Instrumentation Tray Cable
- *NEC Article 760*, Fire Alarm Systems
- *NEC Article 770*, Optical Fiber Cables and Raceways
- *NEC Article 780*, Closed-Loop and Programmed Power Distribution
- *NEC Article 800*, Communications Circuits
- *NEC Article 820*, Community Antenna Television and Radio Distribution Systems
- *NEC Article 830*, Network-Powered Broadband Communications Systems

NOTE

NEC Section 800.52(B) requires that abandoned communication cable be removed. Abandoned cable is defined by the NEC® as: *Installed communications cable that is not terminated at both ends at a connector or other equipment and not identified for future use with a tag.* A contractor who undertakes additions or modifications in an existing building must be careful to consider this issue when bidding on a project.

These classifications and ratings are summarized in *Table 3*. All cable conforming to the requirements of the NEC® is normally marked by the cable manufacturer with the appropriate classification code. Cable types listed for each article are arranged in ascending order of fire resistance. This means that any cable within the listing for an NEC® article may be substituted for any cables listed prior to it in the table. For more detail, refer to the latest edition of the NEC®.

Table 3 Cable Classifications, Ratings, and Usages (1 of 6)

NEC® Reference	Cable Type Marking	Listed Voltage Rating	Listed Usage
NEC Article 725	CL2 or CL3	300V	Power-limited Class 2 or 3 cable for general-purpose use except in environmental plenums, risers, and other environmental air spaces. Resistant to the spread of fire.
NEC Article 725	CL2X or CL3X	300V	Power-limited Class 2 or 3 limited-use cable for installation only in dwellings and raceways. Flame-retardant.
NEC Article 725	CL2R or CL3R	300V	Power-limited Class 2 or 3 riser cable suitable for use in vertical shafts or in runs from floor to floor. Resistant to fire to the extent that flames will not be carried from floor to floor.
NEC Article 725	CL2P or CL3P	300V	Power-limited Class 2 or 3 plenum cable suitable for use in environmental plenums and other environmental air spaces. Has good fire resistance and low smoke-producing characteristics.
NEC Article 725	PLTC	300V	Power-limited cable for use in cable trays. Consists of two or more insulated conductors in a nonmetallic jacket that may be covered with a metallic jacket and an additional nonmetallic jacket. Individual insulated conductors can range from No. 22 to No. 12 AWG. Conductor material may be solid or stranded copper. Conductors can be parallel or twisted or a combination of both. They can be individually shielded or shielded as one or more groups or as a combination of both. Class 2 thermocouple extension wire may also be included. Cable resists flame spread, sunlight, and moisture. Can be used in hazardous locations where permitted, direct buried if marked for that use, and as open limited-length wiring in certain industrial applications.
NEC Article 727	(Per **NEC Section 310.11**)	300V	Instrumentation tray cable (ITC) that can be used only in certain industrial applications. Consists of two or more insulated copper and/or thermocouple alloy conductors covered with a nonmetallic sheath or armor. Can be installed in cable trays, raceways, certain hazardous locations, as aerial cable on a messenger, direct buried if marked for that use, and under raised floors if protected. Conductors can range from No. 22 to No. 12 AWG. Shielding is permitted. Cannot be used on circuits operating at more than 150V or more than 5A; No. 22 AWG is limited to 3A.
NEC Article 760	NPLF	600V	Nonpower-limited fire alarm cable suitable for general-purpose use except in plenums, risers, and other environmental air spaces. Resistant to the spread of fire. Insulated solid or stranded copper multi-conductors are No. 18 AWG or larger.

108T03A.EPS

Table 3 Cable Classifications, Ratings, and Usages (2 of 6)

NEC® Reference	Cable Type Marking	Listed Voltage Rating	Listed Usage
NEC Article 760	NPLFR	600V	Nonpower-limited fire alarm riser cable suitable for use in vertical shafts or in runs from floor to floor. Resistant to fire to the extent that flames will not be carried from floor to floor. Insulated solid or stranded copper multi-conductors are No. 18 AWG or larger.
NEC Article 760	NPLFP	600V	Nonpower-limited fire alarm plenum cable suitable for use in plenums and other environmental air spaces. Has good fire resistance and low smoke-producing characteristics. Insulated solid or stranded copper multi-conductors are No. 18 AWG or larger.
NEC Article 760	NFPL-CI NFPLR-CI NFPLP-CI	—	Circuit integrity (CI) marked cable is nonpower-limited fire alarm, fire alarm riser, or fire alarm plenum cable rated for survivability for a specified length of time under fire conditions and used for critical fire alarm signal and/or control circuits.
NEC Article 760	FPL	300V	Power-limited fire alarm cable and/or insulated, continuous, line-type fire detector cable suitable for general-purpose use except in plenums, risers, and other environmental air spaces. Resistant to the spread of fire. Insulated solid or stranded copper multi-conductors are No. 26 AWG or larger. Coaxial cables with 30% conductivity, copper-clad center conductors are also permitted.
NEC Article 760	FPLR	300V	Power-limited fire alarm riser cable and/or insulated, continuous, line-type fire detector cable suitable for use in vertical shafts or in runs from floor to floor. Resistant to fire to the extent that flames will not be carried from floor to floor. Insulated solid or stranded copper multi-conductors are No. 26 AWG or larger. Coaxial cables with 30% conductivity, copper-clad center conductors are also permitted.
NEC Article 760	FPLP	300V	Power-limited fire alarm plenum cable and/or insulated, continuous, line-type fire detector cable suitable for use in plenums and other environmental air spaces. Has good fire resistance and low smoke-producing characteristics. Insulated solid or stranded copper multi-conductors are No. 26 AWG or larger. Coaxial cables with 30% conductivity, copper-clad center conductors are also permitted.
NEC Article 760	FPL-CI FPLR-CI FPLP-CI	300V	Circuit integrity (CI) marked cable is power-limited fire alarm, fire alarm riser, or fire alarm plenum cable or an equivalent line-type fire detector rated for survivability for a specified length of time under fire conditions and used for critical fire alarm signal and/or control circuits.

108T03B.EPS

Table 3 Cable Classifications, Ratings, and Usages (3 of 6)

NEC® Reference	Cable Type Marking	Listed Voltage Rating	Listed Usage
NEC *Article 770*	OFN or OFC	—	Optical fiber nonconductive (N) or conductive (C) cable for general-purpose use except in risers and other environmental air spaces. Consists of one or more optical fibers. Conductive cable uses metallic strength members and/or sheathing. Resistant to the spread of fire. Composite cables containing optical fibers and electrical conductors permitted, but must be listed as the appropriate electrical cable type. May also be installed in undercarpet protective carrier devices.
NEC *Article 770*	OFNG or OFCG	—	Optical fiber nonconductive or conductive cable for general-purpose use except in risers. Consists of one or more optical fibers. Conductive cable uses metallic strength members and/or sheathing. Resistant to the spread of fire. Composite cables containing optical fibers and electrical conductors permitted, but must be listed as the appropriate electrical cable type.
NEC *Article 770*	OFNR or OFCR	—	Optical fiber nonconductive or conductive riser cable suitable for use in vertical shafts or in runs from floor to floor. Resistant to fire to the extent that flames will not be carried from floor to floor. Consists of one or more optical fibers. Conductive cable uses metallic strength members and/or sheathing. Composite cables containing optical fibers and electrical conductors permitted, but must be listed as the appropriate electrical cable type.
NEC *Article 770*	OFNP or OFCP	—	Optical fiber nonconductive or conductive plenum cable suitable for use in plenums and other environmental air spaces. Has good fire resistance and low smoke-producing characteristics. Consists of one or more optical fibers. Conductive cable uses metallic strength members and/or sheathing. Composite cables containing optical fibers and electrical conductors permitted, but must be listed as the appropriate electrical cable type.
NEC *Article 780*	Hybrid cable [Per **NEC** *Section 800.51(I)*]	—	Hybrid cable for closed-loop and programmed power distribution use consisting of power, communications, and/or signaling conductors all in one jacket, with the power conductors separated from the other conductors. An additional optional outer jacket may be used. Individual conductors are marked in accordance with the appropriate listed use. Signaling conductors may be No. 24 AWG or larger and for voltages of 24V or less, currents may not exceed 1A.
NEC *Article 800*	CMUC	300V	Undercarpet communications wire or cable suitable for use under carpets (for walking weight only). Resistant to flame spread. Insulated solid copper conductors are normally used (typically No. 26 to No. 20 AWG). Typically a flat ribbon cable with twisted pairs. Coaxial cable with copper-clad center conductor is also permitted.

108T03C.EPS

Table 3 Cable Classifications, Ratings, and Usages (4 of 6)

NEC® Reference	Cable Type Marking	Listed Voltage Rating	Listed Usage
NEC Article 800	CMX	300V	Limited-use communications cable suitable for use in dwellings and raceways. Resistant to flame spread. Insulated solid copper conductors are normally used (typically No. 26 to No. 18 AWG). Coaxial cables with copper-clad center conductors are also permitted.
NEC Article 800	CM	300V	Communications wire and cable for general-purpose use except in plenums, risers, and other environmental air spaces. Resistant to the spread of fire. Insulated solid copper conductors are normally used (typically No. 26 to No. 18 AWG). Coaxial cables with copper-clad center conductors are also permitted.
NEC Article 800	Hybrid cable [Per *NEC Section 800.51(I)*]	600V	Hybrid cable for power and communications use with conductors all in one jacket, with the power conductors separated from the other conductors. Power cables are Type NM or NM-B and communications cables are Type CM. Hybrid cable is resistant to flame spread.
NEC Article 800	MP	300V	Multi-purpose communications wire or cable for general use except in plenums, risers, and other environmental air spaces. Resistant to the spread of fire. Insulated solid copper conductors are normally used (typically No. 26 to No. 18 AWG). Coaxial cables with copper-clad center conductors are also permitted.
NEC Article 800	CMG	300V	Communications cable for general-purpose use except in plenums, risers, and other environmental air spaces. Resistant to the spread of fire. Insulated solid copper conductors are normally used (typically No. 26 to No. 18 AWG). Coaxial cables with copper-clad center conductors are also permitted.
NEC Article 800	MPG	300V	Multi-purpose cable for general-purpose communications or power-limited fire alarm use. Resistant to the spread of fire. Insulated solid copper conductors are normally used (typically No. 26 to No. 18 AWG). Coaxial cables with copper-clad center conductors are also permitted.
NEC Article 800	CMR	300V	Communications riser cable suitable for use in vertical shafts or in runs from floor to floor. Resistant to fire to the extent that flames will not be carried from floor to floor. Insulated solid copper conductors are normally used (typically No. 26 to No. 18 AWG). Coaxial cables with copper-clad center conductors are also permitted.
NEC Article 800	MPR	300V	Multi-purpose riser cable for communications or power-limited fire alarm use in vertical shafts or in runs from floor to floor. Resistant to fire to the extent that flames will not be carried from floor to floor. Insulated solid copper conductors are normally used (typically No. 26 to No. 18 AWG). Coaxial cables with copper-clad center conductors are also permitted.

108T03D.EPS

Table 3 Cable Classifications, Ratings, and Usages (5 of 6)

NEC® Reference	Cable Type Marking	Listed Voltage Rating	Listed Usage
NEC *Article 800*	MPP	300V	Communications plenum cable suitable for use in plenums and other environmental air spaces. Has good fire resistance and low smoke-producing characteristics. Insulated solid copper conductors are normally used (typically No. 26 to No. 18 AWG). Coaxial cables with copper-clad center conductors are also permitted.
NEC *Article 800*	MPP	300V	Multi-purpose plenum cable for communications or power-limited fire alarm use in environmental plenums and other environmental air spaces. Has good fire resistance and low smoke-producing characteristics. Insulated solid copper conductors are normally used (typically No. 26 to No. 18 AWG). Coaxial cables with copper-clad center conductors are also permitted.
NEC *Article 820*	CATVX	—	Limited-use community antenna television coaxial cable that is suitable for interior use in dwellings and raceways. Resistant to the spread of fire.
NEC *Article 820*	CATV	—	Community antenna television coaxial cable that is suitable for general-purpose interior CATV use except in risers and plenums. Resistant to the spread of fire.
NEC *Article 820*	CATVR	—	Community antenna television coaxial cable suitable for interior use in vertical shafts or in runs from floor to floor. Resistant to fire to the extent that flames will not be carried from floor to floor.
NEC *Article 820*	CATVP	—	Community antenna television coaxial cable suitable for interior use in plenums and other environmental air spaces. Has good fire resistance and low smoke-producing characteristics.
NEC *Article 830*	BMU	300V	Medium-power multimedia network cable rated for circuit voltages up to 150V and 250VA. May consist of a jacketed factory-assembled coaxial cable, a combination of coaxial and individual conductors, or a combination of optical fiber cable and multiple conductors. Type BMU is suitable for underground use.
NEC *Article 830*	BM	300V	Medium-power multimedia network cable rated for circuit voltages up to 150V and 250VA. May consist of a jacketed factory-assembled coaxial cable, a combination of coaxial and individual conductors, or a combination of optical fiber cable and multiple conductors. Type BM is suitable for general-purpose use except in risers and plenums. Resistant to the spread of fire.

108T03E.EPS

Table 3 Cable Classifications, Ratings, and Usages (6 of 6)

NEC® Reference	Cable Type Marking	Listed Voltage Rating	Listed Usage
NEC Article 830	BMR	300V	Medium power, multimedia network cable rated for circuit voltages up to 150V and 250VA. May consist of a jacketed factory-assembled coaxial cable, a combination of coaxial and individual conductors, or a combination of optical fiber cable and multiple conductors. Type BMR is suitable for use in vertical shafts or in runs from floor to floor. Resistant to fire to the extent that flames will not be carried from floor to floor.
NEC Article 830	BLU	300V	Low power, multimedia network cable rated for circuit voltages up to 100V and 250VA. May consist of a jacketed factory-assembled coaxial cable, a combination of coaxial and individual conductors, or a combination of optical fiber cable and multiple conductors. Type BLU is suitable for underground use.
NEC Article 830	BLX	300V	Low power, multimedia network cable rated for circuit voltages up to 100V and 250VA. May consist of a jacketed factory-assembled coaxial cable, a combination of optical fiber cable and multiple conductors. Type BLX is a limited-use cable suitable for use outside, in dwellings, and in raceways. Resistant to flame spread.
NEC Article 830	BLP	300V	Low power, multimedia network cable rated for circuit voltages up to 100V and 250VA. May consist of a jacketed factory-assembled coaxial cable, a combination of coaxial and individual conductors, or a combination of optical fiber cable and multiple conductors. Type BLP cables are suitable for use in risers, plenums, and other environmental air spaces. Has good fire resistance and low-smoke-producing characteristics.

108T03F.EPS

NOTE

NEC Article 310 covers single-conductor power wire used for installation of Class 1 circuits under *NEC Article 725* and nonpower-limited fire alarm circuits under *NEC Article 760*. Both types of circuits shall be installed in accordance with *NEC Chapter 3*. Insulation of single-conductor power wire shall be rated at 600V and shall comply with *NEC Article 310* for sizes larger than No. 16 AWG. For No. 18 and No. 16 AWG, the insulation shall be Type KF-2, KFF-2, PAFF, PF, PFF, PGF, PGFF, PTFF, RFH-2, RFHH-2, RFHH-3, SF-2, SFF-2, TF, TFF, TFFN, TFN, ZF, or ZFF for nonpower-limited fire alarm or Class 1 single-conductor wire. In addition, insulation Type FFH-2, PAF, or PTF is allowed for Class 1 single-conductor wire.

In addition to the cable substitutions allowed within the various cable types for any one classification, cables for other classifications may also be substituted (*Figures 3, 4,* and *5*).

3.2.0 PTLC, Fire Alarm, and Class 2/3 Cable Styles and Construction

Figure 6 shows three types of cable used in PLTC, fire alarm, and Class 2/3 applications. Conductor sizes range from No. 12 to No. 24 AWG, depending on the number of conductors in the cable. Conductors can be tinned or bare, solid or stranded, and twisted or parallel. Shielding, if used, is usually an aluminum-coated Mylar® film with one or more **drain wires** (ground wires) inside a jacket that, along with the conductor insulation, is rated for the applicable usage. To be

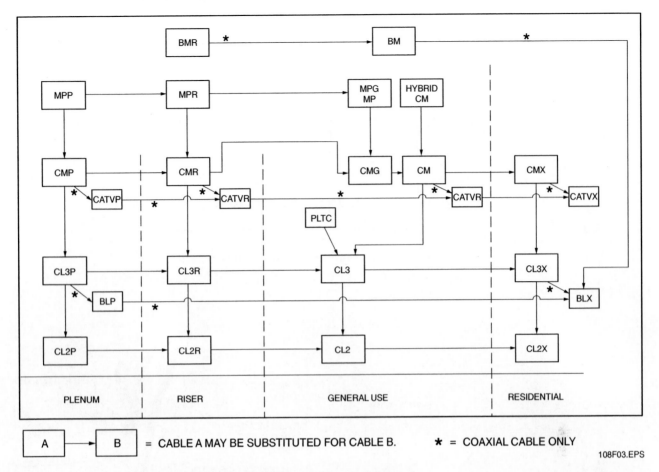

Figure 3 ◆ Permitted communication, Class 2, and Class 3 cable substitutions.

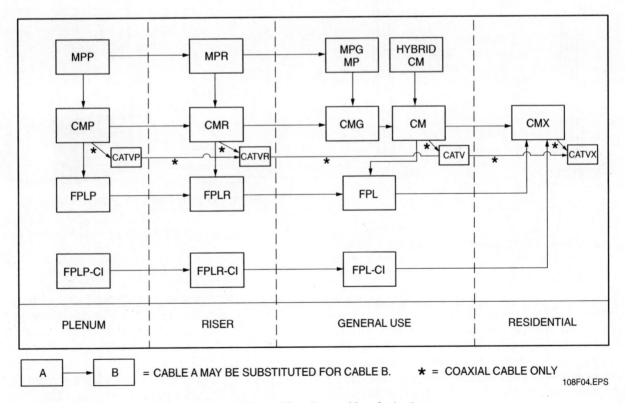

Figure 4 ◆ Permitted communication and power-limited fire alarm cable substitutions.

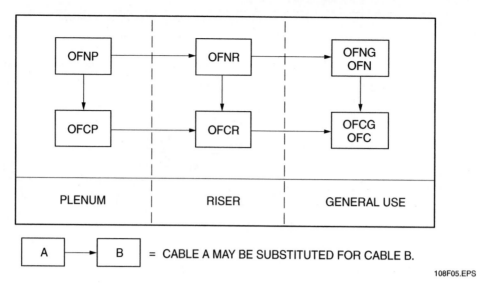

Figure 5 ◆ Permitted optical fiber cable substitutions.

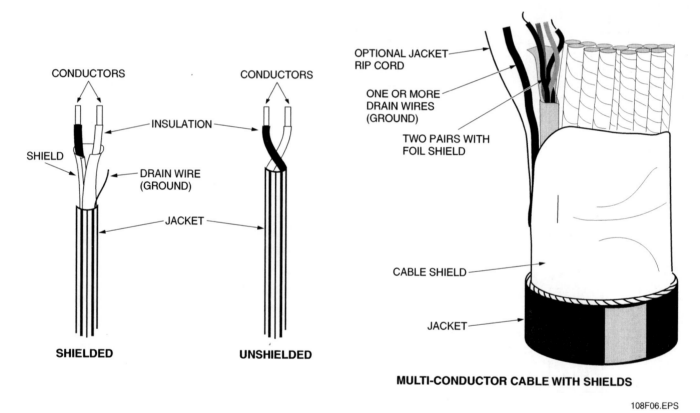

Figure 6 ◆ Typical PLTC, fire alarm, and Class 2/3 cables.

effective, the shielding drain wire(s) must be grounded. The installation loop diagrams or instructions for the system equipment will indicate if all cabling shields are connected together and grounded at only one point, or whether each cable is grounded at both ends or only one end. If only one end is grounded, the drain wire at the other end is folded back and taped to the cable.

This is called floating the ground. If problems ever develop with the drain wire at the other end, the taped drain wire can be untaped and used. Color coding of the conductors is generally dictated by the manufacturer. The outer jackets of fire alarm cable supplied from some manufacturers may be colored red to identify the cable as a fire alarm circuit cable.

3.3.0 Communication Cable Styles and Construction

Some of the communication cables (*ANSI/TIA/EIA-568B* and *EIA-570*) described in the following paragraphs are available with jackets/conductors that are labeled by the manufacturer with feet and/or inch markings to help with the installation of the cable/conductor. In other cases, the cables are available and marked for use as direct-buried cable or for use as aerial cable supported by a steel wire **messenger** (*Figure 7*). Some cables may have thin outer jackets that are color coded (usually yellow) to identify them as communication cable.

3.3.1 Unshielded Twisted-Pair Cable (UTP)

Unshielded **twisted-pair cable** (*Figure 8*) has been used for many years for both voice and data transmission. Currently, it is the most widely used type of cable in these applications. It consists of one to 1,800 pairs of solid copper conductors. The conductors range in size from No. 24 to No. 22 AWG. In cables exceeding 600 pairs, an overall aluminum-steel shield is used to enclose the cable conductors. Each pair of conductors has a nominal **impedance** of 100 ohms (Ω). They are currently available as

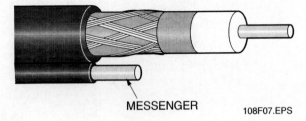

MESSENGER

108F07.EPS

Figure 7 ◆ Cable with messenger.

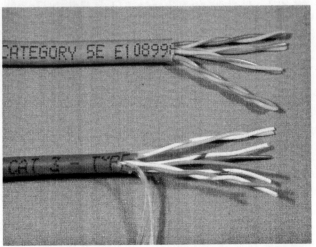

108F08.EPS

Figure 8 ◆ Typical UTP cable.

Category 3 (transmission rates to 16MHz), Category 4 (20MHz), Category 5 or 5e (100MHz), and Category 6 (250MHz) cables. Category 1 and 2 cables, known as Level 1 and Level 2 cables, are not used for new installations; however, they may exist in old Bell System **private branch exchange (PBX)** installations or in residential installations for voice applications. They range from three-wire or four-wire twisted cable (one to two twists per foot) to very large, parallel, multi-pair cables using the old Bell System conductor color codes. They can only be used for analog phone systems.

NOTE

Category 4 and Category 5 are part of the installed base, but are no longer recognized by the standards.

Category 3 cable is the minimum grade acceptable for new installations; however, Category 5e is recommended. When properly installed, Category 5e or higher cable can support high-speed data and multi-media communications.

UTP cable pairs consist of conductors referred to as the tip and ring conductors. The tip conductor is normally connected to a positive DC signal voltage and the ring conductor is connected to the return or negative signal voltage. Originally, these terms came from early telephone systems where operators used **patch cords** to connect calls. The patch cord plug had three conductive portions separated by insulators. The very end of the plug was the tip. This was followed by a ring section that was, in turn, followed by a grounded sleeve section. The original colors used for the tip, ring, and ground (sleeve) wires of telephone equipment were green for the tip (L1), red for the ring (L2), and yellow (G) for the ground. Many old three-wire residential Bell System installations and telephones are wired using this color code. In new communication system installations, only the tip and ring conductors are required.

UTP cable tip and ring conductors are usually identified with the color code shown in *Table 4*, although other codes may be used. This color code uses five colors for the tip conductor: white, red, black, yellow, and violet (in that order). There are up to five pairs for each tip color as defined by five different ring colors: blue, orange, green, brown, and slate (in that order).

The color code allows the definition of up to 25 pairs of conductors in a cable without repeating a color combination. Some manufacturers add a **tracer** to the tip conductor that matches the corresponding ring conductor color to improve pair

Table 4 Typical Color Codes for Wire Pairs and Binder Groups

	Pair		Binder Group	
Number	Tip	Ring	Color	Pair Count
1	White	Blue	White-Blue	001–025
2	White	Orange	White-Orange	026–050
3	White	Green	White-Green	051–075
4	White	Brown	White-Brown	076–100
5	White	Slate	White-Slate	101–125
6	Red	Blue	Red-Blue	126–150
7	Red	Orange	Red-Orange	151–175
8	Red	Green	Red-Green	176–200
9	Red	Brown	Red-Brown	201–225
10	Red	Slate	Red-Slate	226–250
11	Black	Blue	Black-Blue	251–275
12	Black	range	Black-Orange	276–300
13	Black	Green	Black-Green	301–325
14	Black	rown	Black-Brown	326–350
15	Black	Slate	Black-Slate	351–375
16	Yellow	Blue	Yellow-Blue	376–400
17	Yellow	Orange	Yellow-Orange	401–425
18	Yellow	Green	Yellow-Green	426–450
19	Yellow	Brown	Yellow-Brown	451–475
20	Yellow	Slate	Yellow-Slate	476–500
21	Violet	Blue	Violet-Blue	501–525
22	Violet	Orange	Violet-Orange	526–550
23	Violet	Green	Violet-Green	551–575
24	Violet	Brown	Violet-Brown	576–600
25	Violet	Slate	No Binder	n/a

108T04.EPS

identification. For cables with over 25 pairs, each group of 25 pairs up to the 24th group (600 pairs) are wrapped with a color-coded binder tape or thread that identifies the sequential order of each set of 25 pairs, as shown in the table. The last set of 25 has no binder. For some smaller cables (125 pairs or less), only the ring color may be used since the white tip color can be assumed. For cables over 600 pairs, each group of 600 is wrapped with a super-binder. Each super-binder is identified by a tip color in sequential order: 1 to 600 is white, 601 to 1,200 is red, 1,201 to 1,800 is black, etc. Multi-pair UTP cable is generally used for communication system backbone cable. Four-pair UTP cable is employed as horizontal cable for connection to work area outlets. Some manufacturers may use an outer yellow jacket to denote the cable as part of a communication circuit.

3.3.2 Unshielded Twisted-Pair Patch Cords

Unshielded twisted-pair patch cords use four, twisted-pair (100Ω), stranded copper conductors for flexibility and can exhibit up to 20 percent more attenuation than solid conductors. They are usually equipped with 8-position, 8-contact (8P8C) connectors on the ends. The nominal impedance is 100Ω. Typical color coding for UTP patch cords is given in *Table 5*.

3.3.3 Undercarpet Telecommunication Cable (UTC)

Another form of twisted-pair cable is undercarpet telecommunication cable (UTC) (*Figures 9* and *10*). This cable is available up through Category 5 with nominal impedances of 100Ω and can be either:

Table 5 Typical Color Codes for UTP Patch Cords

Pair	Identification	Conductor Color Code – Option 1	Conductor Color Code – Option 2
Pair 1	Tip	White-Blue (W-BL)	Green (G)
	Ring	Blue-White (BL-W)	Red (R)
Pair 2	Tip	White-Orange (W-O)	Black (BK)
	Ring	Orange-White (O-W)	Yellow (Y)
Pair 3	Tip	White-Green (W-G)	Blue (BL)
	Ring	Green-White (G-W)	Orange (O)
Pair 4	Tip	White-Brown (W-BR)	Brown (BR)
	Ring	Brown-White (BR-W)	Slate (S)

108T05.EPS

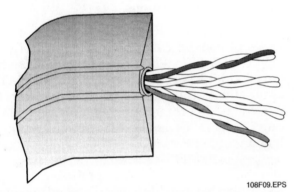

108F09.EPS

Figure 9 ◆ Typical undercarpet cable and support device.

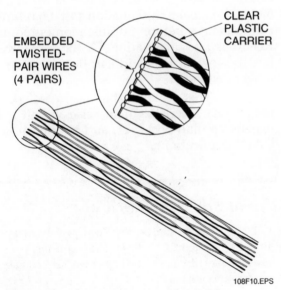

EMBEDDED TWISTED-PAIR WIRES (4 PAIRS)

CLEAR PLASTIC CARRIER

108F10.EPS

Figure 10 ◆ Typical undercarpet ribbon cable.

- Shielded or unshielded, round, twisted, four-pair cable or coaxial cable enclosed or integrated in a support device
- Shielded or unshielded, twisted, four-pair, flat ribbon cable

Optical fiber cable is also being used as undercarpet cabling. Unfortunately, undercarpet cable is often the last choice for new installations due to its susceptibility to damage, its limited reconfiguration ability, and its aesthetically poor appearance due to witness lines that show through carpeting. However, it does offer an effective solution for difficult renovation jobs. When installing undercarpet cabling, high traffic areas, heavy furniture locations, and undercarpet power cables must be avoided.

3.3.4 Screened Twisted-Pair (ScTP) Cable and Patch Cord

Screened twisted-pair (ScTP) cable (*Figure 11*) provides very good rejection of high-frequency electrical noise and interference. It is more expensive than UTP and, with the exception of the foil shield and a drain wire that must be grounded, is essentially the same as UTP cable. It is available up to and including Category 5e cable. ScTP patch cords with four twisted-pair stranded conductors, along with the shield and drain wire, are also available. Like UTP patch cords, they have up to 20 percent more attenuation than solid conductors.

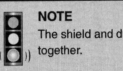

NOTE

The shield and drain wire must not be connected together.

3.3.5 Shielded Twisted-Pair (STP) Cable, Enhanced Shielded Twisted-Pair (STP-A) Cable, and STP Patch Cord

Enhanced shielded twisted-pair (STP-A) cable (*Figure 12*) has two separate foil-shielded twisted pairs and an impedance of 150Ω per pair, with the highest bandwidth (300MHz) of any *ANSI/TIA/EIA-568*

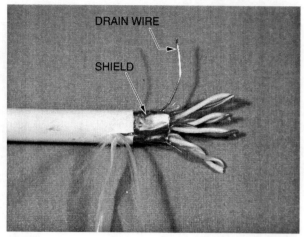

108F11.EPS

Figure 11 ◆ Typical screened twisted-pair (ScTP) cable.

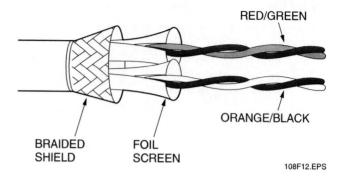

108F12.EPS

Figure 12 ◆ Typical enhanced shielded twisted-pair (STP-A) cable.

approved cable. The foil shields reduce high-frequency interference and provide a positive attenuation-to-**crosstalk** ratio (ACR) throughout the bandwidth. The exterior braid reduces low-frequency interference and provides immunity to other **electromagnetic interference (EMI)**. STP cable has only the exterior braid and a bandwidth of about 16MHz. Conductors for both types are No. 22 AWG solid copper and have a specific color code of green/red for one pair and black/orange for the other pair. STP patch cords use No. 26 AWG stranded copper conductors and exhibit up to 50 percent more attenuation than solid No. 22 AWG conductors. This type of cable is used in high-speed data systems, including **token ring** installations, that do not require more than two pairs.

3.3.6 Coaxial Cable

Figure 13 shows several examples of coaxial cable that are or have been used for data communication. The 50Ω cables are no longer being installed

in data communication systems, but can be found in many audio applications.

- *RG-59, RG-6, and RG-11 coaxial cable* – These types of coaxial cable are used primarily in CATV, video systems, and security systems. Quad-shield is recommended for all CATV applications. These types are available with 60 percent to 95 percent copper or aluminum braid outer shields. Coaxial cable provides a much higher bandwidth and much better protection against EMI than twisted-pair conductors. The aluminum-shielded versions of these cables are less expensive than the copper-braided versions. RG-59, RG-6, and RG-11 cable, also referred to as Series 59, Series 6, and Series 11, respectively, all exhibit the same 75Ω impedance. However, RG-59 has the greatest attenuation and it has limited run distances before amplification is required. RG-6 has less attenuation. Of the three, RG-11 has the lowest loss and can be run for much longer distances.

- *Series 7* – This coaxial cable has higher performance characteristics than Series 6, but is less expensive than Series 11, and is often used in CATV applications.

Bandwidth Characteristics of Twisted-Pair Cable

You have probably heard of Category 3, 4, and 5 cable. What do these designations mean? They refer to the band of frequencies the cable can handle. The categories represent the EIA/TIA-568 standards to which the cables are manufactured. The higher the "Cat" number, the higher the frequency. For example, Cat 3 cable will handle transmissions up to 16MHz, Cat 5 and 5e cables are designed for up to 100MHz, while Cat 6 supports up to 250MHz. The emerging standard for Cat 7 will be 600MHz.

The categories have nothing to do with whether the cables are UTP, STP, or ScTP. In fact, UTP is commonly used unless there is a need to shield the cable because of electronic interference that exists in the operating environment.

Twisted-pair cable is commonly used for telecommunications systems and data networks. It is also used to carry audio in commercial applications.

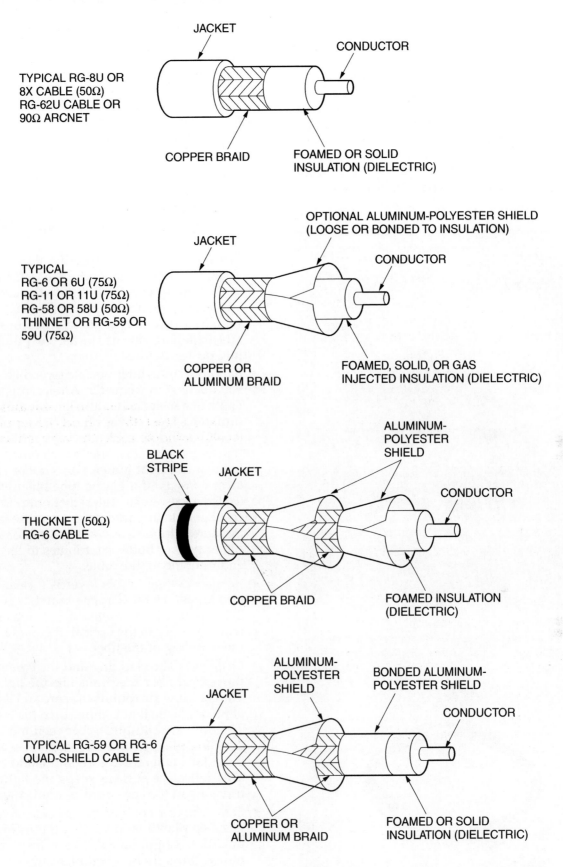

TYPICAL RG-8U OR
8X CABLE (50Ω)
RG-62U CABLE OR
90Ω ARCNET

JACKET

CONDUCTOR

COPPER BRAID

FOAMED OR SOLID
INSULATION (DIELECTRIC)

TYPICAL
RG-6 OR 6U (75Ω)
RG-11 OR 11U (75Ω)
RG-58 OR 58U (50Ω)
THINNET OR RG-59 OR
59U (75Ω)

JACKET

OPTIONAL ALUMINUM-POLYESTER SHIELD
(LOOSE OR BONDED TO INSULATION)

CONDUCTOR

COPPER OR
ALUMINUM BRAID

FOAMED, SOLID, OR GAS
INJECTED INSULATION (DIELECTRIC)

THICKNET (50Ω)
RG-6 CABLE

BLACK
STRIPE

JACKET

ALUMINUM-
POLYESTER
SHIELD

CONDUCTOR

COPPER BRAID

FOAMED INSULATION
(DIELECTRIC)

TYPICAL RG-59 OR RG-6
QUAD-SHIELD CABLE

JACKET

ALUMINUM-
POLYESTER
SHIELD

BONDED ALUMINUM-
POLYESTER SHIELD

CONDUCTOR

COPPER OR
ALUMINUM BRAID

FOAMED OR SOLID
INSULATION (DIELECTRIC)

NOTE: RG-59, RG-6, AND RG-11 CABLES ARE ALSO REFERRED TO AS SERIES 59, SERIES 6, AND
SERIES 11, RESPECTIVELY.

108F13.EPS

Figure 13 ◆ Typical shielded coaxial cables.

- *Special RG-8 (IEEE 802.3 Thicknet) and RG-58 (IEEE 802.3 Thinnet)* – These types of coaxial cable are no longer installed for new data systems. They were used in **thicknet (10 base 5)** and **thinnet (10 base 2)** bus-type networks. RG-8 cable has a maximum segment length of 1,640' (500 m). The maximum segment length for RG-58 cable is 606' (185 m). Cable marked RG-8 or RG-58 should also be marked IEEE 802.3 or either thicknet or thinnet (as applicable) to ensure that the cable is compatible for that use.

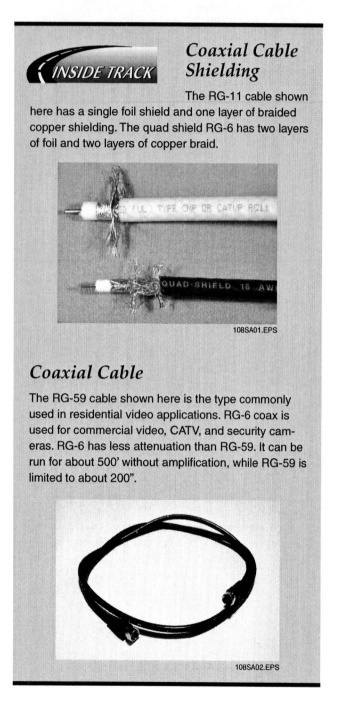

3.4.0 Optical Fiber Cable

Optical fiber cable is used to conduct a light signal instead of an electrical current. *Figure 14* shows a typical simplex (single) optical fiber cable with its optical fiber light conductor and sheathing. The components shown are described below.

- *Jacket* – An outer layer that may be constructed of various types of materials, from flexible metal to soft PVC. The jacket coloring usually identifies one of two types of fiber used inside. Yellow is used for single-mode and orange is commonly used for multi-mode, although other colors are used.

- *Strength member* – Normally, these are non-metallic fiber strands under the jacket that provide strength and flexibility to the cable. They are usually made of aramid (Kevlar®) yarn to which certain types of connectors can be attached. They can also be used to pull the cable into position at installation.

- *Buffer layer* – An intermediate layer that is usually 900 microns in diameter. A micron is one millionth of a meter and is also known a micrometer (μm). This layer can be one of two types, tight or loose. For indoor cable, the layer is a soft plastic that is tight against the layer below it and is known as a tight buffer. For outdoor cable, the layer consists of a plastic tube filled with a gel (called a loose-tube buffer) that protects the optical fiber from impact damage, damage from temperature extremes, or water infiltration damage. Either type of buffer contributes to the strength and flexibility of the cable.

- *Acrylate coating* – This layer is a clear coating, also known as the acrylate buffer, that is about 250 microns in diameter. It provides strength and flexibility to the optical fiber and improves the handling of the fiber.

- *Cladding* – The cladding and the core make up the optical fiber that transmits the light signal. The cladding surrounds the core and is made of glass or plastic that is purer than the core glass. The difference in purity between the core and cladding glass or plastic results in a reflective boundary where the core and cladding meet. This reflective surface keeps the light signals traveling in the core from escaping the core.

- *Core* – This part of the fiber is made of very pure glass or plastic and carries the information-modulated light signals when they are transmitted through the fiber. Light travels through the core as a result of total internal reflection. As the light travels through the core, it is reflected

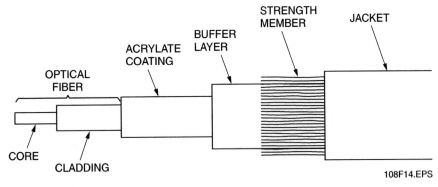

Figure 14 ◆ Typical simplex optical fiber cable.

off the boundary between the core and cladding at a shallow angle that allows the light to continue through the core. Light travels in the core on a path called a mode. The number of modes depends on the core diameter. Fiber is classified as either single-mode or multi-mode fiber. In any installation where optical fiber cables will be joined together, it is essential that cables with the same size core and cladding be used. Joining cables with different cores or cladding will result in unacceptable signal losses.

– Single-mode core fiber (*Figure 15*) has a core diameter of 8 to 9 microns and carries one light wave at a time. The cladding diameter is usually 125 microns. Cable with this type of fiber is usually used for long-distance transmission outdoors up to 9,840' (3,000 m) due to its low loss. The light source for this type of fiber is usually a laser-emitting wavelength of 1,310hm and 1,550hm. The jacket of single-mode core cable is usually yellow.

– Multi-mode core fiber (*Figure 16*) is required to transmit many modes of light at one time down the fiber and, as a result, has a much bigger core than single-mode core cable. The two most common core diameters are 50 microns or 62.5 microns with a cladding diameter of 125 microns. Cables with these fibers are called 50/125µm or 62.5/125µm cables. Core diameters at 100 microns with 140 micron cladding, 200 microns with 230 micron cladding, and others are also available. Multi-mode core cable is typically used only for short distances (under 2 kilometers) because the losses in this type of cable are higher than single-mode core cable. The light source is usually light-emitting diodes (LEDs).

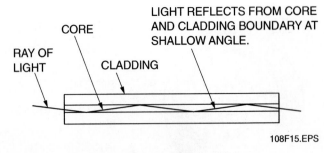

Figure 15 ◆ Single-mode core fiber.

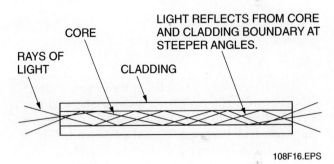

Figure 16 ◆ Multi-mode core fiber.

Like individual fiber cables, optical multi-fiber cable is supplied as tight-buffered (*Figure 17*) or loose-tube (*Figure 18*) cable. The tight-buffered cable is used mostly indoors and the loose-tube cable is normally used outdoors. The gel buffer in loose-tube cable allows the fiber to expand and contract with changes in temperature. It also protects the fiber from any external impact damage to the cable.

Either type of cable can be single-mode or multi-mode fiber. Backbone (riser or plenum) or horizontal cable can be multi-mode or single-mode (the choice depends on the equipment connected to it).

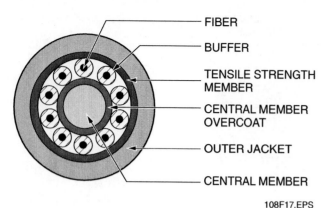

FIBER

BUFFER

TENSILE STRENGTH MEMBER

CENTRAL MEMBER OVERCOAT

OUTER JACKET

CENTRAL MEMBER

108F17.EPS

Figure 17 ◆ Tight-buffered optical multi-fiber cable.

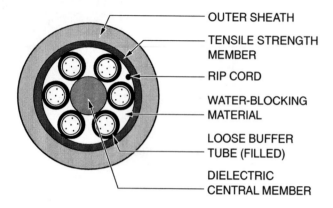

OUTER SHEATH

TENSILE STRENGTH MEMBER

RIP CORD

WATER-BLOCKING MATERIAL

LOOSE BUFFER TUBE (FILLED)

DIELECTRIC CENTRAL MEMBER

108F18.EPS

Figure 18 ◆ Loose-tube optical multi-fiber cable.

Table 6 Optical Multi-Fiber Cable Strand Color Code

Fiber Number	Color
1	Blue
2	Orange
3	Green
4	Brown
5	Slate
6	White
7	Red
8	Black
9	Yellow
10	Violet
11	Rose
12	Aqua
13	Blue/Black Tracer
14	Orange/Black Tracer
15	Green/Black Tracer
16	Brown/Black Tracer
17	Slate/Black Tracer
18	White/Black Tracer
19	Red/Black Tracer
20	Black/Yellow Tracer
21	Yellow/Black Tracer
22	Violet/Black Tracer
23	Rose/Black Tracer
24	Aqua/Black Tracer

108T06.EPS

ANSI/TIA/EIA-598 defines the color coding of optical multi-fiber cable strands, as shown in *Table 6*. If included, strands 13 through 24 are the same as strands 1 through 12 with the addition of a black tracer (except for the black strand, which has a yellow tracer). The tracer may be a dashed or solid line.

4.0.0 ◆ COMMERCIAL CABLE INSTALLATION

Cabling is installed by pulling it through horizontal and vertical pathways, including conduit. A variety of tools and methods are used to pull cable, including **fish tapes** and mechanical pulling equipment. The method selected depends on the amount and weight of the cable. A single cable can be pulled readily through a short run of conduit using a fish tape. A building backbone cable being pulled vertically in a ten-story building will require mechanical pulling equipment.

4.1.0 Fish Tapes

Fish tapes can be made of flexible steel, fiberglass, or nylon and are available in coils of 25' to 200'. It should be kept on a reel to avoid twisting. A fish

UTP *versus* Optical Fiber Cable

A significant advantage of optical fiber cable is its ability to handle much higher data transfer rates than copper media. As the demand for higher speed networks has grown, so has the use of fiber. Another distinct advantage of optical fiber cable is that it is not subject to the same distance limitations as copper.

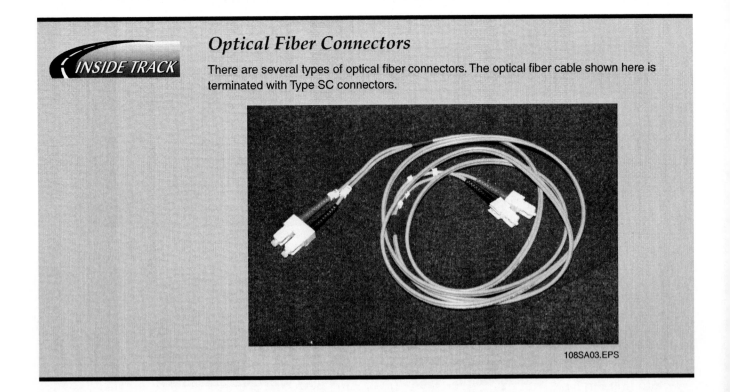
tape has a hook or loop on one end to attach to the conductors to be pulled (*Figure 19*). A broken or damaged fish tape should not be used. To prevent electrical shock, fish tapes should not be used near or in live circuits.

The fish tape is fed through the conduit from its reel. The tape usually enters at one outlet or junction box and is fed through to another outlet or junction box.

4.2.0 Power Conduit Fishing Systems

String lines can be installed by using different types of power fishing systems (*Figure 20*). The power system is similar to an industrial vacuum cleaner and pulls a string or rope attached to a piston-like plug (sometimes called a mouse) through the conduit. Once the string emerges at the opposite end, either the cable or a pull rope is attached and pulled through the conduit manually or with power tools.

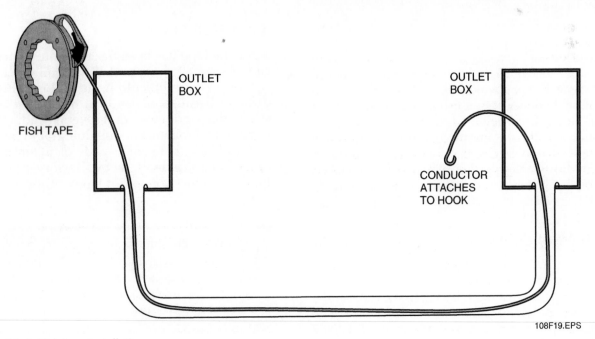

OUTLET BOX

OUTLET BOX

FISH TAPE

CONDUCTOR ATTACHES TO HOOK

108F19.EPS

Figure 19 ◆ Fish tape installation.

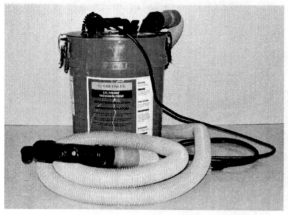

VACUUM/BLOWER UNIT

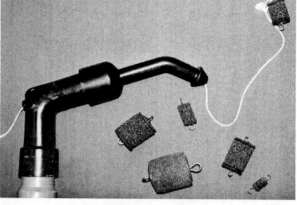

FOAM PLUGS

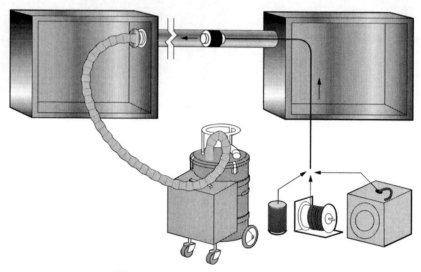

FISHING SYSTEM IN VACUUM MODE

108F20.EPS

Figure 20 ◆ Power fishing system.

The hose connection on these vacuum systems can also be reversed to push the mouse through the conduit as (see *Figure 21*). In other words, the system can either suck or blow the mouse through the conduit, depending on which method is best in a given situation. In either case, a fish tape is then attached to the string for retrieving through the conduit.

Once the string is installed in the conduit run, a fish tape is connected to it and pulled back through the conduit. Cables are then attached to the hooked end of the fish tape or connected to a **basket grip**. In most cases, all required cables are pulled at one time.

4.3.0 Wire Grips

Wire grips are used to attach the cable to the pull tape. One type of wire grip used is a basket grip. A basket grip is a steel mesh basket that slips over the end of a large wire or cable (*Figure 22*). The fish tape hooks onto the end and the pull on the fish tape tightens the basket over the conductor.

4.4.0 Pull Lines

After the tape has been inserted into the conduit run, you must determine if the pull on the wire will be easy or difficult. If the pull is going to be difficult because of bends in the conduit or the size of the conductors, or if several conductors are to be pulled together, a pull line should be used.

A pull line is usually made of nylon or some other fiber. It is made with a factory-spliced eye for easy connection to fish tape or conductors.

 WARNING!

When using pull lines, exercise extreme caution and *never* stand in a direct line with the pulling rope. If the rope breaks, the line will whip back with great force. This can result in serious injury or death.

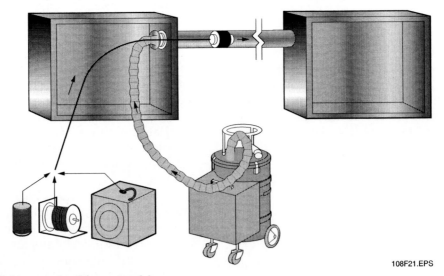

108F21.EPS

Figure 21 ◆ Power fishing system (blower mode).

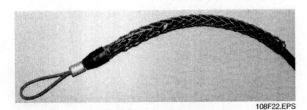

108F22.EPS

Figure 22 ◆ Basket grip.

4.5.0 Safety Precautions

The following are several important safety pre-cautions that will help to reduce the chance of being injured while pulling cable:

- To avoid electrical shock, never use fish tape near or in live circuits. If wires must be pulled into boxes that contain live circuits, use rubber blankets over the exposed live circuitry.

- Read and understand both the operating and safety instructions for the pull system before pulling cable.
- When moving reels of cable, avoid back strain by using your legs to lift (rather than your back) and asking for help with heavy loads. Also, when manually pulling wire, spread your legs to main-tain your balance and do not stretch.
- Select a rope that has a pulling load rating greater than the estimated forces required for the pull.
- Use only low-stretch rope, such as multi-ply and double-braided polyester, for cable pulling. High-stretch ropes store energy much like a stretched rubber band. If the rope, pulling grip, conductors, or other component in the pulling system fails, this potential energy will suddenly be unleashed. The whipping action of a rope can cause consid-erable damage, serious injury, or death.

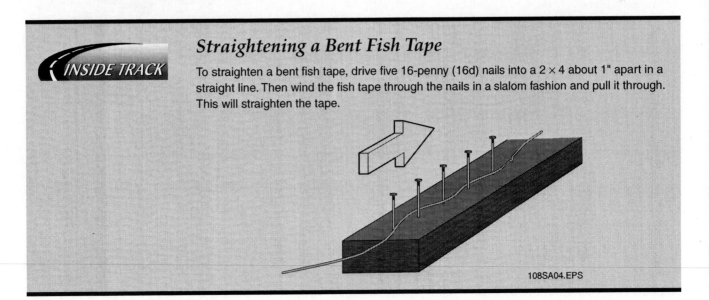

Straightening a Bent Fish Tape

INSIDE TRACK

To straighten a bent fish tape, drive five 16-penny (16d) nails into a 2 × 4 about 1" apart in a straight line. Then wind the fish tape through the nails in a slalom fashion and pull it through. This will straighten the tape.

108SA04.EPS

- Inspect the rope thoroughly before use. Make sure there are no cuts or frays in the rope. Remember, the rope is only as strong as its weakest point.
- When designing the pull, keep the rope confined in conduit wherever possible. Should the rope break or any other part of the pulling system fail, releasing the stored energy in the rope, the confinement in the conduit will work against the whipping action of the rope by playing out much of this energy within the conduit.
- Wrap up the pulling rope after use to prevent others from tripping over it.

4.6.0 Pulling Equipment

Many types of pulling equipment are available to help pull conductors through conduit. Pulling equipment can be operated both manually and electrically. A manually operated puller is used mainly for smaller pulling jobs where hand pulling is not possible or practical (*Figure 23*). It is also used in many locations where hand pulling would put an unnecessary strain on the conductors because of the angle of the pull involved.

Electrically driven power pullers are used where long runs, several bends, or large conductors are involved (*Figure 24*).

The main parts of a power puller are the electric motor, the chain or sprocket drive, the **capstan**, the **sheave**, and the pull line.

The pull line is routed over the sheave to ensure a straight pull. The pull line is wrapped around the capstan two or three times to provide a good grip. The capstan is driven by the electric motor and does the actual pulling. The pull line is unwound by hand at the same speed at which the capstan is

pulling. This eliminates the need for a large spool on the puller to wind the pull line.

Attachments to power pullers, such as special application sheaves and extensions, are available for most pulling jobs. Follow the manufacturer's instructions for setup and operation of the puller.

In all but very short runs, the wires should be lubricated with wire lubricant prior to attempting the pull, and also during the pull. Some of this lubricant should also be applied to the inside of the conduit.

Wire dispensers are helpful for keeping the conductors straight and facilitating the pull. Many different types of wire dispensers are now marketed that handle virtually any spool size. Some of the smaller dispensers can handle up to ten spools of cable; the larger ones can handle a lot more. These dispensers are sometimes called cable caddies or cable trees (*Figure 25*).

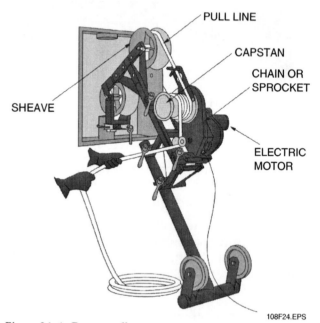

PULL LINE

CAPSTAN

CHAIN OR SPROCKET

SHEAVE

ELECTRIC MOTOR

108F24.EPS

Figure 24 ◆ Power puller.

108F23.EPS

Figure 23 ◆ Manual wire puller.

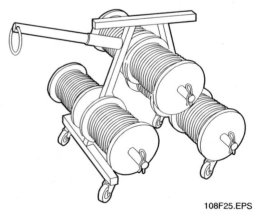

108F25.EPS

Figure 25 ◆ Cable caddy.

4.7.0 Planning the Installation

The importance of planning any wire pulling installation cannot be over-stressed. Proper planning will make the work go easier and much labor will be saved.

Large cables are usually shipped on reels, involving considerable weight and bulk. Consequently, setting up these reels for the pull, measuring cable run lengths, and similar preliminary steps will often involve a relatively large amount of the total cable installation time. Therefore, consideration must be given to reel setup space, proper equipment, and moving the cable reels into place.

Whenever possible, the cables should be pulled directly from the shipping reels without pre-handling them. Usually, this can be done through proper coordination of the ordering of the conductors with the job requirements. Although this requires closely checking the drawings and on-the-job measurements (allowing for extra cable for pull boxes, elbows, troughs, connections, splices, service loops, and outlet service slack), the extra effort is well worth the time.

When the lengths of cable have been established, the length of cable per reel can be ordered so that the total length per reel will be equal to the total of a given number of pathway lengths, and the reel so identified.

The individual cables of the proper length for a given number of runs are reeled separately onto two or more reels at the factory.

With individual cables shipped on separate reels, it is necessary to set up for the same number of reels as the number of conductors to be pulled into a given run, as shown in *Figure 26*. Smaller and/or shorter cables are available on spools or in boxes with up to 1,000' in a box.

Several styles of boxes are used. One is called a pay-out pack and another is called a reel-in-a-box. The reel-in-a-box types can be stacked and the cable is unreeled through a hole in the end of the box. The pay-out packs are used for shorter lengths of cable and cannot be stacked. The cable is dispensed from a large hole in the box, similar to electrical cable. Like electrical cable boxes, this type of box imparts a twist to the cable as the cable is dispensed.

As an extra precaution against error when calculating the lengths of the cables involved, it is a good idea to actually measure all runs with a fish tape before starting the cable pull, adding for makeup to reach the terminations, slack to create service loops at each end, and accounting for discarding the cable underneath the pulling sleeve or pulling wrap, as it will have been excessively stressed during the pull. Check these totals against the totals

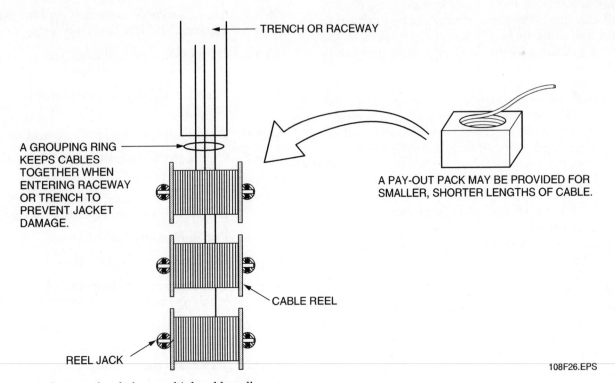

Figure 26 ◆ Staggered reels for a multiple cable pull.

Measuring Tape

A waterproof polyester tape with permanent markings every foot from 0' to 3,000' is available on reels for use in measuring conduit/raceway runs. It can be fished through the run manually or using a power fishing system.

indicated on the reels. Under normal cable delivery schedules, when the pathways have been installed at a relatively early stage of the overall building construction, it may not delay the final completion of the installation to delay ordering the cables until the pathways can actually be measured.

When pulling conductors directly from reels in boxes, care must be taken to ensure that each given run is cut off from the reel so that there is a minimum amount of waste. This is to avoid the possibility that the final run of cable taken from the reel will end up being too short for that run.

4.7.1 Pulling Location

Each job will have to be judged separately as to the best location for pulling setups. The number of setups should be reduced to a minimum in line with the best direction of the pull. For example, it is usually best to pull cables downward rather than up to avoid having to pull the total weight of the cable at the final stages of the pull and also the possibility of injury to workers should the conductors break loose from the pulling line on long vertical pulls. On the other hand, it may not be practical to hoist the cable reels and setup equipment to the upper locations in the building. Also, a separate setup might have to be made at the top of each rise, whereas a single setup might be made at a ground floor pull box location from which several floors are served with the same size and number of cables.

The equipment required depends on the direction of the pull. For instance, if a large cable or a bundle of cables is pulled up vertically or horizontally, a tugger, similar to a winch, may be needed to aid in applying pulling force to a pull line. If pulling down vertically, reel brakes may be needed to prevent the weight of a large, heavy cable or bundle of cables from causing an uncontrolled unreeling of cable called a runaway. Two-way communication devices that allow co-workers to keep each other informed of the pulling progress are essential in every cable pull. Everyone must be alert to inform the person pulling the cable to halt if the cable twists, kinks, or binds in some way.

The location of the pulling equipment determines the number of workers required for the job. For example, a piece of equipment that can be

moved in and set up on the first floor by four workers in an hour's time may require six workers working two hours when set up in the basement or the top floor of a building.

It is a simple operation for a few workers to roll cable reels from a loading platform to a first-floor setup, whereas moving them to upper floors involves much handling and usually requires a crane or other hoists. After the pulling operation is completed, reels, jacks, tuggers, cable brakes, etc. all have to be removed.

4.7.2 Pathway Cable Pull Operations

The following operations are performed in almost all cable pulls with larger sizes of cables:

Step 1 Measure or recheck runs and establish communication between both ends of the pull. Secure the area with barricades and/or caution tape.

Step 2 If needed, set up and anchor pulling equipment and/or reel brakes.

Step 3 Move the cable to the setup point using a cable caddy or by moving reels or boxes.

Step 4 If necessary, move the reel jacks and mandrel to the setup point and mount the reels.

Step 5 Prepare the cable ends and label the cable(s).

Step 6 Install the fish tape, pulling line, or rope.

Step 7 Connect the fish tape, pulling line, or rope to the cable(s).

Step 8 If the cable is being pulled through conduit, lubricate the cable if necessary.

Step 9 Pull and secure the cable(s).

Step 10 Disconnect the pulling line.

Step 11 Create the service loops, label the cable(s) at the reel or box end, and cut the cable(s).

Step 12 Remove the reels or boxes and pulling equipment.

Step 13 Terminate the cables.

Step 14 Check and test.

NOTE

In some instances, the following additional operations are involved, depending upon the exact details of the project. Other items of importance will be discussed later in this module.

- Remove the lagging or other protective covering from the reels.
- Unreel the cable and cut it to length.
- Re-reel the cable for pulling.
- Replace the lagging on the reels.
- Operate auxiliary equipment, such as cable brakes, guide-through cabinets or pull boxes, and signal systems between reel and pulling setups.

EQUIPMENT CHECKLIST

- ❏ PORTABLE ELECTRIC GENERATOR (IF NEEDED)
- ❏ EXTENSION CORDS WITH GFCI
- ❏ WARNING FLAGS, SIGNS, BARRICADES
- ❏ RADIOS OR TELEPHONES
- ❏ GLOVES
- ❏ FISH TAPE OR STRING BLOWER/VACUUM
- ❏ PULL LINE OR ROPES
- ❏ CAPSTAN-TYPE ROPE PULLER
- ❏ SHORT ROPES FOR TEMPORARY TIE-OFFS
- ❏ SWIVELS
- ❏ BASKET-GRIP PULLERS
- ❏ REEL ANCHOR
- ❏ REEL JACKS
- ❏ REEL BRAKES
- ❏ CABLE CUTTERS
- ❏ CABLE-PULLING LUBRICANTS
- ❏ 50' MEASURING TAPE
- ❏ BULLWHEELS
- ❏ PULLEYS
- ❏ TELESCOPING POLE WITH HOOK
- ❏ REMOTE-CONTROLLED TOY

108F27.EPS

Figure 27 ◆ Cable pulling equipment checklist.

Each of the pulling operations is discussed in detail in this module.

4.8.0 Setting Up for Cable Pulling

As mentioned previously, much planning is required for pulling the larger sizes of cables or cable bundles in pathways. There are several preliminary steps required before the actual pull begins.

The proper use of appropriate equipment is crucial to a successful cable installation. The equipment needed for most installations is shown in the checklist in *Figure 27*. Some projects may require all of these items, while others may require only some of them. Each cable pulling project must be taken on an individual basis and analyzed accordingly; seldom will two pulls require identical procedures.

4.8.1 Setting Up the Cable Reels or Boxes

When reels of cable arrive at the job site, it is best to move them directly to the setup location whenever possible. This prevents having to handle the reels more than necessary. However, if this is not practical, arrangements must be made for storage until the cable is needed. The exact method of handling reels of cable depends upon their size and the available tools and equipment.

In many cases, the reels may be rolled to the pulling location by one or more workers. Smaller reels or spools can be mounted on and transported to the setup site on a cable reel transporter, as shown in *Figure 28*.

108F28.EPS

Figure 28 ◆ Transporting cable reels.

Replacing the Hook on a Metal Fish Tape

The hook on a fish tape can be replaced using a propane torch. *IMPORTANT:* Always work in an appropriate environment, and wear the necessary protective equipment.

Hold the fish tape securely in a pair of pliers, heat the end with a propane torch until it softens, then use a second set of pliers to form a hook in the fish tape. Allow it to air cool.

Payout packs or reel-in-a-box containers can be stacked on a pallet and moved by forklift or stacked on a hand truck and manually wheeled to the setup site. For reels up to 24" wide × 40" in diameter, a cable reel transporter can be used to transport the cable reel; it also acts as a dispenser during the pulling operation.

For reels 14" or more in diameter, a crane or similar hoisting apparatus is usually necessary for lifting the reels onto reel jacks supported by jack stands to acquire the necessary height. *Figure 29* shows a summary of proper and improper ways to transport reels of cable on the job site.

ON THE RIMS OF THE SPOOL (MOVING EQUIPMENT DOES NOT COME INTO CONTACT WITH CABLE)

ON THE FLAT SIDE OF THE SPOOL OR ON THE CABLE (MOVING EQUIPMENT COMPRESSES INSULATION AND MAY DAMAGE CABLE)

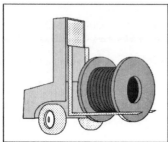
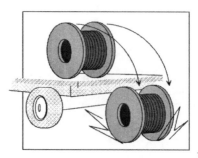
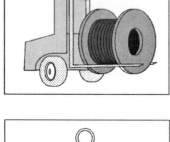

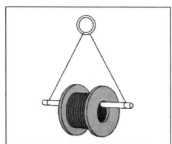

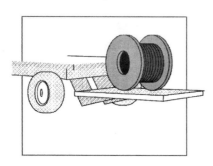
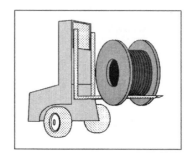
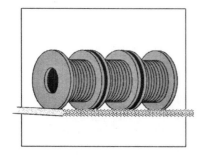

108F29.EPS

Figure 29 ◆ Proper and improper ways of transporting cable reels.

Figure 30 shows several types of reel stands, including the spindle. For a complete setup, two stands and a spindle are required for each reel. The stands are available in various sizes from 13" to 54" high to accommodate reel diameters up to 96". Extension stands used in conjunction with reel stands can accommodate 8", 10", 12", and 14" reels.

Reel-stand spindles are commonly available in diameters from 2⅜" to 3½" and from 59" to 100" in length for carrying reel loads up to 7,500 pounds. However, some heavy-duty spindles are rated for loads up to 15,000 pounds.

4.8.2 Preparing Conduit Pathways for Cables

A preliminary step prior to pulling cables in conduit systems is to inspect the conduit itself. Few things are more frustrating than to pull cables through a conduit and find out when the pull is almost done that the conduit is blocked or damaged. Such a situation usually requires pulling the cables back out, repairing the fault, and starting all over again.

Figure 31 shows several devices used to inspect conduit systems, as well as to prepare the conduit for easier and safer cable pulls. Go and no-go steel and aluminum mandrels are available for pulling through runs of conduit before the cable installation. Mandrels should be approximately 80 percent of the conduit size.

A test pull will detect any hidden obstructions in the conduit prior to the pull. If any are found, they can be corrected before wasting time on an installation that might result in cable damage and the possibility of having to re-pull the cable. See *Figure 32*.

The conduit swab in *Figure 31* can be used to swab out water and debris from the pathway and spread a uniform film of pulling compound inside the conduit for easier pulling.

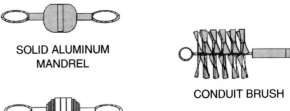

Figure 31 ◆ Devices used to inspect, clean, and lubricate raceway systems.

The conduit brush in *Figure 31* is used to clean and polish the inside of the conduit before the cable is pulled. The brush will remove sand and other light obstructions. Note that this brush has a pulling eye on one end and a threaded rod on the other. The design allows it to be pushed or pulled through the conduit.

One final step before starting the pull is to measure the length of the conduit, including all turns in junction boxes and other devices. A fish tape may be pushed through the conduit system and a piece of tape used to mark the end. When it is pulled back out, a tape measure may be used to measure the exact length. An easier way, however, is to use a power fishing system to push or pull a measuring tape through the conduit run. Details of this operation are explained in the next section.

When measuring the conduit run length, be sure to allow sufficient room where measurements are made through a pull box. Cables should enter and leave pull boxes in such a manner as to allow the greatest possible sweep for the cables. Large cables are especially difficult to bend, but with proper planning, you can simplify the feeding of these cables from one conduit to another.

Figure 30 ◆ Typical reel stands.

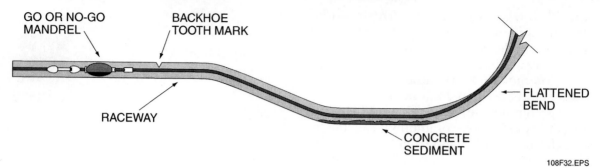

GO OR NO-GO
MANDREL

BACKHOE
TOOTH MARK

FLATTENED
BEND

RACEWAY

CONCRETE
SEDIMENT

108F32.EPS

Figure 32 ◆ Faults that may be detected with a conduit mandrel.

For example, if a conduit run makes a right-angle bend through a pull box, the conduit for a given cable should come into the box at the lower left-hand corner and leave diagonally opposite at the upper right-hand corner, as shown in *Figure 33*. This gives the cable the greatest possible sweep, eliminating sharp bends and consequent damage to the cable insulation.

Runs should also be calculated to allow for terminations, service loops, and end wastage due to pulling.

In some cases, inner duct (*Figure 34*) is installed inside conduit, on cable trays, or other supports to simplify cable pulling for initial cable installations and subsequent additions or alterations. Inner duct is a nonmetallic electrical tubing available in either plenum or nonplenum forms and in a variety of colors used to identify the type of circuits contained within the duct. Basically, red is used for fire protection circuits, blue for power circuits, and yellow for signal and communication circuits. Inner duct is also available with or without pull lines installed.

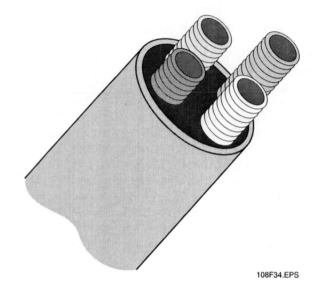

108F34.EPS

Figure 34 ◆ Conduit with inner duct installed.

4.8.3 Installing a Pull Line in Conduit or Inner Duct

At one time, pull-in lines were frequently placed in conduit runs as they were installed. However, in recent times, with modern cable-fishing equipment, this practice is seldom used except in the case of inner duct, where pre-installed pull lines can be ordered.

In conduit or inner duct without pull lines, pull lines or ropes are sometimes manually fished through the conduit using a steel fish tape, but much time can be saved by using a blower/vacuum fish tape system. In general, a **conduit piston**, sometimes referred to as a mouse or missile, is blown with air pressure or vacuumed through the run (*Figure 35*). The foam piston is sized to the conduit and has a loop on both ends. In most cases, **fish line** or measuring tape is attached to the piston as it is blown or vacuumed through the conduit run. The measuring tape serves two purposes: it provides an accurate measurement of the conduit run and the tape is used to pull the cable-draw pulling line or rope into the conduit run. In some cases, if the run is suitable, the pulling line or rope is attached

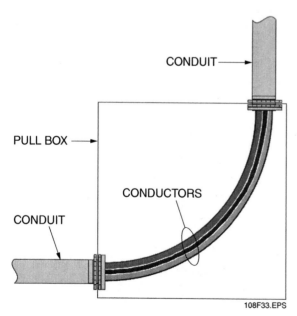

CONDUIT

PULL BOX

CONDUCTORS

CONDUIT

108F33.EPS

Figure 33 ◆ Obtaining the greatest possible cable sweep in a pull box.

A FLEXIBLE FOAM PISTON
PROVIDES AN AIRTIGHT SEAL.

PISTONS ARE AVAILABLE
IN SIZES FROM ½" TO 6".

FINS ARE SOMETIMES UTILIZED
ON PISTONS FOR LARGER SIZES
OF CONDUIT TO KEEP THE PISTONS
FROM TUMBLING.

108F35.EPS

Figure 35 ◆ Types of pistons in common use.

directly to the piston and vacuumed into the run. Most of these units provide enough pressure to clean dirt or water from the conduit during the fishing operation.

WARNING!

Before blowing anything through a conduit, find out what is at the other end of the conduit run. Make sure that no one is looking into or near the other end of the conduit. Also, ensure that no live electrical wiring is in the pull or termination box at the other end of the conduit.

Ensure that the tensile strength of the pulling line or rope is sufficient for the cable run to be pulled. Any rope used must be specially designed so that it does not stretch appreciably under tension and can withstand the friction generated by a power tugger.

There are certain precautions that should be taken when using a power fish tape system:

- Read and understand all instructions and warnings before using the tool.
- Never attempt to fish runs that might contain live power.
- Be prepared for the unexpected. Make sure that your footing and body position are such that you will not lose your balance in any unexpected event.
- Use blower/vacuum systems only for specified light fishing and exploring the pathway system.
- Never use pliers or other devices that are not designed to pull a fish tape. They can kink or nick the tape, creating a weak spot.

4.8.4 Installing a Pull Line in Open Ceilings

Installing cables in open ceilings requires that a pull line be fished across supports or through plenums above the ceiling. Cables may be supported by beam

Cable Blowing

Lightweight cables, especially optical fiber cable, can be floated through conduit using a special high-pressure blower unit.

clamps that hold bridle rings, D-rings, wire hooks, or J-hooks (preferred). The supported cable weight and the distance between the supports must comply with all applicable codes. Ensure that any changes in direction for the cables are gradual enough that the minimum bend radius for the cables is not exceeded. High-performance cables are not normally supported by bridle rings, D-rings, or wire hooks. As an alternative, the cable can be pulled through the structural supports for the floor or ceiling above. If extensive cable will be pulled across open ceilings, cable trays or ladder racks should be installed.

Like conduit pulls, a pull line with adequate tensile strength or a pull tape may be used to pull cable in open ceiling runs. The pull line can be threaded when the supports are installed or it can be threaded over ducts and through supports or plenums using one or more of the following methods:

- Line attached to a rubber ball (tennis ball) and thrown over supports
- Remote-controlled toy
- Telescoping pole (up to 25' long) with a hook to lift the line and place in supports

The use of a telescoping pole reduces the number of ceiling panels that must be removed to place the pull line. Each 90-degree change of direction constitutes a new pull point. A technician must be stationed at each pull point or a pulley must be used to assist in pulling the cable.

4.8.5 Preparing Cable Ends for Pulling

The pulling line or rope must be attached to the cable in such a way that it cannot part from the cable during the pull. Four common methods include:

- Connection by means of a pulling grip or cable basket placed over the cable/cable bundles and taped to the cable/cable bundle to prevent slippage. See *Figure 36*.
- Connection of a pull line or rope to the cable/cable bundle using a rolling hitch knot (*Figure 37*).
- Direct connection with the copper cable conductors (core hitches) of the cable/cable bundle. *Figure 38* shows two different core hitch methods. These methods may not be applicable with some types of high-performance cable.

- For optical fiber cables without pre-installed connectors, connection to the aramid yarn strength member (*Figure 39*).

In some cases, manufacturers can supply large, multi-pair backbone cable with a factory-installed pulling eye.

Most pulling lines or ropes have a **clevis** as an integral component. However, when using pulling grips or baskets, a clevis that is part of the basket is normally used to facilitate connecting the pulling rope to the wire grip. The clevis allows the pulling line or rope on the cable to twist, eliminating any tangling of the rope and cable during the pull.

For high-speed data cable, the pulling tension must not exceed 25 foot-pounds per cable. In these cases, a breakaway clevis or link that is also rated at 25 foot-pounds can be used to protect the cable.

4.8.6 Types of Pulling Lines

The type of pulling line or rope selected will depend mainly on the pulling load, which includes the weight of the cable, the length of the pull, and the total resistance to the pull. For example, Greenlee's **multiplex** cable pulling rope is designed for low-force cable pullers. It has a low stretch characteristic that makes it suitable for pulls up to 2,000 foot-pounds. Lengths are available from 100' to 1,200'. For heavy cable installations, special-purpose rope is recommended because it does not stretch appreciably and can withstand the friction heat generated by a power tugger.

WARNING!

Any equipment associated with the pull must have a working load rating in excess of the force applied during the pull. All equipment must be used and mounted in strict accordance with the manufacturer's instructions.

Care must be used when selecting the proper line or rope for the pull, and then every precaution must be taken to ensure that the cable pulling force does not exceed the rope capacity. Normally, tensile strength ratings are provided on the pull line or rope box by the manufacturer.

Be Sure to Check the Pulling Rope Rating

Many pulling ropes available today are made of synthetic materials designed for pulling by hand or with a winch-type puller. However, friction-type capstan pullers generate a lot of heat, so it is important to make sure the synthetic rope you are using is rated for that use. Otherwise, the rope could melt or fail quickly during capstan slippage.

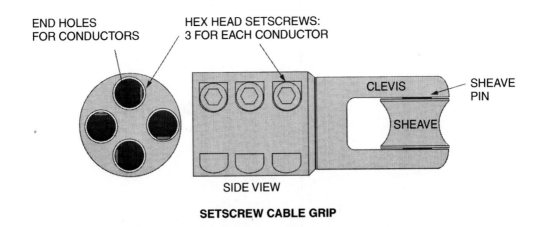

END HOLES
FOR CONDUCTORS

HEX HEAD SETSCREWS:
3 FOR EACH CONDUCTOR

CLEVIS

SHEAVE
PIN

SHEAVE

SIDE VIEW

SETSCREW CABLE GRIP

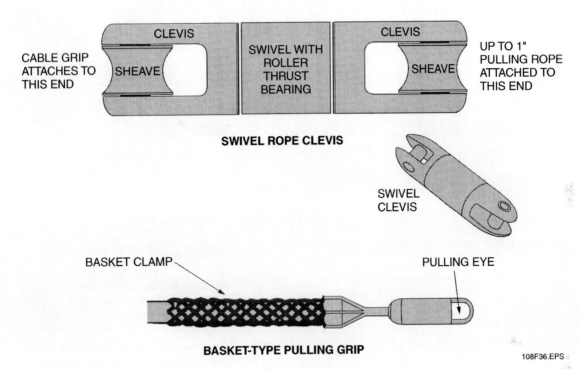

CLEVIS

CABLE GRIP
ATTACHES TO
THIS END

SHEAVE

SWIVEL WITH
ROLLER
THRUST
BEARING

CLEVIS

SHEAVE

UP TO 1"
PULLING ROPE
ATTACHED TO
THIS END

SWIVEL ROPE CLEVIS

SWIVEL
CLEVIS

BASKET CLAMP

PULLING EYE

BASKET-TYPE PULLING GRIP

108F36.EPS

Figure 36 ◆ Typical pulling grip and clevis used during cable installation.

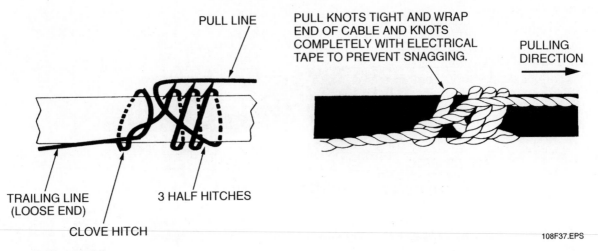

PULL LINE

PULL KNOTS TIGHT AND WRAP
END OF CABLE AND KNOTS
COMPLETELY WITH ELECTRICAL
TAPE TO PREVENT SNAGGING.

PULLING
DIRECTION

TRAILING LINE
(LOOSE END)

3 HALF HITCHES

CLOVE HITCH

108F37.EPS

Figure 37 ◆ Rolling hitch knot.

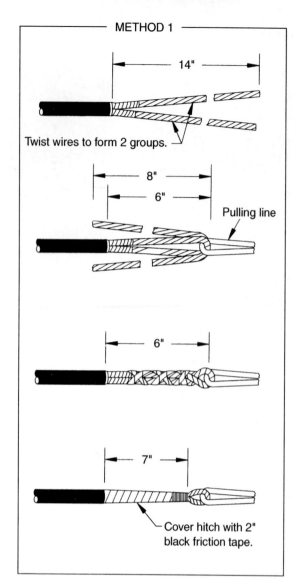

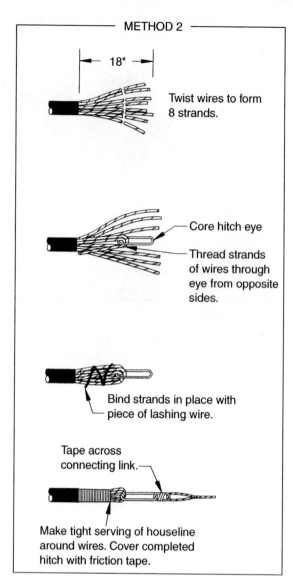

METHOD 1

14"

Twist wires to form 2 groups.

8"

6"

Pulling line

6"

7"

Cover hitch with 2" black friction tape.

METHOD 2

18"

Twist wires to form 8 strands.

Core hitch eye

Thread strands of wires through eye from opposite sides.

Bind strands in place with piece of lashing wire.

Tape across connecting link.

Make tight serving of houseline around wires. Cover completed hitch with friction tape.

NOTE 1: There is a maximum pulling tension for each type of cable. For example, the pulling tension may not exceed 25 pounds on high-speed data cable. Check the manufacturer's instructions for the type of cable you are pulling.

NOTE 2: The methods shown above may not be applicable to certain types of high-performance cable.

108F38.EPS

Figure 38 ◆ Core hitches.

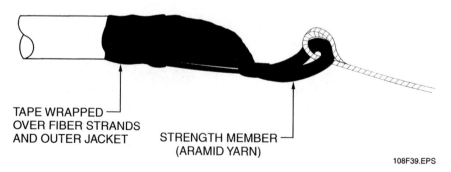

TAPE WRAPPED OVER FIBER STRANDS AND OUTER JACKET

STRENGTH MEMBER (ARAMID YARN)

108F39.EPS

Figure 39 ◆ Connection to optical fiber strength member.

4.9.0 Using Cable Pulling Equipment

Except for short cable pulls, hand-operated or power-operated tuggers or winches are used to furnish the pulling power. In general, cable reels are set in place at one end of the pathway system and the tugger is set up at the opposite end. One end of the previously installed pulling line or rope is attached to a clevis, basket, or the cable. The other end of the rope (at the cable tugger) is wrapped around the rotating drum on the tugger (*Figure 40*).

When pulling in conduit, pulling lubricant—sometimes referred to as **soap**—is inserted into the empty conduit and applied liberally to the front of the cable. One or more operators must be on hand to help feed the cable, while one worker is usually all that is required on the pulling end.

CAUTION

Always use a pulling lubricant that is compatible with the type of cable being pulled. Check with the cable manufacturer for their recommendations and always contact the lubricant manufacturer about the compatibility of their products with specific cables.

Table 7 lists some lubricants suitable for most cable pulls.

The number of wraps on the puller drum decides the amount of force applied to the pull. For example, the operator needs to apply only 10 pounds of force to the pulling rope in all cases.

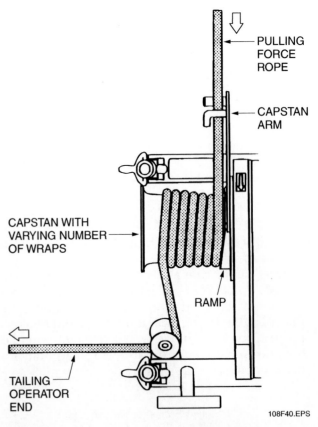

Figure 40 ◆ Basic parts of a power cable tugger.

With this amount of force applied by the operator, and with one wrap around the rotating drum, 21 pounds of pulling force will be applied to the pulling rope; with 2 wraps, it will be 48 pounds; with 3 wraps, it will be 106 pounds; each new wrap roughly doubles the amount of pulling

Table 7 Cable Pulling Lubricants Suitable for Most Applications

Name of Lubricant	Manufacturer
Flaxoap	Murphy-Phoenix, Cleveland, OH
Gel Lube 7/5	Richards Manufacturing, Irvington, NJ
Ivory Snow	Procter & Gamble, Cincinnati, OH
Polywater A, C, G, and J	American Polywater, Stillwater, MN
Quelube	Quelcor, Media, PA
Slip X-300	American Colloid, Skokie, IL
Slipry Loob SWP	Thomas/Jet Line Industries, Matthews, IL
Slipry Loob MWP	Thomas/Jet Line Industries, Matthews, IL
Wire Lube and Aqua Gel	Ideal Industries, Sycamore, IL
Wirepull	MacProducts, Kearney, NJ
Wire-Wax	Minnerallac Electric, Addison, IL
Y-er Eas	Electro Compound, Cleveland, OH
U.S. Gypsum	United States Gypsum, Des Plaines, IL

108T07.EPS

Cable Pulling

force. This principle is known as the capstan theory and it is the same principle that is applied to block-and-tackle hoists.

Table 8 gives the amount of pulling force with various numbers of pull line wraps when the operator applies only 10 foot-pounds of tailing force. Reducing the tailing force reduces the pulling force proportionately (for two wraps, one foot-pound of operator force would produce 4.8 foot-pounds of pulling force).

Table 8 Typical Pulling Forces for Various Wraps

Number of Wraps	Operator Force (foot-pounds)	Pulling Force (foot-pounds)
1	10	21
2	10	48
3	10	106
4	10	233
5	10	512
6	10	1,127
7	10	2,478

108T08.EPS

4.10.0 Pulling Safety

Adhere to the following precautions when using power cable pulling equipment:

- Read and understand all instructions and warnings before using any tool.
- Use compatible equipment (that is, use the properly rated cable puller for the job, along with the proper rope and accessories).
- Always be prepared for the unexpected. Make sure that your footing and body position are such that you will not lose your balance in any unexpected event. Keep out of the direct line of force in case of rope failure.
- Ensure that all cable pulling systems, accessories, and rope have the proper rating for the pull.

- Inspect tools, rope, and accessories before using; replace damaged, missing, or worn parts.
- Personally inspect the cable pulling setup, rope, and accessories before beginning the cable pull. Ensure that all equipment is properly and securely rigged.
- Ensure that all electrical connections are properly grounded and adequate for the load.
- Use cable pulling equipment only in uncluttered areas.

WARNING!

Make absolutely certain that all communication equipment is in working order prior to the pull. Place personnel at strategic points with operable communication equipment to stop and start the pull as conditions warrant. Anyone involved with the pull has the authority to stop the pull at the first sign of danger to personnel or equipment.

4.11.0 Vertical and Horizontal Pathway Cable Pulls

The following paragraphs outline the general methods and precautions for pulling cable in vertical and horizontal pathways.

NOTE

It is extremely important that during the installation of backbone or horizontal cable, adequate service loops for each cable be provided in the equipment room and each telecommunications room to allow for corrections or future changes to the wiring. Service loops for cables entering these rooms should be long enough to reach the farthest corner of the room and, at that corner, also reach from the floor to the ceiling.

Software Programs

CAUTION

When handling, installing, bending, or creating service loops with backbone cable, the minimum bending radius is normally 10 times the diameter of the cable. For high-performance four-pair cable, the minimum bend radius is four times the diameter of the cable. For optical fiber cable, the minimum bend radius can range from 10 to 30 times the diameter, depending on the cable. Manufacturer's recommendations for maximum pulling tensions must also be followed.

WARNING!

Wear goggles, gloves, and a hard hat when pulling cable.

4.11.1 Vertical Backbone Cable Pulls from the Top Down

This is the simplest method of placing backbone cables in vertical pathways because no power pulling equipment is required and long, heavy cables can be readily accommodated. After the cable reels or boxes are positioned and supported at the highest floor and the vertical pathways are determined to be clear, complete the following procedure:

Step 1   Double check the length of the pathways to ensure adequate cable will be available.

NOTE

Communication cable should not be spliced.

Step 2   Ensure that adequate support facilities, such as brackets and clamps, are installed or available on each floor to secure the cable after the pulling is completed. In some open pathways, steel cables are secured to the top and bottom floors, and the communication cables are clamped to the steel cable for support. In this type of system, wire ties that pass through the steel cable strands are used to secure the communication cable every 3' or 4' before the steel cable is put under tension.

Step 3   Set up a reel brake (*Figure 41*).

Step 4   If the weight and length of the cable or cable bundle is excessive, set up a pulley or bullwheel (*Figure 42*) to guide the cable entering the pathway to prevent damage to the cable. Ensure that the pulley or bullwheel is securely fastened to the building structure or to a swing fixture anchored to the floor or building structure.

Step 5   Prepare the end(s) of the cable with an appropriate pulling device if a factory pulling eye has not been installed.

Step 6   As necessary, fish an adequate pull line or rope through the pathway and connect it to the end of the cable to be pulled.

Step 7   Position co-workers with communication devices on each floor to view, aid, and communicate the progress of the descending cable. For additional safety purposes or other purposes on long pulls or with heavy cable, temporary restraining devices for the cable should be installed. One of the most common methods uses sheaves to secure the rope to the building structure. These are attached to the descending cable on every floor or every three or four floors using a rolling hitch knot (*Figure 43*) and are used to **snub** (catch) the descending cable.

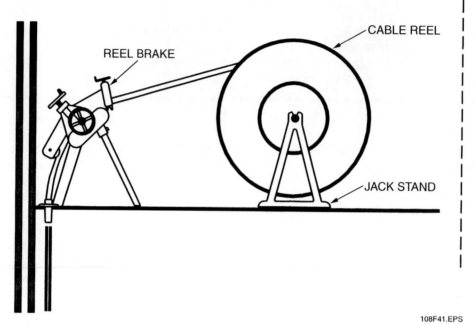

Figure 41 ◆ Typical reel brake for cable reel.

108F41.EPS

 WARNING!

If the cable is very heavy and/or if many floors must be crossed and the accumulated weight of the cable will exceed the tension strength of the cable, the descending cable may have to be lowered in increments of every 4 to 10 floors or so. This can be accomplished by snubbing the cable with a rolling hitch at a selected floor and feeding a certain length of cable out of the pathway onto the floor above. The cable is then snubbed above that floor and the accumulated length is fed down to the lower floors. This process is repeated every 4 to 10 floors until the cable reaches the lowest level desired.

Step 8 Lubricate any sleeves or conduit that the cable will pass through unless inner duct is installed and used.

Step 9 Commence the pull slowly, with co-workers carefully observing the process. Lubricate the cable as needed. When the cable reaches the lowest level, make sure that enough is pulled out to allow termination. Secure the cable at that level with the appropriate clamps or other devices (*Figure 44*). Progressing upward to each floor, pull enough cable down at each floor to create a service loop in the telecommunications room and then secure the cable at that floor.

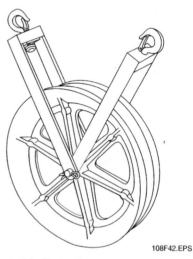

108F42.EPS

Figure 42 ◆ Typical bullwheel.

 NOTE

Another method of securing cable at each floor uses a vertical split mesh grip that is placed around the cable and closed by weaving a pin through the mesh. A ½" (13 mm) steel rod is inserted in the top loop of the grip. The cable is then allowed to slide down until the rod rests on the pathway opening. The mesh grip then tightens, holding the cable. Alternatively, the top loop of the grip can be anchored to the building structure. The cable may also be tied to steel cable that is stretched from the top floor to the bottom floor.

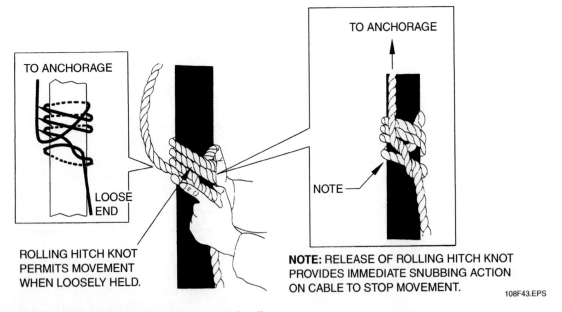

NOTE: RELEASE OF ROLLING HITCH KNOT PROVIDES IMMEDIATE SNUBBING ACTION ON CABLE TO STOP MOVEMENT.

108F43.EPS

Figure 43 ◆ Rolling hitch knot used to snub cable in vertical pulls.

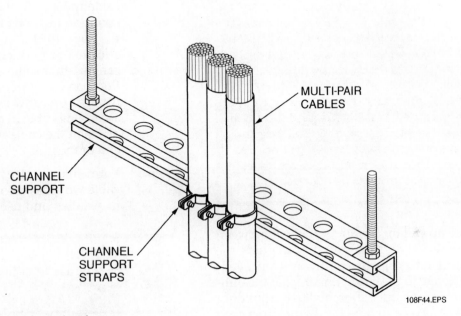

108F44.EPS

Figure 44 ◆ Typical support channel with straps.

Step 10 Label the cable with identification at all appropriate locations. Document the vertical backbone cable information on the building plans/blueprints and cable as follows:

- Type of cable installed
- Origin and termination of each cable
- Conduit (or other pathway) used for each cable
- Application for each cable

4.11.2 Vertical Backbone Cable Pulls from the Bottom Up

This method of placing backbone cables in vertical pathways is more difficult because power pulling equipment is required and long, heavy cables cannot be readily accommodated. After the cable reels or boxes are positioned and supported at the lowest floor and the vertical pathways are determined to be clear, proceed as follows:

Step 1 Double check the length of the pathways to ensure that adequate cable will be available.

NOTE

Communication cable should not be spliced.

Step 2 Ensure that adequate support facilities, such as brackets and clamps, are installed or available on each floor to secure the cable after the pulling is completed. In some open pathways, steel cables are secured to the top and bottom floors and the communication cables are clamped to the steel cable for support. In this type of system, wire ties that pass through the steel cable strands are used to secure the communication cable every 3' or 4' before the steel cable is put under tension.

NOTE

If any multi-pair cable is very heavy and/or if many floors must be crossed and the accumulated weight of the cable will exceed the tension strength of the cable, smaller cable or cable bundles combined with multiple pulls may be required to eliminate the problem. A more time consuming method would be to pull the total amount of the cable required for the vertical pathway (including all required slack) to an intermediate level. The cable would be secured below that level. Then, the power tugger would be moved to the next intermediate level and the process repeated until the top level is reached.

Step 3 Set up pulleys and a bullwheel between the reel(s) and the pathway to guide the cable entering the pathway to prevent damage to the cable. Ensure that the bullwheel is securely fastened to the building structure or to a swing fixture anchored to the floor or building structure.

Step 4 Prepare the end(s) of the cable with an appropriate pulling device if a factory pulling eye has not been installed.

WARNING!

Make sure that the rope used is rated to handle twice the weight of the amount of cable that will be lifted in any one pull.

Step 5 As necessary, fish the appropriate rope through the pathway and connect it to the end(s) of the cable to be pulled.

Step 6 Mount the power tugger securely to the floor at the desired pulling level. If possible, position the tugger far enough from the pathway so that a reasonable amount of slack cable can be pulled into the area (*Figure 45*).

WARNING!

Make sure the power tugger is securely bolted to the floor. If it breaks loose during a heavy cable pull, it may cause severe injury or death, as well as property damage.

Step 7 Position co-workers with communication devices on each floor to view, aid, and communicate the progress of the ascending cable. For safety and other purposes on long upward pulls or with heavy cable, temporary restraining devices for the cable must be installed. One of the most common methods uses sheaves to secure the rope to the building structure. The sheaves are attached to the ascending cable with a rolling hitch knot at the top floor, on every floor, or on every three or four floors and are used to snub the ascending cable in case of pulling failures or when the cable must be secured at the end of the pull.

Step 8 Lubricate any sleeves or conduit that the cable will pass through unless inner duct is installed and used.

CAUTION

Do not exceed the rated pulling tension of the cable.

Step 9 Using the tugger, and with the correct number of capstan wraps, commence the pull slowly, with co-workers carefully observing the process. Lubricate the cable as needed. When the cable reaches the tugger level, ensure that enough cable is pulled out to allow service loops at each floor, plus termination at the top floor. It may be necessary to restrain the cable at the tugger level, disconnect the pulling rope from the cable eye, and reconnect it to the cable with a rolling hitch knot close to the pathway so that additional cable can be drawn into the tugger level. This action must be repeated until an adequate

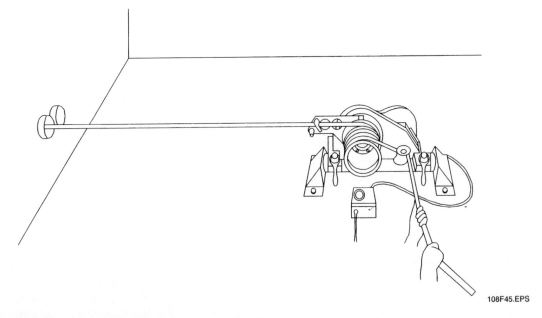

Figure 45 ◆ Power tugger positioned and secured to a concrete floor.

amount of cable is accumulated. When the pulling is complete, restrain the cable at all temporary locations to prevent it from falling.

 CAUTION
Do not allow the cables to wrap around the tugger capstan, as damage to the cables will occur.

Step 10 Secure the cable at the lowest level with the appropriate clamps or other devices. Progressing upward to each floor, lower enough cable at each floor to create a service loop in the telecommunications room and then secure the cable at that floor.

 NOTE
One method of securing cable at each floor uses a vertical split mesh grip that is placed around the cable and closed by weaving a pin through the mesh. A ½" (13 mm) steel rod is inserted in the top loop of the grip. The cable is then allowed to slide down until the rod rests on the pathway opening. The mesh grip then tightens, holding the cable. Alternatively, the top loop of the grip can be anchored to the building structure. The cable may also be tied to steel cable that is stretched from the top floor to the bottom floor.

Step 11 Label the cable with identification at all appropriate locations. Document the vertical backbone cable information on the building plans/blueprints and cable as follows:

- Type of cable installed
- Origin and termination of each cable
- Conduit (or other pathway) used for each cable
- Application for each cable

4.11.3 Horizontal Backbone Cable Pulls

Horizontal backbone cable is normally run between equipment closets. Like bottom-up vertical pulls, horizontal pulls can be difficult because the entire weight of the cable must be dragged over or through the cable supports. Horizontal backbone may be supported by conduit runs with or without inner duct, cable trays, J-hooks and beam clamps, lay-in pathways, or other such devices. *ANSI/TIA/EIA-569-A* guidelines require that horizontal pulls for communication cables be no longer than 98' (30 m) between pull points.

 CAUTION
High-performance cable has a maximum pull tension of 25 foot-pounds. Exceeding this limit can damage the cable.

Guiding and Lubricating Conductors

When guiding conductors into a conduit/raceway during a pull, the conductors may tend to twist, overlap, or become crossed during the pulling operation, especially if fed from boxes instead of reels. Excessive twisting, overlaps, crossovers, etc. can cause binding of the conductors in conduit/raceway turns, create bunching obstructions in the conduit/raceway, and can contribute to insulation burns. Operators at the feeding end of the pull must attempt to keep the conductors as straight as possible during the pulling operation and lubricants should be applied liberally during the pull to allow the conductors to slide against each other and the sides of the run.

Usually, large cables must be placed individually to manage their weight. In no case should different size cables be pulled together. The pulling force required for the larger cable can damage the smaller cable.

In some cases, a power tugger may be required due to the cable weight. After the cable reels or boxes are positioned and supported and the pathways are determined to be clear, proceed as follows:

Step 1   Double check the length of the pathways to ensure adequate cable will be available.

NOTE

Communication cable should not be spliced.

Step 2   If the pathway is open and the cables will be supported by J-hooks or the equivalent, ensure that the spacing of each hook is such that it will support less than 25 foot-pounds of cable weight.

Step 3   Set up pulleys and bullwheels between the reel and the pathway to guide the cable entering the pathway to prevent damage to the cable. Ensure that the bullwheel is securely fastened to the building structure or to a swing fixture anchored to the floor or building structure. On open pathways, it may be desirable or necessary to mount pulleys along the entire path of the cable at locations near the J-hooks or support devices (*Figure 46*) to ease the pulling of the cable and reduce the stress on the cable. Once pulled, the cable can be transferred to the J-hooks or other support devices and the pulleys can be removed. If cable trays are used, use cable rollers, conveyor pulleys, or bullwheels, as shown in *Figures 47* through *50*.

Step 4   Prepare the end(s) of the cable with an appropriate pulling device if a factory pulling eye has not been installed.

WARNING!

Make sure that an appropriate rope is used and that it is rated to handle the weight of the cable that will be pulled.

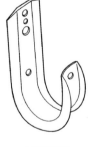

BEAM CLAMP   J-HOOK   SUPPORT RING (BRIDLE)

(NOT USED FOR HIGH-PERFORMANCE CABLE)

108F46.EPS

Figure 46 ◆ Beam clamps and J-hooks.

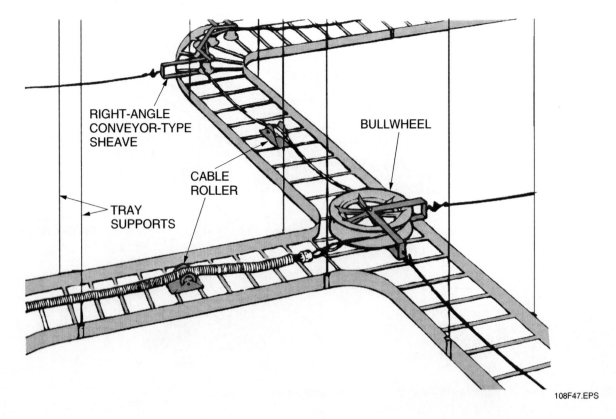

RIGHT-ANGLE
CONVEYOR-TYPE
SHEAVE

BULLWHEEL

CABLE
ROLLER

TRAY
SUPPORTS

108F47.EPS

Figure 47 ◆ Typical cable tray pulling arrangement.

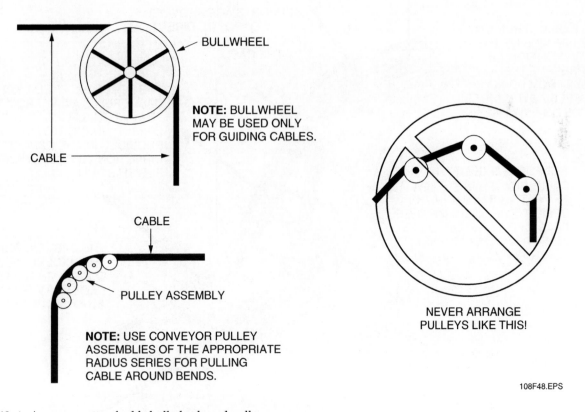

BULLWHEEL

NOTE: BULLWHEEL
MAY BE USED ONLY
FOR GUIDING CABLES.

CABLE

CABLE

PULLEY ASSEMBLY

NOTE: USE CONVEYOR PULLEY
ASSEMBLIES OF THE APPROPRIATE
RADIUS SERIES FOR PULLING
CABLE AROUND BENDS.

NEVER ARRANGE
PULLEYS LIKE THIS!

108F48.EPS

Figure 48 ◆ Arrangements of cable bullwheels and pulleys.

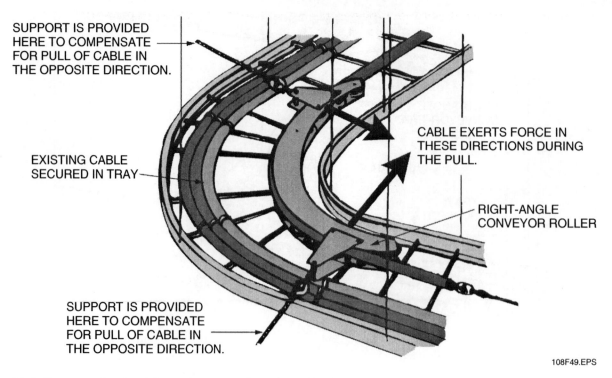

SUPPORT IS PROVIDED HERE TO COMPENSATE FOR PULL OF CABLE IN THE OPPOSITE DIRECTION.

EXISTING CABLE SECURED IN TRAY

CABLE EXERTS FORCE IN THESE DIRECTIONS DURING THE PULL.

RIGHT-ANGLE CONVEYOR ROLLER

SUPPORT IS PROVIDED HERE TO COMPENSATE FOR PULL OF CABLE IN THE OPPOSITE DIRECTION.

108F49.EPS

Figure 49 ◆ Support points for right-angle turns and existing cable placement.

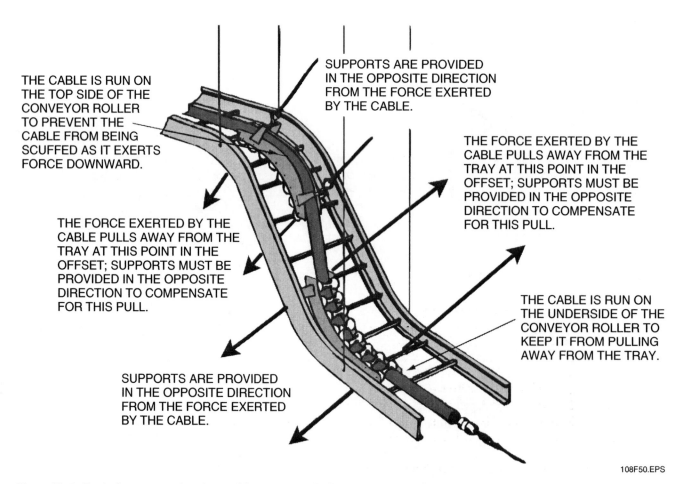

THE CABLE IS RUN ON THE TOP SIDE OF THE CONVEYOR ROLLER TO PREVENT THE CABLE FROM BEING SCUFFED AS IT EXERTS FORCE DOWNWARD.

SUPPORTS ARE PROVIDED IN THE OPPOSITE DIRECTION FROM THE FORCE EXERTED BY THE CABLE.

THE FORCE EXERTED BY THE CABLE PULLS AWAY FROM THE TRAY AT THIS POINT IN THE OFFSET; SUPPORTS MUST BE PROVIDED IN THE OPPOSITE DIRECTION TO COMPENSATE FOR THIS PULL.

THE FORCE EXERTED BY THE CABLE PULLS AWAY FROM THE TRAY AT THIS POINT IN THE OFFSET; SUPPORTS MUST BE PROVIDED IN THE OPPOSITE DIRECTION TO COMPENSATE FOR THIS PULL.

THE CABLE IS RUN ON THE UNDERSIDE OF THE CONVEYOR ROLLER TO KEEP IT FROM PULLING AWAY FROM THE TRAY.

SUPPORTS ARE PROVIDED IN THE OPPOSITE DIRECTION FROM THE FORCE EXERTED BY THE CABLE.

108F50.EPS

Figure 50 ◆ Typical support points for a cable tray vertical offset.

Step 5 As necessary, fish the proper type of rope through the pathway and connect it to the end(s) of the cable to be pulled.

Step 6 If it is required for the pull, mount a power tugger securely to the floor at the desired pulling location. If possible, position the tugger far enough from the pathway so that a reasonable amount of slack cable can be pulled into the area.

WARNING!
Ensure that any power tugger used is securely bolted to the floor. If it breaks loose during a heavy cable pull, it may cause severe injury or death, as well as property damage.

Step 7 Position co-workers with communication devices at the reel end of the pull to view, aid, and relay the progress of the cable.

Step 8 Lubricate any sleeves or conduit that the cable will pass through unless inner duct is installed and used.

Step 9 Commence the pull slowly, with co-workers carefully observing the process. If the cable is being pulled through conduit, lubricate the cable as needed.

CAUTION
Do not exceed the rated pulling tension of the cable.

Step 10 When the cable reaches the tugger (if a tugger is used), make sure enough cable is pulled out to allow the remaining run to the final destination, plus a service loop and termination slack. It may be necessary to secure the cable with a rolling hitch knot and a rope. After the cable is temporarily secured, disconnect the pulling rope from the cable eye and reconnect it to the cable with a rolling hitch knot close to the pathway so that additional cable can be drawn at the tugger location. This action must be repeated until an adequate amount of cable is accumulated. Make sure that the cable is secured at any open support locations. Create service loops in the telecommunications rooms and then secure the cable within the rooms using appropriate clamps, brackets, or ties.

CAUTION
Do not allow the cables to wrap around the tugger capstan, as damage to the cables will occur.

Step 11 Label the cable with identification at all appropriate locations. Document the horizontal backbone cable information on the building plans/blueprints and cable as follows:

- Type of cable installed
- Origin and termination of each cable
- Conduit (or other pathway) used for each cable
- Application for each cable

4.11.4 Optical Fiber Backbone Cable Pulls

Optical fiber cable is generally used as backbone cable. It is usually installed in inner duct, which simplifies the pull. Normally, inner duct is installed in conduit, through sleeves, and on cable trays. However, inner duct can be run in vertical shafts, ducts, plenums, or across open ceilings with appropriate support. If inner duct is installed, make sure that it terminates inside the optical fiber equipment located in the telecommunications room and that it also has a large service loop inside the closet. After the cable reels or boxes are positioned and supported and the pathways are determined to be clear, proceed as follows:

Step 1 Double check the length of the pathways to make sure adequate cable will be available. Verify the continuity of each fiber while the cable is on the reel (cable must be ordered with access to both ends specified.) A light source must be applied to one end and the other end checked for consistent light output.

WARNING!
Never look into the end of a previously installed optical fiber cable. A laser light source that is not visible may be present that can severely damage the retinas of your eyes.

Step 2 If the pathway is open and the cables will be supported by J-hooks or the equivalent, make sure that the spacing of each hook is such that it will support less than 25 foot-pounds of cable weight.

Step 3 Set up pulleys and bullwheels between the reel and the pathway to guide the cable entering the pathway to prevent damage to the cable. Make sure the bullwheel is securely fastened to the building structure or to a swing fixture anchored to the floor or building structure.

Step 4 On open pathways, it may be desirable or necessary to mount pulleys along the entire path of the cable at locations near the J-hooks or support devices to ease the pulling of the cable and reduce the stress on the cable. Once pulled, the cable can be transferred to the J-hooks or other support devices and the pulleys can be removed. If cable trays are used, make sure the inner duct is secured before pulling commences.

Step 5 Prepare the end(s) of the cable with an appropriate pulling device or attach the strength member of the cable to the pull line.

 WARNING!
Ensure that the pull line or rope used is rated to handle the weight of the cable that will be pulled.

Step 6 As necessary, fish a pull line or rope through the pathway and connect it to the end(s) of the cable to be pulled.

Step 7 If it is required for the pull, mount a power tugger securely to the floor at the desired pulling location. If possible, position the tugger so that it is far enough from the pathway so that a reasonable amount of slack cable can be pulled into the area.

 WARNING!
Ensure that any power tugger used is securely bolted to the floor. If it breaks loose during a heavy cable pull, it may cause severe injury or death, as well as property damage.

Step 8 Position co-workers with communication devices at the reel end of the pull and at direction transition points to view, aid, and communicate the progress of the cable. Commence the pull slowly, with co-workers carefully observing the process.

 NOTE
On open pulls, station co-workers at direction transitions so that they can help relieve tension on the cable during the pull.

Step 9 When the cable reaches the tugger (if a tugger is used), make sure enough cable is pulled out to allow the remaining run to the final destination, plus a service loop and termination slack. It may be necessary to secure the cable with a rope and a rolling hitch knot. After temporarily securing the cable, disconnect the pulling rope from the end of the cable and reconnect it to the cable with a rolling hitch knot close to the pathway so that additional cable can be drawn at the tugger location. This action must be repeated until an adequate amount of cable is accumulated.

 CAUTION
Do not exceed the rated pulling tension of the cable. Do not allow the cables to wrap around the tugger capstan, as damage to the cables will occur.

Step 10 Ensure that the cable is secured at any open support locations. If inner duct was not used, create service loops in the telecommunications rooms and then secure the cable within the closets using appropriate clamps, brackets, or ties. Ensure that the clamps, brackets, or ties are not tight against the cable.

Step 11 Anchor all optical fiber cables to the termination cabinet using the strength member of the cable, as specified in the cabinet manufacturer's instructions.

Step 12 Label the cable with identification at all appropriate locations. Document the backbone cable information on the building plans/blueprints and cable as follows:
- Type of cable installed
- Origin and termination of each cable
- Conduit (or other pathway) used for each cable
- Application for each cable

4.12.0 Horizontal Work Area Cable Pulls

Horizontal four-pair cable is normally run between a telecommunications room and each work area outlet on one or more floors. In addition, optical fiber cable may also be run to work area outlets. Sometimes, these types of horizontal pulls can be difficult because they may involve pulling bundles of cables over or through various cable supports. Horizontal work area cable may be supported by conduit runs (with or without inner duct) in walls, floors, and ceilings, or by J-hooks and beam clamps, cable ties, or other such devices, as well as through structural supports in open ceilings. In some cases, a power tugger may be required due to bundled cable weight. After the cable reels or boxes are positioned and supported and the pathways are determined to be clear, proceed as follows:

NOTE
Appendixes A and B provide various alternate procedures for running cable in unfinished commercial or finished commercial and residential areas.

Step 1 Double check the length of the pathways to ensure that adequate cable will be available.

NOTE
Communication cable should not be spliced.

Step 2 If the pathway is open and the cable or cable bundle will be supported by J-hooks or the equivalent, ensure that the spacing of each hook complies with code requirements.

Step 3 If necessary, set up pulleys and bullwheels between the reels or boxes and the pathway to guide the cable entering the pathway to prevent damage to the cable. Make sure the bullwheel is securely fastened to the building structure or to a swing fixture anchored to the floor or building structure.

Step 4 On open pathways, it may be desirable or necessary to mount pulleys along the entire path of the cable at locations near the J-hooks or support devices to ease the pulling of the cable and reduce the stress on the cable. Once pulled, the cable can be transferred to the J-hooks or other support devices and the pulleys can be removed.

Step 5 Identify and label the reels/boxes and then label the end(s) of the cable to be pulled with the corresponding reel identification.

Step 6 Prepare the end(s) of the cable or cable bundle for pulling or, if space permits, apply a rolling hitch knot using the pull line or rope. For optical fiber cable, the strength member is attached to the pull line.

WARNING!
Ensure that the pull line or rope used is rated to handle the weight of the cable that will be pulled.

Step 7 As necessary, fish a pull line or rope through the pathway and connect it to the end(s) of the cable to be pulled. Attach a trailing line to the pull line that can be left for future pulls.

Step 8 If it is required for the pull, mount a power tugger securely to the floor at the desired pulling location. If possible, position the tugger so that it is far enough from the pathway so that a reasonable amount of slack cable can be pulled into the area.

WARNING!
Ensure that any power tugger used is securely bolted to the floor. If it breaks loose during a heavy cable pull, it may cause severe injury or death, as well as property damage.

Step 9 Position co-workers with communication devices at the reel end of the pull to view, aid, and communicate the progress of the cable.

Step 10 Lubricate any conduit that the cable will pass through unless inner duct is installed and used.

CAUTION

Do not exceed the rated pulling tension of the cable.

CAUTION

Do not allow the cables to wrap around the tugger capstan, as damage to the cables will occur.

NOTE

The maximum pulling force for one four-pair No. 24 AWG cable is 25 foot-pounds [110 Newtons (N)]. A breakaway swivel or fishline rated for the maximum pulling force is recommended between the pull line and the cable.

Step 11 Commence the pull slowly, with co-workers carefully observing the process. If the cable is being pulled through conduit, lubricate the cable as needed.

Step 12 When the cable or cable bundle reaches the tugger (if a tugger is used), make sure enough is pulled out to allow the remaining run to the final destinations, plus termination slack. Make sure that the cable or cable bundle is secured at any open support locations. Create large service loops in the telecommunications rooms and then secure the cable within the rooms using appropriate clamps, brackets, or ties.

Step 13 Label the cable with their identification at all appropriate locations before cutting the cable from the reels/boxes. Document the horizontal work area cable information on the building plans/blueprints and cable as follows:

- Type of cable installed
- Origin and termination of each cable
- Conduit (or other pathway) used for each cable
- Application for each cable

Step 14 Apply a temporary label that conforms to the project labeling scheme to each end of all cables. A permanent label must be attached after the cables are terminated.

4.13.0 Conduit Fill for Backbone Cable

ANSI/TIA/EIA-569-A provides fill ratio guidelines for backbone cable installed in conduit. These guidelines (*Table 9*) should be observed when installing cable in conduit, as described in the above procedures. The fill ratios can be increased further by the use of lubricants.

Table 9 Conduit Fill Requirements for Backbone Cable

Conduit			Area of Conduit								Minimum Radius of Bends			
				Maximum Occupancy Recommended										
				AB				CD					E	
Trade Size (in.)	Internal Diameter*		Area = 0.79D² Total 100%		1 Cable, 53% Fill		2 Cables, 31% Fill		3 Cables or More, 40% Fill		Layers of Steel within Sheath		Other Sheath	
	mm	in	mm²	in²	mm²	in²	mm²	in²	mm²	in²	mm	in	mm	in
¾	20.9	0.82	345	0.53	183	0.28	107	0.16	138	0.21	210	8	130	5
1	26.6	1.05	559	0.87	296	0.46	173	0.27	224	0.35	270	11	160	6
1¼	35.1	1.38	973	1.51	516	0.80	302	0.47	389	0.60	350	14	210	8
1½	40.9	1.61	1,322	2.05	701	1.09	410	0.64	529	0.82	410	16	250	10
2	52.5	2.07	2,177	3.39	1,154	1.80	675	1.05	871	1.36	530	21	320	12
2½	62.7	2.47	3,106	4.82	1,646	2.56	963	1.49	1,242	1.93	630	25	630	25
3	77.9	3.07	4,794	7.45	2,541	3.95	1,486	2.31	1,918	2.98	780	31	780	31
3½	90.1	3.55	6,413	9.96	3,399	5.28	1,988	3.09	2,565	3.98	900	36	900	36
4	102.3	4.03	8,268	12.83	4,382	6.80	2,563	3.98	3,307	5.13	1,020	40	1,020	40
5	128.2	5.05	12,984	20.15	6,882	10.68	4,025	6.25	5,194	8.06	1,280	50	1,280	50
6	154.1	6.07	18,760	29.11	9,943	15.43	5,816	9.02	7,504	11.64	1,540	60	1,540	60

*Internal diameters are taken from the manufacturing standard for EMT and rigid metal conduit.

108T09.EPS

These fill requirements do not apply to sleeves, ducts, and straight conduit runs under 50' (15 m) with no bends. The percentage of fill applies to straight runs with offsets equivalent to no more than two 90-degree bends. Column D indicates that conduit bends of ten times the conduit diameter must exist for cable sheaths consisting partly of steel tape. Column E shows that for trade sizes up to 2", conduit bends should be at least six times the conduit diameter. For trade sizes above 2", the bends should be at least ten times the conduit diameter.

5.0.0 ◆ RESIDENTIAL LOW-VOLTAGE CABLE INSTALLATION

For new construction, *ANSI/TIA/EIA Standard 570-A* provides guidelines for the installation of cabling for various types and grades of communication services for single and multi-tenant residential structures. Communication services include telephone, satellite, community antenna television (CATV or cable TV), and other data services such as basic, advanced, or multimedia telecommunications services. Other residential low-voltage systems for fire, security, and automation are normally installed in accordance with the manufacturer's instructions. Low-voltage systems must also be installed in accordance with federal, state, and local codes.

5.1.0 Residential Unit Communication/Data Cabling Requirements and Grades

For any residential unit in a single-tenant or multi-tenant building, the minimum communication outlets recommended by Standard *ANSI/TIA-EIA-570-A* are one outlet location in each of the following residential unit spaces, as applicable:

- Bedrooms (all)
- Family/great room

- Study/den
- Kitchen

Additional outlet locations should be provided within any continuous wall area exceeding 12' (3.7 m) in length and at any point in the space that is 25' (7.6 m) or more horizontally from all other outlets in the space. The outlet heights are determined by local codes.

The level of communication service provided to each of the outlet locations in a residential unit is determined by a standard grading system that defines the telecommunications services (*Table 10*) and cabling infrastructures required for the unit.

5.1.1 Residential Unit Grade 1 Service Cabling

This grade of service provides a generic cabling system that meets the minimum requirements for telecommunications services. Minimum requirements are for one Category 3, four-pair UTP cable and one 75Ω coaxial cable (types meeting *SCTE IPS-SP-001*) at each outlet location. Installation of Category 5e cable in place of Category 3 cable is recommended to enable upgrading to Grade 2 service in the future.

5.1.2 Residential Unit Grade 2 Service Cabling

Grade 2 service provides a generic cabling system that meets the requirements for basic, advanced, and multimedia telecommunications services.

Table 10 Residential Grades Versus Services Supported

Grade	Residential Services Supported			
	Telephone	Data	Television	Multimedia
1	Yes	Yes	Yes	No
2	Yes	Yes	Yes	Yes

108T10.EPS

Minimum requirements are for two Cagetory 5e, four-pair UTP cables and two 75Ω coaxial cables (types meeting *SCTE IPS-SP-001*) at each outlet location. Optionally, installation of one or more dual-optical fiber cables is recommended at each outlet location. Installation of Category 5e cable in place of Category 5 cable is recommended for performance purposes.

5.1.3 Residential Unit Communication/ Data Cable Types

The cable types that can be specified and used for residential unit service are the same as those used for commercial service.

Cable types for outlet cable (horizontal) pathways include the following:

- Four-pair UTP
- RG-59 (Series 59) for patch and equipment cords only
- RG-6 (Series 6) or RG-11 (Series 11) coaxial
- 50/125 mm or 62.5/125 mm multi-mode optical fiber
- Single-mode optical fiber

Cable types for backbone pathways include the following:

- Multi-pair UTP
- RG-59 (Series 59) for patch and equipment cords only
- RG-6 (Series 6) or RG-11 (Series 11) coaxial
- Hard-line **trunk** coaxial
- 50/125 mm or 62.5/125 mm multi-mode optical fiber
- Single-mode optical fiber

5.2.0 Understanding the Job

Because the pathways on a residential job may require onsite planning and layout, the system designer, or the lead electronic systems technician who has been completely briefed on the project, must be present to direct other technicians and see that all the work is done properly. This person must know where each device is going, and what each device is, as well as the appropriate cable from the **head end** (central distribution and/or control equipment) to the devices. This person should also know what equipment comprises the head end and where it is to be located, in addition to any power and ventilation requirements. All dimensions should be known, as well as rough openings for any rack-mounted or other equipment. The head end, whenever possible, should be located somewhere near the center of the building.

This allows the holes that must be drilled for the backbone pathway to be smaller and the cable runs to be shorter.

Once the head end is established, the lead technician and crew must work together to determine the best location for the backbone pathway of the cabling structure. These are the main pathways for all cables leaving the head end. The backbone pathway must be drilled and placed according to all local and national codes, and should be kept well away from power lines/cables; plumbing; and heating, ventilating, air conditioning, and refrigeration (HVACR) equipment.

Special care should be taken to observe the types of construction and materials used on the project and what local and national codes should be applied. Remember that laminated wooden beams cannot be drilled. Also, make sure that other trades do not run their cables through your conduits and holes. Their cables, especially power cables, may cause interference in your system. After the other trades have completed their work and before the finished walls are placed, you should go back to the site and inspect all the cables to make sure none have been damaged. It is also advisable to reinspect at various times throughout the construction process to ensure that the cables and boxes are intact.

5.3.0 Residential Cable Installation Requirements/Considerations

In new construction, horizontal and vertical pathway cable pulls are accomplished in much the same manner as described earlier for commercial installations. In many cases, cable is merely drawn through holes drilled in wood studs, joists, and plates or through pre-punched and bushed holes in metal studs and joists before the walls and ceilings are covered. In other instances, conduit, raceways, ducts, plenums, or sleeves are used as pathways for cable pulls. In a retrofit to existing construction, drilling and fishing of walls, attics, and partitions will be required. Various methods of fishing cable in existing construction are given in detail in *Appendix A*. When installing residential cable, the following requirements and considerations should be observed:

- When working in enclosed attics, be careful not to work too long in high heat. Try to schedule attic work in the morning when it is cool. Be careful not to move too quickly or you may slip off ceiling joists and fall onto or through the drywall ceiling. Walking planks or plywood sheets (¾" thick) should be used on top of joists. To avoid electrocution, do not touch any bare electrical

Coaxial Cable Designations

The RG designations, such as RG-6 and RG-59, that are used for coaxial cable originated many years ago as cable specifications for military applications. These specifications defined the cables in terms of size, construction, and performance. The cables marketed today no longer meet the original specifications, but the designations are still used to represent a type of cable. The terms type and series are used interchangeably with the RG designation.

Home Networks

At the end of 2003 there were an estimated 40 million households with two or more personal computers*. This creates a demand for residential networks that allow residents to share files, video games, and common equipment such as printers. Many newer homes are being built with structured wiring systems. In a structured wiring system, all media enter the home at a common point and radiate from there. Each room contains a single wall jack that has connections for phone, UTP, audio, video, and fiber optics.

So-called smart homes carry this concept further. In a smart home, the occupants can monitor and control appliances, lighting, entertainment, and security systems from a central computer and from remote control devices.

*Source: The Cabling Handbook

108SA05.EPS

---

wires and the box of an electrical fixture at the same time. If the attic has non-covered insulation installed, wear proper respiratory protection and clothing to prevent contact with or inhalation of insulation particles and dust.

- If they are not already installed in new construction, consideration should be given to installing sleeves, metallic or flexible nonmetallic conduits and large boxes (*Figure 51*), cable ducts, or raceways of sufficient size (see *ANSI/TIA/EIA-570-A*) to accommodate future upgrades or expansion of services. This is especially true for multi-tenant structures or large single-family residential units where altering non-ducted concealed pathways cannot be accomplished without considerable expense once the wall and ceiling coverings are in place.

- If conduit and large boxes are not used, the preferred box to use in residential low-voltage new construction is an open-backed box called a mud ring, also known as a dry ring. These

108F51.EPS

Figure 51 ◆ Flexible nonmetallic conduit in wood stud construction.

boxes create a frame for drywall mudding, yet are open to make sure that cables are not bent less than their minimum radius or that wires are not crimped or compressed. Make sure that the mud rings are mounted so that they line up with electrical boxes and are not crooked.

- Underground conduit runs must be planned well in advance. If possible, have any low-voltage conduit runs installed by the electrical contractor in parallel with other conduit. In a retrofit, watch out for other buried pipes and cables. Always have other buried utilities located and marked by a locating company prior to digging. Make sure conduit is large enough to pull cables freely and avoid binding. Never pull new cable over old cable in conduit. Always pull the old cable out after attaching a pulling line and then pull all new cable in. Make sure to use the proper type of cable in the conduit and properly space low-voltage cable from other cables to prevent RFI. As a rule, never run power cables and low-voltage cables in the same conduit.

- Do not drill holes in laminated beams.

- Precautions must be taken to eliminate cable stress caused by pulling. Care should be taken not to deform cables by tightly cinching or clamping or exceeding the minimum bend radius. The bend radius can vary drastically depending on the type of cable used. The minimum bend radius must be observed even when the cable is used inside a junction box or control cabinet. The minimum bend radii for typical cables are as follows:

  - The bend radius for outlet UTP cable shall not be less than four times the cable diameter.
  - The bend radius for one- or two-pair optical fiber cable shall not be less than 1" (25.4 mm) under no load conditions or 2" (50.8 mm) if pulled through pathways under a minimum load of 50 foot-pounds (222N).
  - The bend radius for backbone optical fiber cable shall not be less than 15 times the outside diameter if under tensile loading or 10 times the diameter if unloaded, unless the manufacturer recommends otherwise.
  - The bend radius for coaxial cable shall not be less than 20 times the outside diameter of the cable under tensile load or 10 times the diameter if unloaded, unless the manufacturer recommends otherwise.

- Cables should not be pulled in excess of their maximum rated tensions. Typical tensions for some types of cable are:

  - Series 6 coaxial cable: 35 foot-pounds (150N)
  - Series 11 coaxial cable: 90 foot-pounds (400N)
  - Hardline trunk coaxial cable: refer to the manufacturer's recommendations
  - Four-pair, No. 24 AWG UTP cable: 25 foot-pounds (110N)

- Precautions must be taken to ensure that no drywall screw can reach the cables. If holes are drilled less than 1½" (38.1 mm) from the edge of a stud, steel plates that span the diameter of the hole must be installed on the edge of the stud to prevent drywall screws or nails from being driven into a cable. In addition, cables should be bundled and secured away from the finished wall surface area with the correct fasteners. For instance, metal staples are not acceptable for low-voltage cables. One method is to use cable ties that are fastened to the stud and secured around the cables.

- Cable should be run only on or inside interior walls, partitions, and ceilings to avoid temperature variations that can cause performance problems or damage from siding application.

- Plan ahead when pulling cables. Think about which cables will be pulled before the first pull is started. Pull as many cables as possible at one time. Group the cable reels or boxes together, and label the reels/boxes and associated cable ends. Be careful pulling cables over other existing cables. It is very easy to burn the cable insulation and very difficult to detect this once it has been done. Be careful pulling over sharp objects such as air conditioner vent hangers. Do not pull across attics at an angle. Pull along the sides where the cables will eventually reside. Do not place cables where other workers might trip or step on them. Always route cables along the proper hangers.

- Long runs of cable require the use of larger wire in order to eliminate excessive voltage drop. The amount of voltage drop can be calculated or various tables can be used to determine the required wire size.

- Service loops and slack lengths similar to those required for commercial cabling should be provided in vertical or horizontal residential pathways. Wires should be cut to sufficient length to ensure enough slack for later connection. This is usually between 12" to 18" (304.8 mm to 457.2 mm) but may be more if the connection point is away from the wall (typical for audio equipment). Cable slack must be protected until terminated. This can be accomplished by bagging the slack cable or looping it back into the wall box and loosely fastening it to the box. In some cases, cables may be left behind the walls for later retrieval. In this case, the cables must be properly documented and the use of a photograph for later reference is recommended. Typically, cables are looped in a circle at the side of a stud or rafter and secured out of the way using bundling wire.

- Once installed, all cable runs must be properly labeled and documented on the building plans or drawings as follows:

  - Type of cable installed
  - Origin and termination of each cable
  - Cable wire color code assignments

– Conduit (or other pathway) used for each cable
– Application (use) for each cable

Apply a temporary label that conforms to the project labeling scheme to each end of all cables. Permanent labels must be attached after the cables are terminated. Multiple labels applied at both ends are recommended as a precaution against one of the labels coming off and being lost.

• For non-ducted concealed pathways, consideration should be given to conducting any required or desired field tests before the interior wall or ceiling coverings are installed.

5.4.0 Drilling and Fishing Cable in Existing Construction

In retrofits of existing construction (either commercial or residential), drilling into a blind cavity can produce disastrous results if precautions are not taken to prevent penetrating into various hidden obstacles, such as pipes and electrical wire. The following are general tips and techniques for drilling to accommodate the cabling methods given in *Appendix B*. Always observe proper safety procedures when operating power tools:

• Make sure that you have been properly trained for the tools and accessories to be used.
• Wear proper safety goggles.
• Make sure power cords are not damaged and are approved types.
• Use the right tool and tool bit for the job.

Obstacles are typically located in walls in the following ways:

• Electrical wire is usually located horizontally in walls from receptacle to receptacle at a height of 15" (381 mm) to 24" (609.6 mm) off the floor. Vertical drops for switches are usually stapled to the center of a vertical stud adjacent to the switch box location.
• Water supply lines are usually vertical through plates in the center of stud cavities or are horizontal and located at a height of between 8" (203.2 mm) and 24" (609.6 mm) above the floor.
• Waste and vent lines are usually vertical through stud cavities to the roof or are horizontal and

located at a height of 16" (406.4 mm) to 40" (1.02 m) above the floor.

Do whatever is possible to familiarize yourself with the area to be drilled. Examine the area from above, below, and behind, if possible. Look for obstructions. Whenever possible, use specialized tools to locate studs, pipes, electrical wire, etc. before drilling. For walls, one method is to cut a box hole between the studs with a drywall knife and look inside the wall for obstructions. At the base of the wall, remove the baseboard, then cut a hole to look for obstructions at floor level and to use for drilling through the floor. Holes through the bottom plate (or top plate) of a wall can be drilled using a spade bit, bore bit, or flex bit.

6.0.0 ◆ INTERIOR LOW-VOLTAGE CABLING INSTALLATION REQUIREMENTS

The NEC® specifies requirements for the installation of certain classes of cable in various low-voltage applications in either residential or commercial construction. These requirements are summarized below.

6.1.0 Class 1 Circuits

NEC Section 725.2 defines Class 1 circuits as either power-limited or nonpower-limited remote control and signaling circuits installed between the load side of an overcurrent device or power-limited supply and the connected equipment. **Power-limited circuits** (Class 1) shall have a power supply that is not more than 30V and 1,000VA. **Nonpower-limited circuits** shall not exceed 600V.

Class 1 circuits shall be installed as specified in *NEC Chapter 3*, except as noted in the following paragraphs.

6.1.1 Conductors of Different Circuits in the Same Cable, Enclosure, or Raceway

According to *NEC Section 725.26*, two or more Class 1 circuits can occupy the same cable, enclosure, or raceway, either AC or DC, if all conductors are insulated for the highest voltage of any conductor.

With several exceptions, Class 1 circuits and power supply circuits are only permitted to occupy the same cable, enclosure, or raceway when the equipment being powered is functionally associated with the Class 1 circuits.

According to *NEC Section 725.28*, when Class 1 circuit conductors are in a raceway or cable tray, the conductors, including any power supply conductors, must be derated as specified in *NEC Section 310.15* if the Class 1 conductors carry continuous loads in excess of 10 percent of the conductor **ampacity** and the number of conductors is more than three. If three or more power supply conductors are included with the Class 1 conductors, only the power supply conductors must be derated if the Class 1 conductors do not carry continuous loads in excess of 10 percent of each conductor. The number of conductors permitted in the raceway or tray is determined by *NEC Section 300.17*.

When Class 1 conductors are installed in cable trays, they must comply with *NEC Sections 392.9* through *392.11*.

6.2.0 Class 2 and 3 Circuits

NEC Section 725.2 defines a Class 2 circuit as the wiring between the load side of a listed Class 2 limited or nonlimited power source and the connected equipment. Due to voltage and current limitations, a Class 2 circuit provides safety from a fire initiation standpoint and acceptable protection from electrical shock.

A Class 3 circuit is defined in the same way, except that a listed Class 3 limited or nonlimited power source must be used. Because higher levels of voltage and current are permitted in Class 3 circuits, additional safeguards, including higher-voltage wiring insulation, are specified to provide more protection from electric shock.

The installation requirements for Class 2 and 3 circuits (*NEC Section 725.54*) are summarized in the following paragraphs.

6.2.1 Separation of Class 2 and 3 Circuits from Power Circuits

Class 2 and 3 circuits shall not be placed in cables, compartments, cable trays, enclosures, outlet boxes, device boxes, and raceways with electric power circuits (including electric light, Class 1, nonpower-limited fire protection circuits, and medium power, network-powered broadband communication cables) except as permitted in any one of 1 through 6 below:

1. Installation with power circuits is permitted if the circuits are physically separated by a solid, fixed barrier.

2. Installation with power circuits is permitted if the circuits are connected to the same equipment and as specified in both a and b below:

    a. The conductors and cables of the Class 2 and 3 circuits are separated from the other conductors and cables by at least ¼" (6.35 mm), *and*

    b. The circuit conductors operate at 150V or less and comply with (1) or (2) below:

       (1) The Class 2 and 3 circuits are installed using CL3, CL3R, or CL3P or permitted substitutes, provided these Class 3 cable conductors extending beyond the jacket are separated by a minimum of ¼" (6.35 mm) or by a nonconductive sleeve or barrier from all other conductors, *or*

       (2) The Class 2 and 3 circuit conductors are installed as Class 1 circuits.

3. The Class 2 and 3 circuits may enter an enclosure through a hole along with power conductors if separated by a continuous and firmly fixed nonconductor such as flexible tubing, provided they enter as permitted above.

4. Installation with power circuits is permitted if the circuits are installed in a maintenance hole and the installation meets specified conditions.

5. Installation with power circuits is permitted if the circuits are contained in a rated hybrid cable as defined by *NEC Section 780.6(A)*.

6. Installation with power circuits is permitted if the circuits are in cable trays and the power circuits are separated by a solid, fixed barrier of a material compatible with the cable tray or the Class 2 and 3 circuits are installed in Type MC cable.

6.2.2 Separation in Hoistways

Class 2 and 3 circuits in hoistways shall be installed in RMC, NMC, IMC, or EMT, except for installations in elevator shafts.

6.2.3 Separation in Other Applications

Class 2 and 3 circuits shall be separated by at least 2" (50.8 mm) from all power conductors and medium power, network-powered broadband communication cables except as permitted by 1 or 2 below:

1. Separation of less than 2" (50.8 mm) is permitted if either the Class 2 and 3 circuits or the power/broadband communication cables are in raceway, metal sheathed/clad, nonmetallic sheathed, or Type UF cables.

2. Separation of less than 2" (50.8 mm) is permitted if the Class 2 and 3 circuits are separated by a continuous, firmly fixed barrier in addition to the circuit insulation.

6.2.4 Support of Conductors

Class 2 and 3 circuit conductors or cables shall not be strapped, taped, or attached by any means to the exterior of any conduit or other raceway except for raceways dedicated to that purpose.

6.2.5 Installation in Plenums, Risers, Cable Trays, and Hazardous Locations

For Class 2 and 3 circuits, only plenum-rated cables shall be installed in plenums and only riser or plenum-rated cable shall be installed in risers unless installed in compliance with *NEC Section 300.22*. For one-family and two-family residential installations, CL2, CL3, CL2X, and CL3X shall be permitted for these uses. In hazardous locations, only PLTC-rated cable shall be used and adequately supported, except as noted in *NEC Sections 501.4, 502.4*, and *504.20*. In outdoor cable trays, only PLTC-rated cable may be used.

6.3.0 Instrumentation Tray Cable Circuits

Instrumentation tray cable (*NEC Section 727.4*) shall be permitted for use in industrial establishments only when qualified persons will service the installation. Under this condition, it may be installed in cable trays, raceways, hazardous locations (as defined in the NEC®), and as open wiring when equipped with various versions of a metallic sheath. As open wiring, the cable must be supported and secured at intervals of not more than 6' (1.83 m). Nonmetallic-sheathed cable may be used as open wiring to equipment, provided it is less than 50' (15.24 m) long and is protected from physical damage. ITC cable that complies with Type MC cable crush and impact requirements may also be used as open wiring to equipment, provided it is less than 50' (15.24 m) long. ITC cable may be used as an aerial cable on a messenger or under raised floors in control rooms and rack rooms when protected against damage. ITC cable shall not be used in circuits operating at more than 150V or more than 5A. The cable shall not be installed with electric power circuits of any kind unless its nonmetallic sheath is covered with a metallic sheath or unless it is terminated inside enclosures and separation is maintained by insulating barriers or other means.

6.4.0 Nonpower-Limited Fire Alarm Circuits

Fire alarm circuits are defined as either power-limited (PLFA) or nonpower-limited fire alarm (NPLFA) circuits. Power-limited fire alarm circuits shall be supplied from a listed, power-limited transformer (Class 3) or power supply. Nonpower-limited fire alarm circuits (*NEC Section 760.25*) shall not exceed 600V and shall be installed as specified in *NEC Chapters 1* through *4*, except as noted in the following paragraphs.

6.4.1 Conductors of Different Circuits in the Same Cable, Enclosure, or Raceway

Some of the NEC® requirements for NPLFA circuits are as follows:

• Per *NEC Section 760.26(A)*, NPLFA and Class 1 circuits can occupy the same cable enclosure or raceway, either AC and/or DC, if all conductors are insulated for the highest voltage of any conductor.

Keeping up to Date

The NEC® is revised and reissued every three years. The ANSI/TIE/EIA standards that apply to low voltage cabling are under constant review, and are frequently changed or clarified. Major revisions to these standards are published occasionally. Always be sure you are using the current version of a code or standard. Using an out of date version can result in costly rework.

One way to keep up to date on the status of codes and standards is to become a member of the organization that publishes the document or to join a professional organization that relies on the document. BICSI, NSCA, and NBFAA are examples of the latter. Through their newsletters, they keep members up to date on the status of key codes and standards.

Codes and standards are reviewed and revised by committees made up of industry experts. At some point in your career, you could aspire to be a member of such a committee.

- Per *NEC Section 760.26(B)*, NPLFA circuits and power supply circuits are only permitted to occupy the same cable, enclosure, or raceway when the equipment being powered is functionally associated with the fire alarm circuits.
- Per *NEC Section 760.28*, when NPLFA circuit conductors are in a raceway or cable tray, the conductors, including any power supply conductors, must be derated as specified in *NEC Section 310.15* if the NPLFA conductors carry continuous loads in excess of 10 percent of the conductor ampacity and the number of conductors is more than three. If three or more power supply conductors are included with the NPLFA conductors, only the power supply conductors must be derated if the NPLFA conductors do not carry continuous loads in excess of 10 percent of each conductor. The number of conductors permitted in the raceway or tray is determined by *NEC Section 300.17*. Also, when Class 1 conductors are installed in cable trays, they must comply with *NEC Sections 392.9* through *392.11*.
- Per *NEC Section 760.30*, multi-conductor NPLFA cables may be used on circuits operating at 150V or less and shall be installed when the following conditions apply:

  – In raceways or exposed on the surface of ceilings and sidewalls or fished in concealed spaces

NOTE

When installed exposed, maximum protection against damage must be afforded by the building construction. The cable must be securely fastened at intervals of 18" (457.2 mm) or less to a height of 7' (2.13 m) from the floor. All splices and connections must be made inside listed devices.

  – In metal raceway or rigid nonmetallic conduit where passing through a floor or wall to a height of 7' (2.13 m) unless other protection is provided
  – In rigid metal conduit, rigid nonmetallic conduit, intermediate metal conduit, or electrical metal tubing when installed in hoistways

6.5.0 Power-Limited Fire Alarm Circuits

Power-limited fire alarm circuits [*NEC Sections 760.52(B)* and *760.54*] may be installed in raceway or exposed on the surfaces of walls and ceilings or fished in concealed spaces. Splices and terminations must be made in listed enclosures, devices, or fittings. When exposed, the circuits must be supported and protected against damage by using baseboards, door frames, or ledges. When located within 7' (2.13 m) of the floor, cables must be fastened at intervals of 18" (457.2 mm) or less. The circuits must be installed in metal raceways or NMC when passing through a floor or wall to a height of 7' (2.13 m) above the floor unless protection is provided by baseboards, door frames, ledges, etc. or unless equivalent solid guards are provided. When installed in hoistways, the circuits must be installed in RMC, NMC, IMC, or EMT with certain exceptions for elevator shafts or unless other wiring methods and materials are being used to extend or replace conductors/cables in plenums, risers, or other building areas.

6.5.1 Separation of Power-Limited Fire Alarm Circuits from Power Circuits

Power-limited fire alarm circuits shall not be placed in cables, compartments, cable trays, enclosures, outlet boxes, device boxes, and raceways with electric power circuits (including electric light, Class 1, nonpower-limited fire protection circuits, and medium power, network-powered broadband communication cables) except as permitted in any one of the following three ways:

1. Installation with power circuits is permitted if the circuits are physically separated by a solid, fixed barrier.
2. Installation with power circuits is permitted if the circuits are connected to the same equipment and as specified in both of the following:

    a. The conductors and cables of power-limited fire alarm circuits are separated from the other conductors and cables by at least ¼" (6.35 mm), *and*
    b. The circuit conductors operate at 150V or less and comply with the following:

      (1) The power-limited fire alarm circuits are installed using FPL, FPLR, or FPLP or permitted substitutes, provided that power-limited conductors extending beyond the jacket are separated by a minimum of ¼" (6.35 mm) or by a nonconductive sleeve or barrier from all other conductors, *or*
      (2) The power-limited circuit conductors are installed as nonpower-limited fire alarm circuits.

3. The power-limited fire alarm circuits may enter an enclosure through a hole along with power conductors if separated by a continuous and firmly fixed nonconductor such as flexible tubing, provided that they enter in the ways just explained.

6.5.2 Separation in Hoistways

Power-limited fire alarm circuits in hoistways shall be installed in RMC, NMC, IMC, or EMT except for certain installations in elevator shafts.

6.5.3 Separation in Other Applications

Power-limited fire alarm circuits shall be separated by at least 2" (50.8 mm) from all power conductors and medium power, network-powered broadband communication cables except as permitted by any one of the following ways:

1. Separation of less than 2" (50.8 mm) is permitted if either the power-limited fire alarm circuits or the power/broadband communication cables are in raceway, metal sheathed/clad, nonmetallic sheathed, or Type UF cables.
2. Separation of less than 2" (50.8 mm) is permitted if the power-limited fire alarm circuits are separated by a continuous, firmly fixed barrier in addition to the circuit insulation.

NOTE

These separation requirements are for safety purposes. Additional separation may be required for performance issues, such as EMI suppression.

6.5.4 Current-Carrying Continuous Line-Type Fire Detectors

These types of fire detectors, including the insulated copper tubing of pneumatically operated detectors, are permitted in power-limited circuits. As specified previously, they are installed for power-limited fire alarm circuits.

Power-limited fire alarm circuit conductors or cables shall not be strapped, taped, or attached by any means to the exterior of any conduit or other raceway.

6.5.5 Plenums and Risers

For power-limited fire alarm circuits, only plenum-rated cables shall be installed in plenums and only riser or plenum-rated cable shall be installed in risers unless installed in compliance with *NEC Section 300.22*. For one-family and two-family residential installations, FPL cable shall be permitted for these uses.

6.6.0 Optical Fiber Cable

In accordance with *NEC Sections 770.52* and *770.53*, optical fibers are permitted in composite cables with electric power circuits under 600V (including electric light, Class 1, nonpower-limited fire protection circuits, and medium power, network-powered

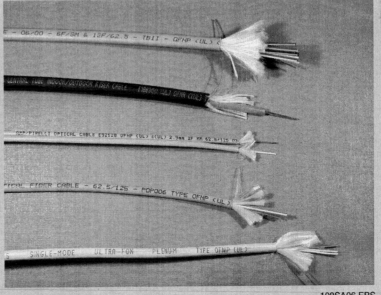

Optical Fiber Cable

This photo shows examples of different types of optical fiber cable. The fluffy looking strands are the strength members that protect the fragile optical fiber from damage.

108SA06.EPS

broadband communication cables) when the fibers and conductors are associated with the same function. Nonconductive optical fiber cables are permitted in the same cable tray or raceway with electric power/broadband communication circuits operating at 600V or less. However, conductive optical fiber cables are not permitted. Both conductive and nonconductive optical fiber cables shall be permitted in the same cable tray, enclosure, or raceway with conductors of Class 2 and 3, power-limited fire alarm, communication circuits, CATV, or low power, network-powered broadband communication circuits.

Composite optical fiber cables containing only power circuits operating at 600V or less are permitted to be placed in enclosures or pathways with other power circuits operating at 600V or less except as specified below. Per *NEC Section 770.52*, nonconductive optical fiber cables are not permitted to be placed in enclosures containing terminations for power/broadband communication circuits except as specified in any one of the following four ways:

1. Occupancy is permitted when associated with the function of the power/broadband communication circuits.

2. Occupancy is permitted if fibers are installed in a factory or field-assembled control center.

3. Occupancy is permitted in industrial settings where maintenance is accomplished by qualified personnel.

4. Composite optical fiber cables are permitted to contain power circuits operating in excess of 600V only in industrial settings where maintenance is accomplished by qualified personnel.

For optical fiber circuits, only plenum-rated cables shall be installed in plenums and only riser or plenum-rated cable shall be installed in risers unless Types OFNR, OFCR, OFNG, OFN, OFCG, and OFC are installed in plenums in compliance with *NEC Section 300.22* or Types OFNG, OFN, OFCG, and OFC installed as risers are encased in metal raceway or are located in a fireproof shaft with firestops on each floor. For one-family and two-family residential installations, Types OFNG, OFN, OFCG, and OFC shall be permitted for these uses.

Any listed optical fiber cable may be installed in hazardous locations and in cable trays. Raceway installations of optical fiber cable must comply with *NEC Section 300.17*.

Plenum, riser, and general-purpose raceways listed for optical fiber cable applications may be used [*NEC Sections 770.51(E)* through *(G)*].

6.7.0 Hybrid Cable

Conductors of listed hybrid cable [*NEC Sections 780-6(A)* and *(B)*] can occupy the same enclosure housing terminations of power circuits only if connectors listed for hybrid cable are used.

6.8.0 Communication Circuits within Buildings

In accordance with *NEC Sections 800.48* and *800.52*, communication circuits are permitted in raceways or enclosures with any other power-limited Class 2 and 3, fire alarm, optical fiber, CATV, and low power, network-powered broadband communication circuits.

6.8.1 Separation of Communication Circuits from Power Circuits

Communication circuits shall not be placed in cables, compartments, cable trays, enclosures, outlet boxes, device boxes, and raceways with electric power circuits (including electric light, Class 1, nonpower-limited fire protection circuits and medium power, network-powered broadband communication cables) except as permitted in either of the following ways:

1. Installation with power circuits is permitted if the circuits are physically separated by a solid, fixed barrier.

2. Installation with power circuits is permitted if the circuits are connected to the same equipment and the conductors and cables of the communication circuits are separated from the other conductors and cables by at least ¼" (6.35 mm).

6.8.2 Separation in Other Applications

Communication circuits shall be separated by at least 2" (50.8 mm) from all power conductors and medium power, network-powered broadband communication cables except as permitted by either of the following:

1. Separation of less than 2" (50.8 mm) is permitted if either the communication circuits are enclosed in a raceway or the power/broadband communication cables are in a raceway or metal sheathed/clad, inner duct sheathed, Type AC, or Type UF cables.

2. Separation of less than 2" (50.8 mm) is permitted if the communication circuits are separated by a continuous, firmly fixed barrier in addition to the circuit insulation.

NOTE
The separation requirements above are for safety purposes. Additional separation may be required for performance issues, such as EMI suppression.

6.8.3 Support of Conductors

Communication circuit conductors or cables shall not be strapped, taped, or attached by any means to the exterior of any conduit or other raceway.

6.8.4 Cable Trays

All communication cable types except CMX may be used in cable trays.

6.8.5 Plenums and Risers

For communication circuits, only plenum-rated cables shall be installed in plenums or in listed plenum raceways per *NEC Sections 300.22(B)* and *(C)*. Only riser or plenum-rated cable shall be installed in risers or in listed riser raceways. Exceptions are specified in the following:

1. The installation is permitted if listed cables are encased in metal raceway or are located in a fire-proof shaft with fire stops on each floor.
2. The installation of types CM and CMX cable is allowed in one-family and two-family residences.

6.8.6 Plenums, Risers, and General-Purpose Raceways

When communication circuits are installed in raceways, the raceways shall be one of the types covered in *NEC Chapter 3* except that listed inner duct plenum, riser or general-purpose raceway conforming to *NEC Sections 800.51(J)* through *(L)* is permitted.

6.9.0 Coaxial CATV Cable Installation within Buildings

Coaxial CATV installation within buildings (*NEC Section 820.52*) is summarized in the following paragraphs.

6.9.1 Separation in Raceways and Boxes

Coaxial cables shall be permitted in raceways or enclosures along with any Class 2 and 3, power-limited fire alarm, communication, nonconductive and conductive optical fiber, and/or low power, network-powered broadband communication circuits. Coaxial cable shall not be placed in raceways and boxes along with electric light, power, Class 1, nonpower-limited fire alarm, and/or medium power, broadband communication circuits unless separated by a barrier or unless the power circuits are supplying coaxial distribution equipment. In this case, the coaxial cables shall be routed to maintain a separation from the power circuits of more than ¼" (6.35 mm).

6.9.2 Separation in Other Applications

Per *NEC Section 820.52*, coaxial cable shall be separated by more than 2" (50.8 mm) from conductors of any electric light, power, Class 1, nonpower-limited fire alarm, and/or medium power, broadband communication circuits except as specified in 1 or 2 below:

1. The circuits are in a separate raceway or metal-sheathed, metal-clad, nonmetallic-sheathed Type AC or Type UF cables or all of coaxial cables are in a separate raceway.
2. The coaxial cables are permanently separated by a continuous and firmly fixed nonconductor such as porcelain tubes or flexible tubing in addition to the insulation on the wire.

NOTE
The separation requirements above are for safety purposes. Additional separation may be required for performance issues, such as EMI suppression.

6.9.3 Support of Conductors

Raceways shall be used for their intended purpose. Coaxial cables shall not be strapped, taped, or attached by any means to the exterior of any conduit or raceway as a means of support.

6.10.0 Network-Powered Broadband Communication System Installation within Buildings

The code requirements for network-powered broadband communication system installation within buildings (*NEC Section 830.58*) are summarized below. Such systems include any combination of voice, audio, video, data, and interactive services.

6.10.1 Separation in Raceways and Boxes

Some of the NEC® requirements for separation in raceways and boxes are as follows:

• Low and medium power, network-powered broadband communication cables, such as long runs of CATV cable, shall be permitted in the same raceway or enclosure.

• Low power, network-powered broadband communication cables shall be permitted in raceways or enclosures along with any Class 2 and 3, power-limited fire alarm, communication, nonconductive and conductive optical fiber, and/or community antenna television and radio distribution system circuits.

• Medium power, network-powered broadband communication cables shall not be permitted in raceways or enclosures along with any Class 2 and 3, power-limited fire alarm, communication, nonconductive and conductive optical fiber, and/or community antenna television and radio distribution system circuits.

• Low and/or medium power, network-powered broadband communication cable shall not be placed in raceways and boxes along with electric light, power, Class 1, nonpower-limited fire alarm, and/or medium power, broadband communication circuits unless separated by a barrier or unless the power circuits are supplying network distribution equipment. In this case, the network-powered broadband communication cables shall be routed to maintain a separation from the power circuits of more than ¼" (6.35 mm).

6.10.2 Separation in Other Applications

Low and/or medium power, network-powered broadband communication cable shall be separated by more than 2" (50.8 mm) from conductors of any electric light, power, Class 1, and nonpower-limited fire alarm circuits except as specified by either of the following:

1. The circuits are in a separate raceway or metal-sheathed, metal-clad, nonmetallic-sheathed Type AC or Type UF cables, or all of the network-powered broadband communication cables are in a separate raceway.

2. The network-powered broadband communication cables are permanently separated by a continuous and firmly fixed nonconductor (such as porcelain tubes or flexible tubing) in addition to the insulation on the wire.

NOTE

The separation requirements above are for safety purposes. Additional separation may be required for performance issues, such as EMI suppression.

6.10.3 Support of Conductors

Raceways shall be used for their intended purpose. Low and/or medium power, network-powered broadband communication cables shall not be strapped, taped, or attached by any means to the exterior of any conduit or raceway as a means of support.

7.0.0 ◆ TELEPHONE SYSTEMS

Alexander Graham Bell's vision of 1876 has become so commonplace that it is often taken for granted. It is hard to imagine what life would be like without the telephone. Between voice, data, and cellular, the telephone industry has exploded over the last ten years. In fact, nearly all forms of electronic communication involve some type of telephone system or technology.

This section covers the methods used for **premises** wiring of voice and data systems. It also covers various types of cables and cable termination devices, as well as installation guidelines and troubleshooting techniques.

7.1.0 Basic Telephone Operation

A basic phone is a fairly simple device; it consists of a transmitter, receiver, dial or pushbutton mechanism, and switch hook.

To complete a call, the receiver is picked up. This releases the switch hook, which closes a circuit and allows a DC current to flow. This current flow is sensed at the central telephone office and causes a **digit receiver** to be connected to the line. The digit receiver provides a dial tone to the caller. The number is then entered using a touch pad or a rotary mechanism, the tones or pulses are decoded by the digit receiver, and the address is sent to the switching circuitry, which then routes the call.

The switching station handling the area of the intended recipient of the call generates an AC signal (ring) which is sent to the called station to make the phone ring. When the called phone is answered, lifting the switch hook completes the DC circuit between the two phones, signaling the **local exchange** to disable the ringing supply. Conversation between the two parties occurs by transferring an AC voice signal from the mouthpiece to the DC circuit between the two phones and routing it to the earpiece of the receiver.

 WARNING!
Care should be exercised when handling telephone wiring as up to 90VAC may be present on the line when there is an incoming call.

The previous example described the procedure for a call within a local area, also called a subscriber's loop. This area may be several blocks to several square miles, depending on the population density. For calls outside of the local area, the call may have to be routed through several switching stations. For transfer between major service areas, the call will be placed on a trunk until it reaches its destination service area, where it will be routed to the receiving station local exchange. These different switching stations are responsible for an increasingly large service area and are set up as shown in *Figure 52*.

As shown in *Figure 52*, a call placed between major regions of the country will normally flow all the way up the line through a **toll center**, **primary center**, and **sectional center** to be transferred between **regional centers** before being sent back down the line to the destination local exchange. If overflow traffic should occur during heavy usage, alternate routes may be selected. This will be determined by the switching stations involved. For example, if a call needs to go from local exchange A to local exchange B, it is usually routed to the regional center before starting back down

the line. However, if all normal circuits are busy and a trunk is available from primary center A to primary center B, the call will be sent that way.

7.2.0 Multiplexing

Obviously, many wires are required to carry the type of voice traffic that is prevalent in the world today. To accomplish this task, telephone transmission cables may contain up to 4,200 pairs of wires. Sometimes, even that is not enough. To solve this problem, a method of transmission called multiplexing is used. Multiplexing permits the simultaneous transmission of multiple signals over a common path (cable or channel) in order to make two or more logical channels. This is typically done either by sending the multiple signals over the common path using a different frequency band (**frequency division multiplexing**) or by sharing the common path at different points in time (**time division multiplexing**). An example of frequency division multiplexing (FDM) is described below.

For Channel 1, a 300 to 4,000Hz voice signal is applied to a mixer to be combined with a 12kHz carrier frequency, giving an output between 12.3 and 16kHz. This signal is applied to a summing circuit. Channel 2 mixes a voice signal with 16kHz, giving an output of 16.3 to 20kHz. This is applied to the same summing circuit. This happens with all 12 voice channels so that the final output from the last mixer will be 12 voice channels with a frequency spectrum of 12 to 60kHz, as shown in *Figure 53*. The equipment where this process takes place is called a multiplexer.

At the other end of the circuit, this summed signal, which may consist of frequencies from 12 to 60kHz, is applied to a bank of bandpass filters. The Channel 1 filter will only pass signals between 12 and 16kHz. This signal is then mixed with 12kHz, leaving the 300 to 4,000Hz voice signal, which is then supplied from the local exchange to the receiving station's phone. The equipment where this process takes place is called a demultiplexer. This must be repeated on a separate cable for the conversations in the opposite direction.

This same procedure is used to combine five standard 12-channel groups to make up a 60-channel supergroup, five supergroups to make up a 300-channel master group, and three master groups to make up a 900-channel supermaster group. Using this many channels requires a higher frequency. For example, a 12kHz carrier could carry three 4kHz channels, but a 100kHz carrier could carry 25 4kHz channels. To carry 900 channels, the carrier frequency must be above 3.6 MHz.

Time division multiplexing (TDM) is used with the transmission of data rather than voice signals.

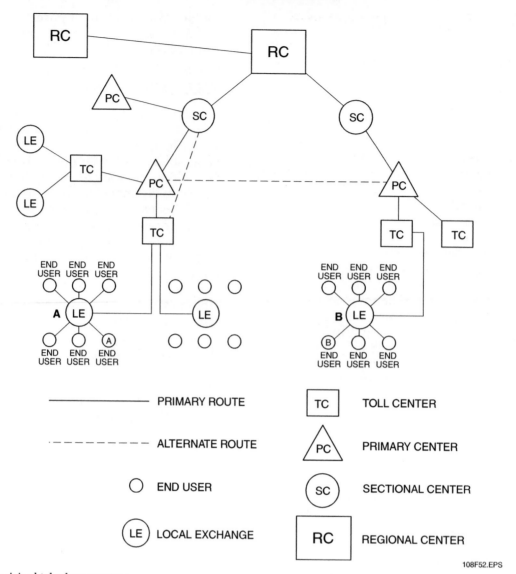

PRIMARY ROUTE

ALTERNATE ROUTE

◯ END USER

(LE) LOCAL EXCHANGE

| TC | TOLL CENTER |

△ PC PRIMARY CENTER

(SC) SECTIONAL CENTER

| RC | REGIONAL CENTER |

108F52.EPS

Figure 52 ◆ Municipal telephone system.

When using TDM, each station, called a node, is allocated a small time interval during which it may transmit a message or portion of a message (for instance, a data packet). During this time interval, the node has exclusive command on a non-interference basis of the common path or channel. The time-shared messages transmitted from all the nodes in a network are sequentially combined (interleaved) for transmission in a multiplexer unit, then demultiplexed by a demultiplexer unit at the receiving end.

7.3.0 Key Systems and Private Branch Exchanges (PBXs)

Key system and private branch exchanges (PBXs) provide customers with additional communication capability and services that are not normally available from standard single-line service. PBX and key systems are like a miniature phone company within a company or building. They provide a means of having a large number of phones share a few common service lines.

What were once quite apparent differences between key and PBX systems have started to blur in recent years. PBX systems are now primarily used in applications with 100 or more stations, generally have a full-time system operator, and users must dial an access number, such as 9, to reach an outside line. Key systems are generally limited to less station-intensive applications and do not require an outside line access number.

Both systems provide for incoming call routing through an operator or attendant, with PBX systems allowing for **direct inward dialing (DID)** trunks to allow a caller to directly dial a PBX extension. However, newer hybrid electronic key systems are also providing a DID capability.

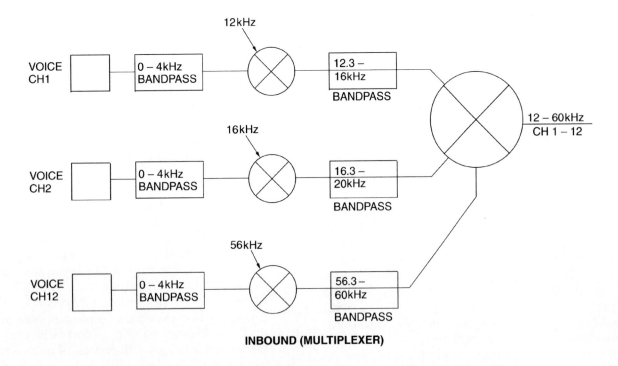

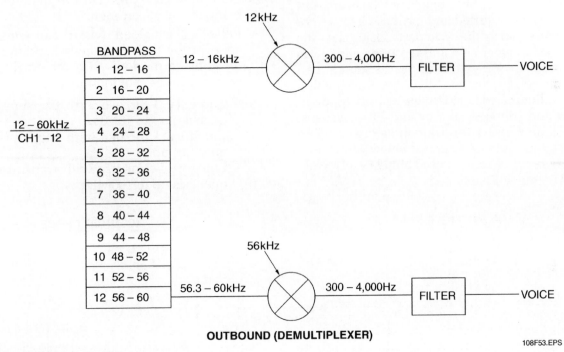

Figure 53 ◆ Frequency division multiplexing.

Installation and maintenance of key systems does not require special certification, as with PBX systems, but specialized training on these systems is highly recommended.

7.4.0 Premises Cable

Cabling systems can be divided into two basic functions: premises wiring and outside plant wiring. The cabling used for premises wiring consists primarily of twisted pair wiring, but may include coaxial and optical fiber cables in larger installations. Outside plant voice transmission includes these mediums, but can also include line of sight radio frequency and satellite transmission. The types of cable commonly used for premises wiring are as follows:

- 100Ω unshielded twisted pair (UTP)
- 100Ω screened twisted pair (ScTP)
- Single-mode or multi-mode optical fiber

The most common type of cable used with telephone systems for voice use is 100Ω unshielded twisted pair. This cable is suitable for both transmission and premises wiring.

- *Two-wire twisted pair (one pair)* – These wires are the basis of all subscriber loop and premises phone systems. They provide for transmission and reception bi-directionally through the same two wires. These two wires are identified by the function they perform for the phone system and are known as tip and ring. The ring wire provides the AC current to operate the ringer, and the tip wire completes the DC path for local exchange notification of a lifted switch hook. *Figure 54* shows a two-wire twisted pair circuit.

- *Four-wire twisted pair (two pair)* – These cables have the same configuration as two-wire twisted pair wiring, except that two pair are used, with each pair handling single direction communication (one pair for transmission and one pair for reception). If two people talk at the same time on a one-pair circuit, both voices will be heard, but they may be distorted and the message may not be understood by the other party. Using separate wires for transmission and reception eliminates this problem and greatly improves sound quality and noise reduction. Two-pair transmission has traditionally been used exclusively for dedicated and private line (key and PBX) systems, but is also used for transmission between switching stations (described below). Additionally, two-pair wiring is used almost exclusively for data transmission.

- *Two-wire to four-wire systems* – Although two-pair operation provides better sound quality transmission, end user equipment can only support two-wire operation. Two-wire to four-wire conversion systems allow the use of four-wire systems for transmission while maintaining end user equipment compatibility. This is accomplished through the use of a hybrid transformer. This hybrid transformer converts the two-wire tip and ring signals to a four-wire format. A typical two-wire to four-wire conversion system and hybrid transformer are shown in *Figure 55*.

- *Packaging* – Twisted pair wires will be found packaged with other twisted pairs in a common cable. The number of wires found in a single cable is dependent upon the application of the cable and ranges from two pairs to 25 pairs. Multiple cables can be combined in assemblies called lay-ups, groups, or units that can contain up to 4,200 pairs of wires. Normally, premises wiring installations will consist of units with no more than 200 pairs, with 8- to 25-pair cables being the most common.

- *Rating* – Unshielded twisted pair wires are categorized by their frequency-handling capability and are marked with the corresponding category for ease of identification:

  - Category 3 for use with transmission frequencies up to 16MHz
  - Category 4 for use with transmission frequencies up to 20MHz
  - Category 5e for use with transmission frequencies up to 100MHz

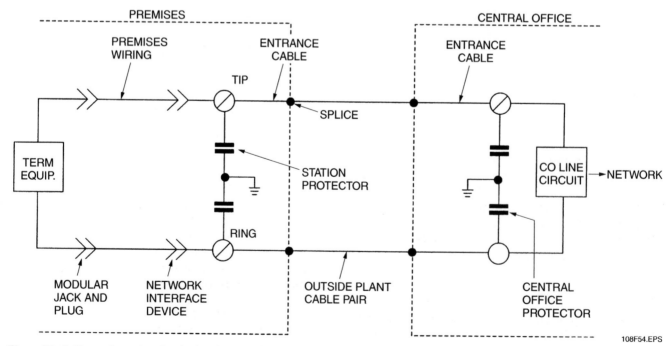

Figure 54 ◆ Two-wire twisted pair circuit.

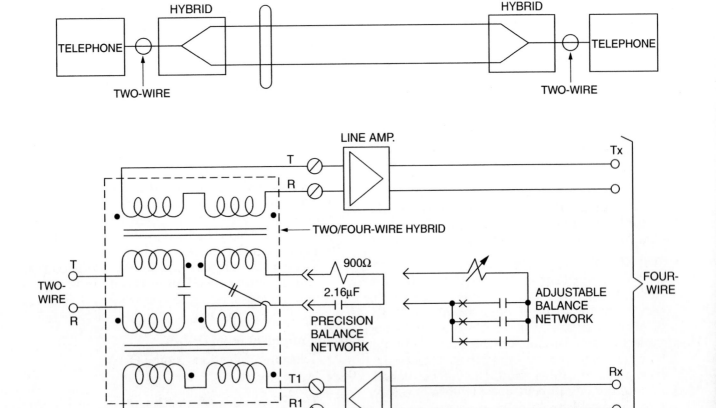

Figure 55 ◆ Two-wire to four-wire hybrid.

Category 3 and Category 5e wiring are the most common.

These transmission frequency limitations give a practical limitation of 12 full duplex voice quality channels up to approximately 200 miles. For more information-carrying capacity, another medium must be used.

Screened twisted pair and optical fiber cable were described earlier in this module.

7.5.0 Installation Standards

Installation of telephone wiring will be concerned with two major areas: outside plant and premises. To review, outside plant wiring is external to the subscriber and premises wiring is within a structure.

With the increasing number of companies making products for the information superhighway, certain standards are required to ensure compatibility of cables, connectors, hubs, and other network devices. Several industry organizations, including the Telephone Industry Association (TIA), Electronics Industry Association (EIA), and the Institute of Electrical and Electronic Engineers (IEEE) combined ideas to establish standardization throughout the industry. Some of these standards are as follows:

- *TIA/EIA-568-A* – Standard for STP and UTP Premises Cabling and Connectors
- *TIA/EIA-569-A* – Standard for Pathways and Spaces
- *TIA/EIA-570-A* – Residential Telecommunication Wiring Standard
- *TIA/EIA-607* – Standard for Bonding and Grounding Requirements for Commercial Buildings

These standards should be consulted prior to commencing any voice or data system installation, as strict compliance will ensure quality results.

7.5.1 Outside Plant

Cable assemblies leaving the local exchange are contained in a cable vault below the building and are usually run underground until they reach the general vicinity of the subscribers for those circuits. They are then either buried, where they will terminate in a pedestal, or run by aerial service to a network interface device (NID). When using a pedestal termination, a service wire is buried to connect the pedestal with the NID at the service location.

Outside plant exchange cables are used to provide service to regular subscribers or private line service (PBX). These cables are categorized according to their service classification, as described in the following:

- *Indoor* – Risers and general internal telephone wiring
- *Aerial* – Combined with a messenger or self supporting; mounted above ground
- *Buried* – Buried directly in the ground
- *Underground* – Installed underground in conduit or a duct

Aerial and underground installations are the most common types of outside plant cabling. They use the following types of transmission mediums:

- *Twisted pair wiring* – Cable cores may be filled with a variety of substances, including jelly or a rubber-like insulator, or they may have an air core with or without pressurization. With smaller cable sizes, filled cores provide better protection against moisture intrusion over time than unpressurized air core cables. Unpressurized air core cables should never be placed underground or directly buried due to moisture intrusion problems.
- *Optical fiber cable* – Currently, optical fiber cable is used for transmission of voice signals only over long distances, such as between toll centers and above. Because of expense and complexity, it has not been used for individual subscriber drops. As the cost of fiber cable decreases, its use will become more commonplace. Special consideration must be given to optical fiber cable installations due to the catastrophic consequences of damage to fiber cables. This cable is almost always either directly buried in the earth or located in conduit or duct underground, and there is specific guidance on installation depth. Most applications call for direct-buried cable to be located at least 24" deep and underground cable to be located at least 36" deep.

It is vitally important to ensure that all buried and underground cables be armored to guard against damage by gophers and other rodents.

Present-day voice transmission requirements call for a minimum of Category 3 unshielded twisted pair wiring. Indoor twisted pair cable is seldom cored, as it is not exposed to varying temperature and moisture extremes. Optical fiber cable, when used in premises, is primarily used for data transmission, but installation criteria are the same as for voice cable.

Premises wiring can be further broken down into commercial and residential installations.

Both of these have similar guidelines and requirements, but different procedures. The first application discussed will be commercial.

7.5.2 Commercial Premises Wiring

The most common way for premises wiring to enter a commercial facility is through underground means. These must use a minimum of 4" diameter, encased Type B, C, or D PVC, galvanized steel, or fiberglass duct with no more than two 90-degree bends. Conduit fill should not exceed 40 percent for more than two cables. The maintenance hole must be equipped with a sump, a pulling iron, cable racks, a grounded ladder, and adequate lighting facilities.

Once on the premises, unshielded twisted pair premises wiring installation can be broken into four main areas:

- Entrance facility (EF)
- Equipment room (ER)
- Telecommunications room (TR)
- Work area (WA)

The EF consists of a pathway for outside service, an interbuilding backbone, and alternate entrance facilities. Entrance facilities contain the termination field, which interfaces the outside cabling to the intrabuilding backbone. Normally, the telephone company will terminate within 50' of building penetration and will provide primary voltage protection.

According to *EIA/TIA Standard 569*, a locked, enclosed, dedicated room is recommended for buildings larger than 20,000 square feet, and is required for buildings having more than 70,000 square feet. Additionally, for buildings up to 100,000 square feet, a wall-mounted termination field made of ½" plywood may be used, but buildings above 100,000 square feet may require rack-mounted freestanding frames. Minimum room sizes are shown in *Table 11*.

The equipment room (ER) is essentially a large closet that contains the main distribution frame, PBXs, and secondary voltage protection. It may also contain the main cross-connect or an intermediate cross-connect. It is often located adjacent to the entrance facility (EF) to make use of common air conditioning, security, lighting, and access control.

Ideally, 0.75 square feet of ER space will be required for each 100 square feet of work area (WA). The room should not have a false ceiling, and no piping, ductwork, or power cabling should be routed through the room. Two separate

Table 11 Entrance Facility Room Size

BUILDING FLOOR SPACE (FT²)	ROOM DIMENSIONS
5,000–70,000	Dedicated room not required
70,000–100,000	12' × 6.3'
200,000	12' × 9'
400,000	12' × 13'
500,000	12' × 15.6'
600,000	12' × 18.3'
800,000	12' × 22.3'
1,000,000	12' × 27.7'

108T11.EPS

15 amp, 115VAC power circuits should be provided, and an emergency alternate power source should be considered. The ER outputs the vertical backbone to the telecommunications room (TR).

The TR is the junction between the vertical backbone and the horizontal cabling. It consists of telecommunications equipment, termination fields, and cross-connect wiring. It may contain intermediate cross-connects or the main cross-connect. A typical telecommunications room is shown in *Figure 56*.

One TR is required for each 10,000 square feet of work area, or if the horizontal cable distance exceeds 300'. Requirements for power, lighting, climate control, and access control are the same as for ERs. For the interconnection of floors, a minimum

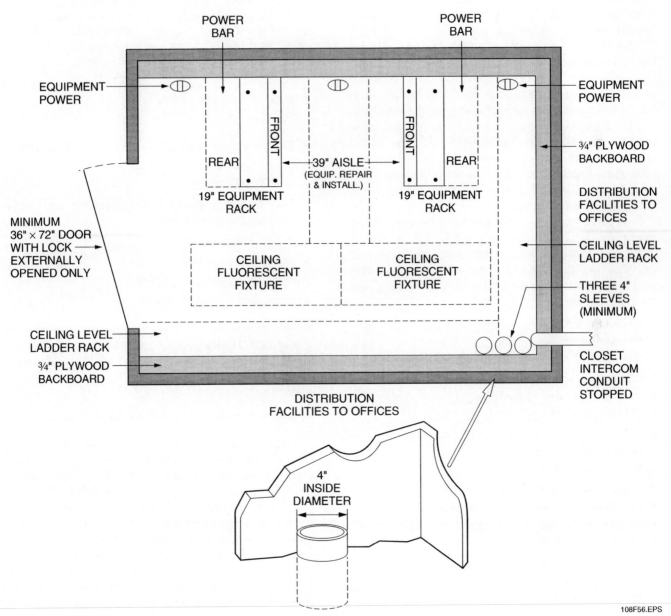

108F56.EPS

Figure 56 ◆ Telecommunications room.

of three firestopped 4" backbone sleeves will be used, and they should be stacked vertically above each other on each floor. Closet interconnections will also use firestopped conduit. The TR outputs horizontal cabling to the work area.

The WA is where the end use equipment is located. It contains connection boxes at each workstation location. The choice of pathways is up to the designer, but the most common method is to suspend cables from J-hooks above the ceiling, fanning out to the work area. The horizontal cables drop from the ceiling through walls or along raceways and terminate at an outlet box. The cable connecting the outlet box to the equipment should be limited to 3 meters (approximately 10').

The installation strategy for data cable is identical to the technique used for voice cabling with the exception of the entrance facility. Unless there is an intrabuilding LAN, there will be no entrance facility for data cables.

The data equipment room will normally be located separate from the voice ER, and will contain the LAN system server, the primary hub routing, and patch panel equipment. This will be the main controlling and monitoring station for the network.

The telecommunications room and work area cabling facilities can be shared with the voice equipment; this is recommended to reduce the cost and duplication of resources. The TR may contain additional hub routers, patch panels, and amplifiers (as required).

A typical premises installation showing these major areas can be seen in *Figure 57*.

Proper handling and installation practices will prevent damage from occurring to the cable. The following precautions should be observed when running cable:

- Maintain a maximum bend radius of four times the diameter.
- Apply cable ties loosely at random intervals.
- Minimize jacket twisting.
- Avoid stretching the cable.
- Handle optical fiber cable gently.
- Make all connections with patch panels or cross-connect blocks.
- Replace any damaged cable.
- Follow length restrictions for UTP and STP.
- Use accepted methods for securing cables.
- Keep cables away from potential EMI sources.
- Do not exceed a 90-degree bend.
- Do not overtighten cable ties.
- Do not overtwist cables.
- Do not exceed 25 lbs pulling tension.
- Do not splice, bridge, tap, or repair cables.

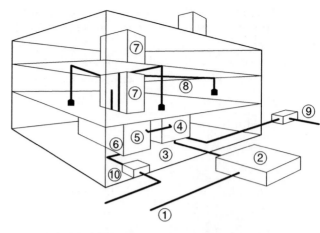

1. TELCO CONDUIT	6. VERTICAL BACKBONE
2. TELCO MANHOLE	7. TELECOM CLOSET
3. ENTRANCE CONDUIT	8. HORIZONTAL CABLING
4. TELCO ENTRANCE FACILITY	9. INTERBUILDING BACKBONE
5. TELECOM EQUIPMENT ROOM	10. ELECTRICAL ENTRANCE FACILITY

108F57.EPS

Figure 57 ◆ Premises wiring.

- Do not run power and phone cable together.
- Do not run UTP cable near the power cables for fluorescent lights.

The accepted methods for dressing and securing cables are as follows:

- Cable ties
- Cable support bar
- Wire management panels
- Releasable Velcro® straps

CAUTION

The use of a standard stapling gun can severely damage the cable. Use only an approved stapling gun.

Cable runs in premises wiring may take many forms. The biggest factors in determining which type will be used are the local wiring code and the preferences of the design engineer. While TIA/EIA standards govern the routing of cables between the EF, ER, and TR, horizontal cabling to the WA is also governed. Cable runs can be broken down into two categories, backbone and horizontal pathways.

Backbone pathways consist of intrabuilding and interbuilding pathways, and include intermediate cross-connects, main cross-connects, and mechanical termination:

- Intrabuilding pathways provide a means of routing cable from the entrance facility to the equipment rooms and the telecommunications room, and use cable trays, conduit, and sleeves.
- Interbuilding pathways interconnect separate buildings, and consist of underground, buried, aerial, and tunnel pathways.

Backbone cabling uses the conventional hierarchical star topology. Recognized cable types for backbone cabling are as follows:

- 100Ω UTP multi-pair backbone cable
- 50.0 or 62.5/125µm multi-mode optical fiber
- Single-mode optical fiber

The maximum allowable distances for backbone cabling are as follows:

- 100Ω UTP: 800 meters for voice; 90 meters for data
- 50.0 or 62.5/125µm multi-mode optical fiber: 2,000 meters
- Single-mode optical fiber: 3,000 meters

Horizontal pathways are used for the installation of media from the telecommunications room to the work area outlet. In accordance with *EIA/TIA Standard 568*, commercial building telecommunication cabling shall be of a star topology, with each work area connected to a TR. The maximum horizontal distance shall be 90 meters, with an additional 10 meters allowed for work area cables and patch cords.

The cables used can include the following:

- Four-pair 100Ω UTP cable
- Four-pair 150Ω ScTP cable
- Two-fiber 50.0 or 62.5/125µm optical fiber cable
- Single-mode optical fiber

A minimum of two telecommunication outlets shall be provided at each workstation, and shall be configured as follows:

- One connector supported by a four-pair 100Ω UTP cable, Category 3 or higher for voice use
- The other shall be one of the following:
    - Four-pair 100Ω UTP cable, Category 5e (recommended)
    - Four-pair 100Ω UTP cable, Category 6
    - Two-fiber 50.0 or 62.5/125µm multi-mode optical fiber cable
    - Single-mode optical fiber

The amount of untwisting of individual pairs shall be less than 0.5" for Category 5e, and less than 3" for Category 3.

Although the EIA/TIA standards describe the requirements for the cabling scheme, they do not specify the route the pathway must take, particu-larly for work area cable runs. The system designer must use the NEC® and local building codes as a reference, as well as considering the desires of the client. Although there are many ways of routing cable through a building, the most common means are as follows:

- Single-level underfloor duct
- Two-level underfloor duct
- Overhead ventilated cable trays
- Perimeter raceways

7.5.3 Residence Premises Wiring

The premises wiring requirements for a residence are quite different than those for a commercial building. The EF, ER, TR, and WA are replaced with the:

- Demarcation point
- Auxiliary disconnect outlet
- Distribution device
- Station wire
- Telecommunications outlet

The demarcation point, also called a network interface device (NID), is the point of interconnection between the service wire and the premises wiring. For single-tenant dwellings, this point will be within 12" of the protection device on the customer's side, or within 12" of entering the premises if a protection device is not installed.

The auxiliary disconnect outlet contains a modular jack for each line supplied to the premises and an input termination for connecting distribution wires. The modular jack allows the end user to disconnect each line for testing or rearranging the wiring configuration. *Figure 58* shows a combination network interface device and auxiliary

108F58.EPS

Figure 58 ◆ Combination NID auxiliary disconnect.

disconnect outlet. The left side of the device shown is the NID, where one pair of conductors is terminated and wires are routed to the auxiliary disconnect. *Figure 59* shows the same unit with the line leading into the residence removed from the auxiliary disconnect device.

The distribution device is a common point for terminating all distribution wire runs and for originating all station wire runs. The station wires connect the distribution device to the modular phone jacks located throughout the premises. The telecommunications outlet is a standard modular phone jack. The precautions for installing residence premises wiring are the same as for commercial premises wiring.

With cable runs, residence premises wiring can follow one of three different schemes, each with its own advantages and disadvantages. These three different methods are as follows:

- Backfeed (method 1)
- Looped (method 2)
- Homerun (method 3)

In the backfeed configuration, the tip and ring wires are run in a circular configuration to each station, returning to the distribution device. The advantage of this configuration is that there is an alternate path to the stations if a wire is cut. The disadvantage of this configuration is that it is hard to pull, especially over a long distance. A solution would be to run two separate wires from the distribution device to the farthest station, and connect the wires in the jack. *Figure 60* shows the wire run for a backfeed installation.

In a looped configuration, the stations are wired sequentially out to the last station, as shown in *Figure 61*. The advantage of this configuration is that it is easy to pull. The disadvantage is that if a wire is cut, all stations after the damaged station will cease to function.

The homerun configuration uses a separate wire run for each station, as shown in *Figure 62*. The advantage is that faults are easy to isolate and a cut wire will not disable any other stations. The disadvantage is that it takes longer to install.

Once the wiring method is decided upon, the cable run should be measured as follows:

Step 1 Measure the distance from the power meter to the ceiling joists or basement joists.

Step 2 Measure the distance from the outlet to the ceiling joists, and double it if using Method 1 or 2. (The cable will be looped through the outlet and back.)

Figure 59 ◆ Auxiliary disconnect removed.

108F60.EPS

Figure 60 ◆ Backfeed installation.

Step 3 Measure the route (at a convenient level) to each outlet.

Step 4 Add the three measurements.

Step 5 Multiply by 1.5 (to allow for error and slack).

In new construction, the measurement and installation process is much simpler than when installing in existing structures. In new homes, the connection boxes are mounted at the same level as the power outlets. Holes are drilled in the joists and studs, and the cabling is pulled through to the connection boxes.

The wiring must be fished through the walls using the existing wiring as a guide in existing structures.

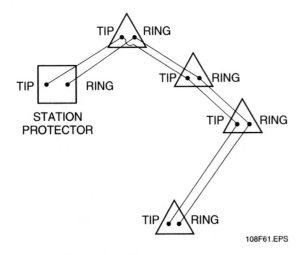

Figure 61 ◆ Looped installation.

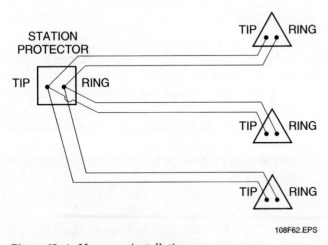

Figure 62 ◆ Homerun installation.

The termination requirements for residence premises wiring is similar to that of commercial wiring, although the normal termination device is an RJ11 plug. This plug can support up to three phone lines. If four lines are required, an RJ45 plug and connector will be used. If an RJ45 plug is used, it must be determined which wiring scheme (T568A or T568B [AT&T]) will be used. The plug wiring arrangements for a residence are shown in *Figure 63*.

7.6.0 Grounding and Bonding

Following the break-up of AT&T in 1984, all premises voice and data cabling became the responsibility of the end user. With the increasing voice and data system complexity, a reliable common grounding system is required to ensure optimum performance. Grounding to a water pipe is no longer satisfactory.

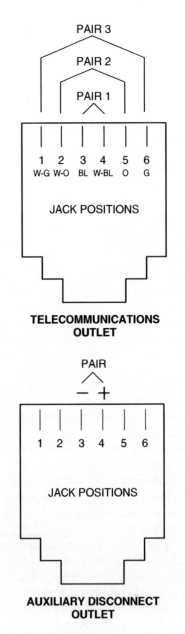

NOTE: JACKS ARE VIEWED FROM FRONT OPENING WITH THE TAB DOWN.

Figure 63 ◆ Plug wiring for residential termination.

For commercial applications, most standards call for a solid copper busbar with insulated standoffs in the EF as well as each ER and TC. Each busbar is drilled with rows of holes for the attachment of bolted compression fittings. Telecommunications equipment racks, frames, cabinets, and voltage protectors are grounded to these busbars. There is a backbone connecting the equipment busbars to the main grounding bus in the EF and a structural steel member on each floor. The EF grounding bus is connected to an earth ground. Grounding and bonding conductors are color coded green and labeled appropriately.

For residential applications, a common grounding conductor must be attached between the auxiliary disconnect device and the network interface device and then attached to the installed grounding rod connected to the power system.

8.0.0 ◆ ELECTROMAGNETIC INTERFERENCE (EMI) CONSIDERATIONS

When installing low-voltage cabling, EMI is one of the primary considerations during the selection and routing of cable. EMI may cause erratic operation of low-voltage circuits. EMI can be the result of coupled or induced currents created from nearby power lines, transformers, fluorescent ballasts, motors, office/factory equipment, or other electrical equipment. Harmonics of 60Hz power can also produce circuit noise. Low-voltage circuits can also be affected by radiated EMI from various noise sources such as variable-speed AC motor drives, generators, electronic equipment, or fluorescent lamps. In some cases, it may be man-made interference such as that caused by radio and television transmission signals or signals used for deliberate jamming purposes.

Adequate physical separation between the low-voltage circuits and any potential EMI sources is the primary solution in most installations. Along with separation, the use of high-performance UTP cable should eliminate most EMI problems. In especially harsh environments, such as industrial facilities, various types of shielded cable or optical fiber cable can be used to reduce or eliminate EMI. Check with cable manufacturers to determine the level of noise immunity offered by various grades of cable.

The following major precautions should be considered to reduce interference from sources of EMI:

- Use grounded metallic pathways to limit inductive or radiated EMI.
- Minimize emission from power conductors by using sheathed power cables or other construction such as taping, twisting, or bundling the conductors to prevent separation of the line, neutral, and grounding conductors.
- Maintain a minimum of 24" (609.6 mm) between electrical power cables and electrical or electronic equipment and unshielded low-voltage cables.
- If at all possible, cross power cables at 90-degree angles.
- For unintentional or deliberate high-noise environments, shielding and/or EMI filters may be required.

INSIDE TRACK

EMI

It is generally assumed that using shielded cable will prevent EMI problems. In reality, shielding is not very effective at frequencies below 100Hz. For that reason, EMI problems are often caused by 60Hz power conductors. The only way to prevent low frequency EMI problems is to use conduit or keep the cable widely separated from 60Hz lines. Shielding will reduce RF interference (RFI) at low frequencies, but has no effect on EMI.

8.1.0 EMI Guidelines

The following general guidelines detail some of the precautions required for increased protection against EMI:

- Twisted-pair cable results in less loop area for inductive pickup and lower inductance per foot of running cable.
- Multiple-conductor cable should consist of twisted conductors.
- Multiple-conductor cable used for transmission of several individual signals should consist of twisted-pair signal leads that are isolated from each other.
- Multiple-conductor cables should have an overall shield to further improve EMI.
- Terminate unused conductors at both ends or remove them altogether.
- Similar signals should be run together and not intermixed (e.g., run power with power and data with data).
- Closely space power leads to maximize cancellation of magnetic fields. Where possible, twist conductors that carry alternating currents.
- Low-level data transmission lines should not be run parallel to high-level power lines.
- Use localized magnetic barriers when signal lines are found close to switchgear.
- Conduit should not be buried below high-voltage transmission lines or in areas with high ground currents.
- Where unshielded cables of different signal conditions must cross, they should do so at right angles, not gradually over long distances.
- Pull boxes and junction boxes may require special attention, such as the need for ground barriers between circuits operating at different signal levels.

- Conduit separation in cable tray should be considered as a potential problem area.
- Tray networks in the floor provide better noise protection than other installations.
- System modifications and additions should be viewed as possible areas of concern.
- Signal return wire should not be shared by more than one signal path. Individual signal return wires must be used.
- EMI source suppression should be considered. Dealing with noise at the source helps to eliminate major corrective action on cabling systems.
- Avoid installing low-voltage circuits in pathways with power circuits, even if separated.
- Do not use isolated grounding circuits unless the equipment manufacturer mandates using isolated circuits.
- Whenever possible, use grounded conduits and enclosures for low-voltage circuits.
- Always follow the equipment manufacturer's instructions for the use and grounding of any cable shields.

Summary

Knowing the different types of low-voltage cables, their construction, how they are rated, and their uses is important to the electronic systems technician when cable must be selected, routed, and pulled for a particular job. The technician must be familiar with the equipment, safety procedures, and techniques of pulling various types of cable in residential and commercial buildings. The procedures for installing low-voltage cable and the various requirements of the NEC® and other standards or considerations covering the installation of low-voltage cable must also be understood.

Review Questions

1. Low-voltage cable typically contains solid wire sizes ranging from _____ AWG.
   a. No. 28 to No. 14
   b. No. 26 to No. 12
   c. No. 22 to No. 10
   d. No. 20 to No. 8

2. Of the following, _____ is used most extensively for cable jackets.
   a. polyvinyl chloride
   b. polyethylene
   c. rubber
   d. crosslinked polyethylene

3. Communications circuits are covered in _____.
   a. *NEC Article 760*
   b. *NEC Article 770*
   c. *NEC Article 780*
   d. *NEC Article 800*

4. A power-limited fire alarm cable that can be used in plenums is marked as _____.
   a. FPL
   b. FPLP
   c. FPLR
   d. CM

5. A limited-use communication cable that can only be used in dwellings and raceways is marked as _____.
   a. CMX
   b. CM
   c. NP
   d. CMG

6. On a shielded cable, floating the ground means _____.
   a. removing the shield
   b. not grounding the shield
   c. grounding both ends of the shield
   d. grounding one end of the shield

7. Category 5e UTP cable has a bandwidth up to _____.
   a. 10MHz
   b. 16MHz
   c. 20MHz
   d. 100MHz

8. The minimum grade of UTP cable acceptable for new telecommunications installations is Category _____.
   a. 2
   b. 3
   c. 4
   d. 5

9. The UTP cable tip color for the first five pairs is normally _____.
   a. red
   b. blue
   c. yellow
   d. white

10. In an optical fiber cable, the _____ creates a reflective boundary.
    a. buffer layer
    b. acrylate coating
    c. cladding
    d. jacket

11. Single-mode optical fiber core is normally _____ in diameter.
    a. 8 to 9 microns
    b. 50 microns
    c. 62.5 microns
    d. 100 microns

12. A power fishing system is used primarily to blow or vacuum a _____ through a raceway system.
    a. cable
    b. wire
    c. string line
    d. heavy rope

13. A vertical pull of a heavy cable from the top down is likely to require _____.
    a. a pull line
    b. reel brakes
    c. a rope tugger
    d. temporary take-up devices

14. Horizontal pulls for backbone communication cable installations must *not* exceed _____ between pull points.
    a. 98'
    b. 295'
    c. 328'
    d. 984'

15. Grade 1 residential service does *not* provide _____ service.
    a. telephone
    b. data
    c. television
    d. multimedia

16. In new residential construction where conduit is not used, cables can be brought through the finished wall by the use of a _____.
    a. mud ring
    b. closed box
    c. sleeve
    d. ceramic tube

17. A _____ is used to prevent cables from being damaged by drywall screws or nails.
    a. wire tie
    b. steel plate
    c. mud ring
    d. sleeve

18. The NEC® allows power-limited fire alarm circuit conductors to be within 2" of insulated power conductors if _____.
    a. they are separated by a continuous barrier
    b. the power circuits carry no more than 15 amps
    c. the fire alarm circuit conductors are shielded
    d. there are no high-frequency broadband cables within 6"

19. A process that allows several different data signals to be carried simultaneously on a common path is called _____.
    a. time domain sharing
    b. time division multiplexing
    c. frequency domain demultiplexing
    d. time domain reflecting

20. To reduce EMI, it is recommended that low-voltage circuits be separated from power circuits by a minimum distance of _____.
    a. 2"
    b. 12"
    c. 24"
    d. 36"

Stephen Clare, Master Instructor

Lincoln Technical Institute

Steve Clare was stocking shelves at a local grocery store when he realized that he wanted to do more with his life. He took charge of his own destiny and obtained the training he needed to start on a career as an electronic systems technician and instructor.

Tell us how you got into the electronics field.
I was 21 years old and working at a job without much of a future. I decided I wanted to do more with my life, so I entered the Job Corps and took up electrical wiring. When my training was complete, I immediately got a job as an electrician's helper, but I was not satisfied. While in this line of work I saw people installing high-tech equipment and decided that's what I wanted to do. I went back to school for two years to study electronics. Once I obtained my state certification as an electronics technician, I was able to get a job as an installer for Eastern Home Solutions, a company that was doing security and home automation systems.

What kinds of work have you done in your career?
Eastern Home Solutions, the company I started with, branched out from security and home automation to cover audio, video, networking, CCTV, access control, fire, voice, and data. This expansion allowed me to get experience in all these areas, and I wound up becoming their head technician.

What do you do in your current job?
As a master instructor, I helped set up the Columbia, MD training program and training facility. In addition to this, I review curriculum to ensure it meets industry standards and national codes. I also teach classes, as well as train new instructors.

What advice would you give to someone just entering the field?
Find out what you like and focus on it. When you enjoy what you're doing, work is more like a hobby than a chore. Try to keep a positive attitude. It makes life easier for you and for those around you.

What factors contributed to your success?
The biggest factor was completing my training and getting my certification. Once I decided I wanted to work in this industry, I dedicated myself to doing whatever I needed to do to reach my goal. I believe that I have good work habits that stem from my desire to do a good job. Hence the passion I have for this industry transitioned into not just settling for working in my chosen field, but improving it.

Do you have an interesting career-related fact or accomplishment to share?
After I had been in the industry for several years, I decided that I wanted to give something back to it, and at the same time, influence the future of training in the industry. I became a subject matter expert for development of the NCCER EST Curriculum. I review the NCCER training materials and help them write new material. I also participate in other organizations. I serve on the System Integration subcommittee for the Security Industries Association (SIA) and I am working with the National Institute for Certification in Engineering Technologies (NICET) on the CCTV Certification. I'm also helping in the development of the system integration section of the World of Electronic Access Control Course (WEAC).

Trade Terms Introduced in This Module

Ampacity: The amount of current, in amperes, that a conductor is permitted to carry continuously without exceeding its temperature rating.

Attenuation: A decrease in the magnitude of a signal. It represents a loss of signal power between two points and is measured in decibels (dB).

Basket grip: A flexible steel mesh grip used on the ends of cable and conductors for attaching the pulling rope. The more force exerted by the pull, the tighter the grip wraps around the cable.

Capstan: The turning drum of a cable puller on which the rope is wrapped and pulled. An increase in the number of wraps increases the pulling force of the cable puller.

CATV: Abbreviation for community access television.

Clevis: A device used in cable pulls to facilitate connecting the pulling rope to the cable grip.

Conduit piston: A foam cylinder that fits inside the conduit and is then propelled by compressed air or vacuumed through the conduit run to pull a line, rope, or measuring tape. Also called a mouse.

Crosstalk: Unwanted coupling of signals from circuit to circuit.

Digit receiver: A piece of equipment at the local exchange that receives and interprets telephone tone or pulse signals.

Direct inward dialing (DID): The ability to call an extension on a PBX or key system without having to go through an operator or receptionist.

Drain wires: Wires running parallel to and in contact with a foil cable shield. They are used to connect the shield to a grounding point.

Electromagnetic interference (EMI): An electrical phenomenon in which undesirable random electrical energy from a source such as adjacent wiring, equipment, etc. is induced or picked up by wiring and subsequently causes problems with equipment connected to the wiring. Also known as radio frequency interference (RFI), noise, and radio interference.

Fish line: A light cord used in conjunction with vacuum/blower power fishing systems that attaches to the conduit piston to be pushed or pulled through the conduit. Once through, a pulling rope is attached to one end and pulled back through the conduit for use in pulling conductors.

Fish tape: A flat iron wire or fiber cord used to pull conductors or a pulling rope through conduit.

Frequency division multiplexing: A means of combining multiple calls on a single line by the modulation of different carrier frequencies.

Head end: The central distribution and/or control equipment that is used in residential installations.

Impedance: A measurement of the opposition to the flow of alternating current (AC).

Key system: A type of private use phone system, usually within a building or company.

Local exchange: The lowest controlling element within a municipal phone system.

Messenger: A strong support member, such as a steel strand used to carry the weight of cables and wiring.

Multiplex: Combining two or more signals into a single wave from which either of the two original signals can be recovered.

Nonpower-limited circuit: A circuit that complies with *NEC Chapters 1* through *4* and is less than 600V.

Patch cord: A connecting cable used with cross-connect equipment and work area cables. It has three conductive portions separated by insulators.

Power-limited circuit: A circuit that has a power source limited to 1,000VA or that is self-limiting to 1,000VA or less.

Premises: Refers to wiring within a structure or building.

Primary center: Connects toll centers within a specific area and connects to a sectional center. One step above a toll center.

Private branch exchange (PBX): A type of private use phone system, usually within a building or company.

Regional center: The highest controlling level within the national phone system. It connects distinct regions of the country.

Sectional center: Connects primary centers within a specific section of the country and connects to a regional center. One step above a primary center.

Sheave: A pulley-like device used in cable pulls in both conduit and cable tray systems.

Snub: Wrapping a rope around a post or other secure object to check the movement of the rope.

Soap: Slang for wire-pulling lubricant.

Thicknet (10 base 5): A specification for a network using a thick 50Ω coaxial cable.

Thinnet (10 base 2): A specification for a network using a thin 50Ω coaxial cable.

Time division multiplexing: A means of combining multiple signals on a single line or channel by incorporating a time-sharing scheme.

Token ring: A network topology in which a token must be passed to a terminal or workstation by the network controller before it can transmit.

Toll center: Routes calls between toll zones and connects to a primary center. One step above the local exchange.

Tracer: A strip or band of color that is different than the insulation color on a wire. The band or strip is used for identification purposes. In older wire, the tracer was a colored thread encased by the insulation.

Trunk: A large group of wires running between specific points.

Twisted-pair cable: A multi-conductor cable consisting of two or more copper conductors twisted in a manner designed to cancel electrical interference.

Installing Cable in Unfinished Areas of Commercial Construction

The following procedures and illustrations are provided courtesy of Labor $aving Devices®, Inc. The tools referred to in the procedures are illustrated and described in *Appendix C*.

NOTE

In the section to follow, we have addressed some of the most common situations facing wire/cable installers. Listed are the basic tools required for the best results, along with a brief explanation of how to proceed. It is purely informative, and in no event can Labor $aving Devices®, Inc. be liable for any special, incidental, or consequential damages.

WARNING!

It remains the sole responsibility of the installer to operate in accordance with any applicable federal, state, county, city, and local building or other codes and to follow official requirements on the use of safety equipment.

OVER FALSE (GRID) CEILINGS

1. LONG RUN (UP TO 125 FEET AT A TIME), SMALL ACCESS AREA, OPEN SPACE

How to proceed:

1. Remove tile from false ceiling; aim the yoke of the **Sling-A-Line** holding it HORIZONTALLY. Push the button on the reel to release the line and put the weight in the leather sling. Shoot.
2. At the other end, attach your wire to a length of **PullCord**, tie the PullCord to the lead weight and reel it back.
3. In areas where cable cannot be resting on the ceiling tiles, attach one **2nd Man Pulley** above the drop ceiling to receive your cable.

Note: Do not remove the ceiling tile in the area you are shooting towards: the weight could drop through the opening and cause injury or property damage. If the line gets tangled over any object, pull the line very slowly with your hand to allow the weight to unravel itself.

2. MEDIUM RUN (UP TO 40 FEET), OPEN SPACE

How to proceed:

1. Remove a tile, rest the wire on the outer "V" of the **Grabbit 18's Ztip**.
2. Push the wire to its destination by extending the Grabbit section by section; if working a two person crew with two Grabbits, the second installer, 40 ft. away from you, will grab the wire with the knifed edges side of the Ztip and pull the wire in collapsing the sections of the Grabbit, one by one.

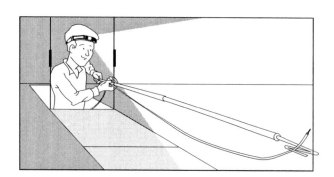

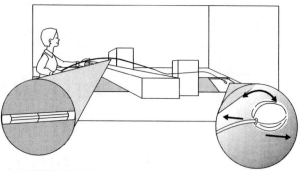

3. MEDIUM RUN, CROWDED SPACE

How to proceed:

1. Attach as many of the **CZ30 sections** as you will need, using pliers to snug the connectors together.
2. With a simple flick of your wrist, the rods will jump up over air ducts, lighting fixtures, cable raceways, etc.
3. The wisp head also raises the end of the Creep-Zit so it can slide smoothly over the grid dividers; turn the end of the Creep-Zit in your hand and the wisp head at the other end will walk from side to side.
4. Attach the wire to the wisp head and bring it back to you, or to the bullnose at the back end.

Note: If pulling multiple cables at once, we recommend you tie them into a **PullSleeve** that you attach to the end of the **PullCord**; also, run with your cables at least one extra length of nylon cord for subsequent cable runs. Also, in areas where cables cannot be resting on ceiling tiles, attach one **2nd Man Pulley** above the drop ceiling to receive your cable.

4. SHORT RUN (UP TO 25 FEET), SEMI-CROWDED SPACE

How to proceed:

1. When working above ceiling in occupied office, the **YFT 30-E**, contained in its round carrying case, can be maneuvered without risk of property or bodily damage.
2. To direct wisp head from side to side. Remove the YFT entirely from its case.
3. Because of its extreme flexibility, the YFT will require some practice to "jump" over obstacles.

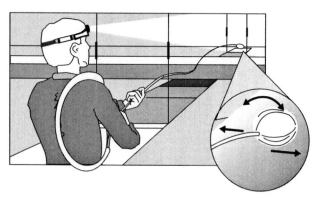

108A01.EPS

5. LONG RUN (100 FEET AND OVER), SEMI-CROWDED SPACE

How to proceed:

1. The **CF50 Fishtix** is a heavy duty version of the Creep-Zit kit, giving you the added <u>rigidity</u> required to pull runs of 100 feet and longer, yet operating the same way the Creep-Zit does (see **medium run, crowded space**).

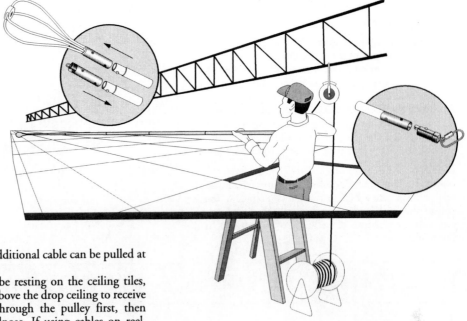

2. When you have extended the Fishtix to its final destination, either attach the male bullnose to the last section, then your cable or PullCord to it and go to the other end to pull it to you, or replace the wisp head up front with the female bullnose, attach cable or pull cord, and pull towards you from the back end. Hint: When pulling long cable runs, it is suggested to pull at least one **PullCord** with the cable to facilitate your work, should additional cable can be pulled at a later date.

3. In areas where cable cannot be resting on the ceiling tiles, attach one **2nd Man Pulley** above the drop ceiling to receive your cable, pass the cable through the pulley first, then attach it to the Fishtix's bullnose. If using cables on reel, place the reels on the Decoil-Zit, just below the ceiling opening.

OVER PIPES OR BEAMS, FROM THE GROUND

How to proceed:

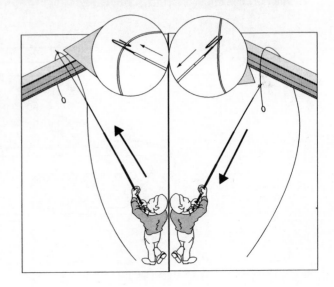

1. If working alone, attach at the end of the wire or **PullCord** a weight (i.e., a golf ball), then "rest" the wire in the outer "V" of the Ztip.

2. Extending the **Grabbit** section by section, pass the wire (PullCord) and the weight over the pipe or beam and release it from the Ztip (the weight will keep the wire from falling back).

3. Now, using the knifed edge side of the Ztip, pull the wire over the beam. Repeat the steps for the next beams.

Note: If working a two person crew with two Grabbits, ignore the weight and just pass the wire to one another over the beam. If pulling multiple cables, tie them in the **PullSleeve**, and attach the Pull-Sleeve to the end of the **PullCord**.

IN RACE WAYS OR OVER PIPES

IN RACE WAYS OR OVER BEAMS AND PIPES NOT MORE THAN 6 FEET APART

How to proceed:

1. Attach the wisp head to the first section, then as you start pushing the **Fishtix** in the raceway or over the beams, snap as many sections together as needed for your run.
2. Attach the male bullnose at the end of the last section (or the female bullnose at the front of the first section after having removed the wisp head), then attach the Pull-cord (or cable) to the bullnose and pull back.

Note: If pulling multiple cables at once, we recommend you tie them into a **PullSleeve** that you attach to the end of the **PullCord**; also, run with your cables at least one extra length of nylon cord for subsequent cable runs.

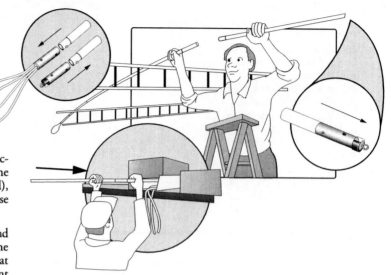

HORIZONTAL TURNS & ELEVATION CHANGES

How to proceed:

1. Snap the hanging strap of the **2nd Man Pulley** off the axle pin and the retaining latch. Attach the pulley to the proper support device, snap the strap back on the axle pin and in the retaining latch, in the same manner, position a 2nd Man Pulley at each horizontal turn, elevation change, each up and down location.
2. Pull the cable through each 2nd Man Pulley.

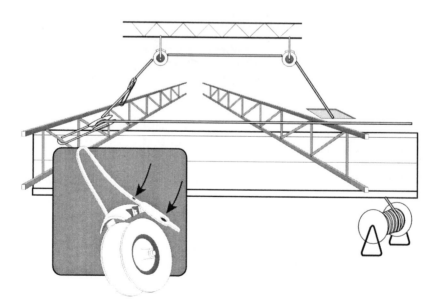

108A03.EPS

Installing Cable in Residential and Finished Areas of Commercial Construction

WHAT?...WHERE?...WHEN?...HOW?...WOW!

In the section to follow, we have addressed some of the most common situations facing wire/cable installers. Listed are The basic tools required for the best and fastest results, briefly explaining how to proceed. It is purely informative, and in no event can Labor Saving Devices® be liable for any special, incidental or consequential damages.

IT REMAINS THE INSTALLERS SOLE RESPONSIBILITY TO OPERATE IN ACCORDANCE WITH ANY APPLICABLE FEDERAL, STATE, COUNTY, CITY AND LOCAL BUILDING OR OTHER CODE(S), AND TO FOLLOW OFFICIAL REQUIREMENTS ON THE USE OF SAFETY EQUIPMENT.

FISHING WIRES INSIDE WALLS

IN EMPTY (INSIDE) WALLS

1. DOWN, FROM THE TOP PLATE TO THE BASE OF THE WALL, ON CONCRETE FLOOR

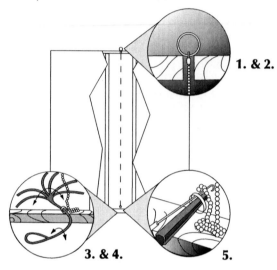

1. & 2.

3. & 4.   5.

How to proceed:

1. In the attic, drill a hole in the top plate with the selected drill bit (**Spear-Zit, Bell Hanger,** or **Pro-Bore®**).
2. Attach the "stop ring" to one end of the ball chain of the **WR24**; drop the chain in the drilled hole.
3. In the room, remove the baseboard and drill a hole at the base of the wall.
4. Bend the flexible retriever of the WR24 and insert in the hole. Move it left to right until the magnet catches the ball chain.
5. Bring the ball chain to the hole; with the **LBS** (or the **Hook-Zit 9"**) pull the chain out. Attach the wire to the chain. (If pulling coax cable or large wires, attach a nylon PullCord to the chain, then the cable to the **PullCord**.)
6. From the top plate, pull the ball chain and the wire. (**Hint:** with concrete floors, run the wire behind the baseboard or between baseboard and tack strip if there is carpet.)

2. DOWN, FROM THE TOP PLATE TO THE CRAWL SPACE OR UNFINISHED BASEMENT

How to proceed:

1. In the attic, drill a hole in the top plate with the selected drill bit.
2. Attach the "stop ring" to one end of the ball chain of the WR24; drop the chain in the drilled hole.

3. Instead of pulling down the molding, this time drill up through the bottom plate from the basement or crawl space.
4. Keep the flexible handle of the WR24 almost straight, with just a light bend on the magnet side. Insert the drilled hole and fish the ball chain. Proceed as above.

3. MULTIPLE CABLE RUNS, DOWN FROM THE TOP PLATE TO LOWER FLOOR(S)

How to proceed:

1. First select the smallest **Drill-Eze** bit size that will accommodate your cable run. Start drilling through the top plate from above, having selected the 2-ft. shaft.
2. Pull the bit back to you and replace the 2-ft. shaft by the smallest next size up (4- or 6-ft.) that will let you reach the next "plate" inside the wall.
3. Once you have drilled through the second plate, pull the bit back to you or add to the shaft the smallest extension that will let you drill through the third "plate".
4. Use extreme caution when drilling the second or following plates in order to avoid drilling through the wall; it is suggested to "rest" the shaft (or extension) against the wall of the first hole.
5. Once you have reached the lower destination point, attach to the end of the last extension a nylon **PullCord**. If pulling multiple cables or pre-connected ones, we recommend the use of the **PullSleeve**.
6. From downstairs, pull the bit, the nylon PullCord and cable will follow.

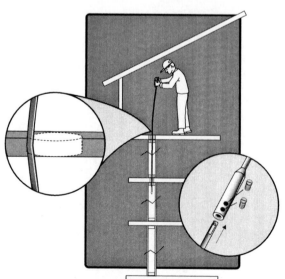

108A04.EPS

IN WALL WITH STAPLED BAT INSULATION

1. DOWN, FROM THE TOP PLATE TO THE BASE OF THE WALL, ON CONCRETE FLOOR

How to proceed:

1. Use the **StudSensor** to locate the inside edge of the stud (or use the TriScanner to locate the stud and check for hot electrical lines along the stud).
2. Cut a 4" **Wire Bit** and at the inside edge of the stud, drill through the ceiling, where it meets with the wall. Remove the drill motor, leaving the wire bit poking through the ceiling.
3. In the attic, using the wire bit sticking up as a reference, measure 3/4" and drill a hole (use **Spear-Zit** or **Bell Hanger**). You will be right in the void between the dry wall and the stapled insulation.
4. Drop the ball chain of the **WR24** in the drilled hole.
5. In the room, first, remove the wire bit (the hole is so small that it will remained unnoticed), then remove the molding and drill a hole at the base of the wall. Insert the flexible handle of the **WR24** and bring the ball chain to the hole. Pull the chain with the **LBS** (or **Hook-Zit**).
6. Attach the wire to the chain and pull from the attic.

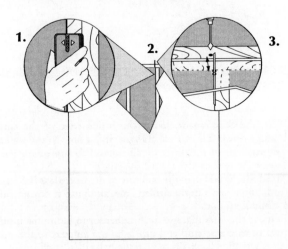

2. DOWN, FROM THE TOP PLATE TO THE CRAWL SPACE OR UNFINISHED BASEMENT

How to proceed:

1. Use the **StudSensor** to locate the inside edge of the stud (or use the **TriScanner** to locate the stud and check for hot electrical lines along the stud).
2. Cut a 4" **wire bit** and at the inside edge of the stud, drill through the ceiling, where it meets with the wall. Remove the drill motor, leaving the wire bit poking through the ceiling.
3. In the attic, using the wire bit sticking up as a reference, measure 3/4" and drill a hole. You will be right in the void between the dry wall and the stapled insulation.
4. Drop the ball chain in the drilled hole.
5. Instead of pulling the molding in the room, this time drill up through the bottom plate from the basement.
6. Keep the flexible handle of the **WR24** almost straight, with a light bent on the magnet side. Insert in the hole and fish the ball chain. Attach the wire to the chain and pull from the attic.

IN WALL WITH INSULATION WITH MOISTURE BARRIER

1. DOWN, FROM TOP PLATE TO BASE OF WALL ON CONCRETE FLOOR... OR... TO CRAWL SPACE OR UNFINISHED BASEMENT

How to proceed:

Same procedure as for Stapled Bat Insulation.

2. DOWN, FROM THE MIDDLE TO THE BASE OF THE WALL, ON CONCRETE FLOOR

How to proceed:

1. Use the **SSZ9 StudSensor** to locate the middle between two studs and mark the wall.
2. Using a small pointed object, poke a hole in the dry wall at a "down angle", making sure not to pierce the moisture barrier.
3. Attach the **WNH-1** to the bullnose of the **LZsec** and enter it through the hole, in the wall, between the drywall and the moisture barrier, until the bullnose touches the bottom plate.
4. Having dropped the base molding, run the **LZO** compass alongside the base of the wall to locate the LZsec magnet.
5. When the red arrow points at the wall, move the compass upward; if the white arrow points this time at the wall, you have located the magnet, not a nail or a pipe.
6. Drill a hole (with **Spear-Zit** or **Bell Hanger**) right where the compass located the magnet, and, with the **LBS** retriever (or **HZ9 Hook-Zit**), pull the ball chain out.
7. Attach the wire (or **PullCord** if running cable) to the ball chain. Pull the rod up.

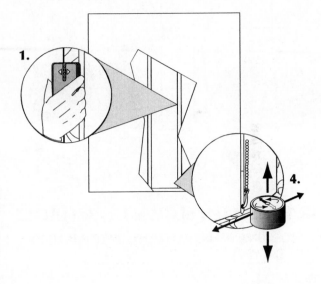

108A05.EPS

IN EMPTY OR INSULATED WALLS, DOWN FROM THE MIDDLE OF WALL, TO CARPETED FLOOR

How to proceed:

1. Pull the carpet and padding from the wall; with a chisel and a hammer, cut a 2" piece of the tack strip.
2. Attach the **BBZ Base-Boar-Zit** to the high speed drill motor, place it against the wall where you cut the tack strip and start drilling, holding the unit firmly against the floor... The drill will go through the molding, the drywall, up the bottom plate (note: always start the bit in a wood molding for it to go up).
3. Push and pull the bit several times to clean the hole, always leaving the drill motor in forward. Remove the bit.
4. Attach the **WNH-1 ball chain** to one of the eyelet of the .047 fish wire provided in the **Base-Boar-Zit Kit** and insert in the hole. (mark the fish wire with tape at the length you need)
5. When the fish wire is in the wall up to the marking tape, insert the HZ9 or LBS in the access hole and fish the ball chain; bring it to the hole and attach the wire or a PullCord. Pull the fish wire from the bottom.
6. Run wire between molding and tack strip (see **fishing wire under carpet, between molding and tack strip**) or down to the basement (see **fishing wire in crawl space, from upstairs with carpeted floor**); replace the padding and the carpet; they will hide the hole in the molding and the wire.

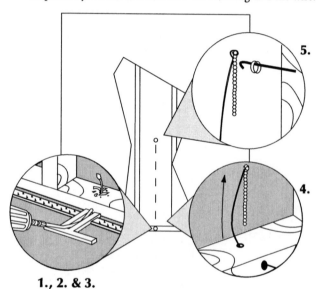

1., 2. & 3.

IN WALL WITH BLOWN-IN CELLULOSE

1. FROM UNFINISHED BASEMENT, UP TO THE MIDDLE OF THE WALL

How to proceed:

1. Cut a 4" Wire Bit and against the wall, drill down through the floor; remove the drill motor, leaving the wire bit in the floor.
2. In the unfinished basement, locate the wire bit sticking through the floor and, with the **Spear-Zit flex bit** or **Bell hanger** and the **directional tool**, drill up the bottom plate immediately behind the wire bit at an angle towards you. This will later direct the **LZsec rod** towards the front drywall. Drill with extreme care so the bit does not go through the wall! (Note: you could also use a right angle drill motor.)

3. Attach the **WNH-1** 1-ft. ball chain to the bullnose of the LZsec; push it up the drilled hole using a jabbing motion; the rod will "ride" against the drywall. (Remember to mark the rod at the length you want to stop.)
4. Back in the room, use the **LZO** compass to locate the magnet of the LZsec; poke a hole in front of the magnet and with the **Hook-Zit 9"** or **LBS** pull the ball chain. Attach the wire or a PullCord and pull the rod down from the basement.

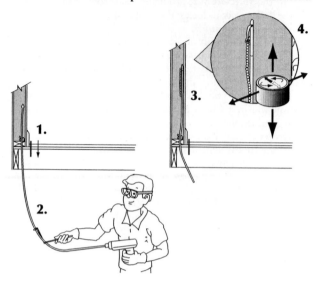

2. DOWN, FROM THE MIDDLE OF THE WALL, TO BASE OF WALL ON CONCRETE FLOOR

How to proceed:

1. With the **StudSensor**, locate the inside edge of the stud. Using a **Spear-Zit** or **Bell Hanger** drill a hole in the wall at a down angle (it will direct the fiberglass fish tape on the back side of the wall cavity, against the stud).
2. Attach the **WNH-1** to the bullnose of the **fiberglass fish tape** (rod) and enter it in the drilled hole, and push it down using a jabbing motion.
3. Remove the molding, use the StudSensor to locate the inside edge of the same stud and drill a hole right next to the stud edge. Use the **Hook-Zit** to grab the ball chain and bring it to you. Attach the wire or a PullCord to the chain. Bring the fiberglass rod up.

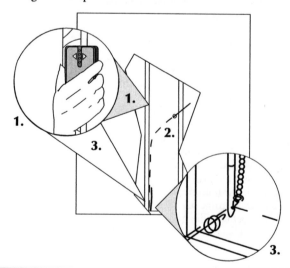

108A06.EPS

INSIDE WALL, DOWN FROM IN-WALL SPEAKER OPENING OR UP FROM SYSTEM'S OUTLET OPENING

How to proceed:

1. With the **StudSensor** locate the two studs in between which you will locate the speaker and mark the wall.
2. If installing a rectangular speaker, use the manufacturer's provided template and mark the contour (use the **pocket level** to guarantee perfect alignment).
3. Adjust the depth gauge of the **Spira-Cut** bit 1/8" longer than the thickness of the material to cut and start the bit into the material at a 45 degree angle. Slowly bring it to 90 degrees and begin to cut clockwise (start and end at the top of the hole). Note: if cutting a round opening, adjust the circular guide of the Spiracut to the diameter to cut, then proceed as above.
4. To run your cable, follow the procedures described above, based on the type of wall (insulation), you are dealing with. If you need to cut an opening for an outlet box proceed as for rectangular speakers: if the box is already installed and you need to cut the drywall covering it, plunge the Spirabit inside the box, guide it to the right until it touches the inside edge of the box: pull the bit out far enough so it is now against the outside of the box and move the Spiracut counter clockwise.

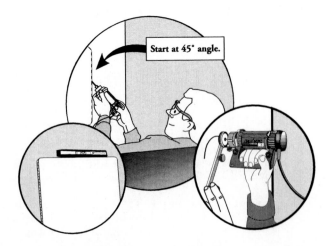

Start at 45° angle.

FISHING WIRES IN FINISHED BASEMENT

BASEMENT WINDOW CONTACT OR IN-WALL SPEAKER, UP TO UPPER FLOOR

How to proceed:

1. From the window header, drill up into the cavity between floor and ceiling using the **Spear-Zit** or **Bell Hanger**; before going upstairs, measure the distance from the drilled hole to the outside wall perpendicular to the one you are working on. If installing in-wall speaker in the basement, use the **Spiracut** to cut the speaker opening (refer to application *inside wall, down from in-wall speaker or up from system's outlet)* then drill up into wall.
2. Upstairs, measure the same distance, from the same outside wall in order to be located between the same floor joists. Pull the carpet and drill down, between molding and tack strip.
3. Attach the stop-ring to the ball chain of the **WR24** and drop chain down the drilled hole; it will pile up on top of the ceiling.
4. Downstairs, insert the flexible handle of the WR24 in the hole drilled through the window header and fish the ball chain in a "twist-pull-back" motion. Bring the chain down to you and attach your wire.
5. Upstairs, pull the ball chain and the wire; from one corner of the room, send the **YFT-10 fiberglass fish tape** between the tack strip and the molding. Attach the wire to the bullnose of the YFT-10; pull it to its destination. If the upstairs floor is not carpeted, run you wire behind the molding or up the wall.

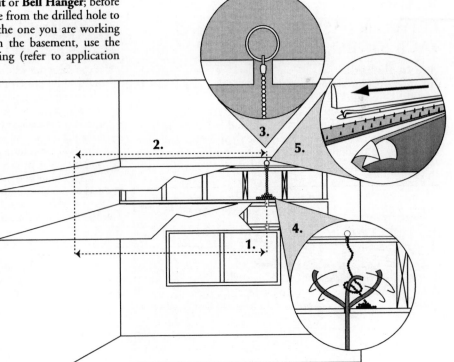

108A07.EPS

CRAWL SPACE OR UNFINISHED BASEMENT

FROM UPSTAIRS, WITH CARPETED FLOORS

How to proceed:

1. Upstairs, pull the carpet and with **Spear-Zit** or **Bell Hanger** drill a hole down, between molding and tack strip.
2. Attach the stripped end of the wire through the hole of the **GR3 GloRod** and flip it back on the flat of the rod (or pass it through the cross hole of the bullnose of the **GR3BB** or **GR3L**).
3. Holding the wire and the GloRod together, pushed them in the drilled hole; still holding onto the wire, jab the push rod to "quick release" the wire. Pull the rod back, the wire will stay.
4. In the crawl space, wearing the **TSP-1** headlight if necessary, extend the **GR12 Grabbit** telescoping pole towards the dangling wire; grab it with the knifed edges side of the Ztip and bring the wire to you.

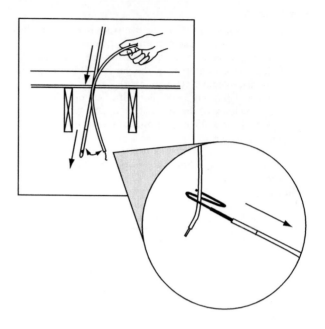

FROM UPSTAIRS, WITH UNCARPETED FLOORS

How to proceed:

Same procedure as above, except that you will have to remove the molding to drill down and run your wire behind it or up the wall.

FISHING WIRE UNDER CARPET

BETWEEN BASE MOLDING AND TACK STRIP

How to proceed:

Pull the carpet in the corner of the room with a pair of needle nose pliers; feed the **YFT fiberglass** rod between the base molding and the tack strip to where your wire is. Attach the stripped wire end to the bullnose of the rod. Pull the rod and the wire back from the corner of the room. Repeat the steps as necessary. The space between molding and tack strip is a "natural" channel to run wires, without having to move furniture.

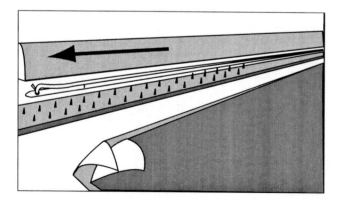

BETWEEN CARPET AND PADDING

How to proceed:

1. If you must run wire under carpet, always run it between carpet and padding to create a double cushion to protect the wire. Never staple or tape the wire as traffic could create damage to the wire jacket resulting in a short.
2. Insert the rolled-up end of the **UCT25 Under Carpet Tape** between carpet and padding from the destination place of the wire; when reaching the other side, strip the end of the wire and attach it to the rolled end of the UCT. Roll back the UCT25 in its case as it brings the wire to you. (The rounded end of the UCT25 is for running over waffle type padding.)

Note: Do not staple or tape the wire; avoid traffic areas.

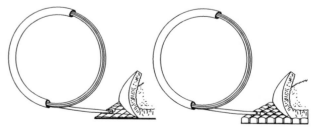

SMOOTH (SHEET ROCK) CEILING MATERIAL

How to proceed:

1. With the **SSZ9 StudSensor**, locate two joists in between which the device will be located and cut a hole a least 2" in diameter with **Spiracut**. Then measure the distance between the hole and the outside wall parallel to the joists.

2. Upstairs, measure the same distance from the same outside wall in order to be between the same joists, against an inside wall perpendicular to the outside wall.

3. Pull the carpet and drill a hole between tack strip and molding (use **Spear-Zit**, or **Bell Hanger**). Attach the "stop-ring" to the **ball chain of the WR24** and drop it in the hole. It will pile up on top of the ceiling.

4. Back downstairs, insert the in the hole cut in the ceiling and locate the "pile" of ball chain. Direct the **CZD Drag-Zit** magnet (screwed on a **CZX section of the CZ-30**) to the pile. Pull the rod slowly back to you so it will feed the ball chain to you .

5. Once you have the chain to you attach to it a minimum of 10 feet of **PullCord**, the wire or cable to the cord.

6. Upstairs, pull the ball chain, the PullCord... The wire (or cable).

ROUGH (LATH & PLASTER) CEILING MATERIAL

How to proceed:

1. With the **SSZ9 StudSensor**, locate two joists in between which the device will be located and cut a hole a least 2" in diameter with **Spiracut**. Then measure the distance between the hole and the outside wall parallel to the joists.

2. Upstairs, measure the same distance from the same outside wall in order to be between the same joists, against an inside wall perpendicular to the outside wall.

3. This time feed a length of thin gauge wire (or **PullCord**) down the drilled hole instead of the ball chain.

4. Back downstairs, screw the **Ztip** on the **CZX rod** of the **Creep-Zit**. With the **Walleye**, locate the wire (or **PullCord**) hanging down and grab it with the knifed edges side of the Ztip. Bring it to you, tie the wire and proceed as above.

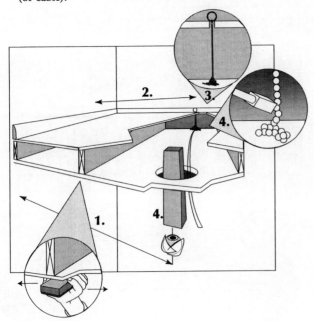

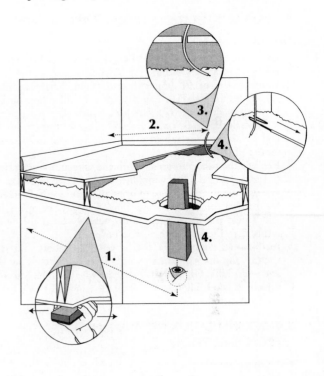

1. LIGHT OR MEDIUM INSULATION, UP FROM WALL DOWNSTAIRS

How to proceed:

1. Using the **Spear-Zit** or **Bell Hanger** drill bit, drill a hole up the top plate.
2. Put the stripped end of the wire through the hole of the **GloRod** and flip it on the flat of the rod. Holding both the rod and the wire, feed it up the hole until it touches the roof line. Holding the wire, pull the rod back a little in order to create a loop in the attic. This can be repeated as often as you have wire runs to bring up the attic.
3. In the attic (wearing the **TSP-1** headlight if necessary) and from a comfortable and convenient location, extend the **GR-12 (12-ft.) Grabbit** towards the first looped wire. With the knifed edges side of the Ztip, grab the wire and bring it to you. The rod will fall back downstairs. Repeat for the following runs. Remember to collect the rods downstairs.

2. MEDIUM INSULATION, FROM A WINDOW HEADER

How to proceed:

1. Using the **Spear-Zit** or **Bell Hanger** drill bit, drill a hole up the window header and the top plate.
2. Insert the 24" or 36" (depending on ceiling height) stainless tube of the **FEK-1 Fish-Eze Kit** into the drilled hole until it its the roof sheeting, then pull back a little.
3. Remove the coiled fish wire of the Fish-Eze kit from its holder and feed it into the tube; the fish wire will coil in the attic, on top of the insulation.
4. Remove the tube and attach both the wire and a nylon line to the eyelet of the fish wire (operating as a two person crew, you will use the nylon line to bring the fish tape back to you for the next run). If operating alone, disregard the nylon line and repeat the above steps using several coiled fish wires rather than the same one over and over.
5. In the attic, extend the **GR-8** or **GR-12** Grabbit with **Jtip** towards the first coiled fish wire. Hit it so the coils lay flat and won't kink. Grab all the loops the wire with the Jtip so it uncoils as you bring it to you. Pull the fish wire, it will bring the wire to you.

3. THICK INSULATION (18" AND MORE), FROM WALL BELOW

How to proceed:

1. Using the **Spear-Zit**, drill a hole up through the top plate.
2. Tie a 30-lb. nylon fishing line to one of the bullnose of the **YFT fiberglass fish tape** and feed it in the drilled hole. When it hits the roof sheeting, pull on the nylon line. The YFT will bend and follow the roof line.
3. You can now go in the attic and pull the YFT and the wire to you or tie the wire to the YFT and pull it back down.

4. IN ATTIC, FROM ONE END TO THE OTHER

How to proceed:

1. Attach as many of the **CZ30** sections as you will need, using pliers to snug the connectors together.
2. With a simple flick of your wrist, the rods will jump up over air ducts, lighting fixtures, cable raceways, etc.

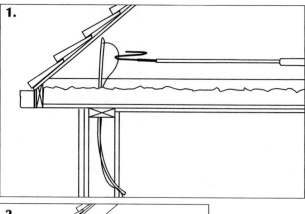

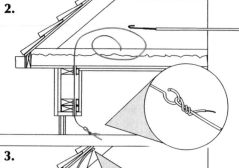

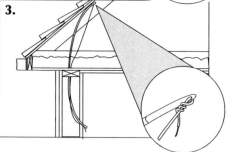

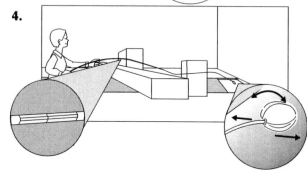

3. The wisp head also raises the end of the **Creep-Zit** so it can slide smoothly over the grid dividers; turn the end of the Creep-Zit in your hand and the wisp head at the other end will walk from side to side.
4. Attach the wire to the wisp head and bring it back to you, or to the bullnose at the back end.
5. If running coax, cat 5 cables or large speaker wires, we recommend you attach a **PullCord** to the wisp head or bull-nose of the Creep-Zit sections, then attach your cable (or the PullSleeve) to the PullCord.

108A10.EPS

Tool Illustrations and Descriptions

Unlike conventional bellhanger bits, the "jobber" bits are aircraft drills Type A specifications for a wider variety of drilling applications:

* Specially designed for drilling through *steel plates*, as well as wood;
* 118 degree point provides more gradual breakthrough; limits the grabbing occurring when using 135 degree point;
* Split point substantially reduces bit "walking";
* Slow design spiral improves bit self-cleaning, eases "pull back".
* All Freeform bits have a 3/16" flexible shank.
* Hole in the drill bit head **AND** chuck end.

PART #	MODEL #	DESCRIPTION
		1/4" BIT
65-118	FF1418F	FREEFORM 1/4 X 18
65-124	FF1424F	FREEFORM 1/4 X 24
65-136	FF1436F	FREEFORM 1/4 X 36
65-148	FF1448F	FREEFORM 1/4 X 48
65-158	FF1458F	FREEFORM 1/4 X 58
65-172	FF1472F	FREEFORM 1/4 X 72
		3/8" BIT
65-218	FF3818F	FREEFORM 3/8 X 18
65-224	FF3824F	FREEFORM 3/8 X 24
65-236	FF3836F	FREEFORM 3/8 X 36
65-248	FF3848F	FREEFORM 3/8 X 48
65-258	FF3858F	FREEFORM 3/8 X 58
65-272	FF3872F	FREEFORM 3-8 X 72
		1/2" BIT
65-318	FF1218F	FREEFORM 1/2 X 18
65-324	FF1224F	FREEFORM 1/2 X 24
65-336	FF1236F	FREEFORM 1/2 X 36
65-348	FF1248F	FREEFORM 1/2 X 48
65-358	FF1258F	FREEFORM 1/2 X 58
65-372	FF1272F	FREEFORM 1/2 X 72

PRO-BORE® DRILL BITS | Larger Bore Drill Bits

Pro-Bore® Wood Boring Bits, for the systems contractor, offer superior drilling capabilities compared to the auger type drill bits. The unique Iso-Tempe® hardening process increases bit life and durability. Pro-Bore bits utilize a self-feeding pilot screw that holds the bit firmly in place and helps draw the bit through the wood. The Pro-Bore has multiple "spurs" that increase the cutting performance of the "bladed" edge.

* Multiple sizes: 1", 1-1/4" and 1-1/2" Bit heads
* Fully reversible.
* Special design makes drilling fast and free of splinters.
* Adjustable feed screws (can lengthen for more pulling power).

PART #	MODEL #	DESCRIPTION
64-500	LSDPB100	PRO-BORE 1" WOOD BIT - HEAD ONLY
64-525	LSDPB125	PRO-BORE 1-1/4" WOOD BIT - HEAD ONLY
64-550	LSDPB150	PRO-BORE 1-1/2" WOOD BIT - HEAD ONLY
64-552	LSDPBS2	2 FT. SHAFT FOR PRO-BORE WOOD BIT 1/4" SHAFT
64-554	LSDPBS4	4 FT. SHAFT FOR PRO-BORE WOOD BIT 1/4" SHAFT
64-556	LSDPBS6	6 FT. SHAFT FOR PRO-BORE WOOD BIT 1/4" SHAFT (FLEX)
61-626	EX225	2 FT. EXTENSION FOR ABOVE SHAFTS
61-726	EX425	4 FT. EXTENSION FOR ABOVE SHAFTS
61-826	EX625	6 FT. EXTENSION FOR ABOVE SHAFTS (FLEX)
64-560	LSDPBK	PRO-BORE KIT (INCLUDES ALL OF THE ABOVE)

Note: For continuous extensions order the EX225, EX425 or EX625

108A11.EPS

SPEAR-ZIT™ DRILL BITS

The Spear-Zit wood drill bit is a perfect diamond shaped head drill bit, allowing the user to drill at any angle. They are fully guaranteed against breakage, and easily field-resharpenable with a file.

Hint: Use any 3/8" Spear-Zit bit as a pilot bit for hole saws to cut holes from 9/16" to 2 5/8" diameter through a top or bottom single plate, with an "up-to-6-ft.-long" shaft hole saw!

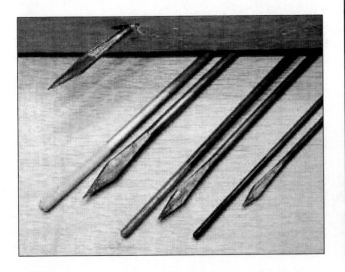

Applications: Any wood drilling application, at any angle; will not catch on and unravel carpet, will go through knots and nails.

Because the spear shape of the head will prevent it from walking, use the directional tool to align the head of a 60" or 72" flex bit in the desired direction.

PART #	MODEL #	DESCRIPTION
61-212	SZ1/4X12	1/4" X 12" SPEAR-ZIT
61-218	SZ1/4X18	1/4" X 18" SPEAR-ZIT
61-224	SZ1/4X24	1/4" X 24" SPEAR-ZIT
61-236	SZ1/4X36	1/4" X 36" SPEAR-ZIT
61-248	SZ1/4X48	1/4" X 48" SPEAR-ZIT
61-260	SZ1/4X60F	1/4" X 60" SPEAR-ZIT, FLEXIBLE SHANK
61-272	SZ1/4X72F	1/4" X 72" SPEAR-ZIT, FLEXIBLE SHANK
		* ALL 1/4" SPEARZITS HAVE 3/16" SHANK
61-312	SZ3/8X12	3/8" X 12" SPEAR-ZIT
61-318	SZ3/8X18	3/8" X 18" SPEAR-ZIT
61-324	SZ3/8X24	3/8" X 24" SPEAR-ZIT
61-336	SZ3/8X36	3/8" X 36" SPEAR-ZIT
61-348	SZ3/8X48	3/8" X 48" SPEAR-ZIT
61-360	SZ3/8X60F	3/8" X 60" SPEAR-ZIT, FLEXIBLE SHANK
61-372	SZ3/8X72F	3/8" X 72" SPEAR-ZIT, FLEXIBLE SHANK
		* ALL 3/8" SPEARZITS HAVE 1/4" SHANK
61-412	SZ1/2X12	1/2" X 12" SPEAR-ZIT
61-418	SZ1/2X18	1/2" X 18" SPEAR-ZIT
61-424	SZ1/2X24	1/2" X 24" SPEAR-ZIT
61-436	SZ1/2X36	1/2" X 36" SPEAR-ZIT
61-448	SZ1/2X48	1/2" X 48" SPEAR-ZIT
61-460	SZ1/2X60	1/2" X 60" SPEAR-ZIT (DO NOT FLEX)
61-472	SZ1/2X72	1/2" X 72" SPEAR-ZIT (DO NOT FLEX)
		* ALL 1/2" SPEARZITS HAVE 5/16" SHANK

The 3/8" (1/4" shank) Spear-Zit can be used as a pilot for deep hole saws, to drill larger holes in single plate.

The flexible extensions (facing page) will give you added flexibility in allowing you to make one drill bit any length you want. **Applications:** see pages 37, 38, 39, 40, 41, 42, 43.

DIRECTIONAL TOOL   Drill Bit Guide

This directional tool (model AT7) is a must for angle drilling with any type of flexible shaft drill or extension. TWO loops to hold and control the bit.

Unlike others you've seen in the past, this one works!

PART #	MODEL #	DESCRIPTION
61-000	AT7	DIRECTIONAL TOOL FOR FLEX BITS

108A12.EPS

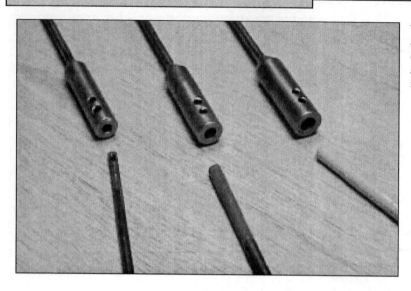

These extensions are made of special *high torque*, extra flexible steel. They are available in 2, 4 and 6-ft. lengths, and receive 3/16", 1/4" or 5/16" bit shanks. Ideal for extending the length of your favorite bit.

3/16" SHAFT EXTENSIONS

PART #	MODEL #	DESCRIPTION
61-512	EX512	2 FOOT EXTENSION FOR 3/16" SHANK
61-514	EX514	4 FOOT EXTENSION FOR 3/16" SHANK
61-516	EX516	6 FOOT EXTENSION FOR 3/16" SHANK
61-522	EX522	2 FOOT EXTENSION FOR 1/4" SHANK
61-524	EX524	4 FOOT EXTENSION FOR 1/4" SHANK
61-526	EX526	6 FOOT EXTENSION FOR 1/4" SHANK
61-532	EX532	2 FOOT EXTENSION FOR 5/16" SHANK
61-534	EX534	4 FOOT EXTENSION FOR 5/16" SHANK
61-536	EX536	6 FOOT EXTENSION FOR 5/16" SHANK

1/4" SHAFT EXTENSIONS

PART #	MODEL #	DESCRIPTION
61-616	EX215	2 FOOT EXTENSION FOR 3/16" SHANK
61-716	EX415	4 FOOT EXTENSION FOR 3/16" SHANK
61-816	EX615	6 FOOT EXTENSION FOR 3/16" SHANK
61-626	EX225	2 FOOT EXTENSION FOR 1/4" SHANK
61-726	EX425	4 FOOT EXTENSION FOR 1/4" SHANK
61-826	EX625	6 FOOT EXTENSION FOR 1/4" SHANK
61-636	EX235	2 FOOT EXTENSION FOR 5/16" SHANK
61-736	EX435	4 FOOT EXTENSION FOR 5/16" SHANK
61-836	EX635	6 FOOT EXTENSION FOR 5/16" SHANK

108A13.EPS

REBORE-ZIT™ DRILL BIT   Retains Existing Wire While Drilling

Rebore-Zit is the only bit that can re-drill and enlarge a hole with a wire already present. It is a counter-sink equipped bit with a pilot and swivel-eyelet to tie the existing wire on.

Applications: Use in situations where the hole needs to be enlarged, and wire has already been run.

PART #	MODEL #	DESCRIPTION
62-338	REB3/8	3/8" REBORE-ZIT WITH 1/4" PILOT
62-348	REB1/2	1/2" REBORE-ZIT WITH 3/8" PILOT
62-368	REB3/4	3/4" REBORE-ZIT WITH 3/8" PILOT
62-388	REB1	1" REBORE-ZIT WITH 3/8" PILOT
62-411	REB 1-1/4	1-1/4" REBORE-ZIT WITH 1/4" PILOT
62-000	REB-P1/4	REPLACEMENT 1/4" PILOT FOR REBORE-ZIT
62-005	REB-P3/8	REPLACEMENT 3/8" PILOT FOR REBORE-ZIT

WIRE BITS   Reference Drill Bits

The wire bit is a .047" spring wire 36" long that can be cut (at an angle) any length to make it the smallest "reference" bit.

Applications: Its primary application is to be used as a reference point to measure from when having to drill in a specific wall cavity (i.e. drilling down through top plate in wall with stapled bat insulation, up from basement in wall with blown-in cellulose or Styrofoam insulation). The hole created is so small that it will remain unnoticeable, even on a ceiling. See page 38.

For use in drill chucks that "fully close".

PART #	MODEL #	DESCRIPTION
84-547	PW36047	PACK OF 10, 36" LONG .047" DIAM. SPRING WIRE

108A14.EPS

For cutting round holes in ceilings, walls and floors. Cuts plasterboard, fiberboard, plywood, wood and acrylic sheets up to 23mm (7/8") depth. Cutting from the opposite sides allows you to cut 45mm (1-3/4") depth.

For cutting round holes in ceilings, walls and floors. Size 1-1/4" to 10-1/4" (30mm to 260mm)(HC10) and 1-1/4" to 12" (HC12).

* Support base steadies the bit while cutting and keeps the cut perpendicular to the surface.
* Transparent cowl prevents chips from flying into eyes while cutting.
* Compression spring absorbs vibrations while cutting.
* Cutting depth is freely adjustable via locknut and compression spring.
* Cutting radius is freely adjustable with supplied balance bars.

Note: Recommended for use with an 18 volt drill.

Included in case, is extra standard blade, 4 counter weights, adjusting wrench, and allen wrench.

PART #	MODEL #	DESCRIPTION
56-000	HC10	HOLE CUTTER
56-001	HC10RB	REPLACEMENT BLADE
56-002	HC10MB	ACCESSORY CARBIDE CUTTING BLADE
56-002	HC12	EXTRA LARGE HOLE CUTTER

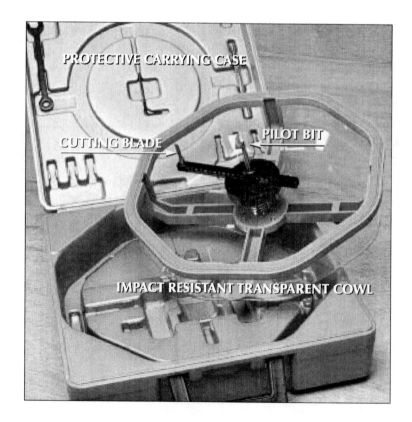

PROTECTIVE CARRYING CASE

CUTTING BLADE

PILOT BIT

IMPACT RESISTANT TRANSPARENT COWL

108A15.EPS

DEEP HOLE SAWS

Bi-metal shatterproof construction, 4/6 variable tooth provides faster, smoother cuts. 3/16" thick backing plate. The deep hole models (1-3/4" deep) will drill through a regular 2x4 in a single pass.

Note: To drill hole 9/16" or larger inside wall, use 3/8" Spear-Zit as pilot drill for your hole saw.

PART #	MODEL #	DESCRIPTION
60-002	BM9/16DH	9/16" DEEP HOLE SAW
60-004	BM5/8DH	5/8" DEEP HOLE SAW
60-005	BM11/16DH	11/16" DEEP HOLE SAW
60-006	BM3/4DH	3/4" DEEP HOLE SAW
60-007	BM7/8DH	7/8" DEEP HOLE SAW
60-010	BM1DH	1" DEEP HOLE SAW
60-011	BM11/8DH	1 1/8" DEEP HOLE SAW
60-012	BM11/4DH	1 1/4" DEEP HOLE SAW
60-014	BM11/2DH	1 1/2" DEEP HOLE SAW
60-020	BM2DH	2" DEEP HOLE SAW
60-021	BM21/8SD	2-1/8" STANDARD DEPTH HOLE SAW
60-025	BM25/8SD	2-5/8" STANDARD DEPTH HOLE SAW
60-102	BM1/4M	REPLACEMENT 1/4" MANDREL FOR HOLE SAW
60-121	BM7/16M	REPLACEMENT 7/16" MANDREL FOR 2-1/8" HOLE SAW

Applications: Use to cut holes from 9/16" to 2-5/8" through everything from wood and plastic to aluminum, brass, copper, cast iron, stainless steel.

DE-PLUG-ZIT™ Hole Saw Arbor

A *must* for anybody using hole saws on a regular basis, the De-Plug-Zit is a hole saw arbor, complete with pilot bit and adapter to fit any size threaded hole saw that eliminates the problem of removing wood "plugs" or steel "washers" from the saw. The saw threads up and down the mandrel, exposing the "plug" on the pilot bit. Just remove the plug, reposition the saw on the mandrel, and be ready to cut the next hole.

PART #	MODEL #	DESCRIPTION
60-700	DPZ-7	DE-PLUG-ZIT HOLE SAW MANDREL

108A16.EPS

STUD SENSOR™

Possibly one of the most "must have" tools for the installer: being non-magnetic, the Stud Sensor is looking for changes in density, not metal, finding hidden wood and metal studs through drywall, plaster, wood, ceilings.

Easy to use – push start button and slowly move across wall. Green LED lights <u>and</u> beeper sounds when you reach the edge of the stud. Mark it with indented notch at top of unit. Go to the other side and reverse the procedure to locate the other edge of the stud. It also has a clip for storing in pocket or attaching to belt.

* Uses 9 volt battery (not included)
* Only 5-1/2" long.

PART #	MODEL #	DESCRIPTION
57-100	SSZ9	STUD SENSOR

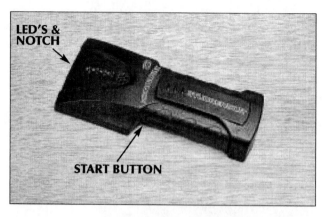

LED'S & NOTCH

START BUTTON

Applications: Use to locate studs and joists prior to fishing inside walls insulated with stapled bat insulation, moisture barrier, blow-in cellulose or Styrofoam, when fishing wires between floors (in ceilings). See Pages 38, 39, 40, 42.

TRISCANNER™ PRO

The TriScanner is an upscale version of the Stud Sensor; it features three different scan modes – Deep scan for wood, metal as well as regular stud scan. It will detect rebar and has an extra AC LED to detect "hot" unshielded electrical wires (romex).

The TriScanner is capable of scanning through drywall, hardwood floors as well as plywood.

Applications: See pages 38, 39, 40, 42.

PART #	MODEL #	DESCRIPTION
57-110	TSCZ3	TRISCANNER

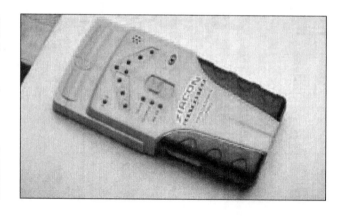

108A17.EPS

MINI SCOPING RETRIEVER — Extendable Pocket Retriever

The Mini Scoping Retriever (model LBS) is a pocket size penclip telescoping retriever with a hook at the end, small enough to pull the chain through a 1/4" hole – only 4" long when collapsed, it extends to 18". See pages 37, 38, 39.

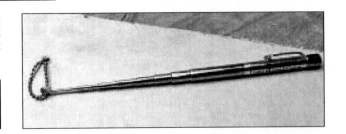

PART #	MODEL #	DESCRIPTION
53-310	LBS	MINI SCOPING POCKET RETRIEVER

HOOK-ZIT™ — Flexible Retriever

Unlike the LBS pocket retriever, the Hook-Zit is flexible, being made of spring steel, .072" in diameter. The small hook at one end and the larger "L" shape at the other end, are faced the same way, so you always know which way the "fishing" hook is facing, even in blind fishing conditions.

Applications: The mini hook end is designed to fish ball chain or wire inside a wall, while the larger "L-shape" hook end is more for fishing a ball of wires in a restricted space, i.e., inside a panel.

In pre-wiring situations, the 18" or 36" Hook-Zit is ideal to pull wire from stud to stud, even 7 feet high, without the use of a step ladder. See pages 37, 38, 39.

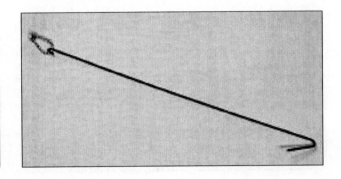

PART #	MODEL #	DESCRIPTION
84-109	HZ9	9" LONG HOOK-ZIT (3 TO A PACKAGE)
84-118	HZ18	18" LONG HOOK-ZIT (3 TO A PACKAGE)
84-136	HZ36	36" LONG HOOK-ZIT (3 TO A PACKAGE)

STEEL FISH WIRES (Recommended for Conduit)

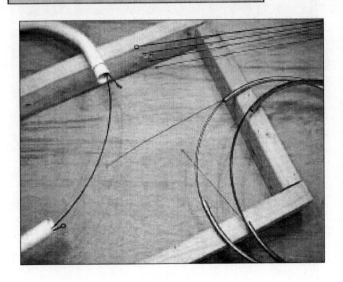

An economical, yet limited, version of the fiberglass push/pull rods, the spring steel fish wires are offered in different diameters, depending on the "flex" required. Each fish wire has a centered eyelet at each end to attach wire or pull cord.

PART #	MODEL #	DESCRIPTION
84-047	FW36047	.047" X 36" SLIM FISH WIRE (5 PACK)
84-062	FW36062	.062" X 36" MEDIUM FISH WIRE (5 PACK)
84-072	FW36072	.072" X 36" HEAVY FISH WIRE (5 PACK)
84-092	FW72092	.092" X 72" HEAVY FISH WIRE
85-410	ICFW10092	.092" X 10FT HEAVY FISH WIRE IN CASE
85-510	ICFW10047	.047" X 10FT SLIM FISH WIRE IN CASE
85-525	ICFW25047	.047" X 25FT SLIM FISH WIRE IN CASE
85-550	ICFW50047	.047" X 50FT SLIM FISH WIRE IN CASE
85-600	ICFW100047	.047" X 100FT SLIM FISH WIRE IN CASE

108A18.EPS

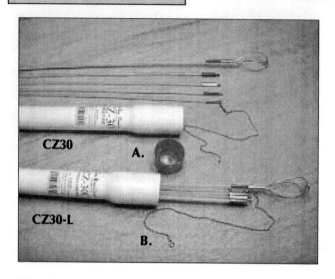

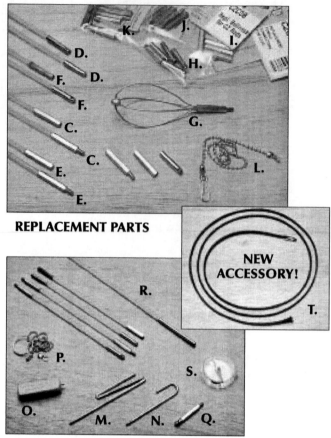

REPLACEMENT PARTS

NEW ACCESSORY!

ACCESSORY ITEMS

The tool that makes a fish tape obsolete., the Creep-Zit kit consists of five 6-ft. green fiberglass rods (.159" in diameter-less than 3/16").

* Four with male/female screw-on connectors
* One with female on one end and a bullet shaped head with cross hole (bullnose) at the other end to attach the wire
* A 1-ft. ballchain attached to the bullnose to grab it easily when inside a wall
* An "eggbeater" shaped head (wisp) used as a guide to keep the rods from getting stuck on obstacles and to provide a "wheel" to "creep" from side to side.

The model **CZ-30L** is made of luminescent epoxy fiberglass rods (stronger and slightly stiffer) that truly glow in the dark after being "charged" in full light. The luminescent rods are interchangeable with the regular green rods.

Multiple accessories are designed for specific applications:

* **DRAG-ZIT™ MAGNET:** fish a ballchain between ceiling and upper floor. See page 42. (Model CZD)

* **ZTIP:** fish wire way back in a cavity where rough surface prevents the use of a Drag-Zit magnet and ballchain. See page 42. (Model Ztip)

* **JTIP:** uncoil coax or other cable. (Model Jtip)

* **LOCATE-ZIT™ ROD (OR LOCATE-ZIT SCREW-ON TIP):** special bullnose with magnet incorporated to be used in conjunction with the LZO compass to fish wires in insulated walls with moisture barrier or blown-in cellulose; locates the tip of the rod before you drill a hole. See pages 38, 39. (Model LZSEC or LZBN)

* **ADAPT-ZIT™ KIT:** combination of 6" fiberglass sections with multiple connector combinations allowing fast conversion of the Creep-Zit section ends. (Includes 1' Ballchain w/ connectors). (Model CZA)

* **DOVE TAIL ACCESSORY 6 FOOT SOCK:** Dove Tail Head screws on to Creep-Zit male end. The 6 foot sock is permanently attached to the dove tail head. Pulls up to 5/16" diameter wire without stripping wire, or the wire pulling sock becomes the pull line! (Model DTS)

Applications: See pages 39, 40, 41, 42, 43, 44.

	PART #	MODEL #	DESCRIPTION
A.)	81-130	CZ30	CREEP-ZIT GREEN FIBERGLASS WIRE RUNNING KIT
B.)	81-230	CZ30-L	CREEP-ZIT LUMINOUS FIBERGLASS WIRE RUNNING KIT
C.)	81-106	CZX	6FT GREEN ROD W/ MALE/FEMALE CONNECTORS
D.)	81-116	CZB	6FT GREEN ROD W/ FEMALE/BULLNOSE CONNECTORS
E.)	81-206	CZX-L	6FT LUMINOUS ROD W/ MALE/FEMALE CONNECTORS
F.)	81-216	CZB-L	6FT LUMINOUS ROD W/ FEMALE/BULLNOSE CONNECTORS
G.)	81-310	CZH	REPLACEMENT WISP (EGGBEATER) HEAD FOR CREEP-ZIT & YFT30-E
H.)	81-320	CZCOB	PACK OF 5 REPLACEMENT BULLNOSE END ONLY
I.)	81-330	CZCOF	PACK OF 5 REPLACEMENT FEMALE CONNECTOR ONLY
J.)	81-340	CZCOM	PACK OF 5 REPLACEMENT MALE CONNECTOR ONLY
K.)	81-350	CZCONN	PACK OF 5 FEMALE, 5 MALE AND 2 BULLNOSE
L.)	85-035	WNH-1L	PACK OF 5 1FT BALL CHAIN, LARGE SNAPHOOKS, #6AA COUPLING
M.)	82-350	ZTIP	ACCESSORY ZTIP FOR CREEP-ZIT AND GRABBIT
N.)	82-370	JTIP	ACCESSORY JTIP FOR CREEP-ZIT AND GRABBIT
O.)	81-360	CZD	ACCESSORY DRAG-ZIT CERAMIC MAGNET
P.)	81-121	CZA	ACCESSORY ADAPT-ZIT KIT
Q.)	81-125	LZBN	ACCESSORY LOCATE-ZIT SCREW-ON BULLNOSE
R.)	81-126	LZSEC	ACCESSORY LOCATE-ZIT 6FT SECTION
S.)	81-127	LZO	ACCESSORY COMPASS FOR LOCATE-ZIT
T.)	81-128	DTS	ACCESSORY DOVE TAIL 6 FOOT SOCK

108A19.EPS

These larger sizes offer more rigidity for fishing long runs. Made from the same material and kit assembly as standard Creep-Zit (5–six foot rods, bullnose head and wisp head in a PVC case).

- **ELECTRICIANS**
- **INSTITUTIONS**
- **SCHOOLS**
- **COMMERCIAL**
- **FIRE INSTALLS**

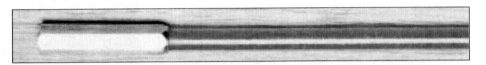

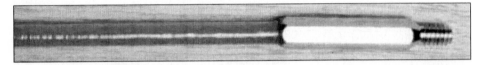

ACTUAL SIZE 1/4" DIAMETER (.250") • **6 FEET LONG**

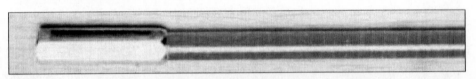

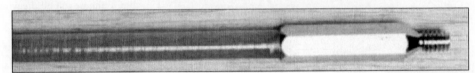

ACTUAL SIZE 5/16" DIAMETER (.3125") • **6 FEET LONG**

PART #	MODEL #	DESCRIPTION
81-430	CZ30 1/4	CREEP-ZIT KIT 1/4" DIAMETER RODS 30 FEET
81-431	CZX 1/4	6 FOOT ROD MALE/FEMALE CONNECTORS
81-432	CZB 1/4	6 FOOT ROD BULLNOSE FEMALE CONNECTORS
81-436	CZ60 1/4	CREEP-ZIT KIT 60 FEET (10-1/4" DIAMETER RODS)
81-439	CZ90 1/4	CREEP-ZIT KIT 90 FEET (15-1/4" DIAMETER RODS)
81-440	CZ120 1/4	CREEP-ZIT KIT 120 FEET (20-1/4" DIAMETER RODS)
81-445	CZ30 5/16	CREEP-ZIT KIT 5/ 16" DIAMETER RODS 30 FEET
81-446	CZX 5/16	6 FOOT ROD MALE/FEMALE CONNECTORS
81-447	CZB 5/16	6 FOOT ROD BULLNOSE FEMALE CONNECTORS
81-460	CZ60 5/16	CREEP-ZIT KIT 60 FEET (10-5/16" DIAMETER RODS)
81-490	CZ90 5/16	CREEP-ZIT KIT 90 FEET (15-5/16" DIAMETER RODS)
81-492	CZ120 5/16	CREEP-ZIT KIT 120 FEET (20-5/16" DIAMETER RODS)
81-495	CZH-LG	REPLACEMENT WISP (EGGBEATER HEAD)

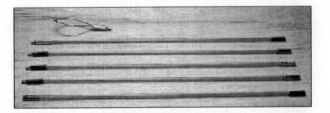

STORED IN PVC CASE

108A20.EPS

FISHTIX WIRE & CABLE KIT | Commercial Installation Kit

The Fishtix (model CF-50) is a highly diverse cable installation system, designed to meet the many needs of today's commercial installation world. It is ideally suited for such environments as drop ceilings, cable trays, raceways, wire mold and raised floors.

The Fishtix kit consists of:

1. Twelve 4-ft. tubular sections (7/8" diameter).
2. One "Cable Glide" or wisp head, used to provide horizontal and vertical steering control and easy tangle-free passage through busy cable ways.
3. One Bullnose section with stainless steel female end.
4. One Bullnose section with quick release button snap male end.
5. One 3/16 Quick Link.
6. One Corex (corrugated polypropylene) Carrying Case.

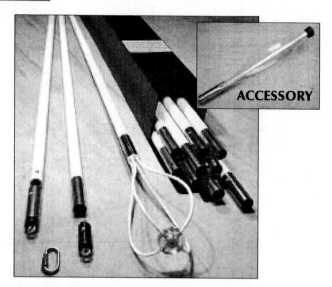

ACCESSORY

PART #	MODEL #	DESCRIPTION
81-500	CF-50	FISHTIX WIRE & CABLE RUNNING KIT
81-502	CFS4	4FT SECTION FOR FISHTIX
81-504	CFW	WISP HEAD FOR FISHTIX
81-505	CFWC	COLLAPSIBLE WISP HEAD FOR FISHTIX (ACCESSORY)
81-506	CFBF	FEMALE BULLNOSE FOR FISHTIX
81-508	CFBM	MALE BULLNOSE FOR FISHTIX
81-510	CFQL	QUICK LINK FOR FISHTIX
81-512	CFCC	CARRYING CASE FOR FISHTIX

The Fishtix has extreme tensile strength. It is capable of handling over 200 pounds of pulling force, and when used in cable trays it can virtually be extended to infinity; it will easily ride over joists, beams, and even with a 5-ft. span, jump obstacles. Once the eggbeater head gets you to your destination, replace it with heavy duty Bullnose to pull the wire.

Applications: See pages 45, 46.

FIBERGLASS FISH TAPE | Continuous Non-Conductive with Shape Memory

Probably the first fiberglass fish tapes that retain their memory to straight. Made of opaque epoxy fiberglass, the YFTs have a diameter of .110", making them capable of handling a much sharper bend that the green fiberglass rods or even the luminous ones. (Initially designed to handle a 90 degree bend–not elbow–in a 3/4" conduit). Offered in three different lengths (10-ft., 15-ft., 30-ft.), these fiberglass fish tapes have a bullnose at each end so wires can be pulled from either direction. The 30-foot is also available with the

Creep-Zit wisp head. Each model is coiled in a PVC storage case, easy to carry over the shoulder, making it easier to handle in crowded places.

When pulling wire we recommend attaching a pull cord or fish line first.

PART #	MODEL #	DESCRIPTION
85-310	YFT10	10FT EPOXY FIBERGLASS FISH TAPE IN CASE
85-315	YFT15	15FT EPOXY FIBERGLASS FISH TAPE IN CASE
85-330	YFT30	30FT EPOXY FIBERGLASS FISH TAPE IN CASE
85-335	YFT30-E	30FT FIBERGLASS FISH TAPE, WITH WISP HEAD
85-351	R-YFT10	10FT REPLACEMENT YFT FISH TAPE W/ BULLNOSES
85-352	R-YFT15	15FT REPLACEMENT YFT FISH TAPE W/ BULLNOSES
85-353	R-YFT30	30FT REPLACEMENT YFT FISH TAPE W/ BULLNOSES
85-354	R-YFT30-E	30FT REPLACEMENT YFT-E FISH TAPE W/ BN & FEM-BN
85-355	YFTBN	PACK OF 5 REPLACEMENT BULLNOSE FOR YFT
85-356	YFTFBN	PACK OF 3 REPLACEMENT FEMALE BULLNOSE CONNECTORS FOR YFT30-E
85-035	WNH-1L	PACK OF 5 1FT BALL CHAIN, SNAPHOOKS, # 6AA COUPLING

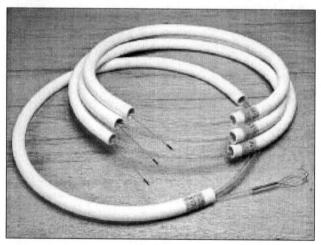

Applications: See pages 39, 40, 41, 43, 44.

GLOROD™ WIRE PUSHER Push Rods

The GloRod wire pushers are fluorescent (reflects light shined on them) green fiberglass rods, .159" in diameter, flexible, yet retain their memory to straight after being flexed. Available in 2-ft., 3-ft., 4-ft., 5-ft. and 6-ft. lengths, the 3-ft. rod is the most popular. Designed to push (*not pull*) wire through top or bottom plate

Applications: Use to push wire through top plate to attic or bottom plate to unfinished basement and pull the wire with a Grabbit; to push wire through a wall. See pages 41, 43.

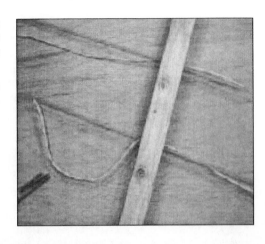

PART #	MODEL #	DESCRIPTION
84-202	GR2	2FT GLOROD WIRE PUSHER
84-203	GR3	3FT GLOROD WIRE PUSHER
84-204	GR4	4FT GLOROD WIRE PUSHER
84-205	GR5	5FT GLOROD WIRE PUSHER
84-206	GR6	6FT GLOROD WIRE PUSHER

FIBERGLASS PUSH/PULL RODS Bull Nose Rods

The fiberglass green and luminous push/pull rods have a bullet shape tip with cross hole (bullnose) on both ends, and, unlike the GloRod wire pushers, these can be used to pull wire as well. The luminous rods are made of phosphorous epoxy fiberglass truly glowing in the dark after being "charged" in full light. The epoxy fiberglass makes them stronger than the regular "green" rods, therefore a little stiffer.

Applications: Same as GloRods, plus pull wires through walls. See pages 41, 43.

PART #	MODEL #	DESCRIPTION
84-232	GR2BB	2FT GREEN PUSH/PULL ROD
84-233	GR3BB	3FT GREEN PUSH/PULL ROD
84-234	GR4BB	4FT GREEN PUSH/PULL ROD
84-235	GR5BB	5FT GREEN PUSH/PULL ROD
84-236	GR6BB	6FT GREEN PUSH/PULL ROD
84-212	GR2-L	2FT LUMINOUS PUSH/PULL ROD
84-214	GR4-L	4FT LUMINOUS PUSH/PULL ROD
84-216	GR6-L	6FT LUMINOUS PUSH/PULL ROD

SLING-A-LINE SLINGSHOT For Long Open Runs

The Sling-A-Line slingshot yoke is made of heavy duty Baltic birch. A fishing reel (with a 10-lb. test line, a #7 swivel and a 3/8 oz. lead weight) is mounted on the yoke. Neither a toy nor a gimmick, it is the fastest tool for pulling long wire runs in open space with limited access area. It is also the very first tool ever offered by Labor Saving Devices.

Hint: For better accuracy, always shoot holding the yoke horizontally.

Applications: See pages 44. (*Maximum range 125 feet*)

PART #	MODEL #	DESCRIPTION
85-202	SAL202	SLING-A-LINE WIRE PULLER
85-210	SALR	REPLACEMENT RUBBER ASSEMBLY

108A22.EPS

The Grabbits are lightweight, shockproof, sturdy friction self-locking telescoping fiberglass poles, indispensable for running (pushing or pulling) wires or cables indoors as well as outdoors, in residential or commercial installations. The inner "V" of the patented "Ztip" has a double knife edge designed to literally "grab" the wire, while the outer "V"–without knife edge–is designed to push wires. The GR12 is made of three sections, and the GR18 has five sections.

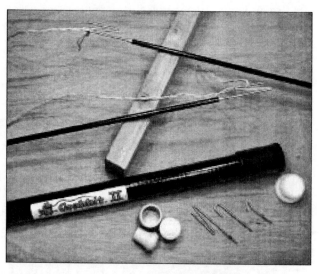

Applications: See pages 41, 43, 44, 45, and below.

PART #	MODEL #	DESCRIPTION
82-108	GR8	8FT GRABBIT (24" COLLAPSED)
82-112	GR12	12FT GRABBIT (51" COLLAPSED)
82-118	GR18	18FT GRABBIT (53" COLLAPSED)
82-045	GR12-1	REPLACEMENT SECTION 1 FOR GRABBIT 12, 18
82-046	GR12-2	REPLACEMENT SECTION 2 FOR GRABBIT 12, 18
82-047	GR12-3	REPLACEMENT SECTION 3 FOR GRABBIT 12, 18
82-074	GR18-4	REPLACEMENT SECTION 4 FOR GRABBIT 18
82-075	GR18-5	REPLACEMENT SECTION 5 FOR GRABBIT 18
82-350	ZTIP	REPLACEMENT PUSH/PULL ZTIP FOR GRABBIT 8, 12, 18
82-360	PTIP	ACCESSORY PULL TIP (TIGHT SPACE) FOR GRABBIT 8, 12, 18
82-370	JTIP	ACCESSORY "UNCOIL" & PULL TIP (FISH-EZE WIRE, CABLES) GRABBIT 8, 12, 18
82-380	GRC	ACCESSORY RUBBER TIPS FOR SECTION 2, 3 AND 4

GOLF STRING
(for fishing overhead pipes or beams without a ladder!)

You asked for it and here it is! Use in conjunction with the 12 or 18 foot Grabbit for pulling wire overhead on high beams, pipes, etc. without the use of a ladder. Insert one side of the loop into the V of ZTIP. Telescoping the Grabbit up, lift the ball and cord and sling over the pipe or beam. The weight of the ball will bring it down to you. If the ball doesn't come down, use the Grabbit ZTIP to pull the cord down to you. Now pull slack in the cord before lifting it up over the next beam with the Grabbit. Repeat this procedure until you reach your destination. Remove the ball and attach your wire to pull! **OR** Simply use this unit as a durable, strong pull cord!

100 feet (400 lb test) polyester coated nylon cord (1/8" diam.) Durable Lexan reel. Easy to re-wind by inserting the bolt in the drill motor.

PART #	MODEL #	DESCRIPTION
85-215	GBS	GOLF STRING UNIT
85-226	GBS-B	REPLACEMENT BALL WITH EYELET
85-227	GBS-R	REPLACEMENT REEL ONLY
85-228	GBS-C	REPLACEMENT 100' CORD ONLY

108A23.EPS

2ND MAN CABLE PULLEY™ — Attachable Pulley

The 2nd Man Cable Pulley device saves time and money by eliminating the need for a second technician to feed the cable up through the ceiling or around turns for a cable pull. Just **snap** the hanging strap **off** the axle pin and the retainer piece, attach the pulley to a proper support device, **snap** the strap back on the axle pin and in the retainer latch. Position a 2nd Man Pulley above the drop ceiling to receive the cable from the supply side of your pull, at each horizontal turn, each elevation change, each up and down location. The 2nd Man Pulley will accommodate up to eight (8) four pair, Category 5 or like-size cables, protect and preserve the integrity of the cable and virtually eliminate friction on the cable.

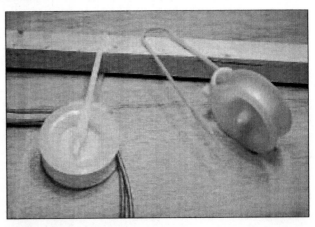

PART #	MODEL #	DESCRIPTION
85-142	DC2M	PACK OF 2-2ND MAN CABLE PULLEYS

Applications: See pages 44, 45, 46.

CONNECTOR PROTECTOR — Wire Pull Wrap

The Connector Protector is a very flexible, heavy duty, "double wall" tight weave monofilament sock designed to pull **pre-connected** cables. Its unique double wall construction reduces the fraying of the sleeve itself, while adding extra protection for the connectors. The sleeve is fused into a bullet shape, high resistance bullnose head with cross hole to make pulling these connected cables as easy as unfinished wires.

PART #	MODEL #	DESCRIPTION
85-950	PS1/2	1/2" CONNECTOR PROTECTOR FOR PRE-CONNECTED CABLES
85-975	PS3/4	3/4" CONNECTOR PROTECTOR FOR PRE-CONNECTED CABLES
85-990	PSNTW	PACK OF 100, 1/4" X .10 REPLACEMENT NYLON TIE WIRES

Applications: See pages 37, 43, 44, 45, 46.

WET NOODLE & RETRIEVER — Fast Fish for Uninsulated Walls

The Retriever component of the WR24 is a flexible, insulated 24" handle with a neodenium magnet attached to one end. This rare earth magnet, unlike an alnico magnet, will not loose its magnetism if it is hit. The "Wet Noodle" consists of 10 feet of .090" (half the size of a regular ball chain) smooth nickel plated steel ball chain, a "stop ring" that will prevent the chain from falling through the drilled hole, a #6 in-ring connector to pull the wire and a #3 "b" coupling to attach a second chain if needed.

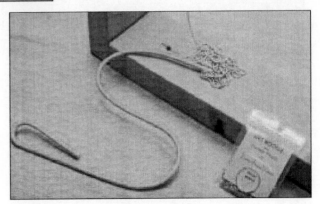

PART #	MODEL #	DESCRIPTION
85-124	WR24	WET NOODLE AND RETRIEVER
85-024	WN10	REPLACEMENT WET NOODLE AND CONNECTORS
85-120	R24	REPLACEMENT FLEXIBLE INSULATED RETRIEVER W/ MAGNET
85-030	WNC	REPLACEMENT CONNECTORS (10 EA. RING, 3B COUPLING, #6 IN-RING)

Applications: See pages 37, 38, 40, 42.

108A24.EPS

UNDERCARPET TAPE

The Undercarpet Tape is 25 feet long annealed stainless steel, 3/4" wide with one end curled up and the other rounded. Run wire between padding and carpet.

Applications: See page 41.

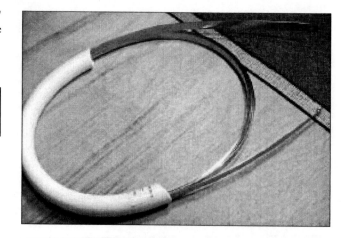

PART #	MODEL #	DESCRIPTION
85-125	UCT25	UNDER CARPET TAPE, 25FT

FISH-EZE™ KIT

Attic Wire Fishing Kit

(One person can fish an attic faster than two without crawling in insulation!)

Makes running wire from any header up to an attic easy! The kit includes two stainless steel tubes, less than 1/4" diameter, 24" (for 8-ft. ceiling) and 36" long (for 9-ft. ceiling), stored in a fiberglass housing, a 12-ft. spring wire, heat treated in a coil .047" diameter with eyelet on both ends, in a circular stainless holder.

Hint: Drill hole up header. Insert tube up header. Insert all the coiled wire through tube. (The coil will miss the sheathing and circle in the attic). Remove the tube and attach your wire to eyelet at window base. Stand in the center of attic and bring the wire to you using the Grabbit with the JTIP! With extra wire in holders (FEKW12) you can fish all the openings at once.

Applications: The kit is primarily designed to run wire from any header up to the attic. See page 43.

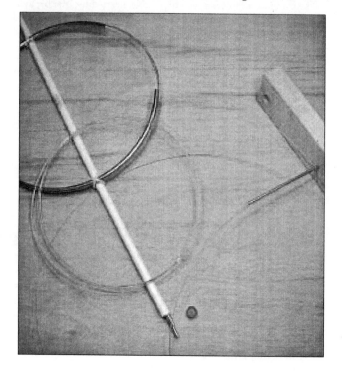

PART #	MODEL #	DESCRIPTION
83-110	FEK-1	FISH-EZE ATTIC FISHING KIT
83-112	FEKW12	FISH-EZE WIRE IN A STAINLESS STEEL HOLDER
83-120	FEKWOH	REPLACEMENT FISH-EZE WIRE WITHOUT HOLDER
83-124	FEKT24	REPLACEMENT 24" STAINLESS HOLLOW TUBE (FISH-EZE)
83-136	FEKT36	REPLACEMENT 36" STAINLESS HOLLOW TUBE (FISH-EZE)
83-140	FEKH	REPLACEMENT STAINLESS STEEL WIRE HOLDER

108A25.EPS

Additional Resources

This module is intended to be a thorough resource for task training. The following reference works are suggested for further study. These are optional materials for continued education rather than for task training.

Audio/Video Cable Installer's Pocket Guide, 2002. New York, NY: McGraw-Hill.

National Electrical Code® Handbook, Latest Edition. Quincy, MA: National Fire Protection Association.

Telecommunications Cabling Installation Manual, 3rd Edition. 2001. Tampa, FL: BICSI. www.bicsi.org.

Telecommunications Distribution Methods Manual, 10th Edition. 2003. Tampa, FL: BICSI. www.bicsi.org.

TIA/EIA Telecommunication Building Wiring Standards, Latest Edition. Englewood, CO: Global Engineering Documents.

The Cabling Handbook, 2nd Edition. 2000. Upper Saddle River, NY: Prentice Hall.

Figure Credits

Topaz Publications, Inc.	108F08, 108F11, 108F20A, 108F20B, 108F22, 108F35B, 108SA01–108SA03, 108SA06, 108SA07
BICSI	108T04–108T09, 108F09, 108F12, 108F13, 108F17, 108F18, 108F34, 108F36, 108F38–108F46,
Carlon	108F51
Image courtesy of SMARTHOME.COM, Inc. Copyright © 2004	108SA05
Labor $aving Devices®, Inc.	108A01–108A25

CONTREN® LEARNING SERIES — USER UPDATE

The NCCER makes every effort to keep these textbooks up-to-date and free of technical errors. We appreciate your help in this process. If you have an idea for improving this textbook, or if you find an error, a typographical mistake, or an inaccuracy in NCCER's Contren® textbooks, please write us, using this form or a photocopy. Be sure to include the exact module number, page number, a detailed description, and the correction, if applicable. Your input will be brought to the attention of the Technical Review Committee. Thank you for your assistance.

Instructors – If you found that additional materials were necessary in order to teach this module effectively, please let us know so that we may include them in the Equipment/Materials list in the Instructor's Guide.

Write: Product Development and Revision
              National Center for Construction Education and Research
              P.O. Box 141104, Gainesville, FL 32614-1104

Fax: 352-334-0932

E-mail: curriculum@nccer.org

Craft _____ Module Name _____

Copyright Date _____ Module Number _____ Page Number(s) _____

Description _____

_____

_____

_____

(Optional) Correction _____

_____

_____

(Optional) Your Name and Address _____

_____

_____

Index

Index

Acceleration, 6.10, 6.11–6.13, 6.33
Accidents
    asphyxiation, 5.19, 5.20, 5.25
    back injury, 5.17
    benefits paid out for, 5.8
    crushing type, 5.1
    direct and indirect cost of, 4.29
    electrocution. *See* Electric shock
    emergency response, 5.5, 5.26–5.27
    engulfment type, 5.25
    escape route, 5.7
    eye injury, 4.29
    falling objects, 5.1, 5.25
    falls, 5.9, 5.25, 5.33
Acetylene, 5.23
Acids, 5.33
Acoustical board, 2.45, 2.46
ACR. *See* Attenuation-to-crosstalk ratio
Acrylate, 8.18, 8.19
Adapt-Zit™, 8.100
Admixture, 2.9, 2.75
Aerial installation, 8.66
Air, compressed, 5.32
Air boot, 2.50
Air conditioning, 1.2, 2.53, 8.50
Air quality. *See* Atmospheric hazards; Atmospheric testing;
    Ventilation
Alarms
    evacuation, 5.26
    fire, 3.1, 8.5–8.6, 8.12, 8.55–8.57
Alcohol use, 1.5
Algebra, 6.19–6.22
ALOA. *See* Associated Locksmiths of America
Alternating current (AC), 8.61, 8.64
Aluminum, 3.6–3.7
American National Standards Institute (ANSI), 1.11, 1.27,
    1.35, 1.36. *See also* ANSI/TIA/EIA standards
American Plywood Association (APA), 2.3, 2.24, 2.75
American Society for Testing and Materials (ASTM)
    International, 2.56, 4.3, 4.4, 4.35
American Wire Gauge (AWG), 8.2, 8.3, 8.4
Ampacity, 8.54, 8.77
Anchor(s)
    bolt, 4.26–4.27, 4.36
    drilling holes in concrete/masonry for, 4.28

    hollow-wall, 4.28–4.30, 4.36
    one-step, 4.25–4.26, 4.36
    screw, 4.27, 4.36
    self-drilling, 4.27–4.28
Angle in a wall, 2.45, 2.46, 2.48
Angles, 6.24, 6.25, 6.34. *See also* Trigonometry
ANSI. *See* American National Standards Institute
ANSI/TIA/EIA standards, telecommunication cabling
    commercial, 8.2
    conduit fill, 8.48
    overview, 1.11, 1.36
    pathways and spaces for, 3.1, 3.38, 8.2
    residential and light commercial, 8.2, 8.49, 8.51
    updates on, 8.55
APA. *See* American Plywood Association
Apprenticeship. *See* Training
Approved, definition, 3.8, 3.43
Apron, 4.9, 5.30
Arc (electric), 5.5
Arc (geometric), 7.8, 7.10
ARC trigonometric function, 6.29
Area, 6.5–6.6, 6.7, 6.33, 6.34
Arguments. *See* Conflict resolution; Misunderstandings
Asbestos, 2.4, 5.30–5.32
Asbestosis, 5.31
Associated Locksmiths of America (ALOA), 1.28
ASTM. *See* American Society for Testing and Materials
ATELS. *See* Office of Apprenticeship Training and
    Employer and Labor Services
Atmospheric hazards, 5.19, 5.20, 5.23–5.24, 5.29–5.30, 5.37
Atmospheric testing, 5.20, 5.23, 5.24, 5.26, 5.27–5.28, 5.31
Attenuation, 8.2, 8.77
Attenuation-to-crosstalk ratio (ACR), 8.16
Attic work area, 8.50–8.51, 8.90, 8.106
Auger, 2.64
Automatic Fire Alarm Association, Inc., 1.28
AWG. *See* American Wire Gauge

Backfeed scheme, 8.70
Backing board, 2.8, 3.38
Bakelite, 3.28
Bandwidth, 8.16
Bar (unit), 6.10
BAS. *See* Building automation systems
Baseboard or base molding, 2.33, 8.88

Base-Boar-Zit, 8.86
Basement work area, 8.84, 8.86, 8.87–8.88
Base number, 6.15, 6.17
BAT. See Bureau of Apprenticeship and Training
Batteries, 5.32–5.33
Batting, 8.85
Beam(s)
    box, 2.23, 2.24
    cable installation over, 8.81, 8.82
    conduit installation through, 3.33
    from engineered wood product, 2.5, 2.6, 2.7, 2.17, 2.32
    I-, 2.17, 2.23, 2.24
    in post-and-beam framing, 2.32–2.33
    from structural steel, 2.12, 3.33
Bell Hanger, 8.84, 8.85, 8.86, 8.87, 8.88, 8.90
Bell System, 8.13
Bender for conduit, 7.2, 7.5–7.6. See also Hand bending of
    conduit
Bend radius, 7.8, 7.24, 8.37, 8.48, 8.52
BICSI. See Building Industry Consulting Service
    International, Inc.
Bill of materials, 1.12
Binary systems, 6.15
Bits. See Drill bits
Blades
    bix tool, 1.20
    saw, 2.63, 2.64
Block, concrete, 2.10–2.11, 2.16, 2.33, 2.34, 2.63, 4.36
Blocking (solid bridging), 2.19, 2.20, 2.22, 2.75
Boards, building, 2.3–2.5
BOCA. See Building Officials and Code Administrators
    International
Body language, 1.7
Boiler, 5.19
Bolt(s)
    anchor, 2.15, 4.18
    eye, 4.18
    J-, 4.18
    machine, 4.4–4.5
    molly, 2.46
    stud, 4.6
    toggle, 4.28–4.29
    torque values for, 4.12
Bore hole, 2.65
Box(es)
    for cable reel, 8.25, 8.27–8.28
    connection to conduit, 3.29, 3.30
    hot, 7.5
    installation, 3.29, 3.31–3.34
    junction, 3.20, 3.21
    low-voltage, 3.29, 3.30
    metallic, 3.27–3.28
    nonmetallic, 3.28–3.29
    pull, 8.30
    for residential cable, 8.51
    speaker back, 3.30
    switch, 3.31
    termination, 3.19, 3.29
Box sill, 2.16
Bracing, 2.23–2.24, 2.25, 2.41
Brake, reel, 8.37
Brick
    clay, 2.11, 2.63
    hollow concrete, 2.10–2.11
    precast concrete, 2.36
Bridging, 2.18–2.19, 2.75
Broadband systems, 8.58, 8.59–8.60
Brush, conduit, 8.29
Bucks, 2.38

Buffer, in optical fiber cable, 8.18, 8.19, 8.20
Building automation systems (BAS), 1.2, 1.3
Building codes, 1.11, 8.79
Building Industry Consulting Service International, Inc.
    (BICSI), 1.28
Building materials, 2.1–2.12
Building Officials and Code Administrators International
    (BOCA), 1.11
Bullwheel, 8.37, 8.38, 8.40, 8.43
Bureau of Apprenticeship and Training (BAT), 1.17, 1.18
Buried cable, 3.26, 3.37
Burns, 5.3, 5.5, 5.24
Busbar, 8.71
Bushings, 3.12, 3.13
Butane, 5.23

CABA. See Continental Automated Buildings Association
Cabinets, 3.26–3.27
Cable
    access to, 3.24, 3.25, 3.26
    buried, 3.24–3.27, 3.37, 8.52, 8.65–8.66
    Class 2/3, 8.5, 8.10–8.12
    coaxial, 1.20–1.21, 3.27, 8.9, 8.16–8.18, 8.49, 8.52, 8.59
    communication, 8.8, 8.9, 8.13–8.18
    distribution system for, 3.34–3.38
    ductwork for, 2.37
    ends, preparation for pulling, 8.32
    for fire alarm circuits, 8.5–8.6, 8.12, 8.55–8.57
    and firestopping materials, 2.56, 2.57
    hybrid, 8.7, 8.8, 8.58
    installation
        aerial, 8.66
        of the backbone cable, 8.36, 8.37–8.46, 8.69
        broadband communication system, 8.58, 8.59–8.60
        commercial, 8.20–8.49, 8.66–8.69, 8.79–8.90
        equipment for, 8.24–8.25, 8.26, 8.27, 8.32, 8.35–8.26
        fire alarm circuits, 8.55–8.57
        horizontal pulls, 8.41–8.45, 8.47–8.48, 8.69, 8.80–8.81
        intervals for fastening, 8.56
        optical fiber, 8.45–8.47, 8.57–8.58
        planning the, 8.25–8.27, 8.52, 8.53
        residential, 8.49–8.53, 8.69–8.71, 8.83–8.90
        safety, 8.22, 8.23–8.24, 8.36
        setting up for cable pulling, 8.27–8.34
        telephone, 8.65
        tension during, 8.38, 8.41, 8.46, 8.52
        tools for, 2.58–2.71
        underground, 3.24–3.27, 8.52
        vertical pulls, 8.36–8.41, 8.84–8.87
        work area pulls, 8.47–8.49
    maximum pull force/tension, 8.41, 8.48, 8.52
    multimedia network, 8.9–8.10
    multiplex, 8.32
    number in conduit, 8.48–8.49
    optical fiber. See Optical fiber
    polyethylene insulated conductor, 3.26
    premises, 8.60, 8.63–8.65
    PTLC, 8.10–8.12
    ribbon, 8.15
    standards, 1.36, 3.1–3.2, 8.2. See also ANSI/TIA/EIA
        standards
    television antenna, 3.27, 8.9, 8.18, 8.49
    tools to work with, 1.20–1.21
    trunk, 8.50
    twisted-pair, 8.64, 8.78. See also Shielded twisted-pair
        cable; Unshielded twisted-pair cable
    undercarpet, 8.7, 8.14–8.15
Cable caddy, 8.24
Cable supports, 3.16–3.17

Cable tester, LAN, 1.22
Cable tray, 3.1, 3.21–3.22, 3.43, 8.5, 8.43, 8.44
Cable tray fittings, 3.22
Cable tray supports, 3.23–3.24
Caddy-fastening device, 3.32
Calcium chloride, 3.6
Calculator, 6.16, 6.17, 6.18, 6.19
Camera, digital, 5.29
Canadian Electrical Code (CEC), 1.11, 1.34
Canadian Security Association (CANASA), 1.29
Canadian Standards Association, 1.11
Cancer, 5.31
Cantilever applications, 2.6, 2.75
Capstan, 8.24, 8.32, 8.35, 8.36, 8.41, 8.45, 8.77
Carbon monoxide, 5.23
Cardiopulmonary resuscitation (CPR), 5.27, 5.29
Carpeting, 8.86, 8.88, 8.106. See also Undercarpet
    telecommunication cable
Caulk, 2.55, 2.57, 2.58
CEA. See Consumer Electronics Association
CEC. See Canadian Electrical Code
CEDIA. See Custom Electronic Design and Installation
    Association
Ceiling access, 2.49, 2.52
Ceilings
    construction techniques
        commercial, 2.43, 2.45–2.52, 2.53
        residential, 2.26–2.27, 2.28
    direct-hung concealed grid system, 2.48–2.49, 3.16,
        8.80–8.81
    exposed grid (direct-hung), 2.45–2.46, 3.16
    fasteners used on, 4.31
    installation of a pull line in, 8.31–8.32
    integrated systems, 2.49, 2.50
    luminous systems, 2.49–2.50
    pan systems, 2.47, 2.51
    special systems, 2.51–2.52
    suspended, 2.45–2.46, 3.34
    suspended drywall furring systems, 2.50–2.51
    vaulted, 2.6, 2.76
Cellulose, blown-in, 8.86
Celsius scale, 6.13, 6.14
Cement, 2.9–2.10, 5.31, 7.4
Centimeter-gram-second system (CGS), 6.2
Ceramic fiber, 8.3
Certificate of Completion, 1.12, 1.15–1.16
Certification and licensing, 1.4, 2.69, 4.24
CEV. See Controlled environment vault
CFR. See Code of Federal Regulations
CGS. See Centimeter-gram-second system
Change order, 1.13
Channel
    framing, electrical, 3.15
    furring, 2.47, 2.50, 2.51
Channel support, 8.39
Chemicals, hazardous, 5.33
Chimney (maintenance hole), 3.24
Chimney (on residential roof), 2.30
Chisels, 2.61
Chord, 2.18, 2.31
Chuck, 2.60, 4.27
CI. See Circuit-integrity cable
Circle cutter, 2.67, 8.96
Circles, 6.6, 6.7, 6.23–6.24, 7.7–7.8
Circuit(s)
    Class 1, 3.1, 8.53–8.54
    Class 2 and 3, 3.1, 8.54–8.55
    communication, within buildings, 8.58–8.59

    de-energized, 5.7, 5.8–5.9, 5.14–5.15
    fire alarm, 3.1, 8.5–8.6, 8.12, 8.55–8.57
    four-wire twisted pair, 8.64
    nonpower-limited, 8.53, 8.55–8.56, 8.78
    power-limited, 8.53, 8.56–8.57, 8.78
    re-energizing, 5.10, 5.13
    remote-control, 3.1
    telephone, 8.61–8.62
    two-wire to four-wire hybrid, 8.64, 8.65
    two-wire twisted pair, 8.64
Circuit breaker, 5.9–5.10
Circuit-integrity cable (CI), 8.6
Circumference, 6.24, 7.8
Cladding, 8.18, 8.19
Clamps, 3.14, 3.16, 3.17, 4.17, 8.42
Cleaning techniques for ceiling panels, 2.52
Cleanup, 8.53
Clearance, of a threaded fastener, 4.2, 4.9, 4.35
Clevis, 8.32, 8.33, 8.77
Clips, 2.46, 2.47, 2.48, 3.32, 4.13. See also Tie wraps
Clothing, 5.6, 5.14, 5.25
CMU. See Concrete masonry units
Code of Federal Regulations (CFR), 5.5, 5.6, 5.8, 5.9, 5.11
Coefficient, 6.20, 6.33
Cold, extreme, 5.25
Cold weather conditions, 2.31, 3.37
Color coding system
    for bonding conductor, 8.71
    for cable jackets, 8.13, 8.14, 8.15, 8.16, 8.20
    for inner duct, 8.30
    for powder charge, 2.69
    for studs, 2.42
Column, lally, 2.16
Combustible materials and atmospheres, 3.14, 5.23, 5.24,
    5.37
Commercial construction
    cable installation, 8.20–8.49, 8.66–8.69, 8.79–8.82
    ceiling, 2.34–2.52, 2.53
    concrete structures, 2.35
    exterior wall panels, 2.35, 2.36
    floor, 2.36–2.37
    interior walls, 2.38–2.45. See also Partition
    studs, 2.38–2.42
Communication
    in confined spaces, 5.29
    professional, 1.6–1.8
    while pulling cable, 8.36
Communication systems
    broadband, 8.58, 8.59–8.60
    cable, 8.7, 8.8, 8.9, 8.14–8.15, 8.58
    circuits within buildings, 8.58–8.59
    distribution, 3.18, 3.36–3.38
    ductwork for, 2.37
    examples, 1.2
    grounding and bonding, 8.71–8.72
    integrated, 1.3
    outlets and raceways for, 3.18–3.21
    residential, 8.49–8.53
    room layout, 3.36, 3.37
    standards, 1.32–1.34, 3.2
Compliance, 1.4, 5.32
Compression web, 2.31
Computers, 3.36, 6.15, 8.51
Concentric bends, 7.7, 7.21
Concrete
    commercial structures, 2.35
    controlled environment vaults, 3.26
    drill bits for, 2.63

Concrete (*continued*)
    drilling holes in, 4.28
    duct, 3.26
    epoxy anchoring systems, 4.30–4.32
    fasteners for, 4.20, 4.28, 4.36
    fireproof openings, 2.56
    floors, 2.36–2.37, 3.21
    flush-mount installation of conduit in, 3.29, 3.31–3.32
    green, 2.9, 2.75
    overview, 2.9–2.10
    plastic, 2.9, 2.75
    post-tensioned, 2.9, 2.76
    pre-stressed, 2.9, 2.75
    reinforced, 2.9, 2.76
Concrete forms, 2.10
Concrete masonry units (CMU), 2.10–2.11
Conductors
    bonding, 3.13, 3.43, 8.71–8.72
    definition, 3.2, 3.43
    of different circuits in the same
        cable/enclosure/raceway, 8.53–8.54, 8.55–8.56
    ring, 8.13, 8.15, 8.70–8.71
    tip, 8.13, 8.15, 8.70–8.71
    wire size within, 8.2
Conduit
    bends in, 3.9, 3.33. *See also* Bend radius; Hand bending of
        conduit
    buried, 3.24–3.27, 3.37, 8.66
    connection to a box, 3.29, 3.30
    cutting, 7.1–7.2, 7.4, 7.17
    definition, 3.2, 3.43
    inspection and measurement prior to pulling cable,
        8.29–8.30
    installation, 3.29, 3.31–3.34
    intermediate metal, 3.4, 3.7
    joining, 7.4–7.5
    reaming, 7.3
    standards, 3.1
    storage of, 3.24
    thinwall, 3.32
    threading, 7.3–7.4
    types, 3.2–3.9
Conduit bodies, 3.10–3.11, 3.12
Conduit body cover, 3.11
Conduit fill, 8.48–8.49, 8.66
Confined spaces
    additional hazards in, 5.24–5.25
    atmospheric hazards in, 5.20, 5.23–5.24
    characteristics and examples, 5.1–5.2
    classification, 5.19–5.20
    nonpermit-required, 5.19–5.20, 5.37
    permit-required, 5.20, 5.37
    responsibilities and duties, 5.26–5.27
Conflict resolution, 1.9–1.10
Constant, 6.6, 6.20, 6.33
Construction materials and methods. *See also* Tools
    building materials, 2.1–2.12
    commercial, 2.34–2.52
    fire-rated and sound-rated, 2.52–2.58
    lath and plaster, 2.7
    project schedules, 2.71–2.72
    residential frame construction, 2.12–2.34
Consumer Electronics Association (CEA), 1.29
Continental Automated Buildings Association (CABA),
    1.28–1.29
Continuity, 3.43
Controlled environment vault (CEV), 3.26
Controllers, 1.3, 6.14, 8.51

Conversion (mathematical), 6.1–6.2, 6.5, 6.8, 6.9–6.10, 6.11,
    6.14, 6.34–6.35
Copper, 8.2
Cord
    extension, 5.10
    flexible, 5.11
    patch, 8.13, 8.14, 8.15, 8.78
Core hitch methods, 8.32, 8.34
Corian, 2.63
Corners, 2.21, 2.22, 2.34, 3.9, 3.19
Corrugated, definition, 2.75
Cosine, 6.28–6.29, 7.22–7.23
Countersink, 2.60
Coupling(s)
    combination, 3.9
    compression, 3.4, 3.5
    expansion, 3.7, 3.8
    metal, 3.10
    raceway-to-conduit connector, 3.20
    setscrew, 3.4, 3.5, 3.10
Courtesy, 1.6
CPR. *See* Cardiopulmonary resuscitation
Cranes, 5.17
Crawl space work area, 8.88
Creep-Zit™, 8.80, 8.81, 8.89, 8.90, 8.100–8.101
Crimp tool, 1.20
Cross-connect, 3.36, 3.37, 3.43
Crosscutting, 2.66, 2.75
Cross-linked polyethylene (XLP), 8.3
Crosstalk, 8.77
Cross ties (cross tees), 2.45, 2.46, 2.48
Crushing accidents, 5.1
Cubes or box-shapes, 6.6, 6.7, 6.8
Custom Electronic Design and Installation Association
    (CEDIA), 1.29
Customers, 1.5–1.8
Cutout tool, 2.67
Cutting tools, 2.66–2.67, 7.1–7.2, 7.5, 8.96–8.97
Cylinders, 6.6, 6.8

Danger signs, 5.12, 5.13, 5.32
Decibel (unit), 6.17–6.18, 6.33
Decimals, 6.1–6.2, 6.15
Decking, 2.11, 2.53, 4.21, 4.22
Decoil-Zit, 8.81
Demarcation point. *See* Network interface device
Demultiplexer, 8.63
De-Plug-Zit™, 8.97
Developed length, 7.10, 7.12, 7.21
Diagrams, 1.12
DID. *See* Direct inward dialing
Dies, 1.20, 4.13, 7.3–7.4
Direct current (DC), 8.61
Direct inward dialing (DID), 8.62, 8.77
Documentation
    backbone cable information, 8.39, 8.41, 8.46, 8.48
    entry permit, 5.20, 5.21–5.22
    lockout/tagout verification, 5.13
    residential cable information, 8.52–8.53
    used on each project, 1.12–1.16
Door openings, 2.21, 2.23, 2.33, 2.38, 2.40
Dormer, 2.32, 2.33, 2.75
Dove Tail 6 Foot Sock, 8.100
Drag-Zit™, 8.89, 8.100
Drawings, 1.12, 1.13, 5.7
Drill bit(s)
    commonly used, 2.60, 2.61, 2.62
    flexible extensions for, 8.94

guide, 8.93
Pro-Bore®, 8.84, 8.92
Rebore-Zit™, 8.95
reference, 8.95
Spear-Zit™, 8.84, 8.85, 8.86, 8.87, 8.88, 8.89, 8.90, 8.93
specifications, 2.63–2.64, 4.10
use during cable installation, 8.92–8.95
Drill-Eze, 8.84
Drilling
    into fire-rated walls, 2.53
    holes for cable access, 2.59
    holes for fasteners, 4.9, 4.10, 4.16, 4.19, 4.20, 4.28
    horizontal directional, 2.65
    into joists, 2.17–2.18, 2.19
    during residential cable installation, 8.53
    techniques, 2.53
    tools, 2.59–2.65, 5.10, 8.92–8.95
Drilling rig, 2.65
Drill rod, 2.65
Drills, 2.59–2.65, 5.10
Drip edge, 2.31
Drug use, 1.5
Drywall
    circle cutter for, 2.67, 8.96
    drill bits for, 2.63
    and fire rating, 2.55
    installation, 2.48, 2.51
    and mud rings, 8.51
    screws for, 4.21–4.22
Duct
    end plug for, 3.21
    inner, 3.3, 8.30–8.31
    monolithic concrete, 3.26
    multiple, 3.19, 3.24
    in underground systems, 3.24, 3.26
Ductwork system, 2.26, 2.37. See also Plenum
Dust, 3.14, 5.23, 5.30, 8.51
Dyne (unit), 6.11, 6.12

Earthquakes, 2.5, 2.20, 2.41
ECTFE. See Ethylene chlorotrifluoroethylene
EFCO Hand-E-Form®, 2.10
EIA. See Electronic Industries Alliance
Electrical metallic tubing (EMT), 3.3–3.5, 3.32, 3.33, 7.1, 7.5
Electrical nonmetallic tubing (ENT), 3.2
Electric shock
    annual number of accidents, 5.2
    effects of current on the body, 5.2–5.5
    emergency response, 5.5
    and fish tape, 8.23
    reducing your risk, 5.5–5.7, 5.24
    and telephone line, 8.61
Electromagnetic interference (EMI), 3.91, 8.16, 8.55, 8.57,
    8.60, 8.72–8.73, 8.77
Electronic Industries Alliance (EIA), 1.11, 1.27, 1.29, 1.31,
    1.36, 8.66. See also ANSI/TIA/EIA standards
Electronic systems, 1.2. See also Low-voltage systems
Electronic Systems Industry Consortium (ESIC), 1.29–1.30
Electronic systems technician
    definition, 1.2
    opportunities, 1.1, 1.2–1.3, 1.22
    responsibilities. See Responsibilities
Elevator shaft, 3.36, 5.33, 8.8
Emergency response, 5.5, 5.26–5.27
EMI. See Electromagnetic interference
EMT. See Electrical metallic tubing
Endothermic materials, 2.56
Energy (work), 6.34

Engineering notation, 6.16–6.17
English system, 6.2, 6.9
Engulfment, 5.25
ENT. See Electrical nonmetallic tubing
Entertainment Services and Technology Association (ESTA),
    1.30
Entertainment systems, 1.2
Entrance facility room, 8.66, 8.67
Entry permit, 5.20, 5.21–5.22
Environmental control systems, 1.2
Environmental Protection Agency (EPA), 5.33
Epoxy anchoring systems, 4.30–4.32
Equipment
    accidents from moving parts, 5.25
    to bend conduit, 7.5–7.7
    pressure-tolerant, 6.11
    protective. See Personal protective equipment
    to pull cable, 8.24–8.25, 8.26, 8.27, 8.32, 8.35–8.26
Equipment room, 3.34, 3.35, 3.36, 3.37, 8.66–8.67
Escape route, 5.7, 5.26
ESIC. See Electronic Systems Industry Consortium
ESTA. See Entertainment Services and Technology
    Association
Ethical principles, 1.4
Ethylene chlorotrifluoroethylene (ECTFE), 8.3
Evacuation, 5.26
Explosion hazards, 2.69, 3.14, 3.15, 5.23, 5.30, 5.32
Exponent, 6.15, 6.33
Exposed location, 3.10, 3.43
Eye, pulling, 8.37

Faceplate, 3.19, 3.30
Fahrenheit scale, 6.13, 6.14
Falling objects, 5.1, 5.25
Falls and fall protection, 5.9, 5.25, 5.33
Fans, 2.52, 5.23
Fastener(s)
    anchors. See Anchors
    apron to carry, 4.9
    clearance of, 4.2, 4.9
    epoxy anchoring systems, 4.30–4.32
    installation of, 4.9–4.13
    keys, 4.1, 4.14
    non-threaded, 4.13–4.17
    pins, 4.14–4.16
    for powder-actuated tool, 2.41, 2.69–2.70, 4.22–4.25
    retainer, 4.13–4.14
    rivets, 4.16–4.17
    screws. See Screws
    special, 4.17–4.18
    studs, 2.42, 2.63, 4.22, 4.23
    threaded, 4.1–4.13
    tie wraps, 3.16, 4.17
    tolerance of, 4.2
Fastening tools
    pneumatic, 2.68–2.69
    powder-actuated, 2.41, 2.69–2.70, 4.22–4.25
FDM. See Frequency division multiplexing
FEP. See Fluorinated ethylene propylene
Ferrule, 4.35
Fiberboard, 2.3, 2.4, 2.26
Fiberglass, 2.38, 2.39. See also Fish tape/line/wire, fiberglass
Fibrillation of the heart, 5.2–5.3, 5.4, 5.37
File, half-round, 7.3
Fill, conduit, 8.48–8.49, 8.66
Filter, air, 5.30, 5.32
Fire alarms and circuits, 3.1, 8.5–8.6, 8.12, 8.55–8.57
Fire detectors, 8.57

Fire hazards, 5.23
Fire-rated construction
 cable, 3.34
 cable ties, 3.16
 conduit, 3.2
 definition, 2.75, 3.43
 interior walls, 2.38, 2.39
 overview, 2.52–2.58
 walls separating occupancies, 2.33–2.34
Fire-resistant materials, 2.5, 2.38, 2.55–2.56, 2.57, 8.5, 8.8
Firestops and firestopping, 2.23, 2.25, 2.34, 2.53, 2.54–2.57, 2.75
First aid, 5.5, 5.27, 5.29, 5.32
Fish-Eze™ Kit, 8.90, 8.106
Fishing system, power, 1.21, 8.21–8.22, 8.23, 8.30–8.31, 8.77
Fish tape/line/wire
 definition, 8.77
 fiberglass (YFT), 8.80, 8.87, 8.88, 8.90, 8.102
 function of, 8.30
 overview, 2.70–2.71, 8.20–8.21
 replacing the hook on, 8.27
 steel, 8.99
 straightening, 8.23
Fishtix, 8.81, 8.102
Fittings. See also Couplings
 cable tray, 3.22
 compression, 3.4, 3.5
 connector protector, 8.105
 flex connector, 3.8
 optical fiber connector, 8.21
 screw-on coax connector, 8.60
 sealing, 3.14, 3.15
 setscrew, 3.5
 takeoff, 3.21, 3.34
Fixtures, 2.57, 2.58
Flammable materials, 3.14, 5.23, 5.24
Flange, 2.18, 2.23, 3.20
Flash point, 3.14
Flexible nonmetallic conduit (flex; FNC), 3.8–3.9, 8.51
Floor construction, 2.13–2.20, 2.36–2.37, 3.20–3.21, 8.89
Floor plan, 1.12
Fluorinated ethylene propylene (FEP), 8.3
FNC. See Flexible nonmetallic conduit
Follow up, 1.8
Footing, 2.10, 2.12, 2.13, 2.75
Foot-pounds, 4.11, 4.35
Force, 6.9, 6.10, 6.11, 6.33, 6.34, 8.36, 8.44
Forced-air systems, 2.53
Formica, 2.63
Foundation, 2.12, 2.13–2.15, 2.45
Frame construction
 balloon, 2.13
 firestop in, 2.54
 with masonry, 2.33
 metal, 2.38–2.42
 plank-and-beam (post-and-beam), 2.32–2.33
 platform floor, 2.15
 residential, 2.12–2.34
 steel, 3.33–3.34
 stick-built, 2.29, 2.31
 truss-built, 2.29, 2.31
 western platform, 2.13
 wood, 3.32–3.33
Framing channel, electrical, 3.15
Frequency division multiplexing (FDM), 8.61, 8.63, 8.77
Furring channel, 2.47, 2.50, 2.51
Furring clip, 2.47
Furring strip, 2.33, 2.34, 2.75
Fuses, 5.6, 5.7, 5.10

Gable, 2.32, 2.33, 2.75
Gain, 7.10, 7.21
Galvanization, 3.4
Galvanized rigid steel conduit (GRC), 3.5, 3.6
Gas. See Vapors and gases
Gasket, 3.11
Geometry
 basics of, 6.22–6.27
 to bend conduit, 7.7–7.8
 working with right triangles, 6.27–6.29, 7.7
Girder, 2.12, 2.14, 2.16, 2.17, 2.75
Glass bead, 8.3
GloRod™, 8.88, 8.103
Glulam, 2.5, 2.6
Golf string, 8.104
Grabbit™, 8.32, 8.80, 8.81, 8.88, 8.90, 8.104
Granite, 2.63
GRC. See Galvanized rigid steel conduit
Gridwires, 3.16
Grips, to pull cable, 8.22, 8.23, 8.32, 8.33, 8.38, 8.41, 8.77
Grommet, 2.67, 3.20
Ground
 for communication systems, 8.71–8.72
 definition, 3.43, 5.2, 5.37
 by electrical metallic tubing, 3.4
 floating the, 8.12
 standards, 3.1, 5.10–5.11
Ground fault circuit interrupter (GFCI), 2.58, 2.59, 2.75, 5.3, 5.10, 5.11
Guardrail, 5.33
Gunpowder. See Tools, powder-actuated
Gusset, 2.31
Gypsum, 2.75
Gypsum board, 2.4, 2.6–2.9, 2.26, 2.40, 2.58

Hacksaw, 7.1–7.2, 7.17
Hair, facial, 5.30
Hammers, 2.60–2.61, 2.62, 2.64, 4.27
Hand bending of conduit
 back-to-back 90-degree bends, 7.10, 7.11, 7.21
 concentric bends, 7.7, 7.21
 cutting, reaming, and threading, 7.1–7.5
 equipment, 7.5–7.7
 45-degree, 7.7
 four-bend saddles, 7.15–7.16
 gain, 7.10
 geometry, 7.7–7.8
 90-degree, 7.7, 7.8–7.9, 7.10, 7.21
 offsets, 3.15, 3.43, 7.10–7.12, 7.21
 parallel offsets, 7.12–7.14
 planning, 7.16
 saddle bends, 7.14–7.16
 segment bend, 7.6, 7.21
Hand-E-Form®, 2.10
Handholes, 2.37
Hanger
 cable, 3.16–3.17
 ceiling, 2.46, 3.16
 threaded rod, 3.23, 3.34
 trapeze, 3.15, 3.23
 Unistrut, 3.34
Hardboard, 2.4
Hard hat area, 5.13
Harness, full body, 5.28
Hazardous locations, 3.14, 8.55. See also Confined spaces
HDO. See High-density overlay
Head end, 8.50, 8.77
Header, 2.5, 2.21, 2.24, 2.26, 2.75, 3.21
Headlight, 8.88, 8.90

Heat exhaustion, 5.25
Heating, ventilating, air conditioning, and refrigeration (HVACR), 8.50
Heating, ventilating, and air conditioning (HVAC), 1.2, 2.53
Heating unit, for PVC conduit, 7.6
Heat stroke, 5.25
Hickey, 7.6
High-density overlay (HDO), 2.5
High-efficiency particulate air filter (HEPA), 5.32
High voltage, 1.27, 5.3
High-voltage work, 1.2
Hitch knot, 8.33, 8.39
Hoists, 5.17
Hoistway, 8.54, 8.57
Homerun scheme, 8.70, 8.71
Hooks for pull line. See Retrievers
Hook-Zit™, 8.84, 8.85, 8.86, 8.99
Hose, 3.8
Hot box, 7.5
Hub, threaded weatherproof, 3.11–3.12
Human body, 5.3–5.4, 5.23
HVAC. See Heating, ventilating, and air conditioning
Hypotenuse, 6.27, 6.28, 7.7, 7.11, 7.22
Hypothermia, 5.25, 5.37
IBC. See International Building Code

I-beam, 2.17
ICBO. See International Conference of Building Officials
ICC. See International Code Council
ICIA. See International Communications Industries Association
ID. See Inside diameter
IEEE. See Institute of Electrical and Electronic Engineers
IMC. See Intermediate metal conduit
Impedance, 8.13, 8.77
Inch-pounds, 4.11, 4.35
Inside diameter (ID), 3.3, 3.7, 8.48
Installation
    cable. See Cable, installation
    conduit and boxes, 3.29, 3.31–3.34
    conduit bodies, 3.12
    electrical metallic conduit, 3.5, 3.32, 3.33
    fasteners, 4.9–4.13
    of a pull line, 8.30–8.31
    raceways, 3.19
    rigid metal conduit, 3.6
    sealing fittings, 3.15
    telephone wiring, 8.65
    wiring, 3.33
Institute of Electrical and Electronic Engineers (IEEE), 1.11, 1.36, 8.17
Instrumentation tray cable (ITC), 8.5, 8.55
Insulation
    of building board, 2.4
    of conductor, 3.6, 8.2, 8.3
    fiberglass, 2.38
    and fishing wire, 8.85, 8.90
    of gypsum board, 2.6
    of intumescent materials, 2.56
    sound, 2.45, 2.47. See also Sound-rated construction
Integrated management systems, 1.2, 1.3
Interlock, 5.9
Intermediate metal conduit (IMC), 3.3, 3.4, 3.7, 7.1
International Building Code (IBC), 2.17
International Code Council (ICC), 1.11
International Communications Industries Association (ICIA), 1.30
International Conference of Building Officials (ICBO), 1.11

Intumescent materials, 2.56
ITC. See Instrumentation tray cable

Jack
    on a cable reel, 8.25, 8.28
    communications, 3.20, 8.51, 8.69
Jacket on cable, 8.12, 8.13, 8.18
J-clamp (J-hook), 3.17
Jewelry, 5.6, 5.7, 5.25
Job plan, 5.7
Job sheet, 1.12, 1.14
Joist(s)
    ceiling, 2.26–2.27, 2.28
    definition, 2.2, 2.75
    floor, 2.15, 2.16–2.17
    metal, 2.42, 2.45
    notches for, 2.17–2.18
    notching and drilling of, 2.17–2.18, 2.19
    trimmer, 2.17, 2.76
Joist hanger, 2.26
Journeyman, 1.18
Jtip, 8.90, 8.100

Kelvin scale, 6.13, 6.14
Kerf, 2.48, 2.75
Kevlar®, 8.18
Key, 4.1, 4.14, 4.35
Key system, 8.62, 8.63, 8.77
Keyway, 4.14, 4.35
Kicks. See Offsets
Knockout, 3.27, 3.28, 3.29

Labor $aving Devices®, Inc., 8.79, 8.84
Ladder, 5.15–5.16
Laminated strand lumber (LSL), 2.5, 2.6
Laminated veneer lumber (LVL), 2.5, 2.6, 2.17
LAN. See Local area network
Lawsuits, 1.12
LBS, 8.84, 8.85
LED. See Light-emitting diode
Ledger, 2.17
Length, 6.2, 6.4–6.5, 6.33, 6.34
Length, developed, 7.12, 7.21
Level (instrument), 7.8, 7.9, 7.12, 8.87
Level (measurement of fluid), 6.4, 6.33
LFNC. See Liquidtight flexible nonmetallic conduit
Liability, 1.12
Lifeline, 5.28
Life safety systems, 1.2, 1.32–1.33, 1.34
Lifting technique, 5.17, 5.18, 8.23
Lifts, 5.17
Light, path inside optical fiber, 8.18–8.19
Light-emitting diode (LED), 8.19
Lighting, 1.3, 2.49–2.50, 3.36, 5.10, 5.23, 5.33, 8.51
Line
    fish. See Fish tape/line/wire
    pull, 8.22–8.23, 8.30–8.33
Liquidtight flexible nonmetallic conduit (LFNC), 3.8, 3.9
Listening, active, 1.7–1.8
Liter, 6.9, 6.33
Local area network (LAN), 1.22, 3.18, 8.68
Local exchange, 8.61, 8.77
Locate-Zit™, 8.100
Lock, kirk, 5.9
Locknut, 3.13, 3.30
Lockout/tagout procedure, 5.7, 5.9, 5.11–5.13
Logarithms, 6.18
Looped scheme, 8.70

Low voltage, 1.27, 5.3
Low-voltage systems
    ANSI/NFPA standards, 1.35
    boxes for, 3.20, 3.21, 3.29, 3.30
    construction, 8.10–8.12
    definition, 1.1
    raceway, 3.18
    residential installation of cable, 8.49–8.53
LSL. *See* Laminated strand lumber
Lubricant
    to cut pipe, 7.2, 7.4
    to pull cable, 8.35, 8.42, 8.78
Lumber
    dimension, 2.2, 2.75
    drill bits and saw blades for, 2.63
    engineered wood products, 2.5–2.6, 2.7
    five categories of, 2.2
    pressure-treated, 2.2
LVL. *See* Laminated veneer lumber
LZO, 8.85, 8.86
LZsec, 8.85, 8.86

Magnetic resonance imaging (MRI), 3.7
Maintenance hole, 3.24, 3.25, 3.26, 3.34, 5.19, 5.25
Mandrel, 4.16, 4.17, 8.29, 8.30, 8.97
Mantissa, 6.17
Masonry
    drill bits for, 2.63, 2.64
    drilling holes in, 4.28
    epoxy anchoring systems for, 4.30–4.32
    fasteners for, 4.20, 4.28, 4.36
    flush-mount installation of conduit in, 3.29, 3.31–3.32
    framing in, 2.33
    materials, 2.9–2.12
    wall between occupancies, 2.54
Mass, 6.2, 6.9, 6.11, 6.33
Master, 1.18
Material safety data sheet (MSDS), 2.2, 2.4, 5.24, 5.30, 5.31
Materials takeoff, 1.12, 1.27
Mathematics
    algebra, 6.19–6.22
    binary systems, 6.15
    conversions, 6.1–6.2, 6.5, 6.8, 6.9–6.10, 6.11, 6.14
    decibels, 6.17–6.18
    engineering notation, 6.16–6.17
    geometry, 6.22–6.27
    logarithms, 6.18
    metric system. *See* Metric system
    powers and roots, 6.18–6.19
    scientific notation, 6.14–6.16
    sequence of operations, 6.20–6.21
    trigonometry, 6.28–6.29, 7.11, 7.12, 7.13, 7.22–7.23
    working with right triangles, 6.27–6.29, 7.7
Medium-density overlay (MDO), 2.5
Mesothelioma, 5.31
Messenger, 8.13, 8.77
Metal construction materials
    in ceiling systems, 2.51
    joists and roof trusses, 2.42, 2.45
    metal framing, 2.11–2.12, 2.38–2.45, 3.32
    plates, 2.16
    steel cross-bridging, 2.19
    strap bracing, 2.23–2.24, 2.25, 2.42, 2.43, 2.44
    trusses, 2.17, 2.18
Meter, 6.4
Meter-kilogram-second system (MKS), 6.2
Methane, 5.23
Metric system
    fundamental units, 6.2–6.4

    length, area, and volume, 6.4–6.9
    mass *vs.* weight, 6.9–6.11
    pressure (force) and acceleration, 6.11–6.13
    temperature, 6.13–6.14
Microcontroller, 6.14
Microprocessor, 1.2, 1.27
Millwork, 2.5, 2.75
Minerallac, 3.14
Misunderstandings, how to avoid, 1.7–1.8
MKG. *See* Meter-kilogram-second system
MMTA. *See* Multimedia Telecommunications Association
Modem, 1.2, 1.27
Moisture barrier, 2.6, 2.19, 2.30, 8.85
Monitoring. *See* Tests
Mouse, 8.21–8.22, 8.30, 8.31
MSDS. *See* Material safety data sheet
Multimedia Telecommunications Association (MMTA), 1.31
Multimeters, 1.22
Multiplex (cable), 8.32
Multiplex (transmission of multiple signals), 3.36, 3.43,
    8.61–8.62, 8.63, 8.77
Mylar®, 8.10

Nailer, pneumatic, 2.68–2.69
Nails, 2.24, 2.46, 2.68
National Burglar and Fire Alarm Association (NBFAA), 1.30
National Center for Construction Education and Research
    (NCCER), 1.19, 1.31
National Electrical Code® (NEC®)
    bends in conduit, 7.6
    cable classification, rating, and usage, 8.4–8.10
    cable installation, 8.53–8.55, 8.58–8.60
    circuits, 8.53–8.56
    conduit, cable, and raceway, 3.1–3.2
    Fine Print Notes, 3.2
    grounding and electrical safety, 5.8, 5.11
    lockout, 5.11
    overview, 1.10–1.11, 1.35
    telecommunications and life safety systems, 1.32–1.33
National Electrical Manufacturers' Association (NEMA), 3.7
National Fire Protection Association (NFPA), 1.10, 1.11, 1.31,
    1.35, 2.17
National Institute for Certification in Engineering
    Technologies (NICET), 1.31
National Systems Contractors Association (NSCA), 1.31
NBFAA. *See* National Burglar and Fire Alarm Association
NCCER. *See* National Center for Construction Education
    and Research
NEC®. *See National Electrical Code®*
Negative-pressure enclosure, 5.32
Negotiating, 1.9–1.10
NEMA. *See* National Electrical Manufacturers' Association
Neoprene, 3.8
Net, safety, 5.33
Network interface device (NID), 8.65, 8.69–8.70, 8.72
Networks
    home, 8.51
    local area, 1.22, 3.18, 8.68
    multimedia, 8.9–8.10
    and multiplexing, 3.36, 3.43, 8.61–8.62, 8.63
Newton (unit), 6.10, 6.11, 6.12, 6.33
Newton's Laws of Motion, 6.10, 6.11
NFPA. *See* National Fire Protection Association
NICET. *See* National Institute for Certification in
    Engineering Technologies
NID. *See* Network interface device
Nipples, offset, 3.12, 3.13
Noise (ambient), 5.25
Noise (signal), 8.72

Nominal size, of a threaded fastener, 4.2, 4.35
Nonpower-limited fire alarm circuits (NPLFA), 8.55–8.56
Notches, 2.17–2.18, 3.32
NPLFA. *See* Circuits, nonpower-limited
NSCA. *See* National Systems Contractors Association
Nuts, 4.6–4.8
Nylon, 8.3, 8.22

Occupational Safety and Health Administration (OSHA)
    asbestos, 5.31
    electrical regulations, 5.10–5.13
    electrical shock safety, 5.5, 5.6
    lockout/tagout procedure, 5.11–5.13
    overall safety, 5.8
    overview, 5.7–5.8
    powder-tool use, 4.24
    protection. *See* Personal protective equipment
    safety philosophy and general precautions, 5.8–5.10
    voltage testing, 5.14–5.15
OD. *See* Outside diameter
Office of Apprenticeship Training and Employer and Labor
        Services (ATELS), 1.18
Offsets
    of a cable run, 8.44
    conduit fittings for, 3.12, 3.13, 3.15
    definition, 7.21
    overview and types of, 7.10–7.14
    sizing techniques, 7.7, 7.22–7.24
Ohm (unit), 6.17, 8.13
Oil, cutting, 7.2, 7.4
On-the-job training (OJT), 1.17–1.19
Optical fiber cable
    backbone, 3.36, 3.37
    bend radius of, 8.37
    blowing unit for, 8.31
    connectors, 8.21
    installation, 8.45–8.47, 8.57–8.58
    NEC® classifications, 8.4, 8.7
    overview, 8.18–8.20, 8.57
    substitutions, 8.12
    for telephone transmission, 8.66
    undercarpet, 8.15
    vs. UTP, 8.20
Oriented strand board (OSB), 2.3, 2.4, 2.17, 2.20, 2.75
Outlets, 3.19, 3.29, 3.31, 3.33, 8.87
Outside diameter (OD), 3.3, 3.7
Overhang of a roof, 2.30
Oxygen deficiency, symptoms, 5.23
Oxygen-deficient atmosphere, 5.20, 5.23, 5.25, 5.30, 5.37
Oxygen-enriched atmosphere, 5.20, 5.23, 5.37

Paint, 2.50
Parallel, 6.23
Parallel offset, 7.10, 7.12–7.14
Parallel strand lumber (PSL), 2.5, 2.6
Particleboard, 2.4
Partition(s)
    backing on a block wall, 2.34
    construction, 2.21–2.23, 2.27, 2.38–2.43, 2.44–2.45
    definition, 2.20
    fire-rated, 2.54
    modular for offices, 3.18
Pascal (unit), 6.10, 6.12
Patch cord, 8.13, 8.14, 8.15, 8.78
Pathways, 1.3, 1.27, 3.19, 3.36–3.38, 3.43, 8.68–8.69
PBX. *See* Private branch exchange
PCB. *See* Polychlorinated biphenyls
Pedestal, 3.26–3.27
Permissible exposure limit (PEL), 5.32

Perpendicular, 6.23
Personal protective equipment (PPE)
    basic, 5.6, 5.7, 5.13–5.14
    drilling, 3.32, 4.28, 8.53
    powder-actuated tools, 4.24
    power tools, 2.58
    pulling cable, 8.37, 8.53
    respirators, 5.28, 5.30
    work in confined spaces, 5.28–5.29
    work with cement, 2.10
    work with solvents, 5.30
pi, 6.6, 6.24, 7.8
PIC. *See* Polyethylene insulated conductor cable
Pier, 2.16
Pins, 4.8, 4.14–4.16, 4.22, 4.23, 8.33
Pipe chase, 2.38
Pipe cutter, 7.2, 7.5
Pipeline, 5.19
Pipes, 2.17–2.18, 2.38, 3.24, 8.81, 8.82
Piston, conduit, 8.21–8.22, 8.30, 8.31, 8.77
Pitch of a roof, 2.26, 2.27, 2.30
Plaster, 2.7, 2.9, 2.63, 3.30
Plastic, 3.6, 3.26
Plates
    cover, 3.29
    in metal framing, 2.42
    sill, 2.2, 2.12–2.13, 2.15, 2.76
    top, double top, and plate, 2.20, 2.21, 2.26, 2.29, 2.75, 2.76
Plenum, 2.53, 2.75, 3.2, 3.16, 3.22, 3.34
PLFA. *See* Circuits, power-limited
Plug set, 7.6, 7.7
Plywood, 2.3, 2.5, 2.17, 2.24, 3.38, 4.36
Pneumatic tools, 2.68–2.69
Pneumoconiosis, 5.30
Points, 6.23
Pole, telescoping. *See* Grabbit™
Pole systems for cables and wires, 3.20
Polychlorinated biphenyls (PCB), 5.33, 5.37
Polyethylene, cross-linked, 8.3
Polyethylene insulated conductor cable (PIC), 3.26, 8.3
Polygons, 6.24, 6.26
Polystyrene foam system, 2.12, 2.14
Polyvinyl chloride (PVC)
    cable insulation, 3.6, 8.3
    conduit, 7.2, 7.4–7.5, 7.17
    duct, 3.6, 3.7–3.8, 3.22
    junction box, 3.28
Post, mushroom, 3.16, 3.17
Pounds per square inch (psi), 6.10, 6.11
Powder-actuated tools, 2.41, 2.69–2.70, 4.22–4.25
Power (mathematical), 6.14–6.16, 6.18–6.19
Power (rate of work), 6.18, 6.34
Power system to a building, 2.37, 3.35
PPE. *See* Personal protective equipment
Premises wiring, 8.60, 8.63–8.65, 8.69, 8.78
Pressure (force), 6.10, 6.11–6.13
Pressure-tolerant equipment, 6.11
Primary center, 8.61, 8.62, 8.78
Private branch exchange (PBX), 8.13, 8.62–8.63, 8.66, 8.78
Probe, shorting, 5.7
Probe kit, tone generator/amplifier, 1.22
Pro-Bore® drill bit, 8.84, 8.92
Professionalism, 1.5, 1.6–1.8, 8.53
Profiles
    Bruce Nardone, RCDD, 2.71
    Jerry Budge, Blonder Tongue Laboratories, Inc., 5.35
    Ken Nieto, PLA Systems, 3.41
    Larry Garter, NSCA University, 4.34
    Mark A. Curry, SimplexGrinnell, 1.25–1.26

Profiles (*continued*)
    Michael Friedman, consultant, 6.31
    Paul Salyers, Copp Systems Integrator, 7.19
    Stephen Clare, Lincoln Technical Institute, 8.75
Project schedules, 2.71–2.72
Propane, 5.23
Pryout, 3.27, 3.28, 3.29
PSL. *See* Parallel strand lumber
PullCord, 8.80, 8.81, 8.82, 8.84, 8.85, 8.89, 8.90
Puller
    for cable or wire, 8.24–8.25, 8.32, 8.88, 8.103
    for fuses, 5.6, 5.7
Pulleys, 8.37, 8.38, 8.40, 8.42, 8.43. *See also* 2nd Man Cable
    Pulley™
Pulling cable. *See* Cable, installation
PullSleeve, 8.80, 8.81, 8.82, 8.84
Punch, knockout, 3.28, 3.29
Punch-down tool, 1.20
Purging, 5.24
Purlin, 3.33, 3.43
Push rod, 8.88, 8.103
Putty, 2.55, 2.57
PVC. *See* Polyvinyl chloride
Pythagorean Theorem, 6.27

Quick-E pole, 3.20

Rabbeted board, 2.48, 2.76
Raceways
    bends in, 3.9, 3.33
    boxes for, 3.20, 3.21, 3.27–3.29
    cellular concrete floor, 3.21
    cellular metal floor, 3.20–3.21
    definition, 3.2, 3.43
    how to handle, 3.24
    pancake, 3.19
    storage of, 3.24
    surface metallic and nonmetallic, 3.18–3.21
    underfloor, 3.20, 3.21
    underground, 3.24–3.27
Raceway supports, 3.14–3.17
Rack-out procedures, 5.9
Radio frequency interference (RFI), 8.52, 8.72
Radius, 6.23, 7.8, 7.24
Rafter, 2.5, 2.29, 2.76
Rankine scale, 6.13, 6.14
Reamer, 7.3
Rebore-Zit™, 8.95
Receiver, digit, 8.61, 8.77
Rectangle, 6.6, 6.7
Reel, for cable, 8.25–8.26, 8.27, 8.28, 8.38
Reel stand, 8.29
Regional center, 8.61, 8.62, 8.78
Reinforcing bars (rebar), 2.12
Rescue operations, 5.5, 5.26–5.27
Residential construction
    cable installation, 8.49–8.53, 8.69–8.71, 8.83–8.90
    ceilings, 2.26–2.27, 2.28
    floors, 2.13–2.20
    framing, 2.12–2.34
    multi-family dwellings, 2.33–2.34, 2.52, 2.54, 8.49, 8.51
Resin, 4.30
Resistance, electrical, 5.3–5.4, 6.18, 8.3, 8.4
Respect, 1.6, 1.8
Respiration, artificial, 5.29
Respirator, 5.28, 5.30, 5.31, 5.32
Responsibilities
    as an employee, 1.4–1.10
    as an EST, 1.2–1.3, 2.55, 5.7, 5.34
    keeping up to date on standards, 8.55
    operating in accordance with the codes, 8.79, 8.84
    of the supervisor, 5.26–5.27
Retrievers for fish wire, 8.32, 8.42, 8.84, 8.85, 8.86, 8.99
Retrofit, 1.2, 1.27, 2.52, 8.50, 8.52, 8.53
RFI. *See* Radio frequency interference
RG designations, 8.51
Ribband, 2.27, 2.28, 2.76
Ridgeboard, 2.29
Rigid metal conduit (RMC), 3.5–3.6, 7.1
Rigid nonmetallic conduit (RNC), 3.7–3.8
Rings
    for box installation, 3.30, 3.31
    bridle, 3.17, 8.32, 8.42
    D-, 3.16, 3.17, 8.32
    dry (mud ring), 8.51
    grouping, for cable installation, 8.25
    retainer fasteners, 4.14
    token, in a network, 8.78
Ripping, 2.66, 2.76
Rise (of a roof), 2.30
Rise (stub-up of conduit), 7.6, 7.8, 7.21
Rivet gun, 4.16
Rivets, 4.16–4.17
RMC. *See* Rigid metal conduit
RNC. *See* Rigid nonmetallic conduit
Roller, cable, 8.43, 8.44
Roof
    components, 2.26, 2.27, 2.29–2.30
    construction, 2.27–2.32, 2.33
    peak, 2.31
    pitch of the, 2.27, 2.30
    sheathing, 2.26, 2.30–2.31
    types, 2.27, 2.28, 2.29
Roofing material, 2.63
Root (mathematical), 6.18–6.19
Rope, 5.6, 8.23–8.24, 8.30, 8.31, 8.32, 8.40
Rubber compounds, 8.3
Runaway, 8.26
Runners, 2.45, 2.46, 2.47, 2.48
Run of a roof, 2.29, 2.30

SAC. *See* State Apprenticeship Councils
Saddle bends, 7.14–7.16
SAE. *See* Society of Automotive Engineers
Safety. *See also* Occupational Safety and Health
    Administration
    asbestos, 2.4, 5.30–5.32
    batteries, 5.32–5.33
    bending conduit, 7.5
    cement, 2.10
    confined spaces, 5.18–5.29
    cutting conduit, 7.2
    drilling rig, 2.65
    electrical shock, 5.2–5.7, 5.24
    fall protection, 5.33
    fastener installation, 4.11
    first aid, 5.29
    heating unit, 7.6
    ladders, 5.15–5.16
    lifting technique, 5.17, 5.18, 8.23
    lifts, hoists, and cranes, 5.17
    metal stud edges, 3.32
    optical fiber, 8.45
    overview, 5.1–5.2
    PCBs, 5.33
    pulling cable, 8.22, 8.23–8.24, 8.31, 8.36, 8.40

raceways, 3.24
scaffolds, 5.16–5.17
solvents and toxic vapors, 5.29–5.30
telephone line wiring, 8.61
tools
    basic principles, 5.17
    pneumatic, 2.68
    powder-actuated, 2.41, 2.69–2.70, 4.24
    power, 2.41, 2.58–2.59, 2.61–2.62, 2.68–2.70, 3.32
Safety gear, 1.6. *See also* Personal protective equipment
Sammy® anchor, 4.26
Satellite communication, 1.3, 8.63
Saws and saw blades, 2.60, 2.63, 2.64, 2.66–2.67, 7.1–7.2, 8.97
SBC. *See* Southern Building Code
Scaffolds, 5.16–5.17
SCBA. *See* Self-contained breathing apparatus
Scheduling, 2.71–2.72
Scientific notation, 6.14–6.16
Scissors, electrician's, 1.20
Screened twisted-pair cable (ScTP), 8.15, 8.16, 8.63
Screw(s)
    to attach boxes in metal studs (selt-tapping), 3.32
    cap, 4.5
    in ceiling construction, 2.46, 2.51
    concrete/masonry, 4.20
    deck, 4.21, 4.22
    drive, 4.22
    drywall, 2.51, 4.21–4.22, 8.52
    lag, 4.19–4.20
    machine, 4.3–4.4, 4.5
    overview, 4.19
    thread-forming and thread-cutting (sheet metal),
        4.20–4.21
    torque values for, 4.12
    wood, 4.19
Screwdriver, 2.60, 2.61, 3.32, 4.11
ScTP. *See* Screened twisted-pair cable
Sealant, 2.55, 2.57, 3.15
2nd Man Cable Pulley™, 8.80, 8.81, 8.82, 8.105
Sectional center, 8.61, 8.62, 8.78
Security Industry Association (SIA), 1.31
Security systems, 8.16
Segment bending device, 7.6
Self-contained breathing apparatus (SCBA), 5.30
Service loop, 8.36–8.37, 8.38, 8.52
Setscrew, 4.6, 8.33
Sewage line, 8.53
Sewer, 5.19, 5.25
Shakes, 2.30, 2.76
Shear point, 4.27
Sheathing
    on conduit, 3.26
    definition, 2.76
    dimensions, 2.3
    functions of, 2.8
    roof, 2.26, 2.30–2.31
    wall, 2.24, 2.26
Sheave, 8.24, 8.43, 8.78
Shield, lag, 4.20
Shielded twisted-pair cable (STP), 8.15–8.16
Shielding for cable, 8.10, 8.12, 8.16, 8.18, 8.72
Shiplap, 2.30, 2.76
Shock. *See* Electric shock
Shrinkage, in offset calculations, 7.11, 7.12, 7.13, 7.14, 7.15
SIA. *See* Security Industry Association
Siding, 2.63
Signage, danger, 5.12, 5.13, 5.32
Sill, rough, 2.20

Sill plate, 2.2, 2.12–2.13, 2.15, 2.76
Sine, 6.28–6.29, 7.22–7.23
Skylights, 2.30
Sleeves
    on anchors, 4.27, 4.30
    on cable, 2.36, 3.36, 3.38, 8.38
    intumescent pipe, 2.57
Sling-A-Line, 8.80, 8.103
Slope of a roof, 2.30
Smart homes, 8.51
Smurf tube, 3.3
Snub, 8.37, 8.38, 8.39, 8.78
Soap, 8.35, 8.78
Society of Automotive Engineers (SAE), 4.3, 4.4, 4.35
Software to calculate pulling tension, 8.37
Soldering iron, 1.20
Soleplate, 2.20, 2.21, 2.22, 2.25, 2.76
Solvents, 5.29–5.30, 7.4. *See also* Vapors and gases
Sound insulation, 2.45, 2.47
Sound-rated construction, 2.34, 2.38, 2.52–2.58
Sound transmission class (STC), 2.38, 2.57–2.58
Southern Building Code (SBC), 1.11
Span of a roof, 2.29, 2.30, 2.31
Speaker, 8.87
Spear-Zit™ drill bits, 8.84, 8.85, 8.86, 8.87, 8.88, 8.89, 8.90,
    8.93
Spira-Cut, 8.87, 8.89
Splice
    in conduit, 3.2, 3.24, 3.25, 8.56
    definition, 3.43
    not appropriate for communication cable, 8.37, 8.40, 8.42,
        8.47
    in a truss, 2.31
Spline, 2.48
Springer, 2.2
Square (geometric), 6.6, 6.7
Square (mathematic), 6.19
Square root, 6.19
Standards
    company, 1.5
    in conflict resolution, 1.10
    importance of, 1.11–1.12
    industry
        cable, 1.36, 3.1–3.2, 8.2
        and compliance, 1.4
        conflicting, in integrated systems, 1.3
        firestopping materials, 2.46
        notches in joists, 2.17
        overview, 1.4, 1.10–1.12
        thread, 4.1–4.3
    international, 1.11
    keeping up to date on, 8.55
Standoff, 3.14, 8.71
Staples for pneumatic stapler, 2.68–2.69, 8.52
State Apprenticeship Councils (SAC), 1.18
STC. *See* Sound transmission class
Steel, corrugated, 2.11, 2.37
Steel framework, 2.12, 2.19, 2.35, 3.33–3.34
Stone, 2.11, 2.12, 2.63, 4.20, 4.28, 4.36
STP. *See* Shielded twisted-pair cable
Straps, 3.14, 8.39
Strength member, 8.18, 8.19, 8.20, 8.34
Striated, 2.45, 2.76
String, 7.5, 8.104
Stringer, 2.76
Stripper, coaxial cable, 1.20
Strongback, 2.27, 2.28, 2.76
Stub-up, 7.6, 7.8, 7.21

Stucco, 2.8, 2.10, 2.76
Stud finder, 2.70, 8.53. *See also* StudSensor™
Stud punch, 2.67
Studs (fastener), 2.21, 2.26, 2.42, 2.63, 4.22, 4.23
Studs (support)
    in commercial construction, 2.38–2.45
    holes or notches in, 3.32–3.33
    king, 2.21
    metal stock, 2.39–2.40
    in residential construction, 2.20, 2.21, 2.26, 2.29
    trimmer, 2.20, 2.21, 2.76
StudSensor™, 8.85, 8.86, 8.87, 8.89, 8.98
Styrene, 3.26
Subfloor, 2.8, 2.19–2.20, 2.25, 2.32, 2.76
Substrate, gypsum board, 2.8, 2.76
Sunlight-resistance, 3.8, 8.5
Supervisor, 1.6, 1.7–1.8, 5.26–5.27
Swab, conduit, 8.29
Switches, 5.10, 5.11
Switching station, 8.61
Swivel, breakaway, 8.48

Tag, danger, 5.12, 5.13
Tagout. *See* Lockout/tagout procedure
Take-up, 7.8, 7.9, 7.21
Tangent, 6.28–6.29, 7.22–7.23
Tape
    Under Carpet, 8.88, 8.106
    fish. *See* Fish tape/line/wire
    measuring, 8.26
Taps, 4.13
Tardiness, 1.5
TDM. *See* Time division multiplexing
Teamwork, 1.8–1.9, 1.12
Teflon®, 8.3
Telecommunication. *See* Communication systems
Telecommunications Industry Association (TIA), 1.11, 1.27,
    1.31, 1.36, 8.65. *See also* ANSI/TIA/EIA standards
Telecommunications room, 3.38, 8.67–8.68
Telephone systems
    basic telephone operation, 8.61
    multiplexing, 3.36, 3.43, 8.61–8.62, 8.63
Telephone test set, 1.22
Tele-Power pole, 3.20
Temperature
    extreme, 5.25, 6.14
    and the metric system, 6.4, 6.13–6.14, 6.35
Tension web, 2.31
Terminal point of conduit system, 3.10
Termination of employment, 5.8
Tests
    atmospheric, 5.20, 5.23, 5.24, 5.26, 5.27–5.28, 5.31
    LAN cable, 1.22
    telephone test set, 1.22
    voltage, 5.7, 5.14–5.15
Thicknet, 8.18, 8.78
Thinnet, 8.18, 8.78
Threader, ratchet, 7.3, 7.4
Threads per inch (TPI), 4.2
Thread standards
    classes, 4.2, 4.35
    grade markings, 4.3, 4.12
    identification, 4.2, 4.35
    series, 4.2
Throat, 3.24
TIA. *See* Telecommunications Industry Association
Tie wraps, 3.16, 4.17

Tile
    anchors for, 4.36
    asbestos-containing, 5.31
    ceiling, 2.46, 2.63, 8.80
    ceramic floor and wall, 2.63
    vitrified, for ducts, 3.26
Tilt-up construction, 2.35– 2.36
Time division multiplexing (TDM), 8.61–8.62, 8.78
Time sheet, 1.12
Tolerance, of a threaded fastener, 4.2, 4.35
Toll center, 8.61, 8.62, 8.78
Tools
    cable-pulling. *See* Fishing system; Fish tape/line/wire
    cable-stripping and termination, 1.20
    cutting, 1.20, 2.66–2.67, 8.96–8.97
    for drilling, 2.59–2.65, 8.92–8.95
    gas-driven, 2.69
    grounded or double-insulated/ungrounded, 5.3, 5.10,
      5.37
    illustrations and descriptions, 8.91–8.106
    pan removal, 2.47, 2.52
    pneumatic, 2.68–2.69
    powder-actuated, 2.41, 2.69–2.70, 4.22–4.25
    rivet gun, 4.16
    for running cable, 2.58–2.71
    safety. *See* Safety, tools
Toppets, 2.46
Torque, 4.8, 4.9, 4.11, 4.12, 6.34
TORX® socket screw, 4.3, 4.5
Toxic atmospheres, 5.23
TPI (threads per inch), 4.2
Tracer, 8.13–8.14, 8.78
Trade associations, 1.28–1.31
Training, 1.17–1.19, 5.12, 5.29, 5.30, 8.63
Transmission, 6.18, 8.16
Trenches, 5.19
Triangles, 6.25–6.29
Trigger, power, 1.21
Trigonometry, 6.28–6.29, 7.11, 7.12, 7.13, 7.22–7.23
Triscanner™ Pro, 8.98
Troubleshooting, 5.11
Trunk, 8.50, 8.78
Truss(es)
    components, 2.31
    construction, 2.24, 2.31, 2.42
    definition, 2.76
    materials used in, 2.17, 2.18
    types, 2.32, 2.39, 2.42
TSP-1 headlight, 8.88, 8.90
Tubing
    electrical metallic, 3.3–3.5, 3.32, 3.33, 7.1, 7.5
    electrical nonmetallic, 3.2
    standards, 3.1
Tugger, cable
    bolt to the floor, 8.40, 8.41, 8.45, 8.46, 8.47
    components, 8.35
    friction heat generated by, 8.32
    relocation of the, 8.40
    when to use, 8.26
Tunnels, 5.19

UL. *See* Underwriters Laboratories
UNC. *See* Unified National Coarse thread
Undercarpet telecommunication cable (UTC), 8.7, 8.8, 8.9,
    8.14–8.15
Underground systems, 3.24–3.27, 3.37, 8.52, 8.65–8.66
Underlayment, 2.4, 2.25, 2.30–2.31, 2.76

Underwriters Laboratories (UL), 3.7, 3.43
Unified National Coarse thread (UNC), 4.2, 4.35
Unified National Extra Fine thread (UNEF), 4.2, 4.35
Unified National Fine thread (UNF), 4.2, 4.35
Unistrut systems, 3.34, 4.35
Unshielded twisted-pair cable (UTP)
    in commercial cabling, 8.69
    conductor pair in the, 3.36
    maximum tension, 8.52
    overview, 8.13–8.14
    in premises cabling, 8.63–8.64
    in residential cabling, 8.50
    vs. optical cable, 8.20
UTC. *See* Undercarpet telecommunication cable

Vacuum/blower of a fishing system, 1.21, 8.22, 8.23, 8.30
Vapor barrier, 2.6, 2.19, 2.30, 8.85
Vapors and gases, 3.14, 5.23–5.24, 5.29–5.30
Variable, 6.20
Vault, 3.26, 5.19
Vector quantity, 6.9, 6.33
Velocity, 6.10
Veneer, 2.3, 2.12, 2.76
Ventilation of confined spaces, 5.28, 5.33
Vents, 2.30
Vise, pipe, 7.3
Voice signal, 3.36, 8.61, 8.66. *See also* Telephone systems
Voltage drop, 3.7, 8.3–8.4, 8.52
Voltage testing, 5.7, 5.14–5.15
Volume, 6.4, 6.6, 6.7, 6.8–6.9, 6.33, 6.34

Waferboard, 2.30
Walkerpole, 3.20
Wall(s)
    bracing, 2.42, 2.43, 2.44
    curtain, 2.34, 2.35, 2.36
    exterior, 2.38
    fire-rated, 2.53, 2.54, 2.55
    fishing wires inside, 8.84–8.87
    interior commercial, 2.38–2.43, 2.44–2.45. *See also*
        Partitions
    metal stud, 2.38–2.45, 3.32
    multi-dwelling, 2.33–2.34
    party, 2.35, 2.54

Wallboard, 2.6, 2.7–2.8, 2.9, 2.26, 2.38, 4.30, 4.36
Wall construction, 2.12, 2.14, 2.20–2.26
Walleye, 8.89
Wall mounting for cable trays, 3.23
Washer, 4.8–4.9, 4.20
Wash station, 5.33
Waste disposal, 5.32, 5.33
Water supply lines, 8.53
Weight, 6.4, 6.9–6.11, 6.33, 6.34
Wet locations, 3.4, 3.6, 3.8, 3.26
Wet Noodle, 8.105
Wet volume, 6.9
Window openings, 2.21, 2.23, 2.33, 2.38, 2.40
Wire
    dispensers, 8.24
    drain or ground, 8.10, 8.12, 8.77
    fish. *See* Fish tape/line/wire
    load current tables, 8.3–8.4
    residential electrical, 8.53
    safety, 4.13
    sizes within cable, 8.2
Wire Bit, 8.85, 8.95
Wiremold, 3.18
Wire puller, manual, 1.21
Wire pull wrap, 8.105
Wire pusher, 8.88, 8.103
Wiring, 3.20, 3.33. *See also* Telephone systems
WNH-1 ball chain, 8.85, 8.86
Wood products, engineered, 2.5–2.6, 2.7, 2.17
Work statement, 1.12
WR24, 8.84, 8.85, 8.87, 8.89, 8.105
Wrench, 4.11

XLP. *See* Cross-linked polyethylene

Yard, aramid, 8.34. *See also* Strength member
YFT fish tape, 8.87, 8.88, 8.90, 8.102

Ztip, 8.89, 8.100